CW00642774

The Crystal Sun

The Crystal Sun

Rediscovering a Lost Technology
of the Ancient World

Robert Temple

(www.robert-temple.com)

Introduction by
Sir Arthur C. Clarke

C
CENTURY · LONDON

Published by Century in 2000

1 3 5 7 9 10 8 6 4 2

First published in the United Kingdom in 2000 by Century
The Random House Group Limited
20 Vauxhall Bridge Road, London SW1V 2SA

Random House Australia (Pty) Limited
20 Alfred Street, Milsons Point, Sydney,
New South Wales 2061, Australia

Random House New Zealand Limited
18 Poland Road, Glenfield,
Auckland 10, New Zealand

Random House South Africa (Pty) Limited
Endulini, 5A Jubilee Road, Parktown 2193, South Africa

Random House UK Limited Reg. No. 954009

A CIP catalogue record for this book
is available from the British Library

Papers used by Random House UK Limited are natural,
recyclable products made from wood grown in sustainable forests.
The manufacturing processes conform to the environmental
regulations of the country of origin.

ISBN 0 7126 7888 3

Typeset by Palimpsest Book Production Limited,
Polmont, Stirlingshire
Printed and bound in Great Britain by
Mackays of Chatham PLC, Chatham, Kent

If they say to you: 'Where do you come from?',
reply to them: 'We come from the light.'

The Gospel of Thomas

Contents

Acknowledgements

I wish to thank my old friend Sir Arthur C. Clarke for triggering the research which led to this book, and for coming full circle and writing the introduction to it.

As always, my manuscript has been immeasurably improved by my wife Olivia, who always reads everything first and makes it better. She also translated for this project, which in so many ways was a joint effort, about 80,000 words of difficult technical French, much of it old-fashioned 18th-century French and maddeningly obscure. She has supported me in this seemingly endless task for all the years in which I was engaged in it, and without her help it simply would not have been possible. She also designed the British bookjacket and advised on and coordinated many other aspects of publication and promotion, including persuading me to make public appearances, and preparation of broadcasting proposals in many revisions.

I owe immense debts of gratitude to my incomparable editor, Mark Booth of Century Books, to Kate Parkin, Liz Rowlinson, and Hannah Black of Century, to Roderick Brown, and to my brilliant agents Bill Hamilton and Sara Fisher, both of A. M. Heath.

My friend Zhenni ('Jenny') Zhu was of invaluable assistance to me over a period of years, accompanying me to countless museums to study lenses, helping me take the photos, dealing with Chinese enquiries, and above all, making it possible for my work in the British Library to be cut in half, by assisting my research in countless ways. I am very grateful for the cheerful and devoted help she gave for so long.

There are seven friends who are no longer alive whom I wish to thank in particular. They are, firstly, our very dear friend Miss Mary Brenda Hotham Francklyn, who died so long ago that it seems both yesterday and an eternity ago; Professor Derek de Solla Price, who didn't live long enough for me to have known him as well as I would have liked; Walter Gasson, an immensely dedicated, generous, warm-hearted man with a boundless enthusiasm for this subject, and who undertook measurements and study of the British lenses at my request for what was meant to be a joint report, which he didn't live to complete with me; Colin Hardie, a delightful and dedicated scholar of great generosity of spirit who helped me with Latin and anything else I asked of him; Professor D. E. Eichholz, one of the most generous and open-minded of classical scholars it would be possible to meet, who undertook to retranslate every relevant passage of Pliny with the greatest of enthusiasm and authorized me to publish his re-translations under his name – he was one of those rare scholars who was unafraid to revise his views, and indeed thrilled at the opportunity to re-examine any matter from a new angle; dear Michael Scott, who gave me Layard's book containing the description of the Layard Lens, with the effusive generosity which marked the actions of his entire life; and finally, I wish to thank my very dear friend Dr Peter Mitchell, one of the most extraordinary men I ever knew, for allowing me first to study and later to acquire from him the ancient Greek lens which can be seen in Plate 11.

I also wish to thank the following:

The New Horizons Research Foundation of Canada for one year's modest financial grant towards the research for this book in the 1980s. It was the only financial aid I received in more than 30 years.

Professor José Álvarez Lopez of Cordoba, Argentina, for discussions and information about the need for optical surveying of the pyramids in Egypt. If Professor Lopez is alive, could he please get back in touch.

My friend Mohammed Nazmy for taking the photograph on the winter solstice, 1998, which appears as Plate 30 of this book. I also wish to thank his colleague Medhat Yehia for escorting me to the Egyptian Museum in Cairo and facilitating my study of the Cairo Lens.

My friend and colleague Ioannis Liritzis for finding Ioannis Sakas for me and accompanying me to see him in Athens. I especially wish to thank Ioannis Sakas for long discussions and supplying me with printed material and photos relating to his amazing recreation of the feat of Archimedes.

My dear friend Fiona Eberts for helping me to find the two Buffon burning-mirrors at Paris. It wasn't easy!

The British School of Archaeology at Athens, and in paricular Helen Brown, for much patient assistance and a great deal of hard work in obtaining permits and information.

Dr Irving Finkel, Deputy Keeper of the Department of Western Asiatic Antiquities at the British Museum, for much friendly discussion and for being of such assistance in my study of the Layard Lens.

William Graham for his extraordinary assistance in the study of the Carthaginian lenses during his time at the Carthage Museum, and for taking such beautiful photos of those lenses. (Could he please get back in touch!)

Marcus Edwards, Lizzie Speller, Lindsay Allen, and Sarah Knight for translating passages of Latin. Anne Dunhill and Rima Stubbs for translating some passages of Italian. Robin Waterfield for translating some strange passages in Greek. Bob Sharples for answering queries about Alexander of Aphrodisias and Theophrastus's *De Igne*. Allan Mills for many fascinating discussions about shadow-catchers, Archimedes, and other matters of mutual interest, and for generously giving me references and copies of articles which he had collected about the burning-mirror of Archimedes. The late Michael Weitzman for help with Hebrew material, as I explain in the main text. Donald Easton and Richard Sorabji for being so helpful about trying to arrange access for me to the Trojan Lenses in Russia. Evie

Wolff for making enquiries for me in East Berlin in the bad old days. Tony Anderson for information about the Prometheus legends of the Caucasus. Buddy Rogers for information about gemstones. Martin Isler, Günter Dreyer, Richard Lóbban, Hugo Verheyen, and John L. Heilbron for their friendly assistance and permissions regarding the use of illustrations. Bob Lomas and Buddy Rogers for helping work out the nature of the Viking 'sun-stone'. Peter D. Leigh, Secretary of the London College of Optometrists, for his help and encouragement. Jenny Kidd for optical advice and good meals in France. Robert Bauval for introducing me to Bill Hamilton and Mohammed Nazmy. The staff of the British Library for their Herculean efforts to provide helpful and cheerful service under difficult circumstances and, often, bad management and adverse conditions; they are invisible heroes.

Robert Temple

Introduction

by Sir Arthur C. Clarke

Of all human inventions, the telescope is the one which produces the most wonderful results with the least material. We now take it for granted – but could anyone ever have imagined that two pieces of glass could abolish space, and perform the miracle of bringing distant objects apparently within reach? And without the telescope, we would still be almost completely ignorant of our place in the universe.

Although Galileo is rightly credited with introducing the telescope to the world in 1609, he certainly did not invent it. As Robert Temple points out in this impressively researched book, excellent rock-crystal lenses had been known for several thousand years, and it seems incredible that Archimedes – or some Chinese or Egyptian inventor even earlier – did not make the obvious and simple experiment of looking through two of them at the same time.

Some historians claim that Ceylon's maverick King Kasyapa, who in the 5th century AD built the rock fortress of Sigiriya (which I once listed among the 'Seven Wonders of the World' in the BBC programme of that name, and which is one of the principal locales of The Fountains of Paradise), used a telescope to keep an eye on his harem. Unfortunately, I have been unable to get any confirmation of this intriguing story.

I hope that this book will encourage museum curators to take a second look at some of their possessions: they may discover that one of mankind's most important inventions is far older – and has had a greater impact on history – than has hitherto been realized.

Arthur C. Clarke
Colombo, Sri Lanka, May 1999

This book is for Xiaoqiao

凌筱崎

SECTION ONE

THE PHYSICAL EVIDENCE

Chapter One

Coming to Light

You are no longer with what the sun illumines/ but in Your depths You seem the burning life/ of the sun's soul. You seem inside the sun . . .
Angelos Sikelianos

Imagine a world where boats have not been invented and transport across water is impossible. In ancient times in such a world, sailing and rowing did not exist – the only means of getting anywhere was by land. Yet this leaves archaeologists and historians with problems: there appears to be evidence that people travelled long distances and even traded. If only they *had* had boats – then it would be simple to say how all this happened. But instead, complicated land routes have to be worked out, to explain all the cultural connections between peoples.

Imagine too, that various bits of evidence are then found which indicate that perhaps boats existed after all. However, these are all dismissed by the experts. Paintings on old vases showing sailing ships are simple poetic fantasies or mythological scenes. Wrecks seen on seabeds are labelled 'excrescences of rock' and are left unexamined. Portions of old ships which are found are not really ships at all: they are 'votive offerings' to the gods. Records in old texts which speak of sailing between lands – of crossing the Mediterranean, for instance – are imaginary records of events which never took place.

What a distorted view of history we would have if we believed all this. All ancient voyages would then be mythological, no more real than claims of flying in the air to Mount Olympus, and we would be convinced that communication by sea never took place in the ancient world. Doubtless a theory would be evolved to show that this truth is indicated by archaic religions: the Earth goddess was worshipped because only by treading upon her could peoples visit one another. Learned professors would solemnly and repeatedly tell their pupils that this was so, and none could challenge the standard or orthodox view. Any troublemakers who did try to suggest that the ancients had ships after all would be branded lunatics and ostracized by respectable people. For *everyone knows* that there were no boats in antiquity.

3

Unfortunately, a lot of people have a tendency to behave in this manner, and nothing is harder to dislodge than a 'conventional notion' held by experts. Ask any expert if there were magnifying lenses in antiquity and he will probably tell you: 'Of course not. There is no evidence of anything like that. I have never seen any. None are known. And there is no record of their having been known in ancient times.'

Nonetheless, this book is devoted to explaining how the view we have had of the ancient world is distorted in a manner similar to the fictitious example given above, about the lack of boats in antiquity. But instead of believing that men in ancient times had no boats, we have believed that they had no optical technology. Because of a lack of the basic information – and due to our certainty that it did not exist – we have misinterpreted any number of things about man's past. History, technology, architecture, religion, mythology, reading and writing, philosophy, theology, craftsmanship, manufacture – all have been subject to a distorted viewpoint. They have all been viewed through misconceptions, which have acted like those mirrors in a fun-house which make us look tall or squat.

It is time to rectify this situation by revealing the truth and presenting the overwhelming evidence. We shall see that there are more than 450 ancient optical artifacts – slightly more than the 'none' which most people presume exist. We shall see that there are many ancient texts which inform us explicitly, and without the slightest doubt, that optical technology was known and used in antiquity. These constitute the proofs. After them come the interpretations, for, armed with the evidence of the existence of these things, we can suggest new meanings of certain familiar motifs. For instance, can it be that the one-eyed Cyclops of *The Odyssey* has some optical connotation and is not just an arbitrary monster invented at random by an epic poet? There are many such possibilities, and we shall be encountering them on our way.

The information we encounter, and the interpretations of the past which it makes possible, will give us a totally new view of what the ancient world was like. Few aspects of antiquity can remain wholly unaffected by this change in our knowledge and our understanding. Much that was puzzling will become clear. On the other hand, much that we had thought clear can now be seen to be incomplete or misleading. The kaleidoscope of history has been twisted, and new patterns are seen, and I dare say they are prettier ones than before. We must never presume that our ancestors are incapable of springing surprises on us. For here they are, rising from the dead with their spectacles on, in the third millennium AD.

It will be necessary to show, in some detail, how certain scholars have fooled themselves into rewriting history by erasing what ancient texts clearly said and putting new words in their place. This will shock many people. However, most of the guilty are long dead and will not lose their chairs as a result. Some who have been tempted to behave like this have seen the error of their ways and recanted: Professor Eichholz, translator of the Roman author Pliny, gave me fresh translations of the optical passages in Pliny and was extremely enthusiastic in doing so. He said that if he had had any idea at the time he originally did his work (I caught up with him in an old folks' home) that there were ancient lenses which had been found by archaeologists, he would not have treated the text in such a way as to 'get round' their non-existence by altering the meaning so that the text appeared not to discuss what it was actually discussing.

This kind of thing has happened time and time again. The scholars who 'edit the texts' of Greek and Latin have taken out many optical words and have said these must be scribal errors. Then, having substituted new words of their own invention, they have said that there is no ancient textual evidence of optics. Yet they are the ones who destroyed it!

Certainly, this will prove to be a strange story. But let us begin. As it is partly a personal saga, I begin with how I began. I wandered, quite unsuspecting, into this maze, and for a long time I didn't see any more clearly than anyone else the obvious facts before my eyes. That's because the story of ancient optical technology is so large that one's immediate reaction is to believe that it is impossible! Otherwise, surely, *everybody would know about it.*

I HEAR ABOUT THE LAYARD LENS

It all began in the unlikely setting of conversations about outer space, though in retrospect, it seems to me that that was wryly appropriate. If the gods were having their little joke, that was the way to go about it. In the spring of 1966 I had begun observing the production of the film *2001: A Space Odyssey* at MGM Studios near London, during a two-week visit to England.[1]

As a result, I met and became friends with the brilliant visionary Arthur C. Clarke, who had written the script for the film based on his own short story 'The Sentinel'. Arthur was not around that often, for even then he was living in Sri Lanka (still then called Ceylon) and only visited England from time to time.

It was either late 1966 or very early 1967 when Arthur and I became particularly friendly. In those days Arthur and a group of science-fiction enthusiasts would meet at a pub in Hatton Gardens called The Globe. Much earlier, Arthur had met his friends at The White Hart, after which he named a book of his science-fiction stories *Tales from the White Hart.* But by the time I knew Arthur, the venue had shifted to The Globe.

The evenings at The Globe tended to be weekly, and were really occasions for all the science-fiction writers to congregate. Because he was the most famous British science-fiction writer by that time, the gatherings often took the form of clusterings around Arthur. Arthur's brother Fred would sometimes be there, and he became a good friend of ours. Sometimes Isaac Asimov would be in town, and he would then join everyone. When Isaac came the Clarke Brothers were all aflutter. And by no means undistinguished science-fiction writers such as Brian Aldiss and John Brunner would frequently be there, so that the coteries of admirers would be distracted by too many star attractions at once. I remember Michael Moorcock being one of the most frequent attenders. In those days he was not so well known, and he gave the impression of being more fan than author, despite the fact that he was already remarkably prolific.[2]

In those days before *2001* made him a world-famous guru figure, Arthur looked and talked like an old-fashioned bank manager. I have always liked Arthur's rather growly, purring voice, partially because he delivers the most outrageous statements about the Universe in the dry tones of a man informing you in a small office of a provincial town that the interest rate has risen by one quarter of a per cent.

I had become a *de facto* member of a loose Arthur Clarke entourage, and so Arthur began to invite me to lunches with some of his more interesting academic friends, as it went down well that I had a degree in Sanskrit. Arthur liked to meet people for lunch near Leicester Square at the Arts Theatre Club, and sometimes we would go to a small Italian place a couple of minutes away for some pasta. And thus it was that I met Derek de Solla Price, who was Avalon Professor of the History of Science at Yale University. It must have been the spring of 1967 when Arthur, Derek and I sat chatting during one of our lunches about curious artifacts from antiquity, and I was set onto the track that has led to this book being written all these years later.

Derek said he knew of a strange crystal artifact. It was in the British Museum right here in London, he said; a crystal lens, Babylonian or Assyrian, no one knew what it really was. It really did seem to have been made as a lens, though there weren't supposed to be lenses at that time. He meant to study it one day when he had time. I expressed my astonishment. Arthur nodded sagely, as Derek had already told him about it. Arthur said: 'You know, there really are a lot of these curious objects from ancient times which are inexplicable mysteries. Alan Mackay has found that a belt buckle has been excavated in China which contains aluminium, which couldn't have existed in ancient times. There's the ancient electrical battery in Iraq. There are some strange things in India and Ceylon which I've seen. And of course, Derek's discovery of the Antikythera Mechanism is a classic case of how the impossible has been proved about knowledge of technology in ancient times, because it was an ancient computing device. I really mean to look into these things too, when I have time. Why don't you write about all these enigmas as well?'

We agreed to continue our fascinating talks. Next time, Arthur said, he would introduce me to yet another researcher into these ancient artifacts. Derek promised to keep in touch, and indeed he did send me his paper on 'A Survival of Babylonian Mathematics in New Guinea' soon after.

We never really had as many lunches after that as we intended. *Life* got in the way. Arthur became too famous because of *2001* and all the world's media couldn't stop interviewing him.

However, before we carry on and become involved in optics and lenses, starting with the Layard Lens, I want first to summarize what the different types of lenses are, so that the reader can be oriented properly. Basically, lenses come in two types: *convex* and *concave*. Convex ones bulge outwards, whereas concave ones curve inwards. When a lens is only curved on one side, however, and is flat on the other, it is called either *plano-convex* or *plano-concave*. In other words, *plano-* means flat on one side. We shall see that the Layard Lens, about to be described, is one of these. Before it was damaged its base was absolutely flat, so we may describe the Layard Lens as being a *plano-convex lens*.

In order to be helpful, I reproduce here as Figure 1 an engraving from a Victorian popular-science book which shows all the types of lenses. The reader can refer back to this from time to time as he has need, in order to remind himself of the sorts of lenses which are being discussed in subsequent chapters. I give in the caption to the figure further basic information.

Another essential thing which I need to point out to the reader is that spectacles and telescopes are generally assumed to be relatively recent inventions. We are told that telescopes were invented and began to be used about the time of Galileo, at the beginning of the 17th century. And as for

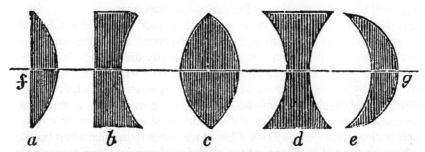

Figure 1. The five types of lenses. a: *a plano-convex lens*, flat on one side and round on the other; b: *a plano-concave lens*, flat on one side and hollow on the other; c: *a biconvex lens*, round on both sides; d: *a biconcave lens*, hollow on both sides (we do not encounter these in this book); e: *a convex meniscus lens*, hollow on one side and round on the other (such as we find forming the crystal eye of the Bull's Head Rhyton from Minoan Crete). Taken simply, a convex lens enlarges and a concave lens diminishes the size of an image. Apart from a considerable manufacture of concave crystal lenses (type b) in Greece, the Aegean and Asia Minor, all the ancient lenses so far found have been of the types a, c, and (rarely, in human or animal heads as eyes) type e. The line f-g is the line of focus. The Layard Lens is more complicated than these simple lenses because it is a plano-convex lens distorted on purpose by being ground toroidally (a torus is a doughnut-shape), to accommodate a case of astigmatism. It might also be helpful to add that the word *lentoid*, 'lens-like', is sometimes used by people to disparage an object which looks like a lens but which they wish to deny is a lens. It is a bit like calling a person you don't like a *humanoid*.

spectacles, whether it was the Chinese or the Italians who were the clever originators, they are accepted as having made their appearance in Italy by the 13th century. After that there is plenty of evidence of them. That is what is conventionally accepted at the present time. The actual truth, on the other hand, will be all too obvious by the time the reader finishes reading this book. Let us now, however, follow the story of the crystal lens in the British Museum which led to this book being written in the first place.

THE STORY OF THE LAYARD LENS

I shall now go into the Layard Lens in some detail, since as well as being the first I encountered, its history in many ways typifies the errors and misconceptions bedevilling all ancient lenses. It is a long story, and anyone interested in all the details should be aware that in the interests of brevity I have moved much of it to the footnotes.

The Layard Lens is Object Number 12091 in the British Museum Department of Western Asiatic Antiquities. It is easy to commence its story, for we know that the Layard Lens was excavated by Austen Henry Layard (1817–94) in 1849. (It is often said that he found it in 1853, but that was really the date when he published his account of it.) The lens has at various times been called the Nineveh Lens, the Nimrud Lens, the Assyrian Lens and the Sargon Lens, but the best policy seems to be to name it after Layard, which more recent writers have done, and which we shall continue to do here.

Layard excavated the Layard Lens in a chamber (labelled Room AB) of the North-West Palace of the ancient Assyrian capital of Kalhu, more often called Nimrud, but in Layard's time thought to be Nineveh. This was during his Second Expedition of excavations in Iraq on behalf of the British Museum. He did not hesitate to declare it a true lens. This is what he said in his published account in 1853:

> Two entire glass bowls, with fragments of others, were also found in this chamber; . . . These bowls are probably of the same period as the small bottle found in the ruins of the north-west palace during the previous excavations, and now in the British Museum. On this highly interesting relic is the name of Sargon, with his title of King of Assyria, in cuneiform characters, and the figure of a lion. We are, therefore, able to fix its date to the latter part of the seventh century BC. It is, consequently, the most ancient known specimen of *transparent* glass, . . . With it were found . . . two larger vases in white alabaster, inscribed with the name of the same king. . . . With the glass bowls was discovered a rock-crystal lens, with opposite convex and plane faces. Its properties could scarcely have been unknown to the Assyrians, and we have consequently the

earliest specimen of a magnifying and burning-glass. [Here he gives a footnote which I shall quote in a moment.] It was buried beneath a heap of fragments of beautiful blue opaque glass, apparently the enamel of some object in ivory or wood, which had perished.

In the further corner of the chamber, to the left hand, stood the royal throne.[3]

Who was Sargon, King of Assyria? He was actually Sargon II, and he ruled from 722 BC to 705 BC, a period of 17 years. We don't know whether he was the younger brother of the previous King (who only ruled for four years) or a usurper.[4] Until the last year of his reign, Sargon lived at his capital Kalhu (Nimrud), which was essentially a military capital. Sargon spent most of his time campaigning to enlarge and protect his empire, and he is believed to have died on campaign against the Cimmerians and the Confederation of Tabal (called Tubal in the Bible) in the Taurus Mountains.[5] Some Assyriologists have thought it likely that Sargon was actually assassinated at this time.[6] Sargon seems to have been prone to megalomania (like his modern successor Saddam Hussein) and he built a new capital in the middle of nowhere called Dur-Sharrukin (the modern village of Khorsabad). He only lived there for about a year before his death; his son used it as a fortress but preferred to make his capital at Nineveh. So Sargon's dream-city, built over the course of ten years by thousands of prisoners of war, was a very brief dream indeed. But we shall see later that, in interpreting the Layard Lens, we must remember that Sargon moved his residence to this place at the end of his life. For at the time of his death, the throne-room of the Palace at Kalhu was not being used as such, and seems to have become a storeroom for precious objects. And, as we have seen, several personal belongings of Sargon were certainly kept there.

Layard's expeditions to Iraq and his astounding discoveries (which filled the British Museum with most of its monumental Babylonian and Assyrian sculpture) were published in a series of massively illustrated volumes. The First Expedition was described in *Nineveh and Its Remains* (2 vols),[7] and the Second Expedition was described in *Discoveries in the Ruins of Nineveh and Babylon*,[8] I found that the footnote given by Layard to the account of the discovery of the lens quoted above reads as follows (I have converted the cumbersome fractions to decimals):

I am indebted to Sir David Brewster, who examined the lens, for the following note: – 'This lens is plano-convex, and of a slightly oval form, its length being 1.6 inch, and its breadth 1.4 inch. It is about 0.9 of an inch thick, and a little thicker at one side than the other. Its plane surface is pretty even, though ill-polished and scratched. Its convex surface has not been ground, or polished, on a spherical concave disc, but has been fashioned on a lapidary's wheel, or by some method equally rude. The convex side is tolerably well polished, and though uneven from the mode

9

in which it has been ground, it gives a tolerably distinct focus, at the distance of 4.5 inches from the plane side. There are about twelve cavities in the lens, that have been opened during the process of grinding it; these cavities, doubtless, contained either naphtha, or the same fluid which is discovered in topaz, quartz, and other minerals. As the lens does not show the polarised rays at great obliquities, its plane surface must be greatly inclined to the axis of the hexagonal prism of quartz from which it must have been taken. It is obvious, from the shape and rude cutting of the lens, that it could not have been intended as an ornament; we are entitled, therefore, to consider it as intended to be used as a lens, either for magnifying, or for concentrating the rays of the sun, which it does, however, very imperfectly.'[9]

Sir David Brewster (1781–1868) was a distinguished Scottish scientist of the time, who specialized in optics. It is unfortunate, therefore, that a typographical error was allowed to appear in Brewster's quoted comments – namely, the statement that the lens was nine-tenths of an inch thick, which it is certainly not! (Its maximum thickness at any point is 6.2 mm.) This bungled quotation from Brewster must have put a lot of people off and dampened any enthusiasm for study of the lens for a long time, since a piece of crystal that thick was liable to be of questionable optical interest, bearing in mind the other dimensions and the fact that the crystal is not biconvex but plano-convex; it would imply a negligible convexity of the superior surface.

Brewster published his own article about the Layard Lens in 1853, the same year that Layard's book came out. Entitled 'On a Rock-Crystal Lens and Decomposed Glass Found at Nineveh', this appeared in the *American Journal of Science*.[10] It contained the same statements quoted by Layard, but it also contained the same typographical error about the thickness of the lens. The error had thus originated with Brewster's manuscript, not with Layard's publishers.

The first published illustration of the lens appeared in October 1883. In a section called 'Summary of Current Researches Relating to Zoology, Botany, Microscopy, etc.', a brief anonymous notice appeared about the Layard Lens in the *Journal of the Royal Microscopical Society*, headed 'Assyrian Lens'. It commenced as follows: 'Sir A. Henry Layard, in his "Nineveh and Babylon", describes a lens which he found in the course of his excavations, and which is now in the British Museum. By the kind permission of Dr Birch, the Keeper of Oriental Antiquities, we have been enabled to figure it here (figs 131 and 132). [See Figure 2.]

'The lens is thus referred to by Sir A. H. Layard: . . .' The remarks commencing 'With the glass bowls was discovered a rock-crystal lens . . .' are then quoted, along with the footnote about Brewster.[11]

Two engraved views of the lens are then given, which are of particular interest in that they show some of the chippings, etc. existed at that time,

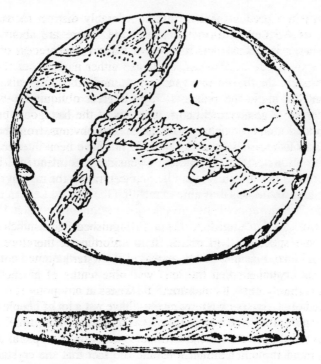

Figure 2. The first illustrations ever published of the Layard Lens, which appeared in the *Journal of the Royal Microscopical Society*, London, in October, 1883. The view of the rim as well as the top view both clearly show the chippings which appear to have been made downwards from the convex surface by someone who prised the lens out of a metal band, presumably of gold. (If the band were of base metal, there would be no point in doing this.) The drawing also accurately shows the flatness of the lens base, which other observers did not always appreciate. But the pressure-flaws in the crystal have been over-emphasized by the artist.

but the pressure-flaws in the crystal were sufficiently over-emphasized by the artist that a footnote was published stating: 'The shading of fig. 131 representing internal striae, is too strong, suggesting more opacity than really exists.'[12]

This *Journal*'s report also corrected the misprint of Brewster's measurement of the thickness of the lens, by changing the text of Layard's footnote citing Brewster to say the lens was one-fourth of an inch thick, and appending a footnote which states that it was nine-tenths 'in the original'.[13] However, it had taken 30 years for a correction of this fundamental measurement to appear in print. And the many readers of Layard's books about exciting excavations in the Middle East can hardly have subscribed *en masse* to the *Journal of the Royal Microscopical Society*, which even for the keenest of scientists is hardly light reading. The correction of Brewster's measurements can thus only have reached a tiny minority of those interested in the lens, if indeed there were any such people about. No microscopists seem ever to have come forward on the subject, from 1883 to the present, and one wonders if they ever will.

The French were the first to sense the importance of the Layard Lens, and the alert and accomplished François Arago learned of the reports of a talk by Brewster in 1852 about the lens, a summary of which in French had been circulated amongst members of the French Academy of Sciences in Paris and published in *l'Athenaeum Français*.[14] The publication of this French translation actually preceded by a year the publication of Brewster's original remarks in English, so that the first publication of the Layard Lens was in French! Arago was thus able to mention the Layard Lens in his book *Astronomie Populaire*, published in Paris in 4 volumes between 1854 and 1857, and published in English as *Popular Astronomy* in 2 volumes in 1855. I quote his remarks from the English edition: 'At the meeting of the British Association, held at Belfast in the year 1852, Sir David Brewster showed a plate of rock crystal worked into the form of a lens, which was recently found among the ruins of Nineveh. Sir David Brewster, so competent a judge in a question of this kind, maintained that this lens had been destined for optical purposes, and that it never was an article of dress.'[15] Arago's mention of this appears in the context of a discussion of Roman lenses, which were beginning to be known from Italy, as well as related Latin texts.

The next mention of the Layard Lens to appear in print was in 1871, when the classicist Thomas Henri Martin published his lengthy and ill-tempered sceptical work 'Sur des Instruments d'Optique Faussement Attribués aux Anciens par Quelques Savants Modernes' ('Concerning Optical Instruments Falsely Attributed to the Ancients by Some Modern Scholars'). He published this in Italy, not in France, possibly because he had been so caustic about so many distinguished French scholars.[16] Martin appears to have been unable to read English, so his knowledge of Brewster's talk was solely through the French translation of Brewster's note in *l'Athenaeum Français* (Martin betrays no knowledge of Arago's earlier discussion, although he was familiar with Arago's book, of which he evidently disapproved, and to which he seems not to have wished to call attention).

Martin dismisses Brewster's conclusions entirely, by saying (translation):

> Sir David Brewster thinks that this little piece of quartz had been shaped to be a true optical lens, and not a simple ornament. This hypothesis of the English scholar seems to us improbable. The crystal was undoubtedly an ornament, like the bronzes and other precious objects with which this Assyrian gem was found, and like various Roman stones of which it remains for us to speak. Meanwhile, it is not impossible that the crystal had been used as a burning-glass.[17]

It will be noticed that Martin contradicts himself in this brief passage. On the one hand, he insists that the Layard Lens was 'undoubtedly an ornament', and then admits it might have been a burning-glass; in that case, the word 'undoubtedly' seems out of place earlier. Martin's entire monograph was dedicated to disproving any and all optical technology in ancient times, so that it can hardly be viewed as a dispassionate account of anything. Martin was a well-known classicist, with a knowledge of many obscure late Greek texts such as the Aristotelian commentaries. It is a pity that such a great scholar was prepared to devote a considerable proportion of his energies to what really amounts to an embarrassingly sustained emotional tirade. It is notable that Martin never examined any ancient lens.

In 1884, Georges Perrot and Charles Chipiez published Volume II of their mammoth work, *Histoire de l'Art dans l'Antiquité* (*History of Art in Antiquity*). In dealing with the art of Chaldaea and Assyria, they briefly mention the Layard Lens.[18] Speaking of Layard's excavations (which they correctly say were at Nimrud rather than Nineveh), they mention (translation): 'It is a rock crystal lens of which the convex face seems to have been prepared fairly roughly, on the lapidary's wheel; it could have served, despite the imperfection of the cutting, as a magnifying glass, or with a very bright sun, as a burning-glass.'[18a]

In 1901, Pierre Pansier published his book *Histoire des Lunettes* (*The History of Spectacles*) at Paris, of which no copy exists in the British Library and the only copy in Britain is deposited in the Library of the British Optical Association in London. In this he writes (translation):

> The ancients were familiar with convex glasses: that is incontestable. In the ruins of Nineveh a rock-crystal lens was found. It was of an oval shape, 16 mm long, 12 mm across; it was plano-convex. Its surface is rough and dulled; the convex surface seems to have been coarsely ground on a wheel, it is quite well polished even though somewhat deteriorated. Despite these imperfections and its bad state of conservation, one can measure the focal distance, which is about 15 cm.[19]

In 1903 the Layard Lens appears in the literature again, this time in Austria. Emil Bock mentions it in his monograph of 62 pages, *Die Brille und Ihre Geschichte* (*Spectacles and Their History*).[20] Bock mentions several ancient lenses which had been found by this time, and accepts all except one as true lenses, saying (translation): 'We must assume that these convex lenses were used as magnifying glasses and as burning glasses.' Of the Layard Lens specifically, amongst a list of ancient lenses which he discusses, his comments are (translation): '. . . finally, a plano-convex lens from Nineveh with a 3 cm diameter and a refractive value of 10 dioptres. It is striking that these are all convex lenses.'

It should be noted that the measurement of 3 cm given by Bock for the 'diameter' of the lens implies that it is circular, whereas it is really an oval,

The Crystal Sun

whose true dimensions are 4.2 cm for its major axis and 3.43 cm for its minor axis. We can see that most of these discussions of the Layard Lens are taking place far removed from direct observation, and few are making any attempt to study the lens and get an accurate description of it. It appears, however, that Pansier must have personally examined the lens.[21]

In 1922, the *British Museum Guide* appeared. The Layard Lens was listed as item 222, and its description stated:

> Oval plano-convex piece of rock crystal with flaws and striae. The edge has been ground and bevelled, presumably for setting in a mount or inlaying. When this object was brought from Nimrud about the year 1850 it was thought by some to be a lens, which had belonged to an astronomical instrument; but this is not the case, and the piece of crystal was probably part of a personal ornament.

The length is given as 1 5/8 inches, the width 1 3/8 inches, and the maximum thickness 3/16 of an inch. This is the first hint that anyone had ever believed the lens to be from an astronomical instrument. It must have been an oral opinion expressed by someone at the Museum, as I have never found anything in print prior to 1930 expressing such a view (see Barker, below).

In 1924 the lens was briefly mentioned by the German Assyriologist Meissner. In Vol. II of *Babylonien und Assyrien*, he says (translation):[22]

> . . . the ancient Babylonians and Assyrians possibly had already been making use of ground lenses for the elimination of the impediments of short-sightedness and long-sightedness [myopia and presbyopia]. In fact, in the ruins of Kalach a rock crystal lens with a convex surface and a plane surface has been found, which, as its rough cutting suggests, was probably not an article of jewellery but may actually have served as a magnifying-glass and burning-glass.

Meissner actually cited the 1922 *British Museum Guide* in a footnote when making these statements, so his comments were thus an unmistakeable public challenge to the anonymous British Museum official who wrote the catalogue's description of the lens as an ornament. The fact that the *British Museum Guide*'s comments could not go unchallenged within Assyriology for as much as two years shows that there were some who considered that the official concerned had overstepped the bounds of scholarly disinterested-ness by making a dogmatic statement in contradiction of Brewster, Layard and Pansier without any actual evidence to support it. This was an abuse of his position, since he hid behind anonymity and issued an official descrip-tion (owing to his access to authorship in the *Guide*) which arrogantly dismissed contrary opinions but gave no justification. Meissner, at least, was clearly irritated and made his position publicly clear.

At last, in 1927, a British scholar finally gave some attention to the Layard Lens once more. With the exception of the *Museum Guide*, 44 years had elapsed since the lens's last mention in print in Britain, when the engravings of it were published in the *Journal of the Royal Microscopical Society* of 1883. The author in this instance was H. C. Beck, and he read his lecture 'Early Magnifying Glasses' to the Society of Antiquaries in London on 1 December 1927; it was published in *The Antiquaries Journal* for 1928. Beck enthusiastically insisted that the ancients had magnifying lenses, and gave several examples: Egyptian, Carthaginian, and Minoan. But he was dismissive of the Layard Lens, which he called the 'so-called magnifying glass of Sargon':

> We have not at present got any magnifiers from Mesopotamia. The so-called magnifying glass of Sargon is wrongly named as, although it is polished, the surface is entirely irregular and it does not magnify. In that country also the glass, particularly the clear glass, from the earlier layers is generally in a very bad state of preservation.[23]

In 1930, the distinguished optician W. B. Barker, President of what is today called the College of Optometrists in London, dedicated an entire article to 'The Nineveh Lens', which was thus the first extended study and treatment of the subject by anyone since Brewster first examined the lens in 1852.[24] Although Barker made the same mistake that everyone makes – stating that the lens was discovered in 1853, whereas that was really the date of its publication by Layard – he went on to give the most detailed description yet of the lens. He gave measurements as '1.6 inches long and 1.4 inches broad, and about .25 inch thick'. Barker noticed that Brewster's report had been in error, and said of it: 'Some of the dimensions given by Brewster are inaccurate and are possibly clerical errors.'

It was Barker who was the first to note the important point that the convex superior surface was 'an irregular toroid, with an average curvature of +5.00 dioptres, the maximum curve being +8.00 and the minimum +4.00'. This point would be raised again later by the ophthalmic optician Walter Gasson, and we shall see that it is fundamental to a consideration of the true purpose of the lens. 'Toroidal' comes from 'torus', which is a doughnut-shape. It is obvious that the shape of a torus is very different from that of a sphere. If the grinding of a convex lens surface is not done spherically, but instead is done toroidally, the result will not be 'even' in the conventional sense and to the casual observer, but it is nevertheless 'even' in its own terms, for it has been produced that way on purpose. Such lenses are necessary to correct for the unevenness of vision in people suffering from astigmatism. It is sufficient to know this without going into the detail of the grinding process.

Barker misinterpreted the 'flaws in the internal structure' of the crystal, due to lack of familiarity with these old crystal lenses (his expertise being

15

in glass), because he says they 'were obvious fissures in the piece of mineral which was used as the raw material'. But having studied at least 150 old crystal lenses by now, I am well aware that the prominent 'flaws' which he mentions, and which previous authors called 'striae', are pressure-flaws which were not present originally in the lens but came about as a result of blows, weight of rubble, burial, etc. If one does not realize this, one can easily draw wrong conclusions about the original purpose of the lens.

Barker's powers of observation were otherwise very acute, and although he misinterpreted the pressure-flaws, he could see that far too much attention had gone into the manufacture of the lens for it to have been intended as a mere ornament. The grinding and polishing of rock crystal is a hard business, and it would have been senseless for such extraordinary attention to have been lavished on this small object if it had been an inlay, quite apart from the fact that since it was originally perfectly clear, it would have been so transparent an inlay that it would have been essentially invisible! (There are some male archaeologists today who have tried to interpret many surviving Greek crystal lenses as women's jewellery, but they overlook the key point that women are not noted for choosing to wear invisible jewellery!)

Barker's remarks are:

The several authorities have asserted that this and similar lenses were most probably used for ornament or, alternatively, as burning glasses. The writer is distinctly of the opinion that neither of these surmises are correct. In the first place, there has been too much deliberate fabrication of the lens for merely ornamental purposes, and, additionally, its dimensions and shape do not support such a contention. To suggest its use as a burning glass is also by no means obvious, as it concentrates the rays of the sun very imperfectly, and a lens of high dioptric power would have done such work better. Further, the relatively small size of the lens would render it rather inefficient for such a purpose. . . . It is possible that the history of this lens is much more romantic; its shape and size suggest that it was made to cover the orbital aperture ['eye socket' in ordinary English] fairly accurately, and its focus certainly suggests that it was deliberately designed to magnify some special kind of near work. . . . It is reasonable to assume that . . . masterpieces [of ancient art such as the Portland Vase] would only have been produced after a great deal of experience and the acquisition of a great deal of skill, and that the artist would very likely have reached, therefore, an age of presbyopia [long-sightedness, requiring spectacles for a modern man]. A lens such as this, held or fixed before his work, would enable him to see detail with great exactitude, and it is only by assuming such magnifying aids were procurable by the workers, that the fineness of the carving on many ancient gems, and similar treasures, can be accounted for.

Barker then addresses possible implications for ancient astronomy of the discovery of the Layard Lens, and thus we learn more of the hint given in the 1922 *Museum Guide* on this subject:

> The age of the lens has not been definitely fixed, but it possibly dates from the seventh century before the birth of Christ. This suggested date has prompted a still further conjecture as to its probable use. Mr A. C. [*sic*, should be R. Campbell] Thompson, a former assistant in the Assyrian Department of the British Museum, has published a series of reports of the 'Astronomers of Nineveh and Babylon', which were found recorded on a large number of tablets of the period of Assur-barri-pal [*sic*, should be Assurbanipal], BC. 668–625. On these tablets are to be found records of observations of the planet Dilbat, which cannot be seen with the naked eye, but is visible with the aid of a fairly strong glass. This fact leads to the further suggestion which has been made by one Assyriologist, that lenses such as the Nineveh lens were used by the ancient astronomers who must have called to their aid some optical apparatus for magnifying. The former theory, however, has its appeal, and the assumption, surely, is warranted that this historic lens, 25 centuries ago, was used as an aid to vision for exacting close work, and as such, it merits the attention of opticians of modern times.
>
> By the courtesy and kind co-operation of the Director of the British Museum, we are enabled to print a photographic illustration, showing a full and also an edgewise view of the lens.

Thus, it was Barker in late 1929 who evidently commissioned the well-known early photos of the Layard Lens, and he was the first to publish a photo of it anywhere. See Plate 34.

The astronomical texts to which Barker referred were the ones published by R. Campbell Thompson in 1900.[25] The planet called Dilbat is now thought to be Venus, which certainly does not require a telescope to be seen. But the question of 'invisible' outer planets, of the Galilean moons of Jupiter and of the rings of Saturn being familiar to ancient astronomers is one which has never been entirely resolved, together with the possibility of rudimentary telescopes in antiquity.[26] Amongst both the ancient Greeks and the ancient Chinese there were traditions implying an astronomical knowledge of these two planetary phenomena in our solar system which cannot be discerned by the naked eye, and knowledge of both is also possessed by the Dogon tribe of Mali in West Africa, and ancient telescopes could have been the source of this knowledge. However, ancient telescopes could not possibly have explained the Dogon knowledge of the white dwarf star Sirius B, because of its proximity to the star Sirius A and the impossibility of resolving the parallax, not to mention the equally insoluble problem of brightness. Nor does the Layard Lens by itself seem to have the necessary physical characteristics to have had any use in a telescope (owing to its toroidal grinding), so that this question may be entirely disregarded as a red herring as far as it is concerned.[27]

It was in 1957 that a major historian of science first turned his attention to the Layard Lens, when R. J. Forbes published Volume V of his *Studies in Ancient Technology*. However, Forbes was extraordinarily brief in his treatment. Despite the fact that he published altogether many volumes concerning ancient technology, Forbes only devoted a meagre two pages to the entire subject of ancient lenses![28] Therefore, despite his reputation for extended treatment, Forbes actually had less to say on this subject than most people. He accepted that various ancient lenses which he mentions were magnifying glasses 'excellent for engraving work'. Of the Layard Lens itself, all he says is: 'The "plano-convex lens from Nineveh", the so-called glass of Sargon is about 3 cm in diameter and if its polished surface had been regular it would have been a lens of some 10 dioptres, but in its present state it does not magnify.' This statement is actually incorrect (see later discussion).

The next year, 1958, another significant historian of astronomy and optics, Henry C. King, wrote an article entitled 'Lenses in Antiquity', showing lack of awareness of most literary sources, but mentioning a number of ancient lenses.[29] He discussed the Layard Lens at length, saying:

Assyrian craftsmen made a small amount of glass ware, barely meeting the demands of a limited home market. From Assyria comes the earliest known example of the lens-grinder's art. During excavations in 1853 of the great mound which overlaid the ancient city of Nimrud, Sir Henry Layard discovered a primitive lens. . . . It dates from 700 BC . . . Fashioned from a piece of transparent quartz, it has an oval shape, 1.6 inches by 1.4 inches, and is about 0.25 inch thick. One surface is almost perfectly flat, the other is convex, but irregularly so. The convex surface is akin to an irregular toroid, that is, it gives rise to different optical powers in different directions across the lens. The focal length is therefore different for each direction or meridian, the maximum focal length being about 17 inches and the minimum only 8 inches. The convex surface has indications of having been ground on a lapidary's wheel. This would account for the numerous facets which cause the differences in surface curvature, but the polish is nevertheless quite good. Originally, this lens may have been used solely as an ornament, less likely as a burning glass, but hardly as an occasional magnifier, that is, an aid to vision. Although the quartz is now badly flawed, it doubtless formed one clear piece; had its surface been truly spherical, it would have been useful in magnifying special kinds of fine work, as for example, in gem-engraving or reading fine cuneiform script.

The Nimrud lens is by no means the only known example of a transparent stone in lentoid form.

Dr King was thus the first person to state clearly that the Layard Lens had once 'formed one clear piece' of rock crystal, a point which previous writers had not taken in. He did not repeat the silly theories about inherent flaws, naphtha leaking out of cracks, and so forth, but realized that the reason why the lens bore flaws today was because of *damage*. By the time I contacted Henry King in May 1980, to ask him about his notes on various ancient lenses he had examined, he was within a month of retirement and he wrote me a letter containing the following depressing information (21 May 1980):

> The articles to which you refer, particularly my own, were not of much academic merit – my efforts depended on secondary sources and could hardly be called research. As a corpus they sketch the field of enquiry and open up sundry lines of study, but in general they lack rigour. I prefer to consign mine to oblivion! That, in fact, has been realised. Almost all my optical material, and much else besides, has been destroyed . . . Anyway, I wish you every success in your enquiries and congratulate you on tracking down the lenses of Woodward's collection.

King's further unpublished information was thus lost. King actually inspected a number of ancient lenses personally, which is more than many of his predecessors had done, and I believe he was thus a bit hard on himself.[30]

In 1962 the great scholar of the history of Chinese science, Joseph Needham, with whom I was later to be associated and even travel to China, published the volume dealing with Physics in his series of volumes, *Science and Civilisation in China*.[31] In his section on Optics, he mentions various Western ancient lenses in passing, commencing as follows: 'In the West, acquaintance with rock-crystal is of ancient date; a famous worked piece of Babylonian [*sic*: should be Assyrian] provenance (assessed at the ninth century BC) was described by Layard.'[32]

In 1965, the optometrist James R. Gregg published his book *The History of Optometry* in America. Chapter Two is entitled 'Early Knowledge of Glass and Lenses'. In it, he writes:

> The ruins of Ninevah [*sic*], about 700 BC, produced the most famous of all ancient lenses. Now in the British Museum, this lens is flat on one side, convex on the other, apparently polished for a purpose. Still there is no evidence as to what the Chaldaeans used it for, and it is speculative to attribute any optical use to it, though it would be ideal as a burning lens.[33]

During the late 1960s a number of people interested in curious phenomena learned of the Layard Lens and it began to become much discussed and speculated upon outside of scholarly and optical circles. This was when Derek Price began to talk about it to people like myself and Arthur Clarke. As I said earlier, Derek was at that time Avalon Professor of the History of Science at Yale University and his comments carried some weight. He had discovered the Antikythera Mechanism, a complicated ancient Greek computing mechanism which had been found in a shipwreck, and of which at the time I met him he was making the definitive study, eventually published in 1974.[34] Derek said to me he wished to make a proper study of the Layard Lens. Unfortunately, he died early, before he could carry out that task at which he would have excelled, and the len's unavailability for many of the relevant years made it impossible for him to do so for part of that time in any case.

As a result of the grapevine of gossip in the 1960s about strange phenomena – it was a hothouse decade for such subjects – news of the Layard Lens circulated widely amongst fringe scientists and scholars, and even more so amongst the wholly unqualified who were merely sensation-seekers. A number of 'nuts' began to lay siege to the British Museum making enquiries about the Layard Lens. Of course, a number of other interested enquirers approached the Museum, who were not 'nuts' at all, but a certain degree of panic and disdain seems to have set in amongst the staff, and who was to say who was a 'nut' and who was not? The situation reached a climax when the controversial Erich von Däniken referred obliquely in 1969 to the Layard Lens in his book *Chariots of the Gods?*, a worldwide bestseller which sold tens of millions of copies, and according to press reports at the time, had outsold the Bible. Von Däniken was convinced that 'God was an astronaut', and that countless unusual artifacts were from outer space, left behind by visiting spacemen. He wrote of ancient lenses the following vague and puzzling claim:

> In Egypt and Iraq there were finds of cut crystal lenses which today can only be made by using cesium oxide, in other words an oxide that has to be produced by electro-chemical processes.[35]

He offers no explanation of this strange statement, and I confess not to know what he is talking about, except that he seems to be saying that the Layard Lens (which he does not name) required electricity for its production! In his Plates Section, however, von Däniken reproduces a photo of the Layard Lens with this caption: 'An Assyrian crystal lens from the seventh century BC. To grind such a lens requires a highly sophisticated mathematical formula. Where did the Assyrians get such knowledge?' There seems little connection between the text of the book and the text of the plate caption. It was clearly the plate which attracted the most attention, so that the Layard Lens was seen by tens of millions of people, with the name of the British Museum clearly visible on the ruler beside the lens – a guarantee that the Museum would be swamped by cranks enquiring about the object. I personally recall in the early 1970s hearing dozens of people chatting about the crystal lens in the British Museum at dinner parties, on buses, and in just about every setting. The Layard Lens at that point entered briefly into public folklore, though no one knew its name or the details. I recall that people liked savouring the mystery of a crystal lens sitting hidden in the British Museum – a lens jealously guarded by paranoid archaeologists to whom the public might, if they only had the energy and the inclination, lay siege in their thousands. But of course, part of the attraction of the mystery was that it must on no account be solved; that would ruin everything. The British Museum unwittingly contributed to the public frenzy by not letting anybody near the lens for years!

Another serious enquirer, but a more important one, who was frustrated at the same time was Walter Gasson, an ophthalmic optician who was a leading historian in his field. He had resumed his historical studies in the 1960s (his first published work of this kind appeared in 1939), and he had completed a great deal of important work. But he could not obtain access to the Layard Lens, which he was told was being 'remounted'. The 'remounting' took many years!

About 1972, under considerable pressure, the Museum finally put the Layard Lens back on display. Gasson found it in that year restored to view as Exhibit Number 6 in the Babylonian Gallery, labelled as dating between *circa* 900 BC and *circa* 700 BC. The Keeper of Western Asiatic Antiquities in 1972 then allowed Walter Gasson to inspect the lens and measure it scientifically, resulting in its first proper scrutiny since Brewster in 1852, 120 years before. The results were published by Gasson in his seminal article 'The Oldest Lens in the World: A Critical Study of the Layard Lens', in the journal *The Ophthalmic Optician* at the end of 1972.[36] It is an unfortunate title for the article, since the Layard Lens is *not* the oldest lens in the world by any means.

In his article, Gasson recounted his difficulties in getting access to the Layard Lens (which he told me at greater length in conversation), and after lengthy preliminaries and quoting Brewster's report, he got down to the results of his analysis:

This slightly cloudy rock crystal lens as mentioned earlier, was mounted not as in the illustration (1930) [the Barker photo], but inset in a Perspex stand as shown in the diagrams (Figure 1). [Plate 34]

These lens measurements are in agreement to those found in 1930 by Barker. [My own recent measurements are more precise, but nearly the same, varying at most by 2 mm.] On careful inspection under a hand magnifier there was a slight peripheral bevel as shown in the edge view. This suggests that the lens was probably retained in some sort of a mounting – long since perished. The writer with some trepidation was allowed to measure with a lens spherometer [an instrument with three adjustable pins which gives an accurate reading of curvature of the surface expressed in dioptres] the surface of the lens itself. One side reasonably well polished as mentioned by Brewster, has a fairly good plano surface. [In other words, it was flat.] The other rather faintly scratched convex spherical surface was toroidal in curvature, varying from +4.0D to +8.0D [D = dioptres] again confirming the recordings made by Barker in 1930. The angular direction of +4.0D was approximately 165° to the shorter axis of the lens. The two dioptric meridians were approximately at right angles to each other.

If the lens would be turned through an angle of 90° in the direction used as a spectacle lens, it could be reasonably considered as being +4D sph/ +4.0D cyl axis 75°. The dioptric difference made by the refractive index of rock crystal being 1.523, for which the lens spherometer was calibrated, does make a small difference in the powers [as expressed in dioptres; he gives formulae and corrects these to 4.25D and 8.5D respectively, which is not of any great consequence] . . . It seems rather incongruous that an eminent scientist of Sir David Brewster's standing could pass unnoticed the printer's error giving the lens thickness as 9/10 inch instead of 1/4 inch. This shows that the printer's proofs could not have been checked. In any case any casual observation could have shown this gross error to any layman inspecting the lens itself, even from a distance in its showcase. . . . The almost perfect oval shape of the lens creates some interesting speculation. A circular shape ground by a lapidary is much easier to fashion. A spherical curvature is also much easier to grind than a toroid, especially as this ancient craftsman was able to make a fairly good plano back surface. Any amateur lathe-turner knows this from experience. . . . It seems to the writer that the lens powers and shape were of deliberate design and fabrication. The 41 x 35 mm almost perfect oval shape conforms to the facial orbital aperture [the eye socket]. The possibility of the lentoid being used by a scribe in the palace library having perhaps a marked presbyopic error [i.e. who was long-sighted] is of conjectural interest. . . . The lens shape itself is interesting as the 41 x 35 mm size almost conforms to the old-fashioned pre-1930 '000' eye size. Those of the older generation of practising opticians will no doubt remember the astig frames and rimless *pince-nez* spectacles of 0, 00, and 000 eye sizes. This oval shape 41 x 35 mm is almost exactly that as laid down by the 1927 Optical Standards Committee, with an axial difference of approximately 6 mm.

At this point, Gasson gives a footnote to a 1935 textbook on ophthalmic lenses, which I have consulted. It gives a drawing of the shape represented by the Layard Lens which is quite astonishing.[37] The visual evidence thus is even more impressive than Gasson's statements, since the resemblance is seen at a glance.

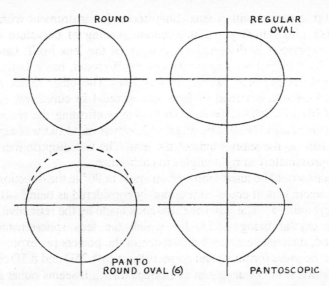

Figure 3. The four types of pre-Second-World-War '000'-size spectacle lenses, as illustrated by Emsley and Swaine in their textbook *Ophthalmic Lenses* (1935/1940). The 'regular oval' shape at the top right is practically identical to the Layard Lens, as first noticed by Walter Gasson. Both the modern lens and the ancient lens are precisely regular ovals; the modern major and minor axes are 2.95 cm and 3.85 cm, whereas the Layard Lens's major and minor axes are 3.43 cm and 4.2 cm, giving differences therefore of less than 5 millimetres for the minor axis and 3.5 millimetres for the major axis. A more precise 'fit' for a spectacle lens shape could hardly be achieved.

Gasson points out that the lens would have been of little use as a burning-lens:

> Since the lens with its fairly high astigmatic configuration would not focus the sun's rays too well, one meridional line focus being approximately 24 cm. and the other 12 cm., the circle of least confusion value being sph + cyl over 2=4 + 4 over 2 = 6.0D = f is 16 cm. approximately.
>
> The sun's image is not sufficiently concentrated for the lens to be effectively used as a condensing-burning glass. The Minoan lens on the other hand, discovered in Crete by Forsdyke in 1927, was circular with a diameter of over an inch, with a focal length of about an inch, giving a dioptric power of approximately + 40.0D. . . . Ancient burning glasses were generally of a much shorter focal length [than the Layard Lens] for better concentration of the sun's rays.

Gasson also points out that:

> The lens according to the museum authorities as well as earlier writers, was considered to have been made for ornamental purposes such as a

plaque or locket. It may perhaps have been used as a badge of office, or solely as a means of decoration or even as an amulet to ward off evil influences. There is however no conclusive proof of any of these suppositions.

Gasson correctly identified the flaws in the lens as pressure-flaws:

The several flaws appear under a hand magnifier to be in the back plano-surface. No doubt these have been made by external pressures and surface deterioration caused by the centuries that have elapsed since the lens was originally made.

Gasson also stresses that the lens was found at Nimrud, not Nineveh as believed by Layard at the time, and proposes that the best name for the lens is the Layard Lens 'after its celebrated Victorian discoverer'.

In the 1970s people interested in oddities and curious phenomena used to talk a great deal about the American William R. Corliss and his *Sourcebooks*. In these, he gathered *précis* of odd facts about nature and man, for he was an indefatigable researcher of such things. In 1976, Corliss published privately a pamphlet entitled *Strange Artifacts: A Sourcebook on Ancient Man.*[38] This was actually his second pamphlet on the subject of strange artifacts from antiquity. He had come across Brewster's report of the Layard Lens in 1853 in the *American Journal of Science* and he summarized it; Corliss had nothing to add other than that. But by virtue of the fact that Corliss had mentioned the lens, a wide circle of people outside scholarly circles came to know about it for the first time, and many of the members of the American public who had seen the photo published with a mere caption by von Däniken were thus able to learn a few actual facts concerning the mysterious object for the first time.

In 1978, the catalogue entry for the Layard Lens which I copied down at the time took this form: 'Nimrud. NW palace, Room AB. Oval lens of ground quartz with one plane and one convex surface. Probably inlay element from an ornament. Diam. $1\frac{1}{4}$ inches to $1\frac{5}{8}$ inches and thickness *c.* $\frac{1}{4}$ inch.' The 1922 *certainty* that the lens could only have been an ornament (as stated in the Museum Guide) had by this time been softened to a *probability*, which was far more scientific! The earlier dogmatism has obviously been found too embarrassing and arrogant and had been abandoned. It was in 1978 that I commissioned new photos of the Layard Lens showing it being held up to an eye socket, thereby visually demonstrating Gasson's point, and also magnifying the print of a newspaper. These photos have never been published, as they are my copyright. They may be seen in Plates 35, 36 and 37.

By 1980, the display card for the Layard Lens at that time in the

Assyrian Basement, Case 4, Number 13, had taken another step back from dogmatism, reading:

> From the NW Palace, Kalhu (Nimrud). Plaque of rock crystal with one flat face and the other convex. It has some optical properties and could be a lens. Alternatively, it may have been meant as a decorative inlay.

At last the British Museum staff had formulated a description of the object which was not tendentious, and was genuinely neutral as regards the object's purpose.

In 1981, Leonard Gorelick and A. John Gwinnett published two articles in the American archaeological magazine *Expedition* in which they considered the problem of how miniature work was done in antiquity. They dismissed the idea of lenses having been used, and concluded that ancient engravers were myopic![39] This extraordinary conclusion was reached in ignorance of the existence of any ancient lenses other than the Layard Lens; they said 'excavated examples [of lenses] would be needed' to convince them that lenses were used. No further publication by them is known on this subject, so presumably they never did learn of the existence of the hundreds of extant ancient lenses which litter the world's museums. From some unspecified published measurements of the Layard Lens, Gorelick and Gwinnett commissioned 'an expert lapidary, Mr Martin Walter, to copy it in rock crystal . . . This piece was then refracted by an optician who reported "a magnification of 2 diopters but significant distortion"'. They do not specify which of the various differing published sets of measurements they used, nor do they give any reference, so the reported results are useless; for instance, did they follow the misprint in Brewster's report giving a thickness of nine-tenths of an inch? We do not know. The cutting of a replica sounds good, but the report remains anecdotal and uncalibrated, since there are no details given! And yet the authors seem to think that proceeding in this vague manner is adequate, and that their findings are entitled to be considered final. The level of substantiation of these opinions is not really any higher than what is found in Erich von Däniken; he too made replicas of things and made claims on the basis of them without giving the details.[40]

In 1996, Peter James and Nick Thorpe published their book *Ancient Inventions*, which I reviewed favourably in *Nature*.[41] They published a photo of the Layard Lens and a page of commentary. They concluded:

> . . . its most likely purpose was for magnification. The use to which the ancient Assyrians would have put such optical aids is easy enough to guess. Their craftsmen followed a long tradition in Mesopotamia of manufacturing intricately carved seals, . . . As a matter of course archaeologists study these impressions with photographic enlargements or by

using a magnifying glass – simply because the details on many seals are not clearly visible to the naked eye. It seems reasonable enough that the craftsmen themselves employed some optical aid. . . . the lens found by Layard is extremely feeble, being just strong enough to 'demonstrate magnification'. (It enlarges things by 0.5 times.) [This is inaccurate; parts of it magnify up to two times. James and Thorpe clearly did not measure the magnification themselves.] Nevertheless this was sufficient to start a controversy that has been simmering for well over a century.[42]

James and Thorpe severely criticize Gorelick and Gwinnett (1981), and point out the astonishing inconsistencies of their logic at length.[43]

* * *

We have thus completed a survey of the literature relating to the Layard Lens from 1852 to the present. It is now time to turn our attention to a physical description of the object which goes beyond what has been attempted before. Readers who only want to know the conclusions may skip to the next section. Here is my account of the object, after which we shall learn what it actually is:

REPORT ON THE LAYARD LENS, 1998

Location: Department of Western Asiatic Antiquities,
British Museum, London
Object number: 12091

ROCK CRYSTAL. PLANO-CONVEX, OVAL.

Maximum thickness: 6.2 mm
Minimum thickness: 4.1 mm
Major axis: 4.2 cm
Minor axis: 3.43 cm
Bisections of the two axes forming a St Andrew's Cross give equal measurements of 4.17 cm, indicating a regular ellipsoid shape.

Description: The lens is of uneven thickness, and the rim is remarkable for being heavily but evenly scoured by deep parallel striations cut into the crystal at an angle of about 20° to the horizontal. This was unquestionably done on purpose, methodically and carefully. The intention was presumably to create a rim with a rough but regular texture capable of 'gripping' a mounting very firmly indeed. It is most unusual to do this with a crystal lens, and it would seem to indicate an unnatural degree of anxiety about the lens coming out of its mounting, which could find an explanation if the owner were a very powerful potentate, for instance.

General condition: Substantial-sized clean chips are found on the upper rim, especially at one end of the minor axis. These have no ingrained dirt and no wear, and appear to be modern, or at least subsequent to excavation. It would be more accurate to call them gouges. The worst of these gouges have been made downwards from the superior surface, evidently by a small sharp tool, but appear to have been restricted to what was possible with the lens still being mounted, as they did not extend all the way down the rim. They give an appearance of someone having prised the lens out of a tight mounting. The pattern of this chipping is such that the rim seems to have been protected and very tightly mounted while this chipping was being done, so that the chips were restricted to what could be accomplished by downward strokes from above. Although the Layard excavations were apparently carried out by large numbers of people, and it may be hard to imagine subterfuge on the part of an assistant, the possibility must be considered that a valuable mounting of a precious metal was prised loose from this lens and stolen before Layard saw the object. There is a precedent for this happening: in 1834, a gold mounting was prised off the plano-convex Nola Lens excavated from a Greek grave in Southern Italy by one of the workers in the excavation and sold to a dealer to be melted down, and the lens was handed over to the archaeologist as if it had been unmounted. He later discovered what had happened and remarked in his report that 'its rim was thereby somewhat damaged at one spot', as we see also describes the Layard Lens. (The advantage in prising off a mounting rather than pocketing the entire object is that a mounting of precious metal can be melted down and sold, and its origin becomes undetectable.) The Layard Lens has such a thick rim that if it had a precious metal mounting, the mounting would have had to be at least 5 mm in thickness. This would have had real value to a poor worker, as in bulk it would have been equal to perhaps half a dozen gold rings.

All around the top and bottom of the rim are what appear at first glance to be a regular series of extremely tiny 'chips'. But a minute inspection reveals that these are merely the tops and bottoms of the scoured rim-lines, and not real chips at all. Some ingrained dirt has settled into these at the ends and remains, despite the fact that the lens has obviously been washed several times subsequent to excavation. Dirt has been removed so completely from the scoured rim itself that the cleaning and washing of the lens must have been very heavy and determined.

On the basal surface, there are very small genuine chips along the rim base which are larger than the 'apparent chips' of the emerging scoured rim-lines, but far smaller than the gouges made from above in what we surmise was the attempt to prise the lens free of a mounting. These would appear to be ancient chipping from the time the lens was mounted, due to slight movement in the mount over a period of time.

There are two separate patterns of wear on the superior and basal surfaces of the lens. Both surfaces are very severely scuffed with crisscrossing lines, indicating far-too-excessive post-excavation washing, scrubbing, and rubbing dry or 'polishing'. It appears that a brush has been used at some time, of a not very gentle type (presumably in the 19th century). Beneath the resulting mass of scuff-marks may be perceived – more particularly on the basal surface – a large amount of nearly microscopic pitting, which presumably occurred as a result of the lens's long sojourn underground, a period of approximately two-and-a-half millennia during which the quartz suffered this minor degradation to its surfaces. The nearly microscopic pits contain deeply-ingrained dirt in quantities too small to have been accessible to the macroscopic cleaning, which could not reach into such tiny cavities. The aggregate effect of this dirt trapped in the tiny – almost invisible – pits is to provide a very subtle darkening of the lens, the cause of which, though superficial and not innate to the quartz, is – in terms of determining what it actually is – nearly at the threshold of detection by powerful examining lenses. This, together with the pronounced obscuring effects of the scuffing, means that the lens does not appear to be perfectly clear today. In addition, there are the well-known and extremely prominent pressure-cracks and associated pressure-flaws, which help cloud the lens at the present day. The considerable pitting on the basal surface indicates that during the period of its burial, the lens cannot have been backed, and it is most unlikely that the lens was ever backed, for if it had been, the small chips caused by movement within the mount would have extended further beyond the rim. It should also be pointed out that the quartz would have been wholly transparent in its pristine state, and would have been completely invisible if backed, so that one would only have seen the back and not the quartz except when close enough to handle it.

The lens is today marred by two major pressure-cracks and some associated pressure-flawing, which would not have been an original feature of the object. The pressure-crack which runs more or less longitudinally (though at a substantial angle, about 30° off the major axis) we can call the lateral pressure-crack; it is 3.2 cm long. It forms a rough 'T' shape with a transverse pressure-crack which is also 3.2 cm long. This transverse crack is the more serious of the two, because, unlike the lateral crack, it has worked through to form a crack in the basal surface. Looking downwards from the superior surface, above and beyond the right-hand side of the 'T'-bar, there is a mass of pressure-flawing.

Near the centre of the superior surface is a rough pitted pattern (now cleared of dirt) measuring 2.5 mm in length and forming an unusual branched pattern; as this is directly above the lateral pressure-crack, it would appear to be the mark of the hard, and uneven, object – probably of metal – which struck the lens (presumably in antiquity) and caused the pressure-cracks. The blow was not a broad and flat blow at all, as has so often happened to other crystal lenses which I have inspected. The branching pattern of this blow might be explained by a blow from some metal object which was ribbed or spined in some way, with multiple tiny protrusions, as for instance one finds sometimes in elaborate jewellery or metal-work for small objects. The pattern also could suggest a repetitive action of a tiny, hard piece of metal which bounced several times in rapid succession, since the markings could be interpreted as a rapidly-repeated series of small, hard, sharp blows, as if the spiny end of some long metal rod, for instance, had fallen onto the crystal with tremendous force (being at the end of a very long rod which had fallen over, and thereby acquiring consider-able momentum) and, meeting a substance as hard as the crystal, had bounced and oscillated several times, each time marginally shifting the precise point of impact. Nearby is an arc-shaped chip, which may or may not be connected with the main series of blows.

Finally, there is another patch of superficial damage on the superior surface; looking downwards, it appears above the right half of the trans-verse 'T'-pressure-crack. The heaviest mass of parallel scuffing-lines emanate (towards the centre) from this patch, which thus would appear to be modern. It looks as if a hard steel-wire brush has banged down onto the surface and been dragged towards the centre; approximately eight parallel 'teeth' of some kind seem to have struck the lens here simultaneously and been dragged. One could speculate that in the 19th century, objects such as this were subjected to rough cleaning on site immediately after excavation.

Configuration: Tests with a spherometer prove that the basal surface is perfectly flat in all directions and at all points with a single exception caused by damage: if the three prongs of the spherometer are aligned along the transverse 'T'-pressure-crack, there is a minute deviation of +0.25 dioptre as a result of this serious crack having penetrated to the basal surface and affected it.

Along the major axis the superior surface has +4.25 dioptres. Along the minor axis it has +6.25 dioptres. Following the line of the later pressure-crack, it has +4.00 dioptres. Orthogonal to that it has +7.25 dioptres. Orthogonally taken diagonal measures in the form of a St Andrew's Cross bisected by the major axis yield measures of +4.75 dioptres with the 'T'-bar-pressure-crack on the left for the NW to SE measurement and +5.75 dioptres for the SW to NE measurement.

As has been observed in previous studies by the late Walter Gasson – with whom I did some joint work before his death, and with whom I had extensive discussions regarding this lens in the past – the superior surface of this lens has been 'toroidally ground'. Toroidal grinding of lenses is done today to produce surfaces of purposely uneven convexity to accom-modate cases of human astigmatism. The superior surface (if held upper-most) plunges downwards near the left side of the 'T'-bar to the rim and bulges upwards in the region bounded by the bottom of the left of the 'T'-bar and the lateral pressure-crack. This 'wonky' surface does not appear to be accidental at all, but a purposeful instance of toroidal grind-ing. See *Comments*, p. 30.

Magnification: When raised sufficiently, a magnification of 1.25X is easily obtained anywhere, and of 1.5X with some evident distortion when the major axis is horizontal. With the minor axis horizontal, 1.25X is given by the right half (the 'T' being above) and 1.5X by the left half, which can however reach 2X without significant distortion if raised higher, but this could easily be overlooked today because the cloudiness caused by the surface damage to the lens makes this difficult to observe (a difficulty which would not have appertained originally).

Original condition: This lens, prior to being damaged, would have been perfectly transparent, clear and lustrous. It was originally a superb and indeed perfect piece of quartz.

Comments: Extreme care was taken in the preparation of this object in the following ways:
1. A superior piece of perfect quartz was found, with no ghostly flaws visible after initial cutting. (It is important to note that such a condition of quartz in this regard is generally not known until the cutting is well progressed; this information is gathered from an account of an 18th-century lens grinder.)
2. A perfectly flat base was produced. This is highly unusual. Most 'plano-convex' lenses from antiquity, whether of crystal or glass, have slightly convex bases. To produce a perfectly flat base with no deviation, as verified by a highly sensitive modern lens measure, requires superior skill and technology, as well as determined effort.
3. Extraordinary pains were taken to produce the strange rim. The scouring by parallel lines must have taken a great deal of time and trouble. It is difficult to imagine why this was thought necessary, unless the craftsman were motivated by fear, such as fear of the wrath of some potentate.

SO WHAT WAS IT?

We may draw several conclusions, some definite as well as some probable. The definite ones should close the door on further useless discussion of those points, leaving only the remaining aspects for consideration by future students of the lens. These are some of the definite conclusions which we can safely accept:
1. *Discovery and publication of the lens:* The lens was discovered in 1849. First public announcement was by Brewster in 1852, and first publication was in French in 1852, followed by publication in English by both Brewster and Layard in 1853. First publication of an engraving of the lens was in 1883. First publication of a photo of the lens was in 1930.
2. *Proper studies carried out on the lens:* Only four individuals have carried out proper physical studies of the lens in 146 years: Sir David

Brewster, W. B. Barker, Walter Gasson, and myself. Brewster's report was ruined by a serious typographical error in his measurements, which remained uncorrected for decades afterwards.

3. *Date of the lens:* Not later than the seventh century BC.

4. *Original condition of the lens subsequent to manufacture:* Perfectly clear and transparent with no flaws. It was made from a highly superior piece of quartz, evidently selected in the hope that it contained no 'ghostly flawing', and finally polished when this was confirmed, after cutting. (One can only be certain that 'ghostly flawing' of the crystal is not present after it is cut, since in its uncut state this can only be the subject of an informed guess. The final choice of an unflawed crystal is thus made after cutting and before polishing.)

5. *Mounted or unmounted?* The lens was undoubted mounted, but not backed. There is evidence from a close study of patterns of chipping and wear that the lens was mounted in a precious metal at the time it was found, that it was prised from this mounting by force and handed unmounted to Layard. An incredible amount of care was taken in the original preparation of the rim of the lens, to insure that it would be mounted more firmly than any normal use would seem to require; this clearly indicates extreme anxiety for the safety of the lens.

6. *Was the base of the lens perfectly flat?* Yes. It deviates very slightly now because of a pressure-crack. The perfect flatness of the base indicates a very great deal of care taken and also high professional skill. I have examined scores of crystal lenses which were nearly plano-convex, but they are usually for lack of skill really biconvex, with a slight bulge at the base. Perfectly flat bases are found on Mycenaean lenses which I have examined in Greece, and the Layard Lens was made by craftsmen of at least equal skill.

7. *Was the lens intended or used as a burning-glass?* No. It is not really effective for that.

8. *Is the lens really the size and shape of a human 'orbital aperture' (eye-socket)?* Yes. It actually corresponds to a lens shape specified in official British standards in 1927, and its perfect fit in the human orbital aperture has been demonstrated by a photograph which leaves no doubt.

9. *Does the lens magnify?* Yes. Despite the fact that several people have insisted that it either does not magnify or magnifies to a negligible extent, the fact is demonstrable that the lens *does* magnify to a non-negligible extent. Magnification of 1.25X is easily obtained anywhere across the lens, and this is sufficient to enable a mildly presbyopic (long-sighted) person to read without his spectacles. If held in certain ways, magnification of 1.5X is obtained. And if raised sufficiently and held in a certain way, magnification of 2X is obtainable without significant distortion. The current cloudy state of the lens, which is due to much damage, makes this difficult to ascertain unless one has considerable experience with old crystal lenses and knows how to deal with them and determine their properties. The lens in its

original state would have given these magnifications through a perfectly transparent substance, and thus could have been used by any presbyopic person as a magnifying aid, although with a considerable degree of annoyance because of the irregularity of the magnifications across the superior surface owing to its toroidal grinding. The purpose of the toroidal grinding is the subject of a probable, not a definite, conclusion, but the fact that the lens magnifies at values ranging between 1.25X and 2X without significant spherical aberration (distortion) is a definite fact.

Having established the above facts as definite ones, we can draw the following probable conclusions. Despite their probability, these remain matters of opinion and interpretation.

1. *Was the superior surface of the lens ground 'toroidally' on purpose or because the workman was unskilled?* Despite the belief by several writers on the subject, including Brewster, that the superior surface of the lens was crudely ground, all have agreed that it was given a magnificent polish; however, this seems to offer a contradiction, since why would one so beautifully polish a crudely ground lens? Why not regrind it first? The fine polishing seems to imply an acceptance of the state of the superior surface. And after taking so much care in the preparation of the perfectly flat base, why allow an imperfectly convex superior surface to remain when it could easily be corrected? And why then go to the enormous trouble of meticulously preparing the rim so that this 'crude' lens would never fall out of its mounting? All of these factors militate against the superior surface being genuinely 'crude', and point towards its purposeful execution. I would suggest that the reason why the toroidally ground superior surface was regarded as 'crude' by so many writers was because it was demonstrably irregular, and the conclusion that it must thus be 'crude' is a natural conclusion to draw unless one is familiar with the *optical purpose* of toroidally-ground lenses. Only if one realizes that, does the 'crudeness' become instead an example of sophisticated intention. My conclusion, therefore – and everyone will have his own view – is that the superior surface of this otherwise carefully executed lens was intentional, and was purposely ground in that manner. However, this leads to a rather astonishing further conclusion:

2. *What was the actual purpose of the Layard Lens?* In my opinion, all the evidence points to an intentionally-ground toroidal lens. And toroidally ground lenses have only one use: *to correct for astigmatism.* The significance of all this became clear to me about 1980 when I had lengthy discussions about the Layard Lens with the late Walter Gasson, whom I knew well, although he and I were not yet acquainted at the time he did his study of the Layard Lens in 1972. Gasson had given a great deal of thought to the Layard Lens subsequent to the publication of his 1972 study, but having already published his comments on it at that time, he had no opportunity to publish further ones. In conversation, he told me that, upon further reflec-

tion, he was inclined to take a somewhat more positive view about the possibility that the Layard Lens – which being toroidally ground was suitable for an astigmatic person – was actually produced for such a person intentionally. He was bothered by the fact that the lens had been produced with such care in every other respect, but had the anomaly of the toroidal surface which was only thought to be 'crude' because nobody had the courage to conclude that it could possibly have been done by design, owing to its antiquity. By 1980, Walter was inclined to believe it more likely than not that the lens was produced for an astigmatic individual. He said it would be possible to go out into the street today and, if you accosted enough people, you would eventually find someone who had an individual case of astigmatism which could be perfectly corrected by the Layard Lens. The trouble is that such toroidally ground lenses to correct for astigmatism only began to be produced in Europe about the middle of the 19th century, and only became available to the general public in quantity about the year 1900. And yet here was one which appeared to have been produced no later than the seventh century BC! This is a dilemma which can accurately be described as mind-boggling. Walter and I discussed this problem further, and agreed that we could not assume that the Assyrians (or whoever produced the lens for them, who may have been a foreign craftsman) had sufficient optical theory to be able to *design and execute* a toroidally ground lens on the basis of calculations.

The more conservative view, and the safer one in the absence of any other evidence, was to conclude that the production of such a lens was accomplished by trial-and-error, on an empirical rather than a theoretical basis. But even so, the technological achievement represented by a toroidally ground lens to correct for an individual case of astigmatism cannot be underestimated. Since it would have been such a fantastic feat, the individual must have been very important indeed: to accomplish this result by trial and error must have meant the preparation of a large number of lenses, held up to the eye of the man in succession over a period of months, until the perfect 'fit' was found. All the duds could have been recycled by being ground normally convex and converted into ordinary magnifying glasses.

The fact that the Layard Lens was found in the king's throne room may therefore mean that the lens was essentially a mounted 'monocle' held up to the eye either of the king – possibly of Sargon, whose name was found on associated material – or of some other important personage. It may even be that the king's chief scribe was important enough to warrant being 'fitted' with a customized monocle. We do not have large numbers of crystal lenses from Assyrian sites, but we do have large numbers of them from Troy (49 were excavated by Schliemann), Ephesus (about 30 or 40) and Knossos (a great number including the remains of a crystal lapidary's workshop, so that the total depends on whether one counts certain types of crystals). The three cities just mentioned were all centres of crystal-lens manufacture at various periods of antiquity (Knossos being the earliest of the three, dating from Minoan times).

Such trial-and-error attempts to correct for astigmatism would not have been so difficult in principle at any of those locations, owing to the large crystal-lens industry each possessed. But of course, to command such a degree of time and effort, the person concerned must presumably have been a king or a senior royal official. The best guess seems to be that such an effort was mounted in the Assyrian capital by a visiting foreign craftsman, who was supplied with as much crystal as he needed, and over a considerable period of time succeeded in producing the perfect match to the astigmatic condition of the eye of the Assyrian king or senior official who insisted upon a correction of his visual defect. Having obtained by trial-and-error the correctly ground superior surface to correct the sight of the person, the result was then beautifully polished and with intense care the rim was cut in the manner described above, to be set into a mounting of precious metal – probably gold – from which it was not, under any circumstances, to become detached. One wouldn't want to go to all that trouble and then have the precious lens fall out of its mounting and get scratched or damaged. (And if it were the king's personal monocle, he might be inclined to be seriously wrathful.)

But was the Layard Lens really King Sargon's personal monocle? Let us just consider this more carefully. The fact that Sargon had moved to another city and left it behind seems to imply that it was not actually his. Furthermore, as he was killed in the Taurus Mountains, he evidently went there without the monocle. I believe therefore that the monocle belonged to Sargon *as an inherited or captured item of another potentate*. It might have been his deceased brother's, assuming that the previous King really was his brother; or his father's. In casual conversation one Assyriologist (whom I will not name lest he feel compromised in print) suggested to me that King Hosheah of Israel who had been defeated by Sargon might have owned the monocle, and that it was therefore royal booty. I think something like this is likely. Various countries closer to the customary manufacture of crystal lenses (as we shall see later in this book) than the Assyrians sent gifts and tribute to Sargon during his reign, including King Midas of Phrygia. It makes more sense if the lens had come from somewhere further west, or northwest, where crystal lenses had been made routinely for centuries. For instance, as mentioned a moment ago, Ephesus and Troy were prominent centres of crystal-lens manufacture, and excavations at Troy have yielded 49 specimens, whereas the number found at Ephesus now exceeds 30, though not all have yet been published. Perhaps it had been the personal monocle of a distinguished figure who had died, so that its precious value as a polished crystal was its sole recommendation as a gift, and its optical qualities had been rendered useless by the death of the owner, even though he had been perhaps a king himself. The lens could have been given as a gift described as 'the eyepiece of King So-and-So', a precious curiosity by that time, and still capable of magnifying, albeit irregularly to someone without astigmatism.

To conclude, then, I believe that the Layard Lens was a carefully crafted monocle to correct for the astigmatic condition of a particular individual, possibly a king. It was made to fit the eye socket, was held up to it in a mounting by some means – perhaps something rather like a lorgnette. It was manufactured by a laborious process of trial-and-error, but despite this represents a magnificent technological achievement, even in the absence of theoretical calculations from a full-blown optical science. It is thus probably one of the most remarkable technological artifacts to survive from antiquity.

And so that is what I have to say about this first optical artifact which we shall encounter in this book – an account which I am happy to be able to give, more than three decades after I first learned of its existence.

We shall encounter a bewildering array of further lenses surviving from antiquity – so many, in fact, that we seriously wonder how they can not have been noticed!

LENSES, LENSES EVERYWHERE

A vast number of ancient lenses exist throughout the world in countless museums. I even have one ancient Greek one myself (see Plate 11). The huge quantities of these surviving objects from ancient times make a mockery of the heedless and widespread assumption that 'no ancient lenses exist'. Ancient lenses are all over the place. So why is it that no one sees them?

The situation is truly baffling. There is one Mediterranean museum, of which one of the directors has published an article saying he thinks ancient lenses existed, but he neglects to mention that there are some crystal lenses on prominent display in cases in his own museum! Presumably he hadn't *seen* them! He simply ignores them.

And in the British Museum, the different departments either were or still are unaware of the fact that the other departments possess ancient lenses, and that there are actually several other ones in that building besides the Layard Lens. The optical artifacts in the British Museum are split up between four or five departments who have little communication with one another. As a matter of fact, Greek crystals – which can clearly be seen by every passing visitor to be *magnifying their mountings* – are in display cases in that museum as well, and no one has ever commented on their magnification properties as far as I know.

In order to give some idea of the magnitude of this strange mass-blindness, I give a selection of some of the better-known ancient lenses – ones which have come to have individual names, and which I therefore call 'Named Lenses' in Appendix Two.

That Appendix describes many tantalizing ancient artifacts, including the 'wandering' Mainz Lens excavated in Germany in 1875; the currently missing King of Naples Lens first mentioned in the 18th century; the Cuming Lens excavated in the City of London; lenses discovered by Sir Flinders Petrie in Egypt; and a remarkable lens in my possession which I call the Prometheus Lens. I decided that, fascinating though these accounts are, too many of them at this early stage of the book, would hinder the reader eager to get on with the rest of the subject. So that material is available at the back of this book.

Nonetheless, anyone who is seriously interested in the physical evidence for ancient optics is urged *not* to skip Appendix Two. Discussions about them over the course of modern centuries in the scientific literature of several languages is also given, with full references, so that a considerable part of the story of the subject as a whole is to be found in Appendix Two.

Having said all that, here as a brief indication of the diversity of ancient lenses, and the vagaries of fate that affect them, I will briefly describe just *two* other lenses: the Nola Lens and the Cairo Lens.

THE NOLA LENS

A plano-convex lens was excavated about 1834 from a Greek grave at Nola in southern Italy. It had a diameter of 4.5 cm and was mounted in a gold rim. However, 'the setting was later removed by the worker who had found the object in order to sell it to a second-hand junk dealer, and so the glass was thereby somewhat damaged,' according to Professor A. Kisa, who adds: 'certainly the objects found at Nola and Mainz were magnifying glasses'. The Nola Lens has, however, since disappeared. Kisa, a German professor who died decades ago, forgot to mention *where it was!* In this he resembled Mach and von Sacken, who also forgot to tell us where the Mainz Lens was despite the fact that they were the only ones who ever saw it until today (as I describe in Appendix Two, I have tracked down the Mainz Lens, which is now in Vienna.)

The original report of the Nola Lens was by Baron Heinrich von Minutoli. He was living nearby at Naples when the Lens was discovered at Nola, and he was able to inspect it on site. He was so impressed by the Nola Lens that it convinced him that 'the ancients understood how to grind glass'.[44] However, as von Minutoli wrote in German, the Nola Lens for 67 years was known only amongst German-speakers, as had been the case with the Mainz Lens. In fact, it is the Germans who were interested in the actual lenses themselves, whereas the French were more interested in ancient texts, which they discussed and rediscussed endlessly. We shall be considering ancient texts in a later chapter, and shall have plenty of occasion then to cite the French.[45]

In 1936, Donald B. Harden mentioned the Nola Lens in passing in a book he wrote about Roman glass. He believed that convex lenses originated with the Minoans and that in Roman times 'Their use was widespread . . .' He mentions numerous other ancient lenses of Roman date.[46] In 1961, the arch-sceptic Emil-Heinz Schmitz briefly mentioned the Nola Lens, but dismissed it without much attention, as he does several other lenses, insisting that they are all merely 'pieces of jewellery'.[47] Needless to say, he never inspected this piece of 'Nola jewellery'.

It is most unfortunate that the Nola Lens is, for the present, lost. It was last apparently seen by Kisa, who published his account of it in 1908, and as I mentioned a moment ago, he forgot to say where he saw it. Or it is even possible that he did not actually see it but simply took his information from Minutoli, and that the Nola Lens had actually not been examined since 1834 or 1835! It may be languishing in the basement drawer of a southern Italian museum, unlabelled and unloved. And if so, Appendix Two will show that it is by no means alone.

THE CAIRO LENS

I examined and photographed this lens – one of the four lenses found at Karanis in Egypt between 1924 and 1929; they are discussed further in Appendix Two – in November 1998, in what is now called the Egyptian Museum at Tahrir Square in Cairo, the museum formerly called The Cairo Museum (see Plate 5). (Since a new museum is being built in Cairo, this object may possibly be moved within a few years' time.) The staff in the Egyptian Museum were among the most helpful and efficient I have ever encountered anywhere, and located the lens from the catalogue number I gave them within minutes. I was told it was in a display case upstairs on the *première étage* (first floor); the Egyptians still use a lot of French. Up we went, and found the lens within about ten minutes of my having walked in the door of the museum. It was in Case B, Room 49, in 'Section 2' of the Museum. The next day the Curator of Section 2, Dr Mahmoud el Helwagy, joined me beside the case. Benches were placed either side of us to stop the public walking past, a table and chair were provided, and the case was opened not only with a key but by cutting a wire seal. The lens was removed and I was able to inspect it.

The two catalogue entries at Cairo for this lens stated: 'Object resembling plano-convex lens – pale greenish glass. Diameter 0.05 [cm].' and 'Lens like object – pale green. Glass. 3rd century AD.' (The Michigan excavators thought about 100 AD.)

I was surprised when I saw the lens, as I could not detect any greenish quality to the glass, despite the fact that Donald B. Harden, in his book entitled *Roman Glass from Karanis* (1936), and both Cairo catalogues, claimed that it was greenish. Perhaps I am going colour-blind! But all I can do is describe what I actually see, whether it agrees with what I am *supposed to* see or not. Harden also said that the lens had spots of iridescence and many pin-prick bubbles and many black impurities, as I just quoted above. But I saw no bubbles or impurities, or any iridescence, though I did see a lot of surface dirt, which he does not mention. I found the maximum thickness to be 72 mm, whereas Harden found it to be 75 mm. I measured the diameter as it varied (something other scholars never seem to do), and discovered that it varied between 4.93 cm and 5.03 cm, as the lens is not perfectly round. Harden merely said the diameter was 5 cm. The rim thickness varied between 0.6 mm and 1 mm, whereas Harden simply said the edges were sharp and less than 1 mm thick.

The base of the lens appears to be perfectly flat, and shows prominent circular grinding patterns across the whole of the base, which indicate clearly that the lens was subjected to rotary grinding in its manufacture. But the circular patterns have a great deal of ingrained dirt in them. There are no chips or damage at all, and the lens is marvellously intact. It shows no evidence of ever having been mounted. The polish of the lens is excellent, and the surfaces are perfectly smooth. The most wonderful thing about this excellent Romano-Egyptian lens is that *the glass is still wholly transparent*, and only the dirt gets in the way. It was thus easy to measure the magnification directly – which is not often possible with ancient *glass* lenses – and although it was zero when resting, when raised the magnification was 1.5X. It was therefore a perfect reading lens for a long-sighted person. The quality of this lens is absolutely first-rate, the glass is superb, and this all indicates a highly sophisticated level of manufacture at Karanis in the third century AD.

BEYOND NAMED LENSES

It may seem to the reader of Appendix Two as if I have discussed many lenses, but the 'named lenses' there are only a fraction of the known ancient lenses. There are in excess of 450 ancient optical artifacts surviving, and I have frankly lost count. Everywhere I go, more appear; it is like an avalanche. At one time I thought I could list every one, and for years I steadfastly adhered to that ideal. But at last I was overwhelmed and had to admit defeat. No one can enumerate them all – it is just too vast a job. I have been working on this problem for more than 30 years, and the lenses have not stopped coming: there are always more, and more, and more.

There are huge bulk-collections. There are the Carthaginian Lenses, the Mycenaean Lenses, the Minoan Lenses, the Rhodes Lenses, and the Ephesus Lenses, which are concave rather than convex and *reduce* images by 75 per cent, thus being good for myopic (short-sighted) people. In

Scandinavia there are more than 100 crystal lenses, all but a handful of which I have studied and measured individually (it took me a month in three countries some of these are described in Appendix Ten). There is a substantial number of ancient British Lenses. See Appendix Five and Eleven. And then there are all the Roman glass objects used for magnification, huge quantities of which are to be found in Germany, for instance. It goes on and on and on. Not one book but *ten* would be required to give even the briefest of descriptions of them all. Even a descriptive catalogue of the ones I have found would seem to be beyond the bounds of possibility.

This book does not have space for reports on the larger lens collections which I found. For instance, 49 convex crystal lenses were excavated at Troy by Schliemann, and some may be seen in Plate 40, including the brilliant perforated lens, which enabled an engraver's tool to be inserted through the middle, while magnifying all around. I was on the trail of the Trojan lenses for 20 years, and twice sent a friend into what was then the sinister world of East Berlin, under the old regime, to try to cultivate the uncooperative museum officials there and discover what had happened to the 49 lenses. All we were told was lies, about how they had been destroyed by Allied bombing in the Second World War. Later, the Russians admitted that they had the famous Trojan gold excavated by Schliemann, and eventually it came out in the mid-1990s that the crystal lenses were with the gold. Colour photos and partial measurements of many of them are to be found in the book *The Gold of Troy*.[49] But all the lenses shown in this book are called 'lens' in quotes, because the authors cannot bring themselves to believe the evidence of their own eyes and admit that they are really and truly lenses! It seems to me remarkable that when confronted with 49 lenses, people can still say they don't 'see' them! It seems unlikely that these 'invisible' lenses will ever leave Russia, as their fate seems to be linked with that of the gold, and the Russian Government apparently does not wish to return that to Germany.

My findings will have to be reserved for the three reports I am doing for Scandinavian archaeological publications except that my report in Appendix Ten is published here in English because its only other publication will be in Swedish translation, in *Gotländskt Arkiv*. When, for example, shall I have the opportunity to describe how the Vikings navigated the sea when it was cloudy by using a quartz 'sun-stone' to 'see' the sun through the clouds? I will probably write about this for a Swedish journal. They used the polarization of sunlight to locate the sun through the clouds.

In fact, the substance probably most commonly used for a 'sun-stone' was iolite cordierite, otherwise known as 'water sapphire', which is found in Scandinavia. It is bipolar, or dichroic, and a thin slice of it would polarize the light seen through clouds so that the sun's location could be readily determined, thereby effectively 'abolishing' the clouds as an obstacle to maritime navigation. There is a clear textual description of the use of a 'sun-stone' in one of the Icelandic sagas which has not been translated into English, but a translation of the relevant passage was done for me by a Swedish friend in Gotland, (which may be found in Appendix Nine). I hope at some point to write a proper account of this subject. This was the secret technology which enabled the Vikings to reach America.

As I have already made clear, in Appendix Two I have tried to deal with some of the lenses which for one reason or another have taken on individual personalities. But just as the number of people in a crowd who are irresistibly fascinating individuals may be a small percentage, so too the number of 'named lenses' is really just a small sampling of all the ancient lenses known to exist. And of course, there are bound to be many which are not yet known to exist. They say that people who buy a particular car suddenly begin seeing those cars everywhere as they drive around. It is like that with ancient lenses. Once you know what you are looking for, it is impossible to stop finding them. We shall learn more about the vast quantities of lenses which have not been discussed yet as we proceed.

GLASS BURNING-GLOBES

In addition to the many lenses I have touched on, the huge numbers of glass burning-globes which existed in Roman times is a subject unknown to almost everyone at the present day. And yet I found that at least 200 whole and broken ones survive in museums – until I stopped counting, that is. But they are not recognized for what they are. They are generally called 'makeup globes'. Because many of them have been found with the dried remains of a pink powder, it has been assumed that these globes once contained makeup of some sort. I believe the powder is the residue of a preservative or colouring agent put into water, either to tint it or to stop it going bad from bacterial action. In fact, I can actually *prove* that the glass globes were not makeup containers – and proof is a rare thing in such matters! How can I do this? I shall tell what happened in Bonn, where all is revealed.

I was touring various German museums – and I do highly recommend the museums to be found in such places as Cologne and Trier – studying Roman glass objects. Then one day I went to a small museum in the sleepy town of Bonn, better known for politics than antiquities. And in that cosy little museum, things were a bit more at the human level and less bureaucratic than in the larger ones. So I engaged a woman who worked there in conversation about the glass globes, telling her that I could prove to her that they were not the makeup globes she had been told they were. She was intrigued. Furthermore, I told her I could show her how the globe functioned optically. She was finding this offer hard to resist, when I popped my condition: in order to do this, I needed to fill the little glass globe I was holding with water. She agreed to my going over to a nearby sink, where people wash their hands after examining antiquities, and filling the globe with water. I brought it back to her and first showed her how it magnified (see my Plate 50) and how it focused the rays of light coming even from a feeble desk lamp (see my Plate 49); unfortunately I wasn't allowed to take it out into the sun and burn anything.

The woman was astonished, but wanted to know how I could prove that the globe had never contained makeup. I then turned the globe upside down and shook it vigorously. She jumped back, expecting to be splashed with water. But no water came out. Then she really was surprised, for no matter how hard she shook it or I shook it, not a single drop could be persuaded to come out of the tiny hole into which I had put it. I then explained to the woman the phenomenon of *surface tension*. The fact was that the hole was so small that it was 'ignored' by the water, and the surface tension of the whole globe kept the water held within the globe. If the globe had really been a makeup globe, no one could ever have used it, because you couldn't get the makeup out!

I explained that such a handy little globe could be put into one's pocket and carried anywhere, and not a drop would leak out. Furthermore, the globes were mass-produced (actually at glassworks based in Germany) and they were thus so cheap to replace it didn't matter if you broke yours and had to buy another.

We suddenly realized that time had marched on, as we had been so preoccupied, and I was about to miss my last train to the next town. And furthermore, she needed to close soon. So I got my things hurriedly and bade my adieux. But as I was leaving, having replaced everything very neatly in the relevant places, the woman panicked: 'How do I get the water out? And if I can't what will I tell the Director?'

I said, all she needed to do was insert a pin and the water would dribble out along it. But I had to rush and couldn't do it for her. The last glimpse I had of her was of a woman terrified of losing her job because she had allowed an object to be tampered with. If there had been any way at all that I could have stayed short of cancelling my reservations, etc., I would have helped her gently out of her predicament. But as it was, I made my train by seconds. I worried about her for a long time. And I hope I will be allowed in the door if I ever come again.

The glass globes are not the only Roman magnifiers and burners made of glass, for there were also some vases on stands which magnified. And one object which I studied in Germany was a vase which actually contained a perfectly ground convex lens *within* it; this object could thus be used for magnifying or burning while resting on a surface, so that it did not need to be held or suspended. The Romans were highly ingenious in the many shapes of these objects, none of which has been recognized until now by any archaeologists for what they were. From time to time the archaeologists will admit that a class of objects is 'strange', and one type of magnifying vase in the shape of a bird so that you could pick it up and set it down by its tail has been admitted to be 'of unknown purpose'. Some of the magnifying objects were coloured or tinted glass, but that did not interfere with their optical functions.

Let us now turn to the textual evidence relating to ancient lenses and other aspects of ancient optics.

Notes

1. Although the set of the film was closed, I was able to get in because I was friendly with all the staff at the studios. I had befriended them all when I was 18, and the carpenters, plasterers, electricians and the guards at the gate welcomed me enthusiastically when I turned up, and quietly ushered me into every inner sanctum where the highly secretive director Stanley Kubrick was at work. I saw the original monolith, which had been cast in transparent perspex – but because that didn't work, Kubrick had to use a black one. I saw the ape costumes (some of which later disappeared, which was a bit of a scandal). I met and befriended all the special effects men such as Wally Veevers, chatted with the cameramen, had long conversations with the technical advisers. One of the latter was an interesting thinker and writer named Fred Ordway, with whom I still keep in tenuous touch today. One of the assistants on the film whom I only met in passing at that time is now a good friend, Andrew Birkin. Sometimes we reminisce together about the extraordinarily weird experience of *2001*. For after I moved permanently to England in October 1966, I visited the set constantly and therefore watched the production for approximately two years. It was quite an education!

   Kubrick was terribly upset at first that I was the only person who could slip under all his security nets (there were 'Absolutely No Entry' signs everywhere), and he kept coming face to face with me in the unlikeliest places, such as the loo, a dark corridor, or chatting amicably to his cameraman. Kubrick never dared to accost me directly, by challenging me or asking who the hell I was. His method of dealing with this unacceptable loss of face at first was to avoid looking at me, and hope that I would go away like a bad dream. It was a classic case of being 'in denial'. But I kept being there. After some weeks of realizing that I was a recurring apparition, he swallowed his pride and began to ask his secretary and his gopher who I was. But they were already my friends, so they cheerfully said that I was Robert Temple who visited the studios from time to time. They didn't feel too much like elaborating because they had already told me so many indiscreet things about Kubrick's working methods and strange lifestyle that they dreaded my coming into direct contact with Stanley in case I blurted anything out which incriminated them as gossips. Whenever I passed Kubrick I would smile and say hello, and he would glumly glance at me and walk hastily on. It was deeply unsettling to him, but I did look pretty harmless, being only a kid at the time. After some time he settled, like an eagle accepting his perch and letting his feathers go sleek. He was reassured: I did not appear to be dangerous. He even met my gaze.

   Then I began to visit Stanley in his office and have discursive chats. He would never ask me who I was, and we seemed mutually to conspire to pretend I was not an intruder who actually had no right to be in the studio at all. At that time he was interested in Nazi memorabilia (his gopher told me he collected them, but kept them at home) and being Jewish was fascinated and horrified at the same time by the whole Nazi movement. I

42

discovered that he had been impressed by a very low-budget film called *It Happened Here*, made by an enterprising young man whom I knew at the time named Kevin Brownlow. The film, more or less made on Kevin's pocket money from what I could gather, portrayed a wartime Britain occupied by the Nazis, whose invasion plan Operation Sealion had succeeded because the Battle of Britain had failed. Stanley had always wanted to meet Kevin Brownlow but it seemed to me that he was too proud to say so. So I took the matter in hand and told Stanley that I would bring Brownlow out to the studio to meet him, which greatly thrilled Stanley and Brownlow alike. Kevin later became famous as a cinema historian, but I haven't seen him since the late 1960s. As for Stanley, I never saw him again after he left for the American premiere of *2001* and recut the film on an ocean liner as he crossed the Atlantic, although I heard a great deal of news of him for some years after through mutual friends and acquaintances.

Postscript: While this book was being edited, Stanley died suddenly. It is now possible to be a bit more explicit about him. His last film, *Eyes Wide Shut*, deals with sexual fantasies, and I have read various articles in the press where people have speculated about Kubrick's personal attitudes towards this subject. Therefore, I think it would be of wider cultural interest for some reliable information to be published about it. What I can say is that even as early as 1966, Stanley's addiction to hard-core pornography was so extreme that he 'had to have' about 40 fresh hard-core pornographic photographs *per day* to satisfy his voyeuristic cravings. He would become desperate if deprived of these.

Many people have speculated also about Stanley's mental state in general. No one can question that he was a brilliant man, and in many ways fascinating. But it is my personal opinion, for what it is worth, that he was 'cracked'. He behaved with reckless, egomaniacal irresponsibility when he was making *2001*. He would keep his entire crew waiting all day at enormous expense and sometimes would not give them any directions as to what to do. I will give one example of just how far he could go in wasting the money of his financiers, MGM. He ordered a specimen of every known type of coathanger in Britain to be collected and spread out over the floor and all the surfaces of his office and the adjoining rooms in the small 'clock tower' building at the front of the studio where he worked. (The entire studio was long ago demolished, which is a shame, as it was the best in Britain.) His personal secretary told me about this incident, which she witnessed. She helped to spread the coathangers all round the building for inspection. It took a long time for the coathangers to be gathered from the manufacturers in the first place, and when they were ready, all work on the production stopped for an entire day. My close friend the secretary said there were 'about a hundred and fifty' types of coathanger. She may have exaggerated the figure somewhat, but there were certainly plenty. Some of them covered her desk so that she couldn't work. Stanley's perfectionism was such that he took hours to choose the ideal coathanger. Everyone looked on puzzled and bemused, seeing 'the genius at work'. Finally he held one up in his hand and said: '*This is the one.*' Someone breathlessly asked: 'Is that the coathanger of the future, Stanley? Are we going to use that in the film as what a coathanger will look like in the year 2001?' Stanley looked surprised and said: 'No. I've been looking for the right kind of coathanger for my wife's new coat.' And that was all it was. He was that removed from reality even at that early date. He nearly bankrupted MGM, but cared no more about that than if he had stepped on an ant when walking across the grass.

Turning to the subject of Arthur C. Clarke, however, my wife Olivia and I would frequently get phone calls from Fred his brother saying, 'Arthur's in town. Let's meet at the Globe.' I remember one evening, Arthur was in a state of great excitement about something which he had concealed in his briefcase. He could barely wait to open it and flash the secret at us. We were the first to see it, then later Arthur flashed it to Michael Moorcock, and eventually over the course of the evening to just about everybody who was there. He even looked wistfully at the door, wishing for more of his friends to turn up so that he could show it to even more people. The mysterious thing in the briefcase was a chatty personal letter from Ladybird Johnson, the wife of Lyndon Johnson (who at

43

that time was President of the United States). Due to his NASA connections, Arthur had met Ladybird and she had taken a great fancy to him. Arthur was so thrilled he was floating on a cloud.

2. For a man famous for his writings about other worlds, Arthur's deadpan ordinariness of manner has always been a delightful irony to me. Arthur had never gone more than 20 miles from his family's Somerset farm until he was 21, as his early friend Val Cleaver told me. But afterwards he made up for that by several light-years.

   My association with Arthur became fairly involved, as I ended up writing a screenplay of his novel *A Fall of Moondust*. I did another of his short story 'The Songs of Distant Earth'. However, despite many moments of promise and of partial funding, letters of commitment from Charlton Heston and Laurence Harvey and all sorts of folk of that kind including a number of directors (even Orson Welles, Joseph Losey, and Alan Pakula were interested in directing at various stages!), these projects came to nothing.

3. Layard, Austen Henry, *Discoveries in the Ruins of Nineveh and Babylon; with Travels in Armenia, Kurdistan, and the Desert: Being the Result of a Second Expedition undertaken for the Trustees of the British Museum*, John Murray, London, 1853, pp. 196–8.

4. Roux, Georges, *Ancient Iraq*, 3rd edition, Penguin, 1992, p. 310.

5. *Ibid.*, p. 317.

6. Ragozin, Zénaïde A., *Assyria: From the Rise of the Empire to the Fall of Nineveh*, The Story of the Nations Series, 2nd edition, T. Fisher Unwin, London, 1888, p. 294.

7. Layard, Austen Henry, *Nineveh and Its Remains*, 3rd edition, John Murray, London, 1849, 2 vols.

8. Layard, Austen Henry, *Discoveries, op. cit.*

9. *Ibid.*, pp. 197–8.

10. Brewster, Sir David, 'On a Rock-Crystal Lens and Decomposed Glass Found at Nineveh', *American Journal of Science*, Vol. 2, No. 15, 1853, pp. 122–3.

11. *Journal of the Royal Microscopical Society*, London, October, 1883, pp. 707–8.

12. *Ibid.*, p. 708.

13. *Ibid.*, p. 707.

14. Brewster, Sir David, Note [of his talk to the British Association in Belfast], *l'Athenaeum Français*, Vol. I (Ière Année), No. 12, 18 September 1852, p. 191.

15. Arago, Dominique François Jean [generally just called François], *Astronomie Populaire*, 4 vols, Paris, 1854–7; English translation: *Popular Astronomy*, 2 vols, London, 1855, Book IV Chapter 4, p. 108.

16. Martin, Thomas Henri, 'Sur des Instruments d'Optique Faussement Attribués aux Anciens par Quelques Savants Modernes', *Bullettino di Bibliografia e di Storia delle Scienze Matematiche e Fisiche*, Rome, Vol. IV, 1871, pp. 165–238.

17. *Ibid.*, p. 210.

18. Perrot, Georges, and Chipiez, Charles, *Histoire de L'Art dans l'Antiquité*, Tome II: *Chaldée et Assyrie*, Librairie Hachette, Paris, 1884, p. 718.

18a. The next person to mention the Layard Lens was Professor Horner of the University of Zurich, in 1887. His first name is unknown, and he merely describes himself as 'Professor Horner'; the British Library catalogue offers no help in this matter, and no one seems to know which Horner he may have been. His brief monograph is entitled *On Spectacles: Their History and Uses*, and it probably appeared initially in German, though I have never located a copy. This monograph of 28 pages was published in English by The Society for the Prevention of Blindness in London. Horner took a very sanguine view of ancient optics, and stated: 'The origin of glasses for assisting defective sight is not known with anything like certainty. That the ancients were acquainted with convex lenses is undoubted. Layard found in Nineveh a plano-convex lens of rock crystal, one and a half inch in diameter with a focus of four-and-a-half inches. In a grave at Nola, a city of Magna Graecia, a plano-convex glass lens mounted in a gold frame was found, . . .' etc. (Horner, Professor, *On Spectacles: Their History and Uses*, The Society for the Prevention of Blindness, London, 1887, p. 1.)

In 1899, the Layard Lens was mentioned in passing in a German ophthalmological encyclopaedia published at Leipzig. Joseph Hirschberg, in his entry for this encyclopaedia concerning 'Geschichte der Augenheilkunde im Alterthum' ('History of Ophthalmology in Antiquity'), takes up an extreme sceptical position with regard to ancient lenses. He refuses to admit that any ancient lentoids are lenses at all. Like Martin, Hirschberg allowed his preconceived argument to blind him in many respects. For instance, he misreads ancient texts, insists that no lenses have been found at Pompeii despite the fact that he cites references which report them, and contradicts himself by admitting that the ancients had burning-glasses and burning-globes, while at the same time insisting that 'There is not the slightest trace to be found in any ancient writings of any optical purpose or optical effect by ground glass or crystal . . .', immediately after noting that the Greek Professor Andreas Anagnostakis had claimed to have examined an ancient lens, and 'Indeed Brewster has maintained the same for a find from the excavations at Nineveh.' (Hirschberg, Joseph, 'Geschichte der Augenheilkunde im Alterthum', in *Gräfe-Sämisch Handbuch der Gesamten Augenheilkunde*, Leipzig, Vol. XII, Part 2, *Pathologie und Therapie*, pp. 174–80. The relevant quote is from p. 176.)

19. Pansier, Pierre, *Histoire des Lunettes*, Paris, 1901, p. 2.
20. Bock, Emil, *Die Brille und Ihre Geschichte*, Verlag von Josef Šafár, Vienna, 1903, pp. 5–8.
21. By 1907, an American had taken an interest. Carl Barck gave a lecture to the Academy of Science of St Louis, Missouri, which was published first in a journal called *The Open Court* for April 1907, and then circulated as a pamphlet offprint with the title *The History of Spectacles*. In this he says:

> Amongst the ruins of old Nineveh an interesting find was made by Sir Henry Layard, namely a lens of rock crystal. This oldest lens in existence is plano-convex, 1 1/2 inch in diameter, with a focus of 4 1/2 inches. It is fairly well polished. But as to its use, and whether this one specimen is indicative of a more general employment of glasses, we are in the dark. Even if the old Assyrians and Babylonians did possess this art, it became lost afterwards. For to the ancient Hebrews and Egyptians spectacles were unknown. (Barck, Carl, *The History of Spectacles*, originally delivered as a Lecture before the Academy of Science, St Louis, published in *The Open Court*, April 1907, and reprinted as a pamphlet, 1907, p. 2.)

The next mention of the Layard Lens was in Germany. In 1916, (Karl) Richard Greeff published an article, in a German ophthalmological journal at Berlin, entitled 'Kritische Betrachtungen über Funde von Brillengläsern und Lupen aus dem frühen Altertum' ('Critical Observations concerning the Discovery of Eyeglasses and Magnifying Glasses from Early Antiquity'). Greeff comments that there are more and more press reports of ancient magnifying-glasses and convex spectacle lenses being found in archaeological excavations, and he lists several of these, among them the Layard Lens, described as 'a plano-convex lens from Nineveh with a diameter of 3 cm. and a refractive power of 10 dioptres'. (He obviously took this directly from Emil Bock. He thus repeats the erroneous measurement and the false implication that the lens is circular.) Greeff admits that the ancients used burning-glasses, but insists that 'the use of convex lenses for the eyes of presbyopes [long-sighted people] was entirely unknown to them'. (Greeff, (Karl) Richard, 'Kritische Betrachtungen über Funde von Brillengläsern und Lupen aus dem frühen Altertum', in *Zeitschrift für Ophthalmologische Optik*, Julius Springer Verlag, Berlin, Vol. IV, Part 3, 1916, pp. 142–6.)

Greeff returned to the subject in 1921, when he published his extended monograph *Die Erfindung der Augengläser* (*The Invention of Eyeglasses*). But in this, he merely repeats the brief statement describing the Layard Lens which he had already published in his 1916 article. (Greeff, (Karl) Richard, *Die Erfindung der Augengläser*, Vol. I of pamphlet series *Optische Bücherei*, Alexander Ehrlich Verlag, Berlin, 1921, p. 24.)

22. Meissner, B., *Babylonien und Assyrien*, Heidelberg, Vol. II, 1924, p. 309.

23. Beck, H. C., 'Ancient Magnifying Glasses', *The Antiquaries Journal*, Vol. 8, 1928, pp. 328–30.
24. Barker, W. B., 'The Nineveh Lens', in *The British Journal of Physiological Optics*, Vol. IV, No. 1, January, 1930, pp. 4–6.
25. Campbell Thompson, R., *The Reports of the Magicians and Astrologers of Nineveh and Babylon in the British Museum*, 2 vols, Luzac's Semitic Text and Translation Series, Vols VI–VII, Luzac and Co., London, 1900.
26. See my book *The Sirius Mystery* for a discussion of perplexing astronomical knowledge in antiquity.
27. Barker's colleague Harry L. Taylor, another ophthalmic optician of London, followed with an article in the summer of the same year on 'The Origin and Development of Lenses in Ancient Times', in which he mentions several examples including the Layard Lens, stresses that magnifying lenses were common in antiquity and apparently originated with the Minoans, criticizes the sceptical German scholar Richard Greeff (1916 and 1921) for doing careless work and says 'he neglects entirely the most vital evidence'. (Taylor, Harry L., 'The Origin and Development of Lenses in Ancient Times', in *The British Journal of Physiological Optics*, Vol. IV, No. 2, July, 1930, pp. 97–103.) Taylor is much more concerned with earlier lenses than the Layard Lens, which he mentions rather dismissively as a late example:

> Neither the Egyptian nor the Sumerian civilisations have provided us with any very early rock crystal lentoid forms, the Nineveh lens, discovered by Layard, in 1853, and now in the British Museum, being as late as 700 BC, a period long after Babylonian supremacy.

He discusses the many Trojan lenses excavated by Schliemann and then adds:

> In the ruins of Tyre, a town of Phoenicia on the Palestine coast, was found another rock crystal lens, also of similar age, and still another, already referred to, at Nineveh, but different in that the form is oval, and its age a few centuries greater.

A one-page article signed only by the initials O.B.S.E. appeared in the spring of 1938 entitled 'The Layard Lens'. (O.B.S.E. [name unknown], 'The Layard Lens', in *The Optician*, London, 15 April 1938.) This was the first time the lens had been given this name, which is the one now commonly used. The author, whose article also contained a photo of the lens, summarizes the statements of Brewster and Barker, commenting of them: 'Both observers found a passably sharp focus of 4 1/2 inches from the plain surface.' He then concludes:

> There has been much speculation, whether this object was a lens at all, or just an ornament. That it was used as a burning-glass – as subsequent glass lenses were used – is open to doubt . . . From its shape, size and weight, it is most unlikely that it was used to correct any error of refraction, but it may be assumed that this lens was used to aid the vision of some craftsman to enable him to execute the fine detail of the decorative work of the period. It is therefore not unreasonable to conclude that the Layard lens was used much in the same way as Roger Bacon used his magnifying glass.

The next discussion referring to the Layard Lens was by a young ophthalmic optician named Walter Gasson, writing his first piece on the history of the subject before getting caught up in the War. In his article. 'A Short History of Refraction', published in 1939, Gasson got the first name of Layard wrong but wrote the following:

> . . . in the Assyrian department of the British Museum there is considered to be the oldest example of a lens-grinder's art. This is the celebrated Nineveh lens discovered by

46

Sir John [*sic*] Layard in 1853 when excavating the ruins of Nineveh and Babylon. This lens is almost plano-convex, made of rock crystal, being approximately 1.6 inches long by 1.4 inches wide and about 0.25 inch in thickness. Its average curvature is +5.0 D. [dioptres]. The maximum about plus 8.0 D. and the minimum plus 4.0 D., the surface being an irregular toroid. Its approximate focal length is about 4.5 inches from its plano surface. The estimated age of this unique specimen is dated from the year BC 700. (Gasson, Walter, 'A Short History of Refraction', in *The Optician*, London, Vol. 98, No. 2540, 1 December 1939, pp. 283–6. Gasson at this point had not examined the Layard Lens, but merely took all this information from his friend Barker.)

The Layard Lens was not discussed again until well after the War was over, when in 1950 the Swedish scholar Otto Ahlström published his article 'Swedish Vikings Used Optical Lenses'. (Ahlström, Otto, 'Swedish Vikings Used Optical Lenses', in *The Optician*, London, 19 May 1950, pp. 459–62. It was the publication of a paper read at a meeting organized by the Worshipful Company of Spectacle Makers and *The Optician* at Apothecaries' Hall, London, on 18 May 1950.) In this article, Ahlström has a section entitled 'The Nineveh Lens', in which he writes:

Having touched upon such written records as exist from centuries long past, we may take note of certain archaeological finds of lenses, or objects resembling lenses. During Layard's exavations in Nineveh in the middle of the last century he found a plano-convex lens of rock crystal, 16 x 12 mm oval. Both surfaces are badly scratched, but in spite of this Sir David Brewster was able to establish the focal length as 150 mm. (These figures are given in Pansier's *Histoire des Lunettes*. [1901].)

28. Forbes, R. J., *Studies in Ancient Technology*, Leiden, Vol. V, 1957, pp. 186–7.
29. King, Henry C., 'Lenses in Antiquity', in *The Optician*, London, 12 September 1958, pp. 221–4.
30. In 1961, the first of many publications about the history of optics by Emil-Heinz Schmitz appeared, entitled *Die Sehhilfe im Wandel der Jahrhunderte (Aids to Vision through the Ages)*. (Schmitz, Emil-Heinz, *Die Sehhilfe im Wandel der Jahrhunderte*, Süddeutsche Optiker Zeitung Verlag, Stuttgart, 1961. An unpublished English translation of this work by Mrs Aileen Fairbanks was presented by her to the Library of the British Optical Association, London, in 1969, and I have taken the liberty of using her translation when quoting this work of Schmitz.) Schmitz adopts a position of truly extreme scepticism, insisting that all the ancient lenses without exception are 'pieces of jewellery'; so determined is he to expunge any ancient optical technology that in discussing the fact that Chinese wore spectacles a few hundred years ago, he insists they did this 'because etiquette and fashion demanded it,' and that they had no optical function! Of the Layard Lens, he says:

The planoconvex polished rock crystal found by Layard in the ruins of Nineveh in old Mesopotamia between the Tigris and Euphrates, for instance, had a refraction power of about +10.0 dioptres . . . However, the prevailing opinion is that not all these spherical segments from olden times were used for utilitarian purposes. On the contrary, they served as pieces of jewellery on sceptres and swords or as buttons on caps and ceremonial garments.

Like previous extreme opponents of ancient optical technology, Schmitz vaguely refers to 'prevailing opinion', without bothering to say whose opinions they were and where they prevailed, other than his own. He had not examined the Layard Lens, yet he implies that all sensible people must know it was either a sceptre top, a sword hilt decoration, or a button for a cap or a ceremonial garment. I do not know of any previous published suggestion by anyone of any of these unlikely possibilities, but Schmitz would have us believe that they unquestionably 'prevailed'.

31. Needham, Joseph; Ling, Wang; and Robinson, Kenneth, Volume IV, Part 1 (*Physics*) of

The Crystal Sun

series *Science and Civilisation in China*, Cambridge University Press, 1962. The section on 'Light (Optics)' is found on pp. 78–125.

32. *Ibid.*, p. 100.
33. Gregg, James R., *The Story of Optometry*, Ronald Press Company, New York, 1965, p. 17.
34. Price, Derek de Solla, *Gears from the Greeks: The Antikythera Mechanism, A Calendar Computer from ca. 80 BC.*, Science History Publications, Neale Watson, New York, 1975, reprinted as a book from article in *Transactions of the American Philosophical Society*, New Series, Vol. 64, Part 7.
35. von Däniken, Erich, *Chariots of the Gods?* (original German title: *Errinerungen an die Zukunft*), originally published in German and English in 1969, this quotation from the Bantam paperback edition, New York, 1971, p. 27.
36. Gasson, Walter, 'The Oldest Lens in the World: A Critical Study of the Layard Lens', in *The Ophthalmic Optician*, 9 December 1972, pp. 1267–72.
37. Emsley, H. H., and Swaine, William, *Ophthalmic Lenses*, 4th ed., Hatton Press, London, 1940, p. 4.
38. Corliss, William R., *Strange Artifacts: A Sourcebook on Ancient Man*, privately published by The Sourcebook Project, Glen Arm, Maryland 21057, USA, Volume M-2 (the second volume devoted to *Strange Artifacts*), 1976. The Layard Lens was classified as Item MMT-008, and a paragraph about it was published on page M2-132; the source listed was Brewster's account of 1853 in the *American Journal of Science*.
39. Gorelick, Leonard, and Gwinnett, A. John, 'Close Work without Magnifying Lenses?', in *Expedition*, Philadelphia, Vol. 23, No. 2, Winter, 1981, pp. 27–32; 'Close Work without Magnifying Lenses [Part 2]: Discussion of Suggestions from Readers of *Expedition*', in *Expedition*, Philadelphia, Vol. 23, No. 4, Summer, 1981, pp. 15–16. In the latter discussion, no other conclusion is reached.
40. Also in 1981, the German Emil-Heinz Schmitz returned to print on the subject of ancient optics (he published something in 1974 on the invention of spectacles, in a German journal of which no copy appears to exist in Britain), by commencing a series of what was to be several volumes under the general title *Handbuch zur Geschichte der Optik* (*Handbook for the History of Optics*). Handbook is hardly the right word in English, however, to describe these lavishly illustrated volumes printed on heavy glossy paper in large format. In this first volume (Schmitz, Emil-Heinz, *Handbuch zur Geschichte der Optik*, Vol. I, *Von der Antike bis Newton* (*From the Ancients to Newton*), Bonn, 1981. The photo of the Layard Lens appears on p. 7, along with the discussion concerning it.), Schmitz says the Layard Lens may be a lens, a burning-glass, or an ornament. His earlier refusal to recognize the existence of any ancient lenses had clearly softened over the two decades since his original book.

In October 1983, the Greek archaeologist Yannis A. Sakellarakis, then Deputy Director of the Herakleion Museum in Crete, excavated two rock crystal lenses in the Cave of Ida on Crete, which he describes as 'of unusually fine optical quality'. As a result of these finds, Sakellarakis made some study of the question of ancient lenses, and with the American George Sines published an article in 1987 in the *American Journal of Archaeology* entitled 'Lenses in Antiquity' (Sines, George and Sakellarakis, Yannis A., 'Lenses in Antiquity', in *American Journal of Archaeology*, Vol. 91, 1987, pp. 191–6.) In this article, Sines and Sakellarakis published photos of three Cretan lenses and briefly surveyed some other ancient evidence. Their general conclusion was that 'lenses were probably used as magnifying glasses . . .' in antiquity. However, they were not very impressed by the Layard Lens, of which they wrote:

The often-mentioned crystal lens found by Layard at Nimrud, in contrast to the lenses described above, does not have sufficient optical quality to be of technical use although it is of sufficient quality to demonstrate magnification. Its optical imperfections have been carefully studied. [Here they give a reference to Gasson's 'Oldest Lens in the World' article of 1972.] This crystal object may have been intended as a crude ornament

48

or it may have been a roughly shaped blank for a lens never finished after a flaw caused internal cracking. . . . The lenses from Knossos are considerably older. The dimensions of the Layard Lens are very similar to those of a modern spectacle lens.

In 1988, Colin B. Fryer published an article entitled 'Glass and Lenses in Ancient Times', containing a section on 'The Nimrud Lens'. (Fryer, Colin B., 'Glass and Lenses in Ancient Times', in *The Optician*, Vol. 195, No. 5139, London, 11 March 1988, pp. 21–33.) Surprisingly, it contains no mention of Walter Gasson or reference to his important study of the lens. Fryer does not correct the date of discovery (he still says 1853). He clarifies the description of the site where the lens was found:

> It was disinterred during excavations of the desert mound on the banks of the River Tigris some 20 miles south east of the present-day oil city of Mosul, named by the Arabs after Nimrud, who is mentioned in the Book of Genesis. Layard believed this mound to be the site of one of the three cities Nimrud is said to have founded, Ninevah [*sic*], but in fact it has subsequently been identified as that of another, the Assyrian Royal capital, Kalhu – the Galah of the Old Testament.

Fryer had seen the published account of the Trojan lenses (though those lenses themselves were lost at that time, secreted in Russia), briefly discussed them in his article, and attempted a comparison of the Layard Lens to them (I have converted his fractions to decimals):

> The lens is slightly cloudy [he was unaware that this was due to pressure and abrasion and thought it was the original condition] and somewhat oval in shape like one of those from pre-classical Troy. It is 1.6 inches long, and 1.2 inches broad, and about 0.25 inch thick, being a little thicker on one side than the other. [This is rather a clumsy way of describing a plano-convex object!] Sir David Brewster, the Scottish physicist who examined the lens shortly after its discovery gives its thickness as 0.9 inch, but this was probably a printer's error. Its edge appears to have been distinctly flattened, but careful inspection under magnification reveals that it is in fact slightly bevelled, which suggests that the lens was once mounted.
>
> Like the earlier lenses, one surface is plane and the other convex. The plane surface is almost perfectly accurate in all directions although now rather badly scratched. The convex surface however, is an irregular sphero-cylinder. This, of course, results in different parts of the lens having different focal lengths. These range from a maximum of about 9.8 inches to a minimum of just half of this amount, although according to Brewster light is brought to a 'tolerably distinct focus at a distance of 4.5 inches from the plane side'. The two main optical meridians are at right angles to each other.
>
> The convex surface bears indications of having been ground on a flat lapidary's wheel – or on a similar device equally as primitive. This would explain the irregular curvature of the surface. [Fryer does not appreciate the true significance of the toroidal surface and believes it to be 'irregular' through lack of skill.] Nevertheless, the polish is still reasonably good. The lens has several flaws in its internal structure. These were obviously fissures in the piece of material from which it was worked. These fissures undoubtedly contained naphtha or similar fluid which is sometimes found in this and other materials. It is possible that these fissures were opened during the process of grinding, although more probably they developed as a consequence of time. [He does not appreciate that the 'fissures' are really pressure-flaws.]
>
> Unfortunately, the exact age of the lens has not been definitely established: but all the available evidence points to it dating from the latter part of the ninth century BC long after the era of Babylonian supremacy.

41. Temple, Robert, 'Technical Wonders of the Past', *Nature*, London, Vol. 374, No. 6521, 30 March 1995, pp. 418–19.

42. James, Peter and Thorpe, Nick, *Ancient Inventions*, Michael O'Mara Books, London, 1995, pp. 157–61.
43. Also in 1996 Jay Enoch, retired Dean of the School of Optometry of the University of California at Berkeley, published an article, in a technical optical journal, entitled 'Early Lens Use: Lenses Found in Context with Their Original Objects', in which he mentioned the Layard Lens:

> . . . these items [ancient lentoids] could be . . . decorative items or jewels. They included the well-known Layard 'lens' located at the British Museum, London (no. BM 90959) [Enoch, like all authors on the subject, still gives the obsolete inventory number, whereas the object is now 12091.] This artifact has been an object of debate/controversy for quite some time. Importantly, the controversy fueled inquiry into the early history of lenses. (Enoch, Jay M., 'Early Lens Use: Lenses Found in Context with Their Original Objects', in *Optometry and Vision Science*, Vol. 73, No. 11, 1996, pp. 707–15.)

Enoch says no more about the Layard Lens, which is peripheral to his main concerns at the moment (he and I met in late 1997 and had extended discussions). Enoch is extremely critical of Gorelick and Gwinnett, and one of his points is that if all ancient engraving was done by myopic individuals, without lenses, then it could only be *seen and appreciated* by myopic individuals, and also: 'an incredible number of highly skilled young myopes would have been needed for all this work!' Enoch is convinced that lenses were known and used in antiquity, giving many examples, and concludes: 'Pertinent lens properties were most probably appreciated early, and were often discovered, lost, and rediscovered.'

The most recent mention of the Layard Lens is by Dimitris Plantzos, who published an article in the July 1997 *American Journal of Archaeology,* entitled 'Crystals and Lenses in the Graeco-Roman World' (Plantzos, Dimitris, 'Crystals and Lenses in the Graeco-Roman World', in *American Journal of Archaeology*, Vol. 101, No. 3, July, 1997, pp. 451–64. The information he gives about the concave lenses from Ephesus excavated by Hogarth is incorrect; the intact one in the British Museum does not reduce images by only 20 per cent, but rather by 75 per cent, so that Plantzos's conclusions are difficult to sustain), in which he mentions the Layard Lens, though he appears not to have examined it, and does not mention Gasson's study of the toroidal grinding of its convex surface. He is dismissive of ancient lenses in general.

44. Minutoli, Heinrich Carl Freiherr [Baron] Menu von, *Über die Anfertigung und die Nutzanwendung der Farbigen Gläser bei den Alten* (*Concerning the Manufacture and Utilization of Coloured Glasses amongst the Ancients*), Berlin, 1836; reprinted at Altenburg in 1838.
45. The Layard Lens was the only ancient lens to attract attention amongst the French (as explained earlier in this chapter) until 1885, when Edouard Gerspach reported his examination of the Pompeii Lens, described in Appendix Two. The Nola Lens was mentioned in passing by Marquardt, Bock, Kisa, Greeff, Theobald, Forbes, and Needham, in conjunction with the Mainz Lens, all of whom have been referred to above. But the Nola Lens was additionally mentioned in 1887 by the Swiss writer Horner, who said: 'That the ancients were acquainted with convex lenses is undoubted,' and cites the Layard Lens and the Nola Lens as the two examples he knows surviving from antiquity. (Horner, Professor [no first name given], *On Spectacles: Their History and Uses*, trans. anonymously, London, 1887.) The Nola Lens, unlike the Mainz Lens, actually entered the French literature in 1901, when it was discussed by Pierre Pansier in a rare book of which there is no copy in the British Library. Pansier only mentions the Nola Lens in passing as evidence of ancient knowledge, saying: 'The ancients were familiar with convex glasses: this is incontestable.' (Pansier, Pierre, *L'Histoire des Lunettes* (*The History of Spectacles*), Paris, 1901, p. 2.)
46. Harden, D. B., *Roman Glass from Karanis*, Ann Arbor, Michigan, USA, 1936, p. 288.

47. Schmitz, Emil-Heinz, *Die Sehhilfe im Wandel der Jahrhunderte* (*Aids to Vision throughout the Ages*), Stuttgart, 1961.
48. Harden, *op. cit.*
49. Antonova, Irina, Tolstikov, Vladimir, and Treister, Mikhail, *The Gold of Troy: Searching for Homer's Fabled City*, Thames and Hudson, 1996. The consultant editor of this book, Donald Easton, a leading expert on Schliemann's work at Troy, was someone I liaised with a lot in my search for these lenses about 1980, and I would like to thank him here for his attempts at that time to help me find the Trojan lenses, which I believe resulted in his realizing for the first time the optical significance of these crystal objects excavated by Schliemann.

SECTION TWO

THE TEXTUAL EVIDENCE

Chapter Two

Really in a Nutshell

'Cicero records that a parchment copy of Homer's poem *The Iliad* was enclosed in a nutshell.'[1]

The original work by Cicero (first century BC) mentioning this fact is lost, but this notice of it is found in the *Natural History* of Pliny (first century AD). Pliny's report appears to be the origin of the common expression which is in daily use today: 'in a nutshell'. Shakespeare, who was well read in the classics, evidently drew his own use of the phrase in *Hamlet* from the Pliny passage. In Act II, Scene 2, Hamlet says to Rosencrantz and Guildenstern:

O God, I could be bounded in a nut-shell and count myself a king of infinite space, were it not that I have bad dreams.

The idea of being bounded in a nutshell undoubtedly comes from the ancient story of a copy of *The Iliad* being written so microscopically that it could fit inside a nutshell.

The fact that a copy of *The Iliad* as small as this was made in ancient times is certainly a bizarre piece of information, and without some familiarity with ancient miniature work and the existence of ancient lenses, one might be inclined to think it was pure fantasy. However, the amount of microscopic writing and carving done in antiquity was vast. And we now know that the lenses certainly existed to enable it to be done.

Because the reader may find it strange to talk about something so small it can really fit inside a nutshell, I have gone to the trouble of finding a modern example and had it photographed with a special lens. It may be seen in Plate 1, and shows the figure of a woman standing inside the half-shell of a walnut. This specimen which I found is Chinese, and I have met the woman who made it. In fact, I saw another specimen of her work where she had made 16 human figures all standing inside a walnut shell. Hamlet could thus have had 15 friends beside him. Such 'shell-art' has been traditional in China for millennia, and bears a close resemblance to what Pliny describes in ancient Rome.

In the same passage, Pliny gives further examples of miniature work:

Callicrates used to make such small ivory models of ants and other creatures that to anybody else their parts were invisible. A certain Myrmecides won fame in the same department by making a four-horse chariot of the same material that a fly's wings would cover, and a ship that a tiny bee could conceal with its wings.[2]

Pliny mentions the subject again at another point with further details:

Fame has been won in the making also of marble miniatures, namely by Myrmecides, whose Four-horse Chariot and Driver were covered by the wings of a fly, and by Callicrates, whose ants have feet and other parts too small to be discerned. So much for the sculptors in marble and the artists who have achieved the greatest fame.[3]

The author Aelian (second/third century AD) records some of these things with additional detail in his *Historical Miscellany* and adds others:

The following are the admired productions of Myrmecides the Milesian [Pliny had not recorded that the man came from Miletus] and Callicrates the Lacedaemonian [Pliny had not mentioned his home either], their miniature pieces: they made four-horse chariots that were concealed beneath the wings of a fly, and they inscribed an elegiac couplet in gold letters on a sesame pod. Neither of these, in my opinion, will earn the approval of a serious person. What are these things except a waste of time?[4]

Aelian, who lived long after Pliny, had obviously not obtained this information from Pliny's work, because he adds details which Pliny did not bother to give. So both clearly drew from some lost common source, which dates at least from the first century BC.

Aelian is very dismissive of the craftsmen who made such miniature masterpieces, saying they were just a 'waste of time', and not worthy of the approval of 'a serious person'. Since Pliny and Aelian were writing 250 years apart, the fact that they both repeated the stories about the famous miniature works means that those tales were widespread and famous for many centuries in antiquity.

The translator of Aelian realized there was something odd about this passage, and he wisely added a footnote, saying:

These two craftsmen are commonly mentioned together. Their date is uncertain. [Marcus] Varro [first century BC], *De Lingua Latina* 7.1., speaks as if he had seen some works by Myrmecides, but he does not say where. One is tempted to speculate that the two were originally experts in carving cameos or sealstones and may even have used lenses.[5]

The miniature work is also mentioned by Gaius Julius Solinus (*circa* 200 AD) in his *Collectanea Rerum Memorabilium*, of which no modern translation exists. However, if we use the quaint and delightful translation of Arthur Golding published in 1587, we find in Chapter Five, the following:

> Cicero maketh report, that the Ilias of Homer was so finely written in Velame [vellum], that it might be closed in a Nutshell. Callicrates carved Ants of Ivory so finely, that some of them could not be discerned from other ants.[6]

It is common for classical scholars to be rude about Solinus, claiming that he simply pinched everything from Pliny and was essentially a plagiarist. But I have found a great deal of fascinating material in Solinus which I rate more highly than that, and I think the lack of a modern edition and translation is a disgrace. In any case, one further detail is evident in the above which was not recorded by either Pliny or Aelian, namely that the miniature ants of Callicrates could not be distinguished from real ones. This indicates that Solinus, like Aelian, was drawing from a common source, rather than from Pliny himself.

The French astronomer François Arago noticed the Pliny and Aelian passages (though not Solinus) in the middle of the 19th century.[7] Arago added: 'There is in a Cabinet of Medals a seal said to have belonged to Michelangelo, the fabrication of which, it is said, ascends to a very remote epoch, and upon which 15 figures have been engraven in a circular space of 14 millimetres in diameter. These figures *are not at all visible to the naked eye*.' Arago cites this information from the second edition (1776) of Louis Dutens's book, *Origine des Découvertes Attribuées aux Modernes* (*Origin of the Discoveries Attributed to the Moderns*). No copy of this edition exists in a British library, and I apparently own the only set in the country. (Only the first and third editions are to be found in the British Library, and all three editions differ from each other in discussions of optics. See, however, footnote 15 of Appendix Two. The gem referred to once belonged to the King of Naples.) Arago comments upon the *Iliad* in a nutshell, mentions the carvings of Myrmecides, and concludes: '. . . these facts establish that the magnifying property of lenses was known to the Greeks and Romans nearly 2,000 years ago.'

The first 'modern' author who inferred the existence of magnifying lenses from the microscopic artisanship of antiquity was the Italian Francesco Vettori, in 1739. Vettori was a connoisseur of ancient gems and he mentions that he had seen some 'the size of half a grain of lentil' which had nevertheless been engraved, and he points out that this was impossible unless the ancient craftsmen had possessed magnifiers.[8] Vettori had been influenced and encouraged in expressing this view openly by reading a book published the previous year by another Italian, Domenico Manni, in which Manni had studied a number of ancient texts and cited Seneca, Pliny, and Plautus as evidence of the existence of lenses in Roman times.[9]

Fifteen years later, a French expert on ancient gems, Laurent Natter, expressed the same opinion as Vettori. In his book on the ancient method of engraving precious stones, published simultaneously in French and English in the year 1754, Natter said:

> The art of engraving in Gems is too difficult for a young Man to be able to produce a perfect Piece; and when he arrives at a proper Age to excel in it, his Sight begins to fail. It is therefore highly probable that the Ancients made use of Glasses, or Microscopes, to supply this defect.[10]

All historians of art have heard of Johann Winckelmann, who lived at the end of the 18th century, for he is generally regarded as the founder of modern art history. In 1776 he also stated that he believed the ancients must have had magnifying glasses in order to have been able to engrave their gems.[11] More than a century later, another important German art historian came forward with the same view. In 1895, Karl Sittl wrote:

> An interesting question arises in connection with this [ancient gem engraving], as to whether the ancient engravers made use of means of optical magnification; however, there is no testimony as to this. But nevertheless, cut stones do exist with incredibly small dimensions, such as the portrait of Plotina [Plotina Pompeia, who died in 122 AD, was a Roman Empress, the wife of Trajan] which measures only 6 millimetres in diameter.[12]

Sittl was obviously unaware of the passages in Pliny and Aelian, and was also unaware of the specific textual evidence for ancient magnification, as well as of the existence of surviving ancient lenses. Sittl was, like Winckelmann before him, merely observing that the miniature work surviving from antiquity could not have been accomplished by the naked eye and must have required magnifiers.

We thus see that suggestions have been made for two-and-a-half centuries that magnifying aids had to have existed in antiquity for miniature work to have been done. The world's museums are filled with microscopic work by ancient and pre-modern craftsmen. In the Stockholm Historical Museum, where I studied a vast collection of rock crystal Viking lenses for two weeks, I was shown eighth-century goldwork by the Vikings, the manufacture of which was clearly impossible without lenses. It is just as well, then, that I found approximately 100 crystal lenses in Scandinavia, all but a few of which I studied and measured individually. I even found a grinding-wheel at Sigtuna, an early Viking site in Sweden. But most important of all, perhaps, was the evidence I found at Sigtuna of a genuine microscopic optical industry. For there are several polished crystal lenses there the size of water drops, which magnify an astonishing three times (3X). The

Swedish archaeologists are probably the most thorough in the world. It is difficult to imagine archaeologists anywhere else even noticing water-drop-sized artifacts, much less preserving them in a museum collection. And they did this without realizing their significance, but simply out of their innate thoroughness and perfectionism. For more about the Scandinavian lenses, see Appendices Four and Ten.

In the Shanghai Museum in China I was likewise shown ancient bronzes from the Han Dynasty (last two centuries BC and first two centuries AD) which contained close-work so minute that it could not have been done with the naked eye. Once again, this work was done at a time and in a culture when crystal lenses are known to have existed, for there are many textual references which describe optical artifacts, such as descriptions in the Han period text, the *Lun Heng*,[13] which I shall discuss later. Unfortunately, all my best endeavours in 1998 to try and see some of the six crystal lenses which have been excavated from tombs in China came to nothing – the only one whose location I was certain of was in a provincial museum in Hubei which was at the time threatened with the worst Yangtse River floods in half a century, so that a visit to the region was impossible. But there is no doubt whatever that the lenses to facilitate the microscopic bronze decoration existed in China at the same epoch as the bronzes.

The famous Henry Schliemann, excavator of Troy, speculated in his book *Troja* in 1884: 'This art of soldering gold to gold, without employing silver or borax, was perfectly well known to the Trojan goldsmith, for all the soldering of the Trojan jewels are perfectly pure, and no dark tint can be seen on them with the strongest lens. Indeed, we cannot look without admiration on the Trojan filigree work (such as the examples on . . . [he gives various examples from another of his books called *Ilios*]), when we see that, in the remote antiquity to which this work belongs, the goldsmiths, without a lens, could solder on such almost microscopic pearls, with an art which now baffles the comprehension of the most skilful of the skilful. This art is lost, and it is doubtful whether it will ever be reinvented.'[14] It is remarkable that Schliemann, who personally excavated no less than 48 ground and polished rock crystal lenses at the site of Troy, should not have made the connection: but perhaps these remarks were made before he discovered the actual lenses themselves. Of course, even allowing for the necessary use of lenses, the question still remains of what technique of soldering could have been used for such microscopic work; it is this problem which is preoccupying Schliemann in this passage. But he seems never to have committed any opinion of the Trojan lenses themselves to writing. Presumably he was completely baffled by them.

One can go from culture to culture in this way and find microscopic art, and generally one can also find the lenses which made it possible. The largest number of examples probably survive from Greece and Rome. Art historians and archaeologists will be familiar with many such, or will suddenly recollect them if prodded in the ribs. It would be a lengthy task to track all of the instances of this sort of thing, and I have not troubled to do it, as I realized pretty early on that it would be endless. In the earlier stages of my research, I thought such instances were rare, and spent considerable effort locating and studying them. I spent a whole day in Cologne studying a codex in a library with miniature writing, which had clearly been written with a magnifying aid. But then I realized that there were masses of microscopic cuneiform texts written on Babylonian and Assyrian baked-clay tablets and cylinder seals, and some ancient Greek coins contained secret inscriptions invisible to the eye, which could only be read through a lens. And there were many engraved seals and gems from Greece and Rome which were either themselves extremely tiny – like the one with the portrait of Plotina – or which contained microscopic work. And so I realized that to try and find all of these examples was pointless. Instead, I concentrated on trying to find all of the magnifiers themselves. But after the number rose beyond 450, I knew that even that was impossible.

Since I have been forced to admit that I have been overwhelmed by an avalanche of evidence, the question poses itself: why has no one else been overwhelmed by a similar avalanche?

It is easier to excuse those who were unaware of the survival of ancient lenses in museums (after all, most of the museum directors didn't recognize them, so how could others be expected to?) than those scholars who failed to notice the very clear passages in ancient literature which describe the use of magnifying aids.

A beginning of sorts was made in 1599 by the remarkable author Guidone (or Guido) Pancirollo (also Pancirollus, Pancirolo, Panciroli, etc.), in his astonishing book *Rerum Memorabilium Iam Olim Deperditarum & contra Recens Atque Ingeniose Inventarum: Libri Duo* (*The History of Many Memorable Things Lost, Which Were in Use among the Ancients: and an Account of Many Excellent Things Found, Now in Use among the Moderns, Both Natural and Artificial*), published at the rather obscure town of Amberg in East Bavaria in the year that Pancirollo died, and posthumously edited by his friend Heinrich (Henricus) Salmuth. Both Pancirollo and Salmuth were jurists and immensely learned scholars. Pancirollo was perhaps best known for an impressive work on the history of Constantinople. Salmuth was narrower in his concerns, having published several definitive works on the highly specialist subject of marital law.

The work by Pancirollo is largely forgotten today, but it had an immense influence for nearly a century and a half after its initial appearance in Latin in 1599, appearing in many editions and different languages until 1727, a continuous publication cycle of no less than 128 years. I have consulted many editions, but cannot claim to have seen them all – and in fact, I doubt if there is certainty about how many there really were. (Two of the British Library's copies were destroyed by German bombing during the Second World War, which did not make my task of comparing the editions any easier.)

In studying the work of Pancirollo, one must differentiate Pancirollo's own text from the even more voluminous annotations by his friend Salmuth (much of which was presumably drawn from Pancirollo's own notes, left undigested at his sudden death). Most editions differentiate between the two texts, but it 'ain't easy'. A highly misleading picture was given to the French readership by the appearance in 1617 of the only French translation of Pancirollo, for this publication omitted all of Salmuth's text in its entirety, and French readers who did not bother to consult the original Latin would never even have known of its existence.[15]

Anyone studying the work of Pancirollo also needs to be aware of a second collection of extensive annotations, not only to Pancirollo's text but to Salmuth's commentary on it. This was published in 1663 by Michael Watson, about whom, unfortunately, I know nothing, except that he was obviously an Englishman or a Scot, though as his book was published in Germany he presumably lived abroad. Watson's extensive commentary was only published in Latin and never translated.[16]

As far as I can determine, then, the first 'modern' author who cited a classical text as evidence for the existence of magnifying aids in antiquity was Pancirollo. What Pancirollo himself wrote (I use the English translation as published in 1715) was:

> Many doubt whether the Ancients had Spectacles or not, because Pliny the most diligent of all Writers, hath not so much as one Word concerning them. But however, you will find them mention'd by Plautus, when he said *Vitram cedo, necesse est conspicilio uti* which cannot be understood of any Thing else, but of those kind of Glasses which are call'd Spectacles.[17]

These comments appear in the chapter called in the original Latin *De Conspiciliis* ('Of Spectacles').[18] Plautus was a Roman comic playright who lived from *circa* 254 BC to 184 BC, 21 of whose plays survive. What ensued from Pancirollo's mention of him was a long dispute in scholarly circles about this reference, and the strange discovery that the quotation can be found nowhere in any known work by Plautus. There are other relevant passages in Plautus, it turns out, but this one apparently cannot be located. Pancirollo gives no actual source for the reference, and he seems to have jotted the passage down from a scholarly work by an earlier French author, Robert Estienne. There seems no doubt that Estienne was in error, a fact unappreciated by Pancirollo, who took the reference on trust. Unfortunately, no work by Estienne is to be found in the British Library.

An early attacker of Pancirollo was William Molyneux, in 1692. In his work *Dioptrica Nova* he pours scorn on those who maintain that any magnifying aids existed in antiquity. (He was unaware of the passage from Seneca describing them clearly, which we shall examine shortly.) Molyneux makes much of the mistaken attribution to Plautus of the use of the optical word *conspicilio*, which he said was a false reference which had been exploded by Abbot Michele Giustiani and discussed also by Christian Beckmann. However, Molyneux fails to give the references to Giustiani or to Beckmann, and the one (Latin) work by Christian Beckmann (published in 1612) which exists in the British Library, which I went through line by line, contains no mention of this. And as for Giustiani, the British Library contains only his Letters published in 1683, which also appear to have nothing in them about this subject. So Molyneux could hardly be described as genuinely helpful on this issue, except that he speculates that perhaps the work by Christian Beckmann in question was his *Oratio de Barbarie & Superstitione Superiorum Temporum*, but admits he has not bothered to check. (I have not been able to find a copy of this work.)

In his commentary on Pancirollo, Salmuth had written:

> *Conspicilia*: some say, 'tis to be read *Conspicillum*; as *Baculus*, *Bacillus*; *Furcula*, *Furcilla*; so *Speculum*, *Specillum*. Though the word *Conspicillum* used here by our Author, doth commonly denote a Place from whence we may see or have a Prospect of any Thing, as in Plautus, his *Medic. In conspicilio adservabam Pallium*; yet here it signifies an Instrument which magnifies Objects and makes them bigger. In which Sense that of Plautus is to be understood (*Vitrum cedo*, &c.) so that 'tis probable from hence, that they were anciently in Use, as it also may appear from Ptolemy's Glass . . .[19]

(Ptolemy's Glass is another issue, to be discussed later on, and we must not allow ourselves to be distracted by it here; it had first entered modern discussions in 1558 with della Porta, but as I say, we must leave that for later.)

This strange business of a mistaken reference from Plautus did nothing to clarify these matters, and a mistake originating either from Estienne or from the uncorrected notes of Pancirollo (who died in the middle of writing his book) led to much unnecessary confusion. The perplexity has still not vanished today. I suspect that the passage attributed to Plautus is taken from some other author, perhaps another Latin playwright. Pancirollo would not simply have invented this, nor would Estienne; it must be that the actual reference is in error. It may even be correctly given in Estienne, if one could ever find the relevant work by him.

But perhaps it is not worthwhile to expend any further effort on this frustrating issue, since it doesn't ultimately matter. Whether Plautus mentioned magnifying aids or not, or whether the passage attributed to him occurs in some other author or not, is irrelevant from the point of view of historical proof of the existence of ancient lenses. For we have other perfectly good and unchallenged passages, such as one from Seneca (first century AD) giving an unambiguous description of ancient magnifying aids, in his scientific work *Natural Questions*. And I wouldn't be a bit surprised if a search were made through the Latin texts of his surviving plays, if the 'Plautus' passage might actually be found there.

In his *Natural Questions*, Seneca states (I, 3, 9):

> Fruits are much larger when seen through glass.[20]

And further on (I, 6, 5), he is more specific:

> I will add that everything is much larger when you look at it through water. Letters, however tiny and obscure, are seen larger and clearer through a glass ball filled with water. Fruits seem more beautiful than they actually are if they are floating in a glass bowl. Stars appear larger when you see them through a cloud because our vision grows dim in the moisture and is unable to apprehend accurately what it wants to. This will be demonstrated if you fill a cup with water and throw a ring into it. For, although the ring lies on the bottom, its image is reflected on the surface of the water. Anything seen through moisture is far larger than in reality. Why is it so remarkable that the image of the sun is reflected larger when it is seen in a moist cloud, especially since this results from two causes? In a cloud there is something like glass which is able to transmit light; there is also something like water.[21]

Here we have an unambiguous description of glass balls filled with water being used for reading purposes by the Romans. In fact, these were extremely common in Roman times, and I have encountered about 200 of

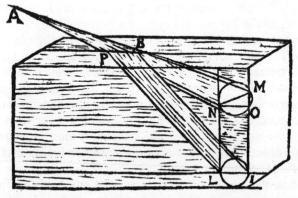

Figure 4. This 17th-century woodcut published by the Rev. Athanasius Kircher in his magnificently illustrated work *Ars Magna Lucis et Umbrae* (*The Great Art of Light and Shadow*) shows the refraction of light rays in water. We see things 'bent' when we look through water because the rays do not go from point B to the circle N-M but are refracted instead by the watery medium at point P and go to the circle L-I. (From the second augmented folio edition of 1671, Amsterdam, p. 593; in the 1646 edition, this woodcut appears on p. 662.) Discussions of 'bent paddles' of boats and other such optical phenomena due to light being refracted in water go back to the Greek philosophers, and are found for instance in Aristotle.

them, either whole or fragmentary, in museums. They were mass-produced, and very cheap. For it was in Roman times that the mammoth glass industry made mass-distribution of magnifying aids possible, and they no longer had to be obtained in the expensive form of ground and polished rock crystal.

Seneca is not the only Roman author who is explicit about glass balls filled with water resulting in magnification. Macrobius (early fifth century AD) wrote in his *Saturnalia* (VII, 14, 1):

> We have just been talking about water, and I would ask you why it is that the images of objects immersed in water appear to be larger than actual objects. For example, most of the dainties which we see exposed to view in eating houses look bulkier than they really are – that is to say, in the little glass jars full of water the eggs seem to be of greater size, the little livers to have thicker fibres, and the onion coils look huge. And, indeed, on what principle does our sense of sight itself depend? . . . Water, replied Disarius, is denser than air (air being a rarified medium), and so sight passes through it more slowly; the visual ray on striking against the water is beaten back, broken open, and recoils. When it returns, thus broken open, it impinges now on the outlines of the object of vision not with a direct blow but from all sides, and so it comes about that the visual image of the object of vision seems to be greater than the object itself. For certainly the sun's orb, too, appears to us to be larger than usual in the morning, because the air between us and it is still dewy from the night, so that the sun's image is enlarged, just as if it were seen [through] water.[22]

The author Aulus Gellius (second century AD) also mentions magnification as seen through water in his book *Attic Nights* (XVI, 18):

> A part of Geometry which relates to the sight is called *optikē* or 'Optics' . . . This science also gives the reasons for optical illusions, such as the magnifying of objects seen in the water, and the small size of those that are remote from the eye.[23]

The Greeks and Romans were well aware of the similarity of a crystal or glass globe filled with water and the water-filled human eye. As Priscian of Lydia wrote in the sixth century AD, in his commentary on a work by Theophrastus (the successor of Aristotle) dealing with sense-perception:

> Why, then, is the eye-jelly of the eye of water?[24]

Later in this book, we shall be considering the many extraordinary ancient Egyptian optical phenomena. But in light of the comment by Priscian which we have just seen, let us look at a few of the Pyramid Texts, Egypt's most ancient religious scriptures, which date from the latter half of the third millennium BC. They are called 'Utterances' and are numbered as they occur in the pyramids, where they are carved in stone in the inner chambers of the Fifth Dynasty pyramid chambers. Not long ago I sat for six hours inside the Pyramid of Unas at Saqqara. This pyramid appears from the outside to be largely ruinous, but its inner shafts and chambers are breathtakingly intact. It was a strange experience to sit beneath the ceilings of carved stars for hours, surrounded by hundreds of carved hieroglyphic 'Utterances'. Here is Utterance 144:

> O Osiris the King, take the Eye of Horus, the water in which he has squeezed out . . .[25]

Utterance 68 also says:

> O Osiris the King, take the water which is in the Eye of Horus . . .[26]

But it is Utterances 62 and 62A which really cause one to wonder:

> O Osiris the King, take the water which is in the Eye of Horus, do not let go of it. O Osiris the King, take the Eye of Horus, the water in which Thoth has seen . . .[27]

These texts suggest that the Egyptians may have been referring to transparent globes filled with water, which magnified. Otherwise, why would the god Thoth have *seen* by means of the water in the Eye? We do not need to assume that they had mastered the art of making globes of glass at that early date – although that is possible – since they could have made them of rock crystal. We have conclusive archaeological proof that they had mastered the art of making complicated vessels from rock crystal as early as the *First* Dynasty. I came across this clear evidence in the Egyptian Museum at Cairo (formerly called the Cairo Museum) in 1998. In that Museum, in Room 43, Case 13, Object Number 37 is a beautifully worked small goblet of rock crystal excavated from the tomb of Hemaka at Saqqara. It is approximately two inches high and flares outward from a narrow base, and the interior is perfectly hollowed out and polished. One does not wish to postulate that such magnificent objects were common, but the indisputable fact is that this object, dating from the very beginning of the dynastic period of Egypt – approximately 3000 BC – shows an absolute technical mastery of the most complex grinding and polishing techniques for rock crystal as well as the ability to hollow out pieces successfully, leaving the interiors as polished as the exteriors. It would be difficult to find a crystal grinder today who could equal the technical feat of producing the Hemaka Goblet. There can thus be no question that the Egyptians could have produced crystal globes if they had wished.

I have seen many convex rock crystal magnifying lenses from Egypt of the Old Kingdom and Middle Kingdom periods, but they will be discussed in a later context. In the meantime, let us return to Greek and Latin literary references.

One might suppose that spectacles had never been mentioned in ancient Greek literature, but one might be wrong! They actually appear to be mentioned in an epigram preserved in the huge collection of ancient Greek poetry generally known as *The Greek Anthology*. Sometimes also called *The Palatine Anthology*, it is a collection of poetry by many poets from the period of the seventh to third centuries BC. In the Loeb Classical Library edition it fills five volumes. The collection preserves in Book VI several dedicatory epigrams by Phanias, who was a grammarian of the third century BC (not to be confused with the Phanias or Phaenias of Eresos in Lesbos, cousin of Theophrastus, who was a disciple of Aristotle in the fourth century BC, or the Phanius who wrote on medicine in the first century AD). The epigrams tend to be wryly humorous. In one, dedicated to an old schoolmaster named Callon, Phanias mentions 'the fennel-rod that lay ever ready to his hand to tap little boys with on the head' as well as 'his one-soled slipper'.[28] But the poem which concerns us is a satire on a scribe named Ascondas, whose writing tools are now set aside because he has taken up the profitable job of a tax-collector, and Paton's translation is as follows:

> Ascondas, when he came in for an exciseman's lickerish sop [a tax collecting job which was highly profitable], hung up here to the Muses [in a Temple to the Muses, of which imaginary offering this epigram is a satirical dedication] the implements of his [former] penury: his penknife, the sponge he used to hire to wipe his Cnidian pens, the ruler for marking off the margins, his paper-weight that marks the place (?), his ink-horn, his compasses that draw circles [for geometry], his pumice [*kisērin* – pumice-stone] for smoothing [making the papyrus surface smooth for writing], and his blue spectacles (?) that give sweet light.[29]

We notice that Paton has used the word 'spectacles' but has inserted a question mark in parentheses, due to his surprise at the reference and his lack of absolute certainty about the word. But what is the Greek word which he has been tempted to render as 'spectacles'? And why are they blue? In fact, the translation 'blue' for *kallainan* should probably be changed to 'green', because the 1996 revised Liddell and Scott Lexikon has corrected the sense of the rare related word form *kallainopoioi* found in the epigram. In earlier editions of the Lexikon it had been thought to mean 'makers of blue dye', but it has now been changed to 'makers of green dye'. The word is a variant of *kalainos* or *kallainos* which means 'shifting between blue and green' and 'greenish-blue', and was applied to the turquoise by Pliny (37, 151). So Paton is not strictly correct to use the translation 'blue'. It should really be 'green' or 'greenish-blue'.

The Greek which Paton translates 'and his blue spectacles (?) that give sweet light' in its entirety is *kai tan hadyphaē plinthida kallainan*. The word *plinthida* is the one Paton translates as 'spectacles'. It is a form of *plinthis*, and the fundamental word is *plinthos*, meaning 'brick'. But a variety of meanings spun off from this, expressed by variant word-forms such as *plinthis*, which from the basic concept of a square or rectangular brick expressed the meanings of 'square', 'rectangle', 'rectangular box', or even 'front frame of a torsion engine'. A *plintheion* was even a 'window frame'. *Plinthida* was thus considered by Paton to refer to greenish squares or rectangles or framed things through which one saw. In Liddell and Scott's Lexikon, there is a slightly pathetic guess that the word as used in this particular epigram might mean: 'paperweight (?)' (meaning 4. under *plinthis*). But since a paperweight has already been referred to, this is most unlikely and was flatly rejected by Paton.

If this were the only isolated reference to greenish lenses in ancient literature, one might be inclined to dismiss it as a fluke, a mistranslation, a misunderstanding, or something of the sort. But in fact there are other references, both to the restful nature of green glass for the eyes, and to actual corrective lenses which were greenish. And in any case, I have examined many ancient Roman lenses which were of greenish glass. So the conclusion is that the Phanias reference is probably acurately translated, though the terminology is obscure.

The Latin word generally used for the material of which greenish lenses were made is *smaragdus*, from the Greek *smaragdos*. Generally speaking, this word means 'emerald', although by extension it describes other green minerals and even green glass. The word is of Egyptian derivation (a point which I was the first to discover). The Greek word comes from Egyptian *shmā* ('emerald' deriving from the word for 'South', since the emerald was the 'stone of the South') – *rāges* ('a variegated stone').[30] *Rāges* probably had reference not only to variegated but coloured stones. The Greek *smaragdos* is thus *shmārāges*, 'an emerald-variegated (or coloured) stone'. The common reference to 'emerald' leaves no doubt. Further lack of ambiguity is due to the fact that the Egyptian word *rāges* is apparently the only instance in ancient Egyptian of a word formed by adding the rare consonant 'g' to the syllable *rā*, and is therefore entirely unambiguous in its sound, which is also an extremely rare fact in the maze and mire of the Egyptian language. This unusual fact may in turn indicate a foreign origin for the Egyptian word!

The word *smaragdos* makes its first recorded entrance into the Greek language in the *History* of Herodotus (fifth century BC), who uses it twice (at II, 44, and III, 41). This is appropriate, as Herodotus lived for some time in Egypt and wrote about that country at great length. It makes perfect sense that Herodotus would be the one to introduce this term into Greek.

The early-19th-century scholar Paul Jablonski believed that the Greek word for 'rock crystal' and 'glass', *hyalos*, had an Egyptian origin, and was also introduced by Herodotus (III, 24).[31] If so, the three materials for use for the optical purposes of magnifying and burning – glass, crystal, and 'smaragdus' – all took their Greek names from the older and more sophisticated culture of Egypt, which was also a culture possessing lenses from at least 3300 BC.

Pliny (first century AD) records a great deal of fascinating lore about the *smaragdus*. Here are some of his remarks:

> The third rank among gemstones is assigned for several reasons to the 'smaragdus'. Certainly, no colour has a more pleasing appearance. For although we gaze eagerly at young plants and at leaves, we look at 'smaragdi' with all the more pleasure because, compared with them, there is nothing whatsoever that is more intensely green. Moreover, they alone of gems, when we look at them intently, satisfy the eye without cloying it. Indeed, even after straining our sight by looking at another object, we can restore it to its normal state by looking at a 'smaragdus'; and engravers of gemstones find that this is the most agreeable means of refreshing their eyes: so soothing to their feeling of fatigue is the mellow green colour of the stone. Apart from this property, 'smaragdi' appear larger when they are viewed at a distance because they reflect their colour upon the air around them [literally: 'tinge around them the air rebounding from them', an old theory about air being involved in optical phenomena]. They remain the same in sunlight, shadow, or lamplight, always shining gently and allowing the vision to penetrate to their further extremity owing to the ease with which light passes through them, a property that pleases us also in respect of water. 'Smaragdi' are generally concave in shape, so that they concentrate the vision.[32]

My friend Buddy Rogers has some unmounted emeralds in his gem collection, which has given me the opportunity to look through large emeralds in a way which is not possible when they are mounted. I suspect that not many people have had this opportunity. Buddy has a 52-carat emerald which is cut as a plano-convex cabochon. If it had been rock crystal or even transparent, it would have been a powerful magnifying lens. Unfortunately, this emerald is not transparent, but it is certainly translucent. I held it up close to my eye and looked through it into a light. It is difficult to describe in words the amazing experience of looking at light through a large emerald. The colour is so indescribably wonderful and soothing that it is somehow unlike any other colour experience. It is indeed true, as Pliny said, that 'no colour has a more pleasing appearance'. It is like being bathed in an optical balm which suffuses the whole of space.

Buddy also has a 24.32-carat emerald cut as a normal faceted gem. It is transparent. It functioned as a magnifier when I placed it over a newspaper. Emeralds certainly are capable of acting as excellent lenses.

Before describing my meeting with Professor Eichholz, the translator of the above passage by Pliny, and the important changes he wished to make to his translation as a result of our discussions, I first quote his published footnote (of 1971) to the last sentence above:

Does Pliny imply that the concave stone could be used as a lens? This is improbable, because a green gemstone would hardly serve that purpose. Moreover, although magnifying mirrors were known in antiquity, there is no certain evidence that anything was known of magnifying lenses, although magnifying lenses of short focus may possibly have been used by engravers. Pliny is presumably theorizing about the beneficial effects of 'smaragdi' on the sight.[33]

In the late 1970s I tracked down Professor Eichholz, who had been in the Classics Department of the University of Bristol in England, but had retired. I found him living in a retirement home in Clifton in Bristol, where he was confined to a wheelchair. He was thrilled to have a visitor, especially one who wished to discuss his greatest passion, Pliny. In the pathetically reduced circumstances to which retirement homes restrict all old people, Eichholz's small room only had space for a few books. A row of Loeb Library volumes kept the lonely man company, and I would have liked to visit him more often for chats about the classics if it had been possible, but I believe I only saw him twice. At that point, he was the world's leading *living* expert on Pliny, but it was clear that he was never consulted, and only occasionally visited. I believe he had a niece who visited him from time to time, so that he was not completely alone in the world.

Unlike some scholars who are highly egotistical and will not tolerate the slightest question of their judgement, Eichholz was wholly open-minded and lacking in ego problems. He was amazed and delighted when I told him that I had found some ancient lenses, and he said if only he had known that they existed when he was doing his translation of Pliny, he would not have been so vague and noncommittal in his translations of the many optical passages, and of course he would have altered his footnotes. He said there was always pressure on Loeb translators to put first the need to 'make it flow' and not be too literal, and added that he had been bothered in his conscience for years about not doing what he thought was full justice to the optical passages in his Pliny translation. We got out the relevant Pliny volumes and pored over them together. I had brought notes of all the references with me, so this was quickly done. He then went over them with me, word by word, and produced revised translations of the passages, which he said he wished I would publish some day under his name so that people would know that he had made amends and done proper justice to the material. I wrote these down and shall refer to them as we go along. Many of these are to be found in Appendix Three, in my translations of Lessing's optical writings. I was deeply touched by Eichholz's scholarly humility and earnestness, which is so rare in his profession. I wish he were still with us, to receive his copy of this book – he would have been one of its keenest readers. And I would like to take this opportunity to thank him, both for all the trouble he took, and for his splendid attitude towards learning. Unfortunately, good men like him do not often rise to the academic heights, because they are genuinely modest and more interested in their scholarly work and teaching than in self-advancement.

I left off the passage of Pliny with the sentence about 'smaragdi' being concave and concentrating the vision. Eichholz went over this and produced this revised version:

> The same stones ['smaragdi'] are generally concave [in shape] so that they collect (or gather together) the vision.

The implication is that the stone does not simply 'concentrate' the vision but 'collects' or 'gathers together' the vision in the sense of rays being focused. This is an important nuance which was missed in Eichholz's published version.

The question of concave lenses in ancient times was one which vexed me for years. Many people, especially German scholars, who had discussed the possibility of lenses in antiquity, had insisted that even if there were convex lenses, no evidence had ever been found of any concave lenses. So Pliny's testimony was not believed.

It was only in 1997 that I finally found that there were a number of surviving concave lenses from antiquity, and was able to locate them in a variety of museums. See Figure 5 and Plate 45 for some of these. The greatest number from any single site were excavated at Ephesus in Turkey. Altogether there must be about 40 of them. I am still tracking down some obscure or unpublished ones, such as one at Brauron near Athens. They are all of rock crystal and perfectly transparent.

In fact, the ability to grind concave lenses had been demonstrated even in Minoan times, *circa* 1500 BC, since the crystal eye in the famous Bull's Head Rhyton found at Knossos is a 'convex meniscus lens', which means that it is convex on the top and concave underneath.

Since concave lenses get thinner rather than thicker in the middle, they are less robust at survival, as they are so much more easily broken. That may be why no intact *glass* concave lens is known to me, and all surviving specimens are of the far stronger rock crystal.

Concave lenses correct for short-sightedness (myopia). Convex lenses correct for long-sightedness, such as that which comes to people when they reach the age of about 45. This condition is a result of the hardening of the

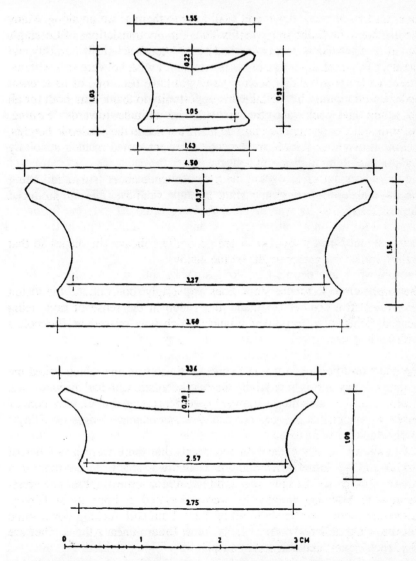

Figure 5. Drawings of three of the concave crystal lenses excavated at Ephesus by Anton Bammer. See his article 'Die Entwicklung des Opferkultes am Altar der Artemis von Ephesos' ('The Development of the Sacrificial Cult at the Altar of Artemis of Ephesus'), in *Istanbuler Mitteilungen (Istanbul Notices)*, of the German Archaeological Institute at Istanbul, Vol. 23/24, 1973/74, pp. 53–62; these drawings are on p. 60. Bammer says of the lenses (translation): 'They all have the shape of a univalvular hyperboloid . . . Their superior surfaces are concave, their bases are slightly convex . . . One crystal is smoky, the others are wholly transparent. . . . Their optical properties are good . . . Looked at physically, they are reducing, diverging lenses. Perhaps they were used by gem cutters who were short-sighted, as working devices. The eyes of the artisans must often in a short time have been ruined by working with the unaided eye on the scarcely visible craftsmanship of stone, ivory, etc. The differing magnifications of the crystals could hint at this, that they were fashioned for the workers at the time. The perforated pieces found in the temple were certainly hollowed out for optical reasons.'

lens in the eye with age, and is called presbyopia. People who have had excellent eyesight all their lives find that they can no longer read without the aid of spectacles, since everything close up is out of focus. This was certainly the most urgent visual defect in antiquity – just as gem engravers and other craftsmen were reaching their peak of skill, and just as scholars were becoming truly learned, their eyes failed and they could neither carve nor read. Hence the vast number of convex lenses which survive from antiquity.

But, as everyone knows, some people are born short-sighted, or develop myopia in childhood. Without concave lenses in spectacles, they can't even see to walk about or recognize the face of anyone who approaches them. We have a description of the Roman Emperor Nero (15–68 AD) which shows clearly that he was myopic. Pliny records (XI, 54) the following bizarre information about the eyes of emperors, culminating in the information about Nero:

> Moreover some people have long sight but others can only see things brought close to them [hence are myopic]. The sight of many depends on the brilliance of the sun, and they cannot see clearly on a cloudy day or after sunset; others have dimmer sight in the day time but are exceptionally keen-sighted at night. . . . Blue-grey eyes see more clearly in the dark. It is stated that Tiberius Caesar alone of mankind was so constituted that if he woke up in the night for a short time he could see everything just as in bright daylight, although darkness gradually closed over him. The late lamented Augustus [Caesar] had grey eyes like those of horses, the whites being larger than usual in a human being, on account of which he used to be angry if people watched his eyes too closely; Claudius Caesar's eyes were frequently bloodshot and had a fleshy gleam at the corners; the Emperor Gaius had staring eyes; Nero's eyes were dull of sight except when he screwed them up to look at objects brought close to them.[34]

This proves that Nero was myopic, a point which we shall see in a moment is a crucial one to establish. If Nero had been long-sighted, he could not have focused on 'objects brought close to' his eyes. Therefore if he had wished to have his sight corrected, he would have required concave, rather than convex lenses. And that brings us back to the passage about 'smaragdi' and introduces us to a notorious controversy. Here is where we left off in quoting Pliny (XXXVII, 64) about 'smaragdi':

> Because of these properties [the ability to gather together visual rays], mankind has decreed that 'smaragdi' must be preserved in their natural state and has forbidden them to be engraved. In any case, those of Scythia and Egypt are so hard as to be unaffected by blows. [These were the only 'smaragdi' which were true emeralds. As Eichholz says in a

footnote here: 'Few precious stones are harder than the emerald.'] When 'smaragdi' that are tabular in shape are laid flat, they reflect objects just as mirrors do. The Emperor Nero used to watch the fights between gladiators in a reflecting 'smaragdus'.[35]

At this very point there is a disputed reading of the Latin, and the text occurs in manuscripts in two versions. In one Nero watches *in smaragdo*, and in the other he watches simply *smaragdo*. Depending on which reading one accepts, the grammar is different, and the meaning changes. Eichholz's published footnote says:

Reading *in smaragdo* with [Manuscript tradition] B. The context shows that Pliny was thinking of a reflecting stone. Probably Nero merely looked at the stone to relieve his eyes from the glare of the arena. The inferior reading [in another manuscript tradition] *smaragdo* has given rise to the belief that Nero used a green stone as an eye-glass.[36]

After our conversations together, Eichholz admitted to me that he had inserted the concept of reflection simply for the sake of trying to achieve clarity. Here is Eichholz's revised translation:

However [*vero*; not 'truly', which would be *vere*] the stones whose body is stretched out, when (laid) on their backs [*supini*] in the same way as mirrors, do give back the images of things. The Emperor Nero used to look at the fights of gladiators in a 'smaragdus'.

We can see that this is a very different interpretation than that which Eichholz gave earlier. Gone is the notion that the 'smaragdus' was acting as a reflecting surface like a mirror. No longer is it necessary for Nero to have turned his back on the gladiators (a thing an emperor could not reasonably do in any case) in order to watch their activities as partial reflections in a small stone. Now he is looking *through* the stone *at* the gladiators. Gone also is the 'sunglasses theory' that the stone was merely being used because its green colour rested his eyes. We already know that Nero was myopic from the other reference, and since he was myopic, he could not possibly have seen the gladiators at all without a concave lens correction to his sight; they would have been just a blur. And we have just been told that 'smaragdi' were specifically ground as concave lenses. Furthermore, about 40 ancient concave lenses in transparent stone exist, all from dates prior to the reign of Nero, so that we know such lenses existed aplenty in his time. So we are left with no other conclusion than that Nero was using a green transparent stone – or perhaps some green transparent glass – ground concave to correct his myopia so that he could bring the gladiators into focus and actually see the combat rather than imagine it from the sounds alone. And as Emperor of Rome, and a demanding one at that, he certainly

Figure 6. The Roman Emperor Nero (reigned 54–68 AD), an engraving of a contemporary bust. He was noted for his thick neck like a bull. Pliny records information about his eyes which shows that he suffered from myopia (short-sightedness). His green concave eye-glass corrected his myopic vision, and he used it publicly when he attended the gladiatorial fights in the Roman Colosseum.

could command the resources to supply himself with this simple visual aid – and it is hard to imagine him *not* doing so.

The subject of Nero's Emerald became world-famous in 1896 when Henryk Sienkiewicz published his international best-selling novel *Quo Vadis: a Narrative of the Time of Nero*. Although it appeared in its original Polish edition in 1896, the sensation was so great that its English translation by Jeremiah Curtin actually appeared in English at London in the same year. This famous historical novel won Sienkiewicz (1846–1916) the Nobel Prize for Literature in 1905. The novel appeared in no less than 27 American editions between 1896 and 1905 alone. The mass hysteria and public adulation of the author, and admiration for the book, were so astounding that the press of the time christened the phenomenon the *epidemia Sienkiewicziana* ('the Sienkiewicz Epidemic'). It is doubtful if there is a major language anywhere in the world in which successive editions of this novel did not appear, and it seems to have sold untold millions of copies. It was still widely read and enormously popular in the 1950s when the Hollywood film of it appeared, in which Peter Ustinov played Nero.

Sienkiewicz was a remarkable scholar of Roman antiquities and he wrote an uncannily accurate novel about the time of Nero, in which Nero appears from time to time as a secondary character. Sienkiewicz had obviously read Pliny and Suetonius very carefully, and noted both their descriptions of Nero's eyes and Pliny's description of his use of the 'smaragdus'. Here is the relevant passage from the novel:

> But at that moment was heard the voice of Acte, who was reclining on the other side of Lygia: 'Caesar is looking at you both.' . . . Vinicius was alarmed . . . Caesar had bent over the table, half closed one eye, and holding before the other a round polished emerald, which he used, was looking at them. For a moment his glance met Lygia's eyes and the heart of the maiden was straitened with terror. When still a child on Aulus' Sicilian estate, an old Egyptian slave had told her of dragons which occupy dens in the mountains, and it seemed to her now that all at once the greenish eye of such a monster was gazing at her. . . . After a while he laid down the emerald and ceased to look at her. Then she saw his prominent blue eyes, blinking before the excess of light, glassy, without thought, resembling the eyes of the dead.[37]

After the worldwide attention called to Nero's Emerald by this popular novel, authors discussing the subject of ancient optics felt compelled to refer to it lest they appear uncultured or uninformed, or out of touch with the times. It was the one thing the public knew about ancient optics, and the one thing they asked about. And a great deal of nonsense was certainly written by some of these authors! It would be too lengthy a task to survey all of the discussion, as it has been so voluminous. However, a reliable summing up of the subject of Nero's Emerald had already been made nine years before the appearance of Sienkiewicz's novel, in a technical book in German by Jakob Stilling. It is a pity that this work was little known and writers in English were especially ignorant of it. The translation of the title is *Inquiries into the Origin of Short-Sightedness*, and the author was an expert, a professor of ophthalmology and a competent classical scholar and historian of science.[38]

I have translated some of the key observations which Stilling made, as they seem to me to sum up the situation very well indeed:

Chapter Ten.
Concerning the History of Concave Spectacles.
There has been controversy over whether the Romans made use of ground concave emeralds for the correction of short-sightedness, and this question has mostly been answered in the negative. However, as I believe can be proved, unjustly so.
Pliny says of the emeralds: *Iidem plerumque concavi ut visum colligant*. This expression in my opinion has not been sufficiently considered

until now, because the philologists are entirely unacquainted with ancient medicine. It is characteristic and too much follows the later authors' usage in order for us not to suppose that Pliny hardly surprisingly expressed an opposing view to that only later adopted by Galen [famous medical writer of the second century AD, a hundred years after Pliny] from the Peripatetics [followers of Aristotle]. The later authors have as a rule *spiritus colligere* instead of *visum colligere*. This expression without any doubt means 'to extend the field of vision'. Thus does [Hieronymus] Mercurialis [who wrote many medical books in the late 1500s and early 1600s] explain the operation of concave spectacles with the words *quare perspicilla* [spectacles] *faciunt pro istis, ut congregentur illi spiritus seu radii pauci et subtiles, ita ut congregati et uniti longius ferantur.* – I find that these passages are not understood properly by any interpreters. [Gotthold Ephraim] Lessing [in 1769] takes them in the sense of *radios colligere* and not in Mercurialis's sense, but in the modern optical sense, and seeks thus to prove that Nero was far-sighted and his emerald through which he watched the gladiators must have been a convex lorgnette. Röttger does not fall into this error, but reads too much into the remark of Pliny . . . He therefore came to the conclusion that *visum colligere* means 'to rest the gaze', and that Nero's emerald must have been a small mirror, which scarcely makes any sense. Horner [1887, a Swiss ophthalmologist who was a believer in ancient convex lenses but doubtful of concave ones] thinks it must have been a protective glass. All of these men were unfamiliar with the medical signification of the expression *visum colligere*.

The Romans knew that short-sightedness could be improved by using ground concave transparent stones. Otherwise there would be no sense to the passage in Pliny [about their not being engraved]. It was forbidden to engrave the *smaragdi* because they aided vision, and because of this they were extensively ground. This passage indicates an already very widespread use of the *smaragdi* as concave lorgnettes. If they were only for the protection of the eyes against glare or for resting the eyes, there would seem to be no apparent point in grinding them or in establishing a prohibition against their being engraved. . . . The well-known controversial question as to whether Nero was short-sighted and his emerald was a concave lorgnette seems to me . . . of a subordinate nature [to questions of ancient understanding of refraction, etc.], and could only have been dealt with so exhaustively because the true meaning of *visum colligere* was not appreciated. Incidentally, this question may be answered in the affirmative. According to Suetonius [*Life of Nero*, 51], Nero was *oculis caesiis et hebetioribus* ['his eyes were grey and dull'], from which absolutely nothing can be concluded. . . . [But we know from Pliny that] Nero's eyes were weak, except if he looked, blinking and close, to objects he encountered. . . . Indeed, in all probability it can be accepted that the ground concave emerald is the oldest form of concave spectacles.[39]

An ancient Greek concave lens of rock crystal, excavated at Ephesus, may be seen in Plate 45. It reduces images by 75%.

In 1899, another distinguished German ophthalmologist, Vincenz Fukala, published his account of *The Science of Refraction in Antiquity* (*Die Refraktionslehre im Alterthum*) and he also concluded:

> The statement of Pliny concerning the concave *smaragdus* of Nero is sufficiently known and proves that such glasses were known in the years BC. . . . there is sufficient evidence to conclude that the ancients long before Christ were acquainted with convex and concave lenses, perhaps even fastened in spectacle frames, for the magnification of fine work or for the improvement of vision.[40]

Fukala even cites two passages from the Roman playwright Plautus (240 BC), mentioned earlier – but not the mysterious 'untraceable' passage – which he believes refer to spectacles. The first is a reference in the play *Cistellaria* (*The Tale of a Trinket Box*), Act One, Scene One, where the young girl Silenia mentions a *conspicillum*, which Fukala believes is a spectacle or lens-shaped instrument through which one sees. The second is a reference in a fragment of the lost play *Medicus*; although only three lines of this play survive, they also contain a mention of a *conspicillum* which Fukala believes to be an optical lens.

Pierre Pansier in 1901 discussed Fukala's views on the Plautus passages but disagrees with his interpretation. The first passage, from *Cistellaria*, can be translated as: 'When I returned to the house, he followed me with a look through his *conspicillum* until I reached the door.' The passage from *Medicus* can be translated as: 'I observed through my *conspicillum*, I kept watch.' Pansier seems strained in maintaining that somehow the meaning of the first is really 'he follows at a distance' and of the second is 'I observed from a distance'. This is not very convincing and seems a desperate dodge to avoid acknowledging the mention of optical aids by Plautus.[41] On the other hand, there are some who believe a *conspicillum* is a vantage point or observation platform – another seemingly strained interpretation, since why would Plautus say the girl was watched from an observation platform? Why not simply say from a balcony or a window?

In 1900, Jakob Stilling published a further study of Nero's Emerald entitled 'Nero's Augenglas' ('Nero's Eyeglass') in an ophthalmological journal.[42] In this he carried his analysis of both the classical evidence and modern discussions much further. He agrees with Fukala that Nero's Emerald could not possibly have been a reflecting mirror of any kind, and that it is ridiculous to suppose that Nero turned round and viewed the gladiators behind him! He concludes:

> The question as to whether Nero used a concave glass is, ultimately,

despite its philological interest, secondary. The main question is this: Were the ancient Romans acquainted with myopia and the effects of a concave glass? The first is established without doubt, and the second, considering the description of Pliny and the medical meaning of *visum colligere*, is to say the least highly probable.[43]

Some writers who have considered ancient optics have wondered why, if there had been lenses in antiquity, they are not specifically mentioned in *The Optics* by Euclid (*circa* 300 BC). There are several comments to make in this connection. For one thing, *The Optics* as it survives is incomplete, and what we have is severely limited in its subject matter. Euclid wrote a work *On Mirrors* which is lost (a work on that subject attributed to him is not thought to be by him). There seems little doubt that Euclid wrote much more about optical matters than what survives, in addition to his apparently lost work on mirrors. *The Optics* which we have today is a very peculiar work, preoccupied with matters of perspective and simple optical illusions, and hardly a thorough-going treatment of optics as a whole. As one would expect from such a famous geometer, the work is highly geometrical, requiring a bewildering array of diagrams relating to lines of sight, and is concerned with questions like how 'to know how great is a given elevation when the sun is shining' or 'If a cone having a circle as its base and the axis at right angles to the base is seen by one eye, less than half the cone will be seen.' These are rather esoteric matters, and Euclid makes absolutely no concessions to any possible readers who are not competent geometers. But even so, near the end there are some intriguing remarks under the proposition 'Objects increased in size will seem to approach the eye'. After his usual specification of a geometrical diagram, Euclid makes these comments:

> But things thought to be greater than themselves seem to be increased, and the things nearer the eye appear greater. So objects increased in size will seem to approach the eye.[44]

What does Euclid mean by the last sentence? It is difficult to think what he could possibly be referring to which would increase in size while remaining still, unless he is referring to the enlargement of an image by a magnifying lens. And as we all know, such enlarged images do indeed 'seem to approach the eye'. I am inclined to believe that this is a casual reference to magnified images in Euclid's usual terse style.

Before we leave the ancient texts behind relating to magnification and corrected vision in antiquity, let's look at a few remaining ones briefly. The early Christian Father Clement of Alexandria (second century AD) in his *Stromata* (*Miscellanies*, Book I) speaks of 'images seen through the water, and things seen through pellucid and transparent bodies'. This is in the context of a theological discussion of First Corinthians XIII, 12, of the New Testament: 'The divine apostle [Paul] writes accordingly respecting us: "For now we see as through a glass"; knowing ourselves in it by reflection . . .' [He means refraction, since reflection does not occur when we see *through a glass*.][45]

Clement seems thus to be thoroughly familiar with both glass or crystal lenses and globes filled with water used for magnification, and he even suggests a translation of the famous passage of First Corinthians which emphasizes a different aspect of looking through a glass; instead of 'seeing through a glass darkly', with the emphasis being on the dimness and darkness of a semi-transparent medium, Clement seems to be suggesting that Paul's true reference was to a wholly transparent lens, the need for which optical aid shall have ceased when we see God face to face. Perhaps Paul was presbyopic (long-sighted) and used a lorgnette which he found irksome and hoped to do without in Heaven!

And this Biblical turn brings us to the last textual references to magnifying aids in antiquity which we shall consider, which as it happens are to be found in the Old Testament of the Bible and in some rabbinical texts of the Jewish rabbis.

These Jewish references are rather complicated, and as I do not read Hebrew, I could not have sorted all this out without the assistance of Dr Michael Weitzman of University College London. Imagine how shocked I was only months later when I read his obituary in the London *Times*, 16 April 1998. Weitzman was the most brilliant Hebrew scholar in Britain but died of a thrombosis aged only 51. I wish to express my profound thanks to Michael Weitzman, albeit posthumously, and my condolences to his family at this sudden and early loss of a remarkable man from their midst.

I discovered the curious references from one of the most obscure references which you could ever hope to find – an article in German published in 1859 in the *Memoirs of the Imperial Academy of Sciences of St Petersburg* in Russia. And a further complication arose because the Jewish writer spelled his surname in no less than three different ways, so that he would fall under two entirely different alphabetical listings in any index.

The author was Daniel Avraamovich Chwolson/ Chwolsohn/ Khvol'son – take your pick of the spelling you prefer! (The middle one is Germanized. I have adopted Chwolson for the sake of simplicity. And the article is entitled (in translation) *Concerning the Fragments of Ancient Babylonian Literature in Arabic Translation*. The extremely learned Chwolson was thus a Hebrew scholar who was also an Arabist, rather like the elderly professor under whom I once studied Islamic history, Professor S. D. Goitein – a Jew who knew more about Islam than most Arabs and whose continual theme in conversation was that Arabs and Jews should be friends and stop squabbling like quarrelsome siblings.

Here first is the passage I translated from German in Chwolson's article:

In the *Zer-ha-Mor* of Abraham Sab'a, a Jewish writer from Spain at the end of the 15th century (compare Wolf, *Bibl. Hebraea*, I, p. 93, Number 127 and III, p. 57, Number 127), three interesting fragments of that Egyptian book [I shall give its identity in a moment] are also found, which the attentive Herr Doktor Steinschneider has most kindly pointed out to me, and which I, because of their great interest, shall communicate here. [I omit the first and third as irrelevant.] . . . And the second passage (fol. 72, col. 4) the author notes by way of elucidation of the word [here he gives a Hebrew word, which transliterated is *toṭafot*] (Exodus XIII, 16) as follows:

[Here there are four lines of Hebrew, a translation of which appears below.]

One certainly usually accepts that the invention of spectacles belongs to the 13th century AD, but one sees from this [passage] that their use is much older by far.[46]

That was about as far as I could get on my own. I contacted Michael Weitzman with my handwritten attempts to copy out the Hebrew, which I had done in the Bibliothèque Nationale in Paris, where the material could not be photocopied or scanned because the book was falling apart. But Weitzman could not read my Hebrew handwriting – I must say I find that all the Hebrew letters seem to look alike! Weitzman said in his letter:

I have tried, but I cannot make the text out properly from this source. This is not surprising: the letters are easily confused, and a dot or short stroke vital for the meaning could easily be overlooked, if one is not expert in mediaeval Hebrew, especially given the frequent use of cryptic abbreviations in such words. In darker moments, I wondered whether the odd word might be missing.

How extremely polite of Weitzman! But at least he could read the single word from Exodus, and informed me as follows:

For what it's worth, I can see that the comment relates to the object . . . [here he gives the Hebrew word] . . . (Exod. 13:16) mentioned in the biblical text. The Bible specifies that this object was to be placed 'between your eyes'. Jewish tradition identifies it as the phylacteries, which are worn by men on the forehead – not literally between the eyes – during prayer. Apparently, however, there were some who instead took this word to mean an aid to sight, which – placed between the eyes [like a pince nez] – would have been spectacles. This interpretation was reached by identifying the Hebrew word (which may be transliterated *toṭafot*) with a similar-sounding Arabic word *ṭuāṭaf*. The latter is a plural noun form; but unfortunately the word is rare in Arabic; and as I don't have time to chase it up in specialized Arabic dictionaries, I cannot confirm what it might mean, and consequently I cannot really tell how a reference to spectacles was arrived at.

To sum up, both Chwolson and Steinschneider were outstanding scholars, and one would expect their work to be well founded. But I cannot really reconstruct what they were saying, from the text as supplied.[47]

Three days later I was able to find the St Petersburg periodical in the British Library, where it had been curiously catalogued (hence my earlier efforts to find it had failed and I had been forced to resort to Paris). This meant that I was able to obtain a photocopy of the Hebrew text which would be legible to Weitzman, and I duly sent it to him on 29 May 1997. On 24 September having finished a book and corrected piles of exam papers, Weitzman replied with his full study of the matter, having at last been able to decipher the Hebrew passage and do the necessary research. He wrote to me as follows:

> The footnote which you sent me deals with three fragments of a mediae-val Hebrew work called the Book of Egyptian Labour (i.e. land cultivation). Three fragments of that book are preserved in quotations in a work by Rabbi Abraham Saba', who was among the Jews expelled from Spain in 1492. (The 'represents a guttural sound, called Ayin.) The second of these quotations discusses the Hebrew word . . . [Hebrew omitted] . . . *totafot* which, according to Deuteronomy 6:8 denotes an object which one has to place between one's eyes. The etymology and hence meaning of this word remain mysterious to the present day. Traditionally, the *totafot* are interpreted as phylacteries, which are in fact placed high on the forehead rather than squarely between the eyes; I think I mentioned this before. Anyway, the passage quoted by Rabbi Abraham Saba' mentions the suggestion that the word instead means 'spectacles':

>> And there are those who say that this word is Egyptian. In the Book of Egyptian Labour, in the tenth section, in the description of old age, you will find it; (namely) that the spectacles which people place between their eyes in order to see well are there called by the name *tuātaf* (in the plural), and *tafaf* in the singular, and also *totafot*; and the root of the three of them is the same. [This is Weitzman's translation of the Hebrew.]

> I have supplied the word shown in brackets.

> The language here said to be spoken in Egypt is evidently Arabic, because the particular relationship between the singular and the plural – *tafaf* turning into *tuātaf* in the plural is typical of Arabic. I do not know if there is any corroborating evidence, though, of this word in Arabic. Anyway, the reason for citing an Arabic word is that it has

long been known that Hebrew and Arabic are sister languages, of common origin, and one way of explaining an obscure Hebrew word is to find a related word in Arabic, which is a far better documented language. On that basis the author suggests that Arabic *ṭafaf/ṭuāṭaf* is the counterpart of the mysterious Hebrew *ṭoṭafot*, and may guide us to its true meaning.

I should mention that there are two types of *t* in Hebrew and Arabic; *ṭ* has a special throaty resonance, unlike ordinary *t*. They were perceived as two quite different sounds, and are represented by two different letters of the alphabet.

The word translated as 'spectacles' is . . . [Hebrew omitted] . . . *mar'ot*, the plural of the word *mar'eh* originally meaning 'sight' but here meaning an aid to sight. The translation 'spectacle' well corresponds to this range.

Although Rabbi Abraham Saba' lived in the 15th century, there is evidently some reason for ascribing the Book of Egyptian Labour to the 13th. No doubt the article [by Chwolson] explains this on some page that I do not have.

I hope that this answers your queries, and I wish you good speed with your research.[48]

I was thrilled by this information, and replied the next day with further eager queries:

. . . it was fascinating to me to see that Rabbi Abraham Saba' was a very well-informed man indeed, for he specifically says the terminology is Egyptian. . . . I was able to look up the Egyptian derivations for these terms. First the word *mar'eh* meaning 'sight' but, as you say, here meaning 'an aid to sight'. This appears to be derived from Egyptian *mar* or *maar*, 'to see'. *Mar-ti* means 'the two eyes' and has a double-eye determinative. *Mau-ḥer* means 'thing by which one sees the face, i.e. mirror'. Or, by extension, 'an aid to sight'. (I am not clear as to whether Wallis Budge was adding 'i.e. mirror' as his own speculation.)

As for the words *ṭoṭafot*, *ṭafaf* and *ṭuaṭaf*, meaning 'spectacles', in Egyptian we find that *teti* means 'to see' and *tet*, *tut*, and *thut* all mean 'image'. [Note: In a later chapter I shall discuss the *Tet* as a possible sighting-device for surveying in ancient Egypt.] Specifically, *tut ma* means 'to collect the eyes, i.e. to gaze intensely, to fix the eyes on something'. I hardly need point out that lenses of spectacles 'collect' (*colligere*) the vision [Note: recall the passage from Pliny using this term, discussed a moment ago.] according to old ideas of light. Since ancient lenses were used more frequently by gem-cutters than by readers, it is interesting that an Egyptian word *teftefa* means 'to work gems into stone, to inlay, to embroider'. It seems to me that linguistically speaking, *teftefa* could be considered cognate with *ṭuaṭaf*. I would be interested to learn from you what the normal Hebrew term for gem-cutting is, and whether it is a related word.[49]

Unfortunately, Michael Weitzman never found time to do further research into these matters, and had no reply to my points. Within only five months he had died. The care he took in preparing his replies to me indicates an extremely generous attitude to scholarship, but if he took that much trouble with everybody, he certainly overstretched himself. Once again, I feel the need to thank him, although he is not here to know of my profound gratitude.

And there we must leave it. I believe that these terms relating to optical aids are Egyptian in origin, and they clearly survive in both Egyptian Arabic and Hebrew. Whether they exist in classical Arabic I do not know. It is clear that a considerable amount of further research could be done on this subject. But it would have to be done by Hebrew and Arabic scholars. I am not qualified.

It seems, therefore, that spectacles were indeed mentioned in both Exodus and Deuteronomy, in the book known as the Old Testament of the Bible to Christians and known as the Torah to Jews.

I want to stress that we should not envisage ancient spectacles having existed of the sort we wear today. There is no evidence whatever that spectacle frames which loop around the ears were ever used in antiquity. Ancient spectacles, which I believe were never very common, appear to have been some form of pince-nez which rested upon the nose, or lorgnettes which were held up to the eye/eyes and put down again. Ancient lorgnettes may often have been monocles, with single lenses, as I believe the Layard Lens may have been. I have inspected many ancient lenses which are either mounted or have unmistakable signs of having been mounted. But modern frames? Never! There is clear evidence, however, that lenses in pairs were indeed sometimes used. Sixteen lenses have been excavated at Carthage (see Plate 3) and of these, a distinct matching pair which are the correct size to fit over eye sockets were found together in the wrappings of a single mummy buried in the necropolis (these may be seen in Plate 2). There can be little doubt that this pair of lenses formed the man's 'spectacles'. But unfortunately, we have no information from the early French excavators of what kind of mounting was involved – and it may well be that soft perishable mountings were used, as leather, skin, or wound cloth would have been more comfortable resting upon the nose, in those days before ear-lopped spectacle frames had been invented.

But I believe that the vast majority of ancient convex crystal and glass lenses used to correct for presbyopia (long-sightedness) were never worn on the face at all. I believe that the ones used by readers were mostly held in the hand and run along the page, so that only the words beneath the lens

Figure 7. This is believed to be the earliest depiction of spectacles to be published in a book, although earlier depictions exist in paintings. The character Speusippus, nephew of Plato, looks here like a hearty German burgher who has just had a good bratwurst for lunch. This appeared in Hartmann Schedel's *Liber Chronicarum* (*Nuremberg Chronicle*), published at Nuremberg in 1493. It was a history of the world from the creation to the year 1492.

were in focus, and the rest of the manuscript was a surrounding blur. As it happens, the early scientist Roger Bacon (*circa* 1214–92) preserves an explicit and precise description of the method of using a reading-lens in this way, which I believe had been traditional for 3,000 years by the time he came to describe it in the 13th century:

> This instrument [a magnifying lens] is useful to old men and those who are of weak sight. . . . If a man looks at letters or other small things through a crystal, a glass, or other transparent body, with the letters placed underneath it, if such object is a small portion of a sphere whose convexity is turned towards the eye and is held in the air, the letters will appear to him clearer and larger . . .[50]

That is what most of our ancestors did, and it still works. I have done this with many ancient lenses now that I am a presbyope, and one can read perfectly well in this way, even with a lens of only 1.25X magnification. Most of the ancient lenses are of 1.5X or 2X magnification. In the old days, people did not read while travelling on trains or planes, and did not carry paperbacks around in their pockets. Reading tended to take place at desks, and with cumbersome manuscripts laid out in front of one. It was thus convenient to have one's reading lens, whether mounted or not, sitting on the desk, and one took it up to run along the page when reading. But as for gem-cutters and other craftsmen, more ingenious means of using lenses were devised, including suspending glass globes filled with water by string-cradles in front of the work they were doing. Sometimes (as with a remark-able crystal lens excavated at Troy, shown in Plate 40) a hole was punched through the middle for the engraving tool, which in no way interfered with the magnification, or even more cleverly – as with some of the ancient British lenses – 'resting-points' protruded from the lenses to enable engraving tools to slip underneath them while they magnified. But more of that later. (See also Appendix Eleven).

Thus we can see from a survey of the ancient textual evidence that what the texts say corroborates what we have found in terms of physical evidence. And of course the physical evidence in turn corroborates the texts. Although the texts have been around since antiquity, few people believed them, because they thought no supporting physical evidence existed. It was presumed that the texts either did not really say what they said, or there had been scribal errors, or that ancient writers were exaggerating or fantasizing. But it turns out that it was the modern scholars who were the ones who were fantasizing, since they wished to deny the reality of the past simply in order to make themselves feel more comfortable. Truth was the victim of this reckless pursuit of ease by slothful and arrogant intellectuals.

Only days before this book goes to the printer for page proofs, I am able to insert an account of a most sensational discovery relating to ancient optical technology. The news of it came to me serendipitously as the result of a visit to an unrelated archaeological site in Egypt in November 1999. I visited the archaeologist Barbara Adams at her dig at the ancient southern predynastic capital of Hierakonpolis in the vicinity of Edfu, a site which is closed and rarely visited by anyone. (My wife Olivia and I were the second and third visitors in 1999.) Hierakonpolis is a site of 140 square kilometres, mostly consisting of mounds of broken pottery as far as the eye can see, undulating in countless pits of robbed tombs, like a World War One battle-field without the mud, and which has turned to dry and desiccated desert. This season they have found an elephant burial, which was one tomb the ancient robbers must have had some trouble with, and a cow buried on a bed of woven palm leaves, scattered with flowers, both from the first half of the fourth millennium BC.

While talking to Dr Adams about ancient optics she told me of a discovery so astonishing that upon returning to Luxor I rushed to a phone to make my appointment to see its discoverer, the Director of the German Institute in Cairo, Dr Günter Dreyer. He is a congenial smiling man who likes to draw analogies from nature to explain very early symbolism: 'Anubis was "on his hill" in the ancient texts because jackals roam the foothills', and so on.

While digging in the predynastic cemetery at Abydos in Upper Egypt, which is known as Omm el Qabb – 'mother of pots' – because it contains literally millions of pieces of pottery sherds, Dreyer excavated an ivory knife handle in the tomb of an unknown predynastic king of the period known as Naqada II. It was made of elephant ivory, rather than hippo ivory, and is dated to *circa* 3300 BC.

What made this knife handle so special – for, after all, Dreyer has found a number of knife handles in his twenty years in Egypt – was that *it was covered in microscopic carvings!* Yes, I said microscopic.

When Barbara Adams first told me about this, she said Dreyer had shown it to her at Abydos and she was baffled because she couldn't see the carving without using a magnifying glass.

The carving may be seen in drawings kindly made available to me by Dr Dreyer in Figures 8 and 9, and in photos which may be seen in Plate 38a. In the first drawing, Figure 8, the figures walking along offering tribute have heads which in the original are *only one millimetre across*. Dreyer told me he spent weeks painstakingly cleaning the knife handle in order to elucidate the details of the carvings on both sides, and for this purpose he had to use the tip of a pin, which was the only tool small enough for the job. He is justly proud of the results.

Figure 8. Drawings of the designs on one side of the 5300-year-old ivory knife handle found by Günter Dreyer at Abydos. The designs are too small to see without a magnifying glass, and could not have been produced without one. The heads of the figures are about one millimetre across. The figures are bearing tribute, and are non-Egyptian, probably Canaanites. The prow of a ship is just visible. In the bottom row, most of the figures are bound, obviously having been taken prisoner. This knife handle was found in the tomb of an unknown predynastic king at Abydos, from the period known to archaeologists as Naqada II, and dates to *circa* 3300 BC. The fact that magnification was being used at that date means that optical technology can truly be said to have been an integral part of high civilization since its very beginnings; from the earliest times known in excavations, it has not been absent. Dreyer's dramatic find pushes back the evidence for it by a further 700 years beyond what was previously known.

This extraordinary find thus could be said to push back the physical evidence for the use of magnifying aids in antiquity by a *further seven hundred years*. Previously, the Egyptian crystal lenses mentioned in the final chapter of this book and dating from *circa* 2600 BC were the oldest physical evidence for ancient magnification. But now we have a microscopic carving produced in 3300 BC which could only have been made by a craftsman using a magnifying aid. If you can only see it with a magnifying glass, you can only make it with a magnifying glass.

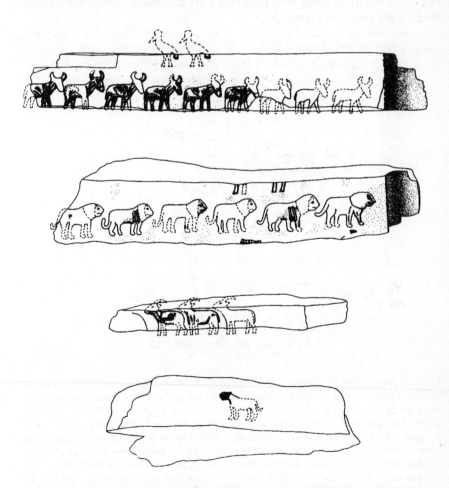

Figure 9. Drawings of the microscopic designs on the other side of the ivory knife handle from Abydos. On this side of the handle, processions of lions and other animals are seen. Are they also showing their respect for the king? Or perhaps they are merely decorative.

There was no shortage of rock crystal around at that time in Egypt. Dr Dreyer assures me that plenty of crystal objects of that date were being produced, and have been excavated, though no lenses have yet been found (or at least nothing recognized as such). However, rock crystal cups were being made, which proves that the art of working quartz was well advanced and highly professional, so that the manufacture of lenses would have been a simple matter by comparison.

Fortunately I am able to report this discovery because it is not an unpublished one and can thus be revealed. Dr Dreyer has already published a preliminary account of the find in the context of an article about predynastic knife handles (in German) in 1999.[51]

The finds being made by Dreyer at Abydos are very important, as this one indicates. But not until I visited Dreyer had the full implications dawned on him of just how important this particular, and rather mystifying, knife handle really was. For it is only in the context of ancient miniature carving and magnifying technology that its true importance can be seen. I am just grateful that fate saw to it that I learned of it just in time to mention it, so that the reader cannot be deprived of this evidence of magnification being used in Egypt 5300 years ago!

Notes

1. Pliny, *Natural History*, Book VII, Chapter 21; translated by H. Rackham, Vol. II of Loeb Classical Library series of Pliny, Harvard University Press, USA, 1969, p. 561.
2. *Ibid.*, pp. 561–3.
3. *Ibid.*, Book XXXVI, Chapter 4, translated by D. E. Eichholz, Vol. X, 1971, p. 35.
4. Aelian, *Historical Miscellany*, Book I, Chapter 17; edited and translated by N. G. Wilson, Loeb Classical Library Series, Harvard University Press, USA, 1997, pp. 39–41.
5. *Ibid.*, pp. 40–1.
6. Solinus, Caius Julius, *The Excellent and Pleasant Worke Collectanea Rerum Memorabilium*, translated by Arthur Golding, facsimile of 1587 edition by Scholars' Facsimiles & Reprints, Gainesville, Florida, USA, 1955, Chapter V (the book is unpaginated).
7. Arago, Dominique François Jean, *Astronomie Populaire* (*Popular Astronomy*), 4 vols, Paris, 1854–7, Vol. II, Book IV.
8. Vettori, Francesco, *Dissertatio Glyptographice Quae Exstant . . . in Museo Victorio* (*Dissertation on Inscriptions* ['*Glyptography*'], i.e. *of Two Gems Which Exist in the Museo Victorio*), 1739.
9. Manni, Domenico, *Degli Occhiali da Naso trattato istorico* (*Historical Tract concerning Spectacles*), Firenze (Florence), 1738. This book was evidently reissued in 1750 at Venice, possibly with a further volume, but I have been unable to consult that edition.
10. Natter, Laurent, *Traité de la Méthode Antique de Graver en Pierres Fines Comparée avec la Méthode Moderne*, London, 1754, p. viii. In the same year, also at London, was published the English translation under the name of 'Laurentius' Natter, *A Treatise on the Ancient Method of Engraving on Precious Stones*, same publisher, London, 1754, also p. viii.
11. Winckelmann, Johann Joachim, *Geschichte der Kunst des Altertums* (*History of Art in Antiquity*), im Akademischen Verlage (The Academy Press), Vienna, 1776, Vol. III, Part I, pp. 551–2.

12. Sittl, Karl, *Archaeologie der Kunst* (*Archaeology of Art*), in Vol. VI of *Handbuch der Klassischen Altertums-Wissenschaft* (*Handbook of the Science of Classical Antiquity*), ed. by Iwan von Müller, Munich, 1895, p. 195.

13. A 4-cm biconvex rock crystal lens was excavated in 1992 from a tomb at Jiangling in Hubei Province. The date of the tomb was the so-called Spring and Autumn Period (722–480 BC); at that time the tomb was in the ancient State of Chu. I have been unable to inspect this lens in person. I believe it is in the small museum in that area, but I was prevented from getting there by floods on the occasion that I tried. The philosopher Wang Chong (Wang Ch'ung in old style) 王充 who was born in 27 AD (in the later Han period) wrote a famous work called the *Lun-Heng* 论衡. In it he mentions burning lenses. Much of the work was translated by Alfred Forke (Forke, Alfred, *Lun-Heng*, 2 vols, 2nd edition, reprinted by Paragon Book Gallery, New York, 1962). He says 'by burning-glasses . . . one may obtain fire from the sun . . .' (Vol. II, p. 132) and 'With a burning-glass one draws fire from Heaven.' (Vol. II, p. 351). And Forke points out that James Legge had found evidence that burning-mirrors were very common during the Zhou Dynasty (1030–221 BC), for which see Forke, Vol. II, p. 497 and the reference he gives to Legge, James, *Sacred Books of the East*, Vol. XXVII, p. 449. An enormous survey of optical lenses in China and India was written by the indefatigable Berthold Laufer in 1915: Laufer, Berthold, 'Optical Lenses', *T'oung Pao*, Leiden, Vol. XVI, 1915: pp. 169–228 and 562–3. I have not space to discuss it. Chinese optics is also discussed by Jin Quipeng in an essay published in English in 1986: Jin Quipeng, 'Optics', in *Ancient China's Technology and Science*, Foreign Languages Press, Beijing, 1986, pp. 166–75. In his essay, Jin quotes Zhang Hua of the Jin Dynasty (265–420 AD) in his book *Record of the Investigation of Things*: 'Cut a piece of ice into a sphere, lift it in the sun and let its shadow fall on a piece of moxa [tinder made from an artemisia related to wormwood]; the moxa will be set alight.' (p. 174). This is the earliest surviving record which I have found of ice being cut to make a burning-lens; later in the book we encounter a Frenchman who did the same thing in the 18th century.

14. Schliemann, Henry, *Troja: Results of the Latest Researches and Discoveries on the Site of Homer's Troy*, reprint, Paul P. B. Minet, Chicheley, England, 1972, p. 109. The original edition was published by John Murray, London, 1884, and had the same pagination.

15. Pancirollo, Guidone, *Livre Premier Des Antiquitez Perdues, et Si au Vif Représentées par la Plume de l'Illustre Juriconsulte G. Panciroli qu'on en Peut Grand Profit de la Perte; Accompagné d'un Second, Des Choses Nouvellement Inventées & Auparavant Incogneües*, translated by Pierre de la Noye, Lyon, 1617. This translation is of Pancirollo's text only and contains no material by Heinrich (Henricus) Salmuth.

16. Watson, Michael, *Theatrum Variarum Rerum Exhibens Excerpta & Annotata in Libb. de Rebus Memoralibus Pancirolli & Salmuthi Quibus Adjecta Est Dissertatio Elenchtica Dealiquot Doctrinis Philosophicis* (*Theatre of Marvels Exhibited Extracted & Annotated from the Book of the History of Many Memorable Things by Pancirollo & Salmuth in Which in Addition is Discussed in a Dissertation Pearls of Philosophical Wisdom*), Bremen, 1663.

17. Pancirollo, Guidone, *The History of Many Memorable Things Lost, Which Were in Use among the Ancients: and an Account of Many Excellent Things Found, Now in Use among the Moderns, Both Natural and Artificial*, translated anonymously, London, 1715, p. 372. (This English translation was reprinted at London in 1727.)

18. Since the only readily available edition of the Latin text by Pancirollo (originally published in 1599) is that of 1660, I give the page reference to that one, which is p. 268. The 1660 edition is a straightforward reprint of the 1646 edition, so the page reference is the same for that. Pancirollo's comments amount to only two sentences. But Salmuth's long commentary, only a fraction of which was translated into English, runs on to p. 273, consisting of five pages of small type in Latin, with considerable citations about the Latin meanings, and a digression into the subject of ancient mirrors.

19. Salmuth, Heinrich (Henricus), commentary on Pancirollo in Pancirollo, *The History, op. cit.* (1715 in English), pp. 372–3.

20. Seneca, Lucius Annaeus, *Naturales Quaestiones* (*Natural Questions*), translated by T. H.

Corcoran, Loeb Classical Library, Harvard University Press, USA, 2 vols, 1971–2; Vol. I, p. 39.

21. *Ibid.*, pp. 57–9.
22. Macrobius, Ambrosius Theodosius, *Saturnalia*, translated by Percival Vaughan Davies, Columbia University Press, New York, 1969, p. 502. I made one small change, indicated in brackets.
23. Aulus Gellius, *Attic Nights*, translated by J. C. Rolfe, Loeb Classical Library, Harvard University Press, USA, 3 vols, 1967–70, Vol. III, pp. 187–9.
24. Priscian of Lydia, *On Theophrastus on Sense-Perception*, 16.10, translated by Pamela Huby, Duckworth, London, 1997, p. 25.
25. *The Ancient Egyptian Pyramid Texts*, translated by R. O. Faulkner, Oxford Press, 1998, p. 28.
26. *Ibid.*, p. 15.
27. *Ibid.*, p. 14.
28. Phanias, Poem 294 in Book VI of *The Greek Anthology*, translated by W. R. Paton, Loeb Classical Library, Harvard University Press, USA, Vol. I, 1960, p. 457.
29. Phanias, Poem 295, in *Ibid.*, pp. 457–9.
30. Wallis Budge, Sir E. A., *An Egyptian Hieroglyphic Dictionary*, London, 1920, pp. 741a and 419a.
31. Jablonski, Paul Ernest, *Opuscula*, Vol. I, Batavia, 1804, p. 250.
32. Pliny, *Natural History*, translated by D. E. Eichholz, Vol. X, Loeb Classical Library, Harvard University Press, 1971, p. 213.
33. *Ibid.*, pp. 212–13.
34. *Ibid.*, translated by H. Rackham, Vol. III, 1983, pp. 521–3.
35. *Ibid.*, translation by D. E. Eichholz, Vol. X, 1971, pp. 213–15.
36. *Ibid.*, p. 214.
37. Sienkiewicz, Henryk, *Quo Vadis: A Narrative of the Time of Nero*, translated by Jeremiah Curtin, London, 1896 (first English edition, which I am fortunate to have), pp. 60–1.
38. Stilling, Jakob, *Untersuchungen über die Entstehung der Kurzsichtigkeit* (*Inquiries into the Origin of Short-Sightedness*), Wiesbaden, 1887.
39. *Ibid.*, pp. 184–7.
40. Fukala, Vincenz, *Die Refraktionslehre im Alterthum* (*The Science of Refraction in Antiquity*), pp. 49–61 in Vol. 39 of *Archiv für Augenheilkunde* (*Archives of Opthalmology*), Wiesbaden, 1899.
41. Pansier, Pierre, *L'Histoire des Lunettes* (*The History of Spectacles*), Paris, 1901, p. 7. The only copy of this book in Britain is in the Library of the British Optical Association in London.
42. Stilling, Jakob, 'Nero's Augenglas' ('Nero's Eyeglass'), in *Zeitschrift für Augenheilkunde* (*Opthalmology Journal*), Vol. 3, No. 1, 1900, pp. 141–6.
43. *Ibid.*, p. 146.
44. Euclid, *The Optics*, translated by Harry Edwin Burton, in *Journal of the Optical Society of America*, Vol. 353, No. 5, May, 1945, pp. 357–72; the quotation is from p. 372.
45. Clement of Alexandria, *Stromata* (*Miscellanies*), Book I; Greek text with Latin translation found in *Klēmentos Alexandreōs ta Euriskomena. Clementis Alexandrini Opera. Graece et Latine quae Extant*, edited by Friderico Sylburgio, Paris, 1641, p. 316, Section D. A translation is to be found in Volume XII of the *Ante-Nicene Christian Library* edited by the Rev. Alexander Roberts and James Donaldson, Vol. II (i.e., Vol. Two of Vol. XII, which is their peculiar system), Edinburgh, 1869, pp. 415–16.
46. Chwolson/Chwolsohn/Khvol'son, Daniel Avraamovich, *Über die Überreste der Altbabylonischen Literatur in Arabischen Übersetzungen* (*Concerning the Fragments of Ancient Babylonian Literature in Arabic Translation*), in *Mémoires Présentés à l'Académie Impériale des Sciences de St Petersburg*, Tome 8, St Petersburg, 1859, p. 341 (p. 13 of the Chwolson tract), note 12. (Chwolson's tract extends from pp. 329–523, and is thus extremely long; pp. 361–8 in the copy I consulted were blank through misprinting.)

47. Fax from Michael Weitzman dated 26 May 1997.
48. Fax from Michael Weitzman dated 24 September 1997.
49. My fax to Michael Weitzman dated 25 September 1997.
50. Excerpts from Roger Bacon quoted by Charles Chevalier and translated into French; I have slightly corrected the sense of Chevalier's rendering, in doing the translation from the French with my wife Olivia. Chevalier gives his reference to the *Opus Majus* of Bacon, to a London edition of 1733, p. 352; I have not bothered to consult this edition in order to obtain the textual reference to Bacon's work because it did not seem necessary. See: Chevalier, Charles, *Manuel des Myopes et des Presbytes, Contenant des Recherches Historiques sur l'Origine des Lunettes ou Besicles, les Moyens de Conserver et d'Améliorer la Vue et un Chapitre Spécialement Consacré aux Lorgnettes de Spectacle* (*Manual of Myopes and Presbyopes, Containing Historical Researches concerning the Origin of Glasses or Spectacles, the Means to Preserve and Ameliorate the Sight, and a Special Chapter Devoted to Lorgnettes*), Paris, 1841, section on 'The Origin of Spectacles', pp. 3–16.
51. Dreyer, Günter, 'Motive und Datierung der dekorierten prädynastischen Messergriffe' ('Motifs and Dating of Predynastic Knife Handles'), in *L'art de l'Ancien Empire Égyptien* (*The Art of the Egyptian Old Kingdom*), Actes du Colloque, Louvre Museum, 1998/1999, pp. 195–226. The paper contains some inaccuracies in designating the scales of reproductions, so that anyone to whom that subject is important should contact Dreyer for the corrections. Dreyer is also unhappy with the quality of the reproduction of the drawings in the Louvre paper for which he has given permission for reproduction here, as the originals were at Abydos and inaccessible.

Chapter Three

Promethean Fire

The other main use of ancient lenses, apart from magnifying, was for burning. This took two forms: cauterization of wounds before the availability of modern antiseptics, and the lighting of sacred fires. But the earliest Greek text which mentions burning-lenses does so in the context of a farcical comedy, *The Clouds*, by the Athenian comic playwright Aristophanes, which was first performed at Athens in 423 BC. This is perhaps Aristophanes's most famous play, because it contains a parody of the philosopher Socrates.

The mention of a burning-lens occurs at lines 765–772 of the text, in Act Two, Scene One, in the context of some banter between Socrates and a character called Strepsiades. Strepsiades says he is plagued by debts, but has an idea of how to escape from them, based upon the fact that wax tablets were used by the debt collectors to write their notes on. Socrates urges him to tell him what it is:

SOCRATES
What is it?

STREPSIADES
Have you ever seen a beautiful, transparent stone at the
druggist with which you may kindle fire?

SOCRATES
You mean a crystal lens [*hyalon*]?

STREPSIADES
Yes.

SOCRATES
Well, what then?

STREPSIADES
If I placed myself with this stone in the sun and a long way
off from the clerk, while he was writing out the conviction,

I could make all the wax, upon which the words were written, melt.

SOCRATES
Well thought out, by the Graces!

STREPSIADES
Ah, I am delighted to have annulled the decree that was to cost me five talents.[1]

As I mentioned in the last chapter, the word *hyalos* meaning 'rock crystal' was introduced into Greek literature by the historian Herodotus (fifth century BC) and has an Egyptian origin. *Hyalos* later came to mean 'glass', but at the time of Aristophanes the burning-glasses were of crystal rather than glass.

This passage in Aristophanes has been mentioned many times by writers on ancient optics, as it is such a clear reference to the existence of lenses in the fifth century BC. The first modern who noticed it in the context of the history of optics appears to be the French scientist Gabriel-Philippe de la Hire, in 1708. He discussed it in a meeting of the French Royal Academy of Sciences, an account of which was published the following year.[2] He also consulted a scholiast (anonymous ancient commentator in Greek) on the play, and de la Hire says:

The Scholiast on Aristophanes says concerning this passage that he is referring to a round and thick glass, expressly made for this purpose . . .

But 30 years later in 1738, Robert Smith in *A Compleat System of Opticks* very sensibly commented:

The famous M. de la Hire has endeavoured to raise the antiquity of lenses or lenticular burning-glasses to a very great height, imagining he has found them in the *Clouds* of Aristophanes, Act II, Sc. 1. towards the end. . . . The Scholiast upon this place says it was a round (*trochoeides*, 'round like a wheel'), thick glass made on purpose for this use . . . the Scholiast conceived it was convex, which shews that in his time, though later than Aristophanes, they used such glasses to kindle fire. He [de la Hire] argues also from the words *apōterō stas* ('standing at a distance'), that this glass was lenticular rather than spherical; because a sphere burns an object only at a very small distance from it.[3]

The crystal must certainly have been a lens rather than a sphere, for it would be quite impossible to melt a wax tablet with a sphere unless it were right next to it.

Prantl, a German editor of the text of Aristophanes, also correctly pointed out the fact 'That Aristophanes took for granted a universal knowledge of such a device by his public is completely obvious . . .'[4]

It is impossible not to conclude, therefore, that in Athens in the fifth century BC, crystal burning-lenses were available in the local shops for anyone who wanted one. And of course, a lens that can burn can also magnify.

The other two main texts about burning-lenses are from Pliny (first century AD). They are really about burning-globes or burning-spheres, rather than lenses. By this time, 500 years after the time of Aristophanes, glass had taken the place of rock crystal for many uses, because it was so much cheaper. Here are Eichholz's published translations of the two passages:

(1) However, the most highly valued glass is colourless and transparent, as closely as possible resembling rock-crystal. But although for making drinking vessels the use of glass has ousted metals such as gold and silver, it cannot bear heat unless cold fluid is first poured into it; and yet glass globes containing water become so hot when they face the sun that they can set clothes on fire. (XXXVI, 67, 199.)[5]

(2) I find that among doctors there is considered to be no more effective method of cauterizing parts that need such treatment than by means of a crystal ball so placed as to intercept the sun's rays. (XXXVII, 10, 28–9.)[6]

Now, here are Eichholz's revised translations of the above passages:

(1) [Eichholz pointed out to me that the passage was really written in the form of a paradox, and the correct translation of the latter part should be in this form:] '. . . it [glass] cannot bear heat unless cold fluid goes first, although when water has been added, glass balls facing the Sun [or 'when the Sun is opposite to them'] begin to radiate so white hot [*candescant*] that they burn clothes.

(2) I find that amongst doctors it is thought that parts of the body which have to be burnt [cauterized] are not otherwise burnt more beneficially than by means of a crystal ball placed in the path of the facing rays of the Sun.

Perhaps I should just say a few words about Pliny's *Natural History*, which I have now quoted several times, and for which I took the trouble to get the revised translations from Professor Eichholz in his retirement home. It is a gigantic work in 37 Books, filling ten Loeb Library volumes (the Harvard University Press series of classics). It is the longest and most comprehensive work on ancient Western science in existence. The historian of science George Sarton has said of this immense work that it 'is perhaps the most important single source extant for the history of ancient civilization'.

Reading it is delightful and fascinating, but using it for scholarly purposes is a nightmare of major proportions. The modern edition and translation of the Loeb Library commenced publication in 1938, and only 33 years later did the final portions of the text and translation finally appear, in 1971 (Eichholz's volume). But Volume XI was supposed to be the Index, and we are still waiting for it to appear 29 years later, or *62 years* after the commencement of publication of the work! With such a voluminous work, it is therefore *impossible to look anything up!*

Now you can imagine what one is up against. If you want to know what Pliny said about lenses or crystal balls, you are 'on your own', and must read through all ten volumes and look for yourself. That is why people still make so little use of Pliny – for no one has time to sit down and read all ten volumes and make notes of every conceivable subject one might want to consult at any time in the future. My volumes are all bristling with bookmarks sticking out of the top – sometimes 20 or 30 per volume – on which I have written notices like these:

Portents from the behaviour of mice
Bull's blood is 'noxious to drink' as it hardens & is thick
Earth divided into parallels – one passes through Delos
Statues of the Sibyl at Rome
Principle of mirrors
Painter who painted portrait of Aristotle's mother
Obelisk represents Sun's rays
Delphic bay leaves burnt
The Sun is the soul or mind of the whole world
How early men found properties of plants
Pompey had two doubles almost indistinguishable from him in appearance

From these titbits, you can gather something of Pliny's weird interests and also why he is such a delight to read.

One is reduced to such methods as my bristling bookmarks by the absolute impossibility of looking anything up in the 37 books filled with scattered information. The situation for optics is made far worse by the fact that a kind of curse has fallen over Pliny, which has rendered many people who refer to him mentally enfeebled. The optical writers who have quoted Pliny for the last century and a half have made the most astonishing number of errors in identifying the passages they quote, so that it is quite impossible to locate those passages. This pernicious habit seems to have begun in earnest with the German writer Emil Wilde, who in his *Geschichte der Optik (History of Optics)*, published at Berlin in 1838, set a bad standard in footnote 1 on page 68, where he gives an erroneous reference to Pliny. From then it was downhill all the way. (I urge all writers to keep a wary eye on page 68 of their works. Almost anything could go wrong there.)

Having found the necessary passages in Pliny despite all obstacles, one's difficulties really begin. For it seems that nearly every relevant passage has variant readings, wildly differing translations and interpretations, or has been the subject of acrid and virulent controversy amongst scholars. Even the Loeb translations are not literal or necessarily accurate, for the instructions given to the translators by the publishers, according to Eichholz, are to aim for fluency and ease of reading, if necessary at the expense of literal meanings. This may be suitable for literature, but when it comes to scientific works like Pliny's *Natural History*, it is a policy which is detrimental to serious studies by historians of science.

Since it is important to find information about the preparation of glass by the ancients which could be used for lenses either for purposes of burning or magnifying, I asked Professor Eichholz about Pliny's passage for which his Loeb translation is: 'Some of it is shaped by blowing, some machined on a lathe and some chased like silver. Sidon was once famous for its glass works, since, apart from other achievements, glass mirrors were invented there.' The word rendered 'machined' is *teritur*, which means 'ground (or polished)' (XXXVI, 66, 193).[7] Eichholz's literal translation, therefore, is:

Some of it is ground by means of a turner's wheel and some of it is chased afterwards like silver.

The word *teritur* is used by Plautus to refer to the grinding of flour between stones, the grinding of something in a mortar, and the rubbing together of wood to make fire. The word *tornus* translated in Eichholz's published version as 'lathe' also means 'a turner's wheel'. We have here attested, therefore, the requisite techniques for the preparation of ground, polished lenses.

There are a number of other explicit references to burning-globes and burning-spheres in ancient literature, but many of them are from extraordinarily obscure sources. For instance, there is the Church father Lactantius, who in 314 AD wrote the theological tract *On the Wrath of God*. I somehow suspect that this is not top of the pops with the man and woman in the street today. He says 'that a ball of glass filled with water, when held up to the Sun, lights a fire even in the coldest weather'.[8] An earlier optical reference by Lactantius occurs in his work *On God's Workmanship*, which he wrote in 304 AD.[9]

The earliest surviving scientific description of ignition by burning-glasses and burning-mirrors occurs in the treatise *On Fire* by Theophrastus, the colleague and successor of Aristotle (fourth century BC). His comments are in the context of trying to understand how combustion was easier by this means than by more conventional means:

73. As to the fact that substances catch fire from the sun by reflection from smooth surfaces but not from fire, the reason is that the sun's rays

have fine particles and, when reflected, the fire is more continuous, while conventional fire is not able to do so because of the irregularity of its particles. Thus the former, by virtue of its concentration and fineness penetrates into the fuel and is able to cause igniting, while the latter, having neither quality, is not able to do this. Fire can be ignited from rock crystal [lenses, by refraction], and (from) copper and silver [mirrors, by reflection], when prepared in a certain way, but not, as Gorgias [an earlier philosopher] says and some others believe, because fire passes out through their pores.[10]

The early Church Father, Clement of Alexandria (born *circa* 150 AD), wrote in his fascinating and erudite *Stromata* (*Miscellanies*), Number VI:

But, as appears, the philosophers of the Greeks, while naming God, do not know Him. But their philosophical speculations, according to Empedocles, 'as passing over the tongue of the multitude, are poured out of mouths that know little of the whole' [a fragment of Empedocles not otherwise preserved]. For as art changes the light of the sun into fire by passing it through a glass vessel full of water, so also philosophy, catching a spark from the divine Scripture, is visible in a few.[11]

Another Church Father, Gregory of Nyssa (fourth century AD, younger brother of St Basil), in his 'Oration Against Eunomius', mentions fire being ignited by water held up to the Sun.[12] So does another Church Father, Caesarius (known to the French as St Césaire), brother of St Gregory of Nazianzus (fourth century AD), in his 'First Dialogue'.[13]

The very obscure Bishop Titus of Bostra in Arabia, whose dates I cannot even discover, wrote a book called *Against the Manicheans*. In it, he refers to the cauterization of wounds, apparently by globes or spheres (II, 13):

The doctor does not worry that he must cauterize a wound by burning it out . . .[14]

Two descriptions of the use of lenses to light sacred fires by the Brahmans of India are given by Philostratus (born *circa* 170 AD) in his mystical work, *Life of Apollonius of Tyana*:

. . . and on (this hill) they worship fire with mysterious rites, drawing fire, according to their own account, from the rays of the sun; and to the Sun they sing a hymn every day at midday. (III, 14.)

Moreover, they neither burn upon an altar nor keep in stoves the fire which they extract from the sun's rays, although it is a material fire; but like the rays of sunlight when they are refracted in water, so this fire is seen raised aloft in the air and dancing in the ether. . . . of a night they intreat the ray of light not to take the night amiss, but to stay with them just as they have brought it down. . . . and they enjoy the sunlight whenever they choose. (III, 15.)[15]

These passages are typical of the fantastic notions promulgated in this book full of magic, hearsay, and imaginary adventures. However, the references to the use of lenses to 'draw down' sacred fire from sunlight are reliable, as this was being done all over the ancient world at that time – certainly from Britain to China. And strangely enough, Philostratus's bizarre work contains a rare clue to what could possibly be an explanation to one of the enigmas of *British* archaeology. For the many crystal balls which have been excavated from female graves in Britain are often accompanied by sieves. No one has ever come up with any explanation for this peculiar fact. But this passage may give a hint:

> . . . there are certain old women who go about with sieves in their hands to shepherds, sometimes to cow-herds, pretending to heal their flocks, when they are sick, by divination, as they call it, and they claim to be called wise women, yea wiser than those who are unfeignedly prophets. (VI, 11.)[16]

This stray item of ancient folklore may even apply to the whole of Europe. As for what the old women actually used the sieves for, or how they divined with them, it is possible that they threw molten lead into cold water to make strange shapes – a method of divination still practised in Austria today amongst the country folk, and demonstrated for me in New York years ago by my friend Mia Agee, who was Austrian – and the sieves were used to fish out the hot pieces of lead. That is just a guess. Otherwise the sieves may have been used for something as simple as fishing egg whites or yolks out of water, after studying the way in which a broken egg descended and mingled, and the shape it made.

Another item of ancient folklore relating to women and relevant to burning-lenses is found in the fascinating five-volume work, *The Cults of the Greek States*, by Lewis Farnell. In Volume III, Farnell says at one point:

> Before endeavouring to sum up the results of this survey of Attic ritual [in ancient Athens], we must see if the records of the Thesmophoria [an annual festival of women] in other parts of Greece can add any further fact of importance to the general account, beyond that which has been already noted, the universal exclusion of men [from the ceremonies]. Of the Eretrian rite [at Eretria in Greece] one other detail is known of some anthropological interest; the women did not use fire, but the sun's heat, for cooking their meat. . . . the sun's fire was purer than that of the domestic hearth.[17]

Farnell does not comprehend what this means, and speculates that it possibly relates to drying the meat in the sun. But it seems clear that what the information really means is that the fire used for cooking the meat – and he does say the meat was *cooked*, in which case, how could *drying* constitute *cooking*? – was obtained by means of burning-lenses, hence was 'pure' heavenly fire. Farnell gives no reference for his information about the Eretrian Thesmophoria traditions, and although I checked in Pausanius, it was not there, so I don't know where he got it from.

Farnell refers explicitly to ancient burning-glasses in Volume V:

> . . . in Greece, according to Plutarch, the method adopted [for kindling the sacred flame on an altar] was ignition by a burning-glass. Now, as ritual is so strongly conservative, this may belong to the original institution of the rite. But a people who had arrived at the use of a burning-glass were under no strenuous need of maintaining a perpetual fire merely for utilitarian purposes. We may suspect rather the direct influence of some religious feeling.[18]

Figure 10. Two 17th-century engravings of ancient depictions of Roman sacrifices on small altars. Above, we see a scene shown many times in ancient art, where a libation is poured onto the altar's sacrificial flame from a small bowl held in the hand of the man at the right. In this picture, a harpist plays sacred music and behind a flautist plays the flute. At left, an ox is held while a man is about to slaughter it with an axe. Behind is an idealized temple. However, the sacrificial scene below (first century AD) seems a bit different. Here we once again have the small altar with the blazing fire and a flautist playing a double flute (or is he acting as a human bellows?). A patrician Roman family stands around this small altar, a boy holds a box probably containing incense which will shortly be offered, and the matron is . . . doing what exactly? At first glance it looks like she too is pouring a libation from a small bowl. But then upon closer examination, one begins to wonder. A round object with a small circle in the centre appears to be duplicated from what she holds in her hand and appears again in the very centre of the fire. From what we now know about lenses being used to kindle sacrificial fires, this picture may well show the matron focusing the sun's rays, and the small circle inside the larger one may be intended to represent the focus which sets the kindling ablaze.

We should consult Plutarch (first century AD) at this point, and we find the relevant passage in his *Life of Numa*, Chapter 9. Numa was the second king of Rome, traditionally dated to 715–673 BC. His name is Etruscan. Some of the traditions about him are legendary rather than properly historical. The text of Plutarch actually refers to burning-mirrors rather than burning-lenses:

> He was also the overseer of the holy virgins called Vestals; for to Numa is ascribed the consecration of the Vestal virgins, and in general the worship and care of the perpetual fire entrusted to their charge. It was either because he thought the nature of fire pure and uncorrupted, and therefore entrusted it to chaste and undefiled persons, or because he thought of it as unfruitful and barren, and therefore associated it with virginity. Since wherever in Greece a perpetual fire is kept, as at Delphi and Athens, it is committed to the charge, not of virgins, but of widows past the age of marriage. And if by any chance it goes out, as at Athens during the tyranny of Aristion [88–86 BC] the sacred lamp is said to have been extinguished, and at Delphi when the temple was burned by the Medes [from Persia], and as during the Mithridatic and the Roman civil wars the altar was demolished and the fire extinguished then they say it must not be kindled again from other fire, but made fresh and new, by lighting a pure and unpolluted flame from the rays of the sun. And this they usually effect by means of metallic mirrors, the concavity of which is made to follow the sides of an isosceles rectangular triangle, and which converge from their circumference to a single point in the centre. When, therefore, these are placed opposite the sun, so that its rays, as they fall upon them from all sides, are collected and concentrated at the centre, the air itself is rarefied there, and very light and dry substances placed there quickly blaze up from its resistance, the sun's rays now acquiring the substance and force of fire. (*Numa*, IX, 5–8.)[19]

Burning-mirrors, burning-lenses, and burning-spheres were essentially interchangeable in these circumstances (remember my description, in Chapter One, of the burning sphere). It seems clear that Plutarch is describing the use of a concave burning-mirror which he had personally witnessed. It did not matter so much which means were used to concentrate the rays, as long as it was the sun's rays which produced the sacred fire.

The reference by Plutarch to an isosceles rectangular triangle is curious, and there may be more to this than meets the eye. Towards the end of this book, when I describe the optical phenomena of the ancient Egyptians, we shall see that one of my discoveries in Egypt relates to optical effects involving triangles. The Pyramid of Khafre at sunset casts a shadow upon the south face of the Great Pyramid on the occasion of the winter solstice which effectively truncates the triangle of the south face and creates a Golden Triangle. (See Plate 30.) This has a multiple significance, to be explained later, and it emanates from conscious planning by the builders of

Justi Lipsi de Vesta

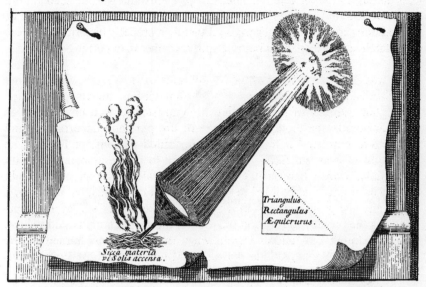

Figure 11. A very determined Sun ignites tinder by his rays on the Altar of the goddess Vesta, as envisaged by an artist in the 17th century. The funnel appears to hold a burning-lens, although the inspiration for the subject was really the description by Plutarch of a burning-mirror of the Vestal Virgins made of joined reflecting metal triangles. The illustration accompanies the article 'On Vesta' by Justus Lipsius which appeared in the compendium *Graevius Thesaurus Antiquitatum Romanorum*, Vol. 5, 1696, pp. 639–40.

the pyramids, who placed the pyramids in such a way that this would happen.

The mention of the triangle in connection with optics here may be part of a cult survival which originated in Egyptian times. My friend Robert Lawlor has made a profound study of ancient Egyptian temple architecture, and in an article on the subject gives diagrams relating to the ground plan of the Temple of Luxor which shows a simple geometric method for generating a series of harmonic progressions by successive truncations of a triangle (reproduced here in Figure 12). He says: 'From this purely geometrical gesture of a repetitive diagonal crossing within a triangular frame we can see that all the musically significant harmonic ratios may be generated without recourse to mathematics or algebra.'[20]

This is precisely what the shadow on the south face of the Great Pyramid does, as it moves daily throughout the winter season. And it may be that once a year a special sacred kindling of the sun's rays took place on the winter solstice, the shortest day of the year and the 'low point' of the sun's strength, to demonstrate its powers of rebirth. If so, such a kindling would have taken place on 'the day of the Golden Triangle'. And we cannot rule out the possibility that Plutarch, who often partially revealed sacred secrets

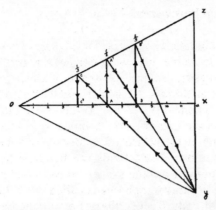

Figure 12. Robert Lawlor's drawing of how the basic harmonic proportions in music can be represented by a triangle crossed by diagonals. He first drew the horizontal line joining 0 with X. Then he raised a vertical line from X to Z (and a corresponding one going down from X to Y); these can all be of any length, since what is being constructed is merely a triangular frame. He takes the midpoint of the line 0X, labelled here by a tiny letter A which can barely be seen, and raises a vertical line above it which cuts the line 0Z. He then joins that point to the point Y, and in so doing the diagonal cuts the central line 0X; at that point where it cuts it, a musical proportion is determined. In this example, it gives the ratio of 2 to 3, which is the musical fifth. The other diagonals give the major third and other basic musical intervals. Such triangular frames of different proportions generate a number of musical ratios by this means, and Lawlor maintains that the ancient Egyptians used such techniques of sliced-triangles to lay out the ground plan of the Temple of Luxor. This makes sense, and the sliced-triangle which I discovered on the south face of the Great Pyramid at the winter solstice must be part of such a tradition, as it creates a 'golden triangle'. See the extended discussion of the Great Pyramid shadow in Chapter Nine.

in his writings which were 'unlawful' to reveal fully, was giving us a bit of a hint. Or it may be that Plutarch had no idea of the further implications of a cult survival which he simply reported.

However, sacred triangles and the pyramids of Egypt are a subject for later on.

Another reference to a fundamental optical phenomenon in the context of an astronomical description is to be found in an esoteric work by the philosopher Macrobius (fifth century AD) entitled *Commentary on the Dream of Scipio*; the *Dream of Scipio* being a cosmological section of Cicero's work *On the Republic*. In fact, the Dream is only preserved by Macrobius. *On the Republic* did not survive as a manuscript and was only found written beneath something else in the Vatican Library in the 19th century, but what was found did not contain the section of the Dream. I have myself published an account of the *Dream of Scipio*, in which I have already described many things of interest which I shall not bother to repeat here.[21]

In Chapter XII, Macrobius writes:

At this point we shall discuss the order of the steps by which the soul descends from the sky to the infernal regions of this life [to be reborn]. The Milky Way girdles the zodiac, its great circle meeting it obliquely so that it crosses it at the two tropical signs, Capricorn and Cancer. Natural philosophers named these 'the portals of the sun' because the solstices lie athwart the soul's path on either side, checking farther progress and causing it to retrace its course across the belt beyond whose limits it never trespasses. Souls are believed to pass through these portals when going from the sky to the earth and returning from the earth to the sky. For this reason one is called the portal of men and the other the portal of gods: Cancer, the portal of men, because through it descent is made to the infernal regions [that is, to life on Earth]; Capricorn, the portal of gods, because through it souls return to their rightful abode of immortality, . . . The soul, descending from the place where the zodiac and the Milky Way intersect, is protracted in its downward course from a sphere, which is the only divine form, into a cone . . .[22] (XII.1–5.)

The actual text describes the soul descending *in conum*[23] – and this image is derived from the cone of focused light that emerges from the transformation wrought upon sunlight by the refractive power of a crystal ball. And just to underline the optical nature of his concepts, a bit later, Macrobius writes:

Indeed, when a ray of light reaches us directly from its starting point, the sun, it carries with it the essence of fire from which it springs. . . . So also with the mirror [*speculum*]: when it reflects the brilliance of a flame set at a distance, it returns only the image of the flame without the heat.[24] (XIX.13.)

The image of the descending soul as a cone of light being emitted from the 'crystal ball' or even 'mini-crystal sun' of its natural spiritual condition into the realms of matter preserves a tradition of a deep metaphysical light-theology which ultimately derives from Egypt, and was preserved in Greece by the mystery schools and the Neoplatonist philosophers like Macrobius and Numenius of Apamea (second century AD, who was responsible for a great deal of the Pythagorean emphasis of Neoplatonism).

The Pythagorean belief that the Sun was literally a gigantic crystal ball in space, far larger than the Earth, will be examined later. But individual souls were envisaged as little crystal suns, emitting their own divine light and fire in cones downwards into matter, in their process of reincarnation.

Some discussion of this subject occurs in the book *Macrobius and Numenius* by Herman de Ley:

In its blessed state the soul is a sphere . . . The predilection of the Greeks for the sphere as 'the most perfect of all figures' is well-known and its connection with the divine substance is attested as early as Xenophanes [sixth century BC; de Ley adds in a footnote: 'It is probably Pythagorean . . .'; he then quotes the philosopher Proclus (fifth century AD):] . . . 'For where there is *nous* [mind/spirit], there is also the spheric . . . all that is intellectual or intelligible must be spherical . . .' [*Commentary on the Timaeus of Plato*, II, p. 77.7–18.][25]

Herman de Ley spends many pages in frustrating and hopeless speculation as to how a cone can be emitted from a sphere, and quotes many other scholars who have fruitlessly attempted to understand this. He quotes one, Professor Leemans, as saying: 'it is not clear . . . how a cone can arise from a globe by means of extension'.[26] And de Ley himself says in exasperation:

The philosophical significance . . . of the quite unique description of the soul as a cone, is not discussed by Elferink, but it is dismissed as a detail that 'has not been explained yet', . . . But why a cone? As far as I know, in no other ancient text the connection of this figure with the generation of the soul has been preserved . . .[27]

What these scholars all needed to know was a few facts about optics.

In a later chapter we shall see the true significance of the myths of Prometheus in ancient Greece. But at this point I just want to point out two things about him: (a) he brought fire to men from heaven, and (b) he was often called the creator of men. From what we now know, *bringing fire from heaven* has a special meaning, for that is what a burning-lens or burning-globe does. And the metaphysical light-theology which we have just encountered concerns the rebirth of men as light-cones descending from heaven. There are several hitherto unsuspected optical aspects to the figure of Prometheus, to whom we will return when we consider the possible existence of ancient telescopes. But we must always keep in mind that underlying even the most banal versions of many ancient myths are surviving shreds of esoteric meaning, unknown perhaps to most of the ancient authors who repeated them, but preserved from earlier times when priests of Egypt and elsewhere wrapped those tales in enigmas which concealed truths unknown to the multitude.

Before we leave Macrobius behind, let us ponder the fact that he is the only ancient author to preserve the tradition of the incarnating soul descending as a light-cone into the world of matter. Who was Macrobius, that he should be the one to tell us this? Although he wrote in Latin, we know that he was not from Italy, and he may have come from North Africa. Despite the fact that he lived as late as the fifth century AD, he was completely untouched by Christian notions, which he never mentions. He was entirely a traditional 'pagan', and indeed made evident efforts to preserve pre-Christian traditions which by his time were under severe threat. Among the other esoteric traditions which Macrobius preserves is the 'Sacred Fraction', 256/243, which divided out gives the value of the Comma of Pythagoras, a universal constant in harmonic theory, a sacred number which Macrobius self-consciously attributes to people who to him were 'the ancients'.[28] (We discuss this number at great length in the final chapter.) Macrobius was thus a conservator of much esoteric knowledge which he seems to have thought it worthwhile partially revealing, because he feared it might otherwise be lost altogether.

Another mystical tradition of lenses drawing down spiritual essences in the form of focused light from heaven is recorded in Ireland. The 18th-century antiquary, Charles Vallancey, inspected and preserved a spectacular engraving (see Figure 12a) of an ancient sacred Celtic stone called the *Liath*

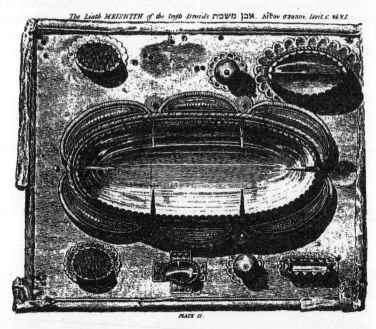

Figure 12a. The Liath Meisicith, or Magical Stone of Speculation, of the Irish. A literal translation of its name apparently means 'Druid Vision-Stone'. Seen here in an engraving from Vol. XIII, Part 3, of Charles Vallancey's *Collectanea de Rebus Hibernica*, Dublin, 1784, Plate II following p. 20. This is the inlaid top of a metal box about two inches deep. Originally, the large central crystal protruded through the lid, but by the time Vallancey examined the box in the late 1700s, the bottom of the crystal had been covered over inside the box. In 1784, this extraordinary object belonged to a Mr T. Kavenagh of Ballyborris, of whom I know nothing further. Anyone who knows the present-day location of this precious object, please contact the author! The central crystal is an inch and a quarter thick, five and a quarter inches long, and slightly more than two inches wide. It was supposed to draw down the *logh*, or heavenly fire, by acting as a burning-lens. But it would have been a good magnifier as well.

105

Meisicith. Vallancey informs people like myself who do not have a familiarity with the Irish language that the Irish word for 'crystal' is *criost-al*, meaning 'a holy stone'.[29] I have not figured out the philological significance of this unexpected cognate word, which is so obviously related to ancient Greek *krystallos*. Did the Irish borrow from the Greeks? Is the word of older Indo-European origin? I am inclined to think that the word was simply borrowed in Christian times from the English. But an expert on Irish would have to be consulted to be sure.

Vallancey says that the Druids used crystals as burning-lenses 'to draw down the *Logh*, the essence of spiritual fire' in religious ceremonies. He describes the *Liath Meisicith*, 'or the Magical stone of speculation', a large ancient Irish crystal burning-lens then (1784) in the possession of T. Kavenagh of Ballyborris. Vallancey tells us that *liath* means 'stone' (cognate with Greek *lithos*, 'stone'). And *meisi* means 'Druidism' and *cith* means 'a vision'. Hence the literal meaning of the name of this stone appears to be 'Druid-vision-stone'. I have no idea what has happened to the stone today, more than two centuries later. I presume it must be preserved in an Irish museum somewhere, considering its importance.

Vallancey also cites two curious Biblical passages about Moses forbidding the Israelites to continue to use their religious scrying stone called *Mashcith* in Hebrew, *lithos skopos* in the Septuagint, and *ebn mithnaggedah* in Samaritan. These references seem never to have been translated accurately in any English version of the Old Testament. Unfortunately, I cannot go back to Michael Weitzman with these further queries. I regret also that I know so little of ancient Irish traditions that I cannot say more about the *logh* – the spiritual fire drawn down by the burning-lens. But clearly this is an area for further research.

I don't know whether *logh* might be cognate with Greek *logos*. But in the Old Testament, in the Book of Genesis (IX.6) where it says man was made in the image of God, the Alexandrian Jewish philosopher Philo (born *circa* 20 BC) interprets this in a most interesting way in his book *Questions and Answers on Genesis*:

> For nothing mortal can be made in the likeness of the most high One and Father of the universe but (only) in that of the second God, who is his Logos. For it was right that the rational (part) of the human soul should be formed as an impression by the divine Logos, since the pre-Logos God is superior to every rational nature.[30]

One might say that as human souls are images of the Logos which have been impressed upon matter, the descent of the Logos is reminiscent of drawing the *logh* down, and may well be a related tradition, both based upon optical inagery, and related to the cones of light of Macrobius.

Lest anyone think I am stretching a point, and Philo did not have ideas related to light-theology, I can cite a passage from Philo's *Questions and*

Answers on Exodus which makes it plain beyond any doubt that he saw souls in terms of light-imagery:

> . . . to the light-bearing stars all their light happens to be brought from the celestial sphere. For just as whatever is luminous in the eyes is irrigated [*ardetai*, – a better translation would be 'watered'] by the soul, for souls are most luminous, so is the radiance of light in the stars wont to receive its illumination from the most pure ether.[31]

Philo clearly believed that the light in the eyes emanated from the luminous soul, and he seems to have believed that the luminous soul entered the world of matter as an image of the divine Logos, which in itself must therefore have been a luminous body. Philo's views are thus not far from those of Macrobius, when one thinks about it.

Some aspects of the focusing of sunlight through a glass globe filled with water were considered so conceptually astonishing that philosophers made heavy weather of them. A perfect example of this is Alexander of Aphrodisias, generally known as the most famous ancient commentator on Aristotle, who lived at the end of the second century and beginning of the third century AD. Being concerned with the natures of substances, Alexander in his *Commentary on the Meteorology of Aristotle* (I, 3), 'wanting to prove that a body could transmit an attribute of which it did not itself partake, says that objects could be set set alight by the heat of the sun passing through a [transparent glass] vase filled with cold water, without the water even being heated in the vase, or at least without heating it enough to explain the combustion.'[32,33]

The really dramatic instances of burning by optical methods were with the ancient burning-mirrors of Archimedes, Anthemius and Proclus (not the same Proclus who wrote philosophy). But these are dealt with later in Chapter Five.

There was a vast theological lore relating to burning-globes and burning-spheres amongst a group of ancient Greeks called the Orphics. Orphism was a religious movement outside the standard pagan state cults, and the Olympian gods were largely ignored by the Orphics. The movement took its name from the legendary figure of Orpheus, and there was a large body of Orphic poetic literature, some of which survives. Orphics used to be a bit of a nuisance in classical Athens. Like certain 'New-Agers' of today, the Orphics often handed out leaflets advocating a cult of salvation, and they even went from door to door like Jehovah's Witnesses trying to spread their gospel. They were very keen on ritual purity and tended to be vegetarians. Many Orphics were uneducated, even wandering vagabonds. But there were also highly educated Orphics, especially amongst the Greek cities of southern Italy.

Fundamental to the Orphic cult is the image of a cosmic egg from which light and fire stream forth. The egg is obviously a crystal ball or glass water-filled globe. In some of the surviving Orphic hymns, a creator-god named Protogonos ('the First Born') bursts forth from a cosmic egg called Phanēs (a form of *phanaios*, 'giving light'). The skin of Phanēs is sometimes mentioned, the Greek word for it being *chrōs*; this is not a normal word for skin, but is the word which means 'the surface (of any body)'. And the verb used for the shooting forth of Protogonos from Phanēs is *apestrapten*, 'to flash forth'. (This is a rare word used by Johannes Tzetzes in Byzantine times to refer to lightning.)

The surviving Orphic fragments were collected by the remarkable Isaac Preston Cory, and published in Greek with English translation in 1832. Cory's admirable collection of *Ancient Fragments*, an attempt to gather the fragments of important lost historical and mythological works from quotations in classical authors, was first published in a slim volume of 129 pages in 1828.[34] But Cory was not satisfied with his book and continued to work indefatigably on enlarging it, so that in 1832 he published his second edition, which had grown to 362 pages.[35] It was in this expanded edition that Cory included the surviving Orphic Fragments, which filled 12 pages of his book (pp. 289–300). Cory's book was reissued in 1876 after his death by a very presumptuous editor named E. Richmond Hodges, who threw out a lot of things he didn't approve of, such as the Orphic Fragments, with the derisory comments:

> Lastly, it remains only for me to say in this place that I have omitted Cory's preface entirely, . . . and have dispensed altogether with the Neo-Platonic forgeries which Cory had placed at the end, bearing the titles respectively of, Oracles of Zoroaster, the Hermetic Creed, the Orphic, Pythagorean, and other fragments, of doubtful authenticity and of little value . . . I have preferred, therefore, in the present edition, to omit this farrago of metaphysico-philosophical nonsense . . .[36]

Hodges claimed on the title page that his third edition was 'A New and Enlarged Edition', but although it did contain some new material, it had actually shrunk from 362 pages to 214 pages of much larger type, so it hardly qualifies as 'Enlarged', however 'New' it might be in having been purged of all dangerous contagion by the paranoid and arrogant Hodges. I am fortunate in owning copies of all three editions, so that I can compare them. Others consulting only a single edition could be forgiven for getting a false impression of the work, depending on which version they used.

So we return to the middle edition for the otherwise unavailable Orphic Fragments. A fragment of one hymn says:

No one has seen Protogonus with his eyes
Except the sacred Night alone: all others

Wondered when they beheld in the Ether the unexpected Light
Such as the surface of the immortal Phanes flashed forth.[37]

Another Orphic hymn says:

> I invoke Protogonus . . . Egg-born, rejoicing in thy golden wings, . . . The
> renowned Light, . . . Ineffable, occult, . . . all-glittering . . . Who bringest
> the pure and brilliant light, wherefore I invoke thee as Phanes, . . . and
> as the dazzling fountain of splendour./ Come then, blessed being, full of
> wisdom and generation, come in joy To thy sacred, every-varying
> mystery. Be present with the Priests of thy Orgies.

This is a clear reference to the light-beam forming part of a religious
ceremony of the Orphics. But another fragment makes clear that it was
meant to be in imitation of the creation:

> What Orpheus has asserted . . . is as follows: . . . 'The Earth was invis-
> ible on account of the darkness: but the Light broke through the Ether,
> and illuminated the Earth and all the material of the creation:' signifying
> by this Light, which burst forth through the Ether, the . . . being who was
> supreme above all things: 'and its name,' which Orpheus learnt from the
> oracle, 'is Metis, Phanēs, Ericapaeus,' which in the common Greek
> language may be translated will (or counsel), light, light-giver . . .[38]

In the treatise *Clementine Homilies*, thought to date from the first century
AD at Alexandria and possibly written by Apion, we find the following
description of what first emerged from the vortex of Creation:

> For just as a bubble is made in water, so a sphere-like hollow form
> gathered itself together from all sides. . . . from within the circumference
> a certain male-female Living Creature is imaged out . . . whom Orpheus
> doth call Manifestor (*Phanēs*) because when he is manifest (*phaneis*) the
> universe shines forth from him, through the lustre of Fire, most glorious
> of elements, perfected in the Moist [Element].
>
> Nor is this incredible, for in the case of glow-worms, for example,
> Nature allows us to see a 'moist light'.[39]

We can see from this that creation myths of some of the esoteric sects in
ancient times involved concepts drawn from the mysterious phenomena of
focused light rays emerging from crystal spheres or glass globes filled with
water, and that part of the 'mystery' was that fire could actually issue from
water, creating what appeared to be a contradiction in terms – a 'moist
light'. Fire and water were meant to be separate elements, and the fact that
sunlight could be focused by water in order to produce fire was thought to
be an astonishing Mystery related to divine Creation.

These mysterious phenomena and images were carried over into the 'heretical' Gnostic sects of early Christianity. One such fascinating sect was known as the Sethians, also known as the Sethian Heresy, although there is some doubt that they were Christian at all, as they never mentioned Jesus.[40] In his *Refutation of All Heresies*, the Christian author Hippolytus of Rome, in the third century AD, describes the doctrines of the Sethians in a way which, cutting through the allegorical quagmire, reminds us of the operation of the burning-globe. He says they have a principle called 'Darkness' and that 'Light descends into the Darkness which is set beneath (it).' But the Darkness has no conventional meaning here; it is specifically a name, he says, for 'an awesome water into which the light is drawn down and transferred.' This Darkness 'makes a slave of the Light-spark . . .' After a bit we come to a mutilated section of the text where we find mention of 'a very minute spark . . . like a ray . . .' And the light which has entered into the 'impure womb' with its water becomes a 'serpent'.[41]

There are some fragments of a Phoenician author named Sanchoniathon preserved by Eusebius. In one, he speaks of the Orphic Protogonos and says he gives birth to three children: fire, light, and flame. These three personified 'found out the method of generating fire . . . and taught men the use of it', which is a distinctly Promethean tradition. And Protogonos is also described as 'stretching forth his hands to heaven, towards the Sun . . .'[42] And another fragment of Sanchoniathon entitled 'On the Serpent' specifies that the serpent is 'of a fiery nature, inasmuch as it exhibits an incredible celerity, moving by its spirit without either hands, or feet, or any of those external organs, by which other animals effect their motion. And in its progress, moving in a spiral course, and at what degree of swiftness it pleases. . . . And when it has fulfilled the appointed measure of its existence, it consumes itself . . .'[43]

Anyone who has used a magnifying glass or glass sphere to start a fire will be aware that the pin-point of light dances and spirals around. This is more pronounced with a suspended sphere or globe than it is with a lens held firmly in the hand. Since the above seem to be references to suspended burning-globes (it is difficult not to interfere with the light if you try and hold it in your hand), we may imagine 'the fiery Serpent' which moves swiftly in circles is the focused light-point. In trying at first to find the focus, the light does, as the text last-quoted says, *assume a variety of forms*. And finally, after its 'appointed time' has elapsed, there is a bursting into flames – 'it consumes itself'.

We have to keep always in view the momentous impact such phenomena must have had on the minds of ancient men. 'How,' they would ask themselves, 'can fire be produced from water?' And the water could even be *quite cold* – it made no difference! Furthermore, the phenomenon of the burning-globe uniquely combines light with all four 'elements': light comes from the *air*, goes into the *water*, produces *fire*, which burns the offering into ashes which are a form of *earth*.

When we consider the phenomenon from the point of view of ancient men, we can realize that it was probably inevitable that everything to do with burning-globes, burning-spheres, or burning-lenses must have had an air of the sacrosanct about it. It is natural for it to have entered into religious allegory as we have found in these texts.

In fact, one wonders about such famous texts as this from the Book of Genesis:

And the Spirit of God moved upon the surface of the waters; and God said, Let there be light, and there was light.

Could 'the waters' have been in a hollow globe which enclosed them? We have already seen in our considerations of Pliny and other Latin texts discussing the use of lenses that *spiritus* came to be substituted for *visum*, so that it was not the 'vision' which was gathered together in a focus, but the 'spirit'. One could conceivably see the Genesis passage as a reference to an optical phenomenon – the light emanating from God encounters the *surface* (*chrōs* in Greek, as in the descriptions of Phanēs) of the globe containing the waters, *and there was focused light*. I do not mean to insist upon this, but merely suggest that light-imagery and the theology of light are to be found in many places, and not only in Macrobius! Maybe the soul as a descending light-cone was a motif in most religions, and we haven't realized it because we have paid no attention to the phenomena of optics which so bedazzled our ancestors. But *the descent of light into matter*, which in so many religions is looked upon as the Creation (whether of Life or of individual incarnating souls-as-light-cones) is naturally referred to in any religion with reference to the awesome optical phenomena which so perfectly seemed to symbolize it.

The image of the serpent as related to light and fire is something to which we will return when we consider the ancient Egyptians, and for instance their *uraeus* serpent, which seems to have symbolized light issuing from the forehead. It may have been a reference to the dancing serpent of light which issues from a crystal sphere suspended in a cradle in the sunlight. The mysterious name of Phanes may even be derived from the Egyptian word *fennu*, which means 'serpent'. But we will return to light-serpents later.

A mystical 'light-theology' permeated Jewish, proto-Christian and early Christian traditions, although as frequently as it appeared it was relegated to the sidelines as 'heresy' by the Organizers, whether they were rabbinical Jews or Catholic Christians, the main concern of both being the erection of systematic edifices of belief which could be conveniently patrolled by themselves as Thought Police. 'Light-theology' always seems to have represented a threat to those who would control others by the establishment of Secondhand-Thinking Systems known as churches or religious institutions, where divergence of opinion is condemned and often results in murder (Giordano Bruno being burnt at the stake by the Inquisition, as an example which took place as recently as 400 years ago). Secondhand-Thinking Systems have as their aim the control of the masses by a ruthless élite.

Although the Judaism which survives today seems to be a rather pale and desiccated form of Pharisaical Rabbinism (the Hassidim who wear ringlets are an exception to this and have affinities with a more mystical Kabbalistic tradition), early Judaism was a richer tapestry of philosophical and theological ideas of a more interesting nature. Many of the more intriguing ideas which died out in Judaism 2,000 years ago survived in the byways of heretical Christianity for many centuries longer. The ideas I am referring to are generally referred to as 'Gnostic', and they incorporate much light-imagery which ultimately derives from ancient Egyptian traditions.

It is impossible here to do justice to this vast field, which is highly complex and requires a knowledge of a variety of languages such as Aramaic, Coptic, Syriac, Hebrew, and even Ethiopic. I hope that scholars familiar with this field will revisit it, now that I have given an account of the optical background in antiquity, and reinterpret many of the passages and ideas in terms of what we now know of ancient optical influences on theology. But I will just give a few brief allusions as examples.

One of the intriguing mysteries of early Judaism is the figure and tradition identified with the name of Melchizedek. F. Legge informs us that his full name of Zorocothora Melchizidek can be translated as 'light-gatherer'.[44] Can part of the intention have been a reference to the 'light-gathering' of lenses? The early Church Father Hippolytus of Rome (third century AD) claimed that in his day there was a heretical Christian sect of followers of a certain Theodotus who honoured 'a greatest power named Melchizidek who was greater than Christ'.[45]

Sacred light imagery suffuses all of these traditions and their texts. Take for example the Gnostic book *Pistis Sophia*, preserved in a seventh-century AD Coptic manuscript, but representing a fascinating Gnostic form of very early Christianity several centuries older than the manuscript. In the Fourth Section of this mystical work, we read:

It came to pass then, when the Saviour had finished speaking these words unto his disciples, that Mary answered and said unto Jesus: 'My Lord, I have heard thee say: "He who shall receive of the mysteries of the Ineffable or who shall receive of the mysteries of the First Mystery, – they become flames of light-beams and light-streams and penetrate all the regions until they reach the region of their inheritance."'

The Saviour answered and said unto Mary:

'If they receive the mystery when still in life, and if they come out of the body, they become light-beams and light-streams and penetrate all the regions until they reach the region of their inheritance.

'But if they are sinners and come out of the body and have not repented, and if ye perform for them the mystery of the Ineffable, in order that they may be removed out of all the chastisements and be cast into a righteous body, which is good and inheriteth the Light-kingdom or is brought into the last order of the Light, then they will not be able to penetrate the regions, because they do not perform the mystery [themselves]. But the receivers of Melchizidek follow them and lead them before the Virgin of Light. . . .'[46]

Here we find an explicit statement attributed to Jesus that souls of the deceased turn into light-rays, which is a kind of reverse of the Macrobius tradition that souls which incarnate also do so as light-rays. It is obvious that common conceptions about the mystical nature of light underlay all of these widespread traditions, which are found amongst Greek and Roman pagans, Jews, and Christians alike.

Finally, I wish to call attention in this connection to the peculiar Jewish text known as *The Book of Enoch*, which seems to have its origins about 200 BC. This bizarre book contains many intriguing passages, but some relate to light-imagery in such a way as to suggest optical concepts. This book is a hodgepodge of different texts stuck together, and the sections generally thought to represent the earliest layer are the ones of possible optical interest. Enoch is a sacred scribe who is called upon by God to rebuke the fallen angels, who are called 'the Watchers', or 'the Watchers of the heavens'. The idea of fallen angels being connected with light-bringing is preserved in the name of Lucifer, a Latin word meaning 'light-bringing', and thus a good descriptive term for Prometheus as well. (Lucifer became also a name for Venus at dawn, or 'the morning star'.)

Enoch has a series of instructional visions which he records, and the surviving text gives these strange, garbled accounts in a form made more confusing by the fact that the original text of the work (thought to have been in Aramaic, but possibly in Hebrew) has been lost for nearly two millennia. We have to rely on an Ethiopic translation and fragments in Greek, so the original terminology can never be known for certain. In his first vision, Enoch says he 'drew nigh to a wall which is built of crystals and surrounded by tongues of fire . . . its portals blazed with fire. . . . [its] heaven was water . . . and it was hot as fire and cold as ice . . .'[47]

Already we are reminded of the many references by early Church Fathers and Neoplatonists to the mystery of how a glass globe filled with water can generate heat and fire while the water inside it remains cold.

Enoch then has a second vision of a house containing a throne whose 'appearance was as crystal'.[48] He then goes on visionary journeys and encounters various precious stones and 'a flaming fire'. Finally he is taken to Sheol, or the Underworld. There he encounters hollow places, 'deep and

113

wide and very smooth'. One of the smooth hollow places was bright and contained water in its midst. It was 'deep and dark to view'. The archangel Raphael then tells Enoch that 'These hollow places have been created for this very purpose, that the spirits of the souls of the dead should assemble therein . . .' Enoch asks why they differ, and Raphael replies that the hollow place which contains 'the bright spring of water' has been made for the collection of the spirits of the righteous. Enoch then saw 'a burning fire which ran without resting'.[49]

For anyone familiar with the optical allusions in ancient texts, the impression can be obtained that these Enoch passages are a garbled record of optical phenomena. The 'hollows' which contain water and 'gather together the spirits' remind us of the 'gathering of the *spiritus*' used to describe the optical properties of water-filled globes. The many references to crystals and streams of fire can also be interpreted optically. It seems that earlier sacred texts or traditions referring to optical phenomena have been drawn upon for use in the Enoch book, which is an Apocalypse, by an author who either did not fully understand the references or chose to veil the true meanings.

The Chinese had traditions not unlike those in the West about the mystical nature of light and of its descent, often expressed in a context connected with the kindling of fire by burning-mirrors like those mentioned earlier by Plutarch. These traditions are contemporary with those at Rome, being at least 2,200 years old. One of the most fascinating of all ancient Chinese books is the *Huai-Nan Tzu*. It is very dense and obscure in many places, but it contains early scientific, cosmological, and mystical ideas which are of the greatest interest. It dates from the second century BC, the period known as the Early Han Dynasty.

One of the earliest descriptions of this ancient philosophical book to appear in English was in 1867, when the system of transliteration of Chinese into English letters was not really standardized, and the book was called the *Hwae nan tsze*. This was by A. Wylie, who in that year published his vast summary catalogue of Chinese literature so that the white devils (which is what the Chinese call us, once seriously, now in jest) could know something about the subject.

Wylie's comments, with the transliteration modernized (according to the Wade-Giles, not the Pinyin, system) and corrected and the characters omitted, were:

A descendant of the first emperor of the Han, named Liu An, holds a distinguished place among the writers of this ['Miscellaneous'] class. His work, in 21 books, is entitled *Huai-Nan Tzu*, he having been prince of Huai-Nan. This treats at large of the doctrine of the *Tao*, or the *Logos* of the Greeks, with its development in the creation and maintenance of the material universe. A second part to the work existed formerly, but is

114

now lost. The oldest and most valued commentary on this treatise is by Kuan Yu.[50]

No complete translation of the *Huai-Nan Tzu* into English exists, but there are two partial translations, as well as many individual passages translated by Derk Bodde and Joseph Needham (the former my professor, the latter my colleague). Bodde's translations occur in his translation of the mammoth work *A History of Chinese Philosophy* by Fung Yu-Lan, which was written in Chinese and which Bodde not only translated itself, but he had to translate the many quotations included in it – one of the great scholarly labours of translation in our time. Fung was greatly impressed by the *Huai-Nan Tzu*, and said of it:

> The book called the *Huai-nan-tzu* . . . was written in the Former Han dynasty by the guests attached to the Court of Liu An . . . Prince of Huainan, who after becoming implicated in a plot against the throne, committed suicide in 122 BC. This book . . . is a miscellaneous compilation of all schools of thought, and lacks unity. Nevertheless it contains passages which explain the origin of the universe more clearly than do any earlier philosophic writings.

He then quotes some amazingly profound passages from Chapter Two which deal with ontology (the 'science of being') in such a way that even Martin Heidegger would have been dumbfounded (such concepts as: 'There was "not yet a beginning of Non-being"'). Eventually, optical allusions begin to intrude into the account of the creation:

> '(5) The state of Non-being was so called because when it was gazed on, no form was seen; when the ear listened, there was no sound . . . It was limitless space, profound and a vast void, a quiescent subtle mass of immeasurable translucency. . . . (7) In the period of 'there was not yet a beginning of the not yet beginning of Non-being,' Heaven and Earth had not yet split apart, the *yin* and the *yang* had not become differentiated, the four seasons were not yet separated, and the myriad things had not yet come to birth. It was like light in the midst of Non-being which retreats and is lost sight of . . .'

Fung then quotes further sections from Chapter Three:

> 'When Heaven and Earth did not yet have this form, there was a state of amorphous formlessness. Therefore this is termed the Great Beginning (*t'ai shih* 太始). This Great Beginning produced an empty extensiveness, and this empty extensiveness produced the cosmos. The cosmos produced the primal fluid (*yüan ch'i* 元氣), which had its limits. That

which was clear and light collected to form Heaven. That which was heavy and turbid congealed to form Earth. The union of the clear and light was especially easy, whereas the congealing of the heavy and turbid was particularly difficult, so that Heaven was formed first and Earth afterward. . . . The hot force of *yang*, being accumulated for a long time, produced fire, and the essence of fire formed the sun. The cold force of *yin*, being accumulated for a long time, produced water, and the essence of water formed the moon. . . . The way of Heaven is to be round, while the way of Earth is to be square. Squareness dominates darkness, while roundness dominates light. Light is an ejection of fluid, and therefore fire is bright externally. Darkness is that which absorbs fluid, and therefore water is bright internally. That which ejects fluid, gives forth. That which absorbs fluid, transforms. Therefore *yang* gives forth and *yin* transforms. . . . The sun is the lord of *yang* . . . Therefore when a *yang sui* 陽 燧 (a kind of mirror) is put under the sun, it becomes hot and creates fire.'[51]

Here we have a reference to a concave burning-mirror in the second century BC coming in a profound discussion of cosmology and the creation of the world. In a recent translation of this passage by Charles le Blanc, the burning-mirror is no longer called a *yang sui* but is called a *fu-sui* 夫 燧:

The *fu-sui* 夫 燧 (burning mirror) gathers fire from the sun . . .

Le Blanc explains this change in a footnote:

Modern editions write *fu yang sui* 夫 陽 燧. I agree with Wang Nien-sun . . . that *yang* should be eliminated, the original text reading simply *fu-sui* 夫 燧. *Yang* was added by later scholars, who misunderstood *fu* here to be an initial particle (read in the second tone) meaning 'now', 'then', or an emphatic 'this'. . . . These scholars, says Wang, were also influenced by a similar passage in *Huai-nan Tzu* 3/2b, where the expression was written *yang-sui*. Wang argues [that the Commentary on another ancient book called the *Chou Li*] . . . explains that *fu-sui* and *yang-sui* are two names for the same object. . . . The commentary on *Huai-nan Tzu* 3/2b describes *yang-sui* as follows: '*Yang-sui* is made of metal. If one takes a metal bowl without a rim (a slightly concave mirror), polishes it vigorously so that it becomes hot, places it directly below the sun at noon and puts mugwort before it, the mugwort will then catch fire.' That we are dealing with heat reflection on the basis of the true focal point is confirmed by *Huai-nan Tzu* 17/19a-b: 'The right way of recruiting men [for government service] may be compared to obtaining fire by means of *yang-sui*; if it is placed too far [from mugwort], it fails to produce fire; if it is placed too close, it fails to hit the center [focal point]; it should be placed exactly between "too far" and "too close".'

116

Besides *fu-sui* and *yang-sui*, the single character *sui* was also used to designate burning mirrors in ancient China; *sui* was sometimes written ... or 燧 .... Needham translated the two passages from *Huai-nan Tzu* quoted in this note. I have modified his translation.[52]

Another phenomenon of optical significance which has been 'missed' by archaeologists of a much earlier period is the double-axe motif (called the *labrys*) of ancient Crete. This prominent religious symbol represents, in my opinion, the pattern made by sunlight through a burning-lens. See Plate 6 for the photo I took of this very pattern made by a lens in my garden. See how it resembles the double-axe of the Minoans as shown in Plate 7 which is actually a *pre*-Minoan artefact, as I explain in a moment.

I found some evidence to confirm my opinion in mainland Greece. I visited the strange prehistoric settlement of Lerna near Argos in the Peloponnese. It has been well excavated, and much of it is on public view beneath a corrugated iron roof, though I suspect the numbers of travellers who actually go to the rather out-of-the-way site are few. In ancient times it was beside the Bay of Argos, though now it is inland. Excavations have shown that the site was inhabited in palaeolithic times, many thousands of years ago. By what is called 'prehistoric' times, *circa* 3000 BC, a people were living there who left an important sacred artifact behind them which I found on prominent display in the nearby Museum of Argos. As for who the pre-Greek people of Lerna were, one should consult the book *The People of Lerna*, though it is rather confusing and extremely technical.[53]

What did I find? It may be seen in Plate 7. This large, beautiful and obviously sacred hearthstone or altar stone has had carefully excavated from its centre an area for the burning of an offering – and this depression is made in the shape of a perfect double-axe. Around its edges, little licking flames are depicted. This stone was intended to celebrate the mystical shape of the focused rays of the sun emanating from a lens. If a lens large enough had been available to form a double-axe pattern of that size, the offering would have been perfectly consumed by the focused rays, which would have precisely matched its outlines. But since the altar stone is so large, the shape was presumably symbolic. (Smaller versions could have accomplished the 'perfect burning' feat, but none is known to survive.)

I regard this extraordinary altar stone as an optical artifact, and considering its date, it may be the second oldest one in the world after the ivory knife handle from Abydos. For the oldest lenses which I have so far found date only from the Fourth and Fifth Dynasties in Egypt, and are of slightly later date than the stone.

As for the large number of Minoan crystal lenses which have been excavated in Crete – traditional home of the double-axe motif – these too lend support to an optical interpretation of the double-axe symbol. For the people to whom the double-axe was of such fundamental importance were a people for whom crystal lenses were commonplace.

Now we will look at the matter of telescopes.

Notes

1. Aristophanes, *The Clouds*, in *Aristophanes: The Eleven Comedies*, translated anonymously, Tudor Publishing Company, New York, 1936, pp. 339–40. For the Greek text, the Loeb Library edition may be consulted, or see *Aristophanes. The Clouds*, with introduction and notes by W. W. Merry, Oxford the Clarendon Press, 1899, p. 31. Merry makes no comment on *hyalos*, but for line 771 translates 'like this' and adds a note saying: 'He throws himself into a posture of a man holding a burning-glass.'
2. de la Hire, Gabriel-Philippe, 'Sur les Verres Ardents des Anciens' ('On the Burning-Glasses of the Ancients'), under *Dioptrique* (Dioptrics) of *l'Histoire* (History) section, in *Histoire de l'Académie Royale des Sciences* (*History of the Royal Academy of Sciences*), Paris, 1708, volume actually published 1709, pp. 112–15. There were three contemporary de la Hires, who are easily confused with one another. The best-known was probably Philippe (1640–1718), who wrote about geometry and mathematics. Gabriel-Philippe (1677–1719), an astronomer, was his son, as also was Jean-Nicolas (1685–1727), who was primarily a botanist but also published a treatise on vision in 1708 at Paris entitled *Quaestio Medica – Potestne Stare Visio Absque Crystallino?* (*Can Vision Exist without Crystal?*) There may have been a family preoccupation with optics in that year; this pamphlet was written from the theoretical ophthalmological point of view. It is important to note that there were thus two optical publications by the two brothers in the same year, so that a reference to 'de la Hire, 1708' could be ambiguous.
3. Smith, Robert, *A Compleat System of Opticks*, 2 vols, Cambridge, 1738, Vol. II, p. 15 at back of volume in section 'The Author's Remarks upon the Whole Work', which commences a new pagination.
4. Cited by Joseph Hirschberg, 'Pathology and Therapy' section of *Geschichte der Augenheilkunde im Alterthum* (*History of Ophthalmology in Antiquity*), in *Gräfe-Saemisch Handbuch der Gesamten Augenheilkunde* (*Gräfe-Saemisch Handbook of Complete Ophthalmology*), Leipzig, Vol. XII, Part 2, *Pathologie und Therapie, p. 178.
5. Pliny, *Natural History*, translated by D. E. Eichholz, Loeb Classical Library, Harvard University Press, USA, Vol. X, 1971, p. 157.
6. *Ibid.*, p. 185.
7. *Ibid.*, p. 153.
8. Gabriel-Philippe de la Hire, *op. cit.*
9. Lactantius, *De Opificio Dei* (*On God's Workmanship*), in *Lactantii Opera Omnia*, Tomus Secundus et Ultimus, in *Patrologiae* Tomus VII, Paris, 1844, p. 37.
10. Theophrastus, *De Igne* (*Peri Pyros; On Fire*), edited and translated by Victor Coutant, Royal Vangorcum Lts., Assen, the Netherlands, 1971, pp. 46–8. Note that I have altered Coutant's translation of *hyelou*, changing the English from 'glass' to 'rock crystal', since the meaning 'glass' came later, and at the time of Theophrastus the rarity of glass was such that the word almost certainly referred to rock crystal, which was the original meaning of this word introduced into Greek by Herodotus.
11. Clement of Alexandria, *Miscellanies*, Chapter 17, in Vol. II of Vol. XII 'Clement of Alexandria' in *Ante-Nicene Christian Library*, translated by the Rev. Alexander Roberts and James Donaldson. Edinburgh, 1869, p. 393. The textual reference is *Stromata VI*, in *Klēmentos Alexandreōs ta Euriskomena. Clementis Alexandrini Opera. Graece et Latine quae Extant*, edited by Friderico Sylburgio, Paris, 1641, p. 688 D (Greek with Latin translation).

12. *Grēgoriou Episkopou Nyssēs ta Euriskomena Sancti Patris Nostri Gregorii Episcopi Nysseni Opera*, Tomus Secundus, Paris, 1638, *Contra Eunomium, Oratio XII*, p. 751 B (Greek with Latin translation).

13. *Sancti Caesarii . . . Dialogi IV*, edited by Joannes Leunclavius, 6 vols, Tomus VI, Venice, 1770, Dialogus I, p. 25 C (Greek with Latin translation).

14. Bishop Titus of Bostra, *Wider die Manichaër (Against the Manicheans)*, in Rössler, Christian Friedrich, *Bibliothek der Kirchen-Väter in Übersetzung und Auszügen, Epiphanius und Alte Häresiologie (Library of the Church Fathers in Translation and Epitomized)*, Leipzig, 1776–81, Book II, pp. 369–70.

15. Flavius Philostratus, *Life of Apollonius of Tyana*, Loeb Classical Library, Harvard University Press, USA, Vol. I, pp. 257–9.

16. *Ibid.*, Vol. II, p. 55.

17. Farnell, Lewis Richard, *The Cults of the Greek States*, Oxford, Vol. 3, 1907, p. 97.

18. *Ibid.*, Vol. V, 1909, p. 353.

19. Plutarch, *Lives*, translated by Bernadotte Perrin, Loeb Classical Library, Harvard University Press, USA, Vol. I, 1959, pp. 339–41.

20. Bamford, Christopher, ed., *Homage to Pythagoras: Rediscovering Sacred Science*, Lindisfarne Press, Hudson, New York, USA, 1994. See Robert Lawlor's article 'Ancient Temple Architecture' (pp. 35–132), pp. 106–8.

21. Temple, Robert, Introduction to *The Dream of Scipio (Somnium Scipionis)*, Aquarian Press, Wellingborough, Northamptonshire, England, 1983.

22. Macrobius, *Commentary on the Dream of Scipio*, translated by William Harris Stahl, Number 48 of the Records of Civilisation, Sources and Studies series, Columbia University Press, New York, 1952, pp. 133–4. This volume does not contain the Latin text, for which see next footnote.

23. Macrobius, *Opera*, Lipsiae, 1774, p. 66.

24. Macrobius, *Commentary, op. cit.*, p. 165; Macrobius, *Opera*, p. 101.

25. de Ley, Herman, *Macrobius and Numenius: A Study of Macrobius, In Somn., 1, c. 12*, Collection Latomus, Vol. 125, Latomus, Revue d'Études Latines, Brussels, 1972, pp. 43–4.

26. *Ibid.*, p. 44.

27. *Ibid.*, pp. 42–4.

28. Macrobius, *Commentary, op. cit.*, II, 1, pp. 188–9.

29. Vallancey, Charles, *Collectanea de Rebus Hiberniae*, Dublin, Vol. IV, 1784, pp. 13–20. The *Liath Meisicith* is illustrated in Plate II opposite p. 20.

30. Philo, *Questions and Answers on Genesis*, translated by Ralph Marcus from the ancient Armenian version of the original [lost] Greek, Philo Supplement Volume I, Loeb Classical Library, Harvard University Press, USA, 1979, pp. 150–1.

31. Philo, *Questions and Answers on Exodus*, translated by Ralph Marcus from the ancient Armenian version of the original [lost] Greek, Philo Supplement Volume II, Loeb Classical Library, Harvard University Press, USA, 1987, p. 129; this passage is from a Greek fragment, not from the Armenian.

32. Martin, Thomas Henri, 'Sur les Instruments Optiques Faussement Attribués aux Anciens par Quelques Savants Modernes' ('On the Optical Instruments Falsely Attributed to the Ancients by Some Modern Thinkers'), in *Bolletino di Bibliografia e di Storia delle Scienze Matematiche e Fisiche (Bulletin of the Bibliography and History of Mathematical and Physical Science)*, Rome, Vol. 4, 1871, p. 216. (The article as a whole extends from pp. 165–238.)

33. Bishop Isidore of Seville (seventh century AD) is another writer who discussed crystal burning-spheres, in his work *Etymologies*, where he also commented upon Nero's emerald. The relevant passages are XVI.7.1 and XVI.13.1. The burning-sphere is described in the section 'On Crystal', the text being *Isidori Hispalensis Episcopi Originum*, in *Auctores Latinae Linguae in Unum Redacti Corpus*, 1585, p. 1220.

34. Cory, Isaac Preston, *Ancient Fragments,* William Pickering, London, 1828.

35. Cory, Isaac Preston, *Ancient Fragments,* William Pickering, London, 2nd edition, 1832.
36. Cory, Isaac Preston, *Cory's Ancient Fragments*, 3rd edition edited by E. Richmond Hodges, Reeves & Turner, London, 1876.
37. Cory, 1832, *op. cit.*, pp. 295–6. I have put 'surface' for 'skin' and 'flashed forth' for 'shot forth', in accordance with the truer meaning as explained earlier.
38. *Ibid.*, pp. 296–7.
39. Mead, G. R. S., *Thrice Greatest Hermes*, John Watkins, London, 1964, Vol. I, pp. 270–1.
40. Legge, F., *Forerunners and Rivals of Christianity*, Cambridge, 1915, Vol. II, p. 76.
41. *Ibid.*, pp. 274–7.
42. Cory, 1876, *op. cit.*, p. 5.
43. *Ibid.*, pp. 22–3.
44. Legge, F., *Forerunners and Rivals of Christianity*, Cambridge University Press, 2 vols, 1915, Vol. II, p. 148. Apparently this translation was first noted by C. W. King in his book *The Gnostics and Their Remains*.
45. *Ibid.*, n. 1.
46. Mead, G. R. S., *Pistis Sophia*, John Watkins, London, 1921, pp. 272–3.
47. *The Book of Enoch*, XIV, 9–13, translated by R. H. Charles, SPCK, London, 1966, p. 41.
48. *Ibid.*, XIV, 18, p. 42.
49. *Ibid.*, XIV, 18 – XXIII, 1, pp. 42–50.
50. Wylie, A., *Notes on Chinese Literature*, American Presbyterian Mission Press, Shanghai, new edition, 1902, pp. 157–8. My own copy is of this edition, and I have not bothered to consult the first edition in this instance, as there was no important reason to do so.
51. Fung Yu-Lan, *A History of Chinese Philosophy: The Period of the Philosophers* (this would later be known as Volume I), translated by Derk Bodde, Henri Vetch, Peiping (Beijing), China, 1937, pp. 395–7.
52. Le Blanc, Charles, *Huai Nan Tzu: Philosophical Synthesis in Early Han Thought: The Idea of Resonance . . . with a Translation and Analysis of Chapter Six*, Hong Kong University Press, 1985, p. 120 and n. 48.
53. Angel, J. Lawrence, *The People of Lerna: Analysis of a Prehistoric Aegean Population*, American School of Classical Studies at Athens, Princeton, New Jersey, and Smithsonian Institution Press, Washington, DC, 1971.

Chapter Four

The Case of the Disappearing Telescope

Before we begin, we need to consider just what a telescope *is*, for many people do not really know. Before people can feel at ease believing that the ancients had telescopes, they need to know just what it means that they really had to have. And the answer is surprisingly simple: all you really need to have to comprise an elementary telescope is two lenses, one in each hand. If you take two ordinary convex lenses, whether of crystal or glass, and hold one closer to your eye and one further from your eye, and look through them both at once – you have a simple telescope! That's all there is to it. Of course, you have to move them back and forth until you get the focus right, but there it is. And since we know that hundreds of ancient lenses survive, is it really possible that no one in the history of the world before the time of Galileo ever thought: *I wonder what would happen if I looked through two of these at once?*

I should hasten to point out that a telescope of the kind I have just described gives you an inverted image – everything is upside down. But if you take a third lens, known as a rectifying lens, and put it in line with the others, it flips the image back right side up again. However, if you are studying the moon or the stars, you don't need to rectify the image by flipping it, as it makes no difference at all whether things are upside down or not. This is presumably the case with the simple astronomical telescopes used in ancient Britain for looking at the moon, which we will consider later in this chapter. But first let us turn to the ancient writer Strabo.

'Strabo' was a Latin nickname for someone whose eyes were deformed or distorted, and who squinted very strongly. As for the writer called Strabo, we don't know a great deal about him. He lived during the early Roman Empire. In fact, he was born in 64 or 63 BC in what is today Turkey and he died about 25 AD. He was a wealthy man, and apparently a Greek, since he wrote in Greek rather than Latin. But we don't know why he was called Strabo, since it was also a Roman surname. And by one of those weird coincidences which sometimes happen in history, considering his importance for our story and the evidence he gives us relating to optics, he had an 'optical name'.

Strabo was extremely rich, and he spent his large inherited fortune studying philosophy initially, and then travelling the world in order to write about peoples and places in immense, almost pedantic, detail. He was probably the greatest of the ancient geographers. And in those days, unless you were rich and had the private money to travel everywhere, you couldn't really be one. He was also fortunate to live at a time when the Mediterranean had been entirely cleared of pirates by the Roman navy, so that it was safe to sail everywhere without fear of being kidnapped or murdered on the high seas.

Strabo's first great work was a History of the World in 47 volumes, not a word of which survives today. But then that is nothing unusual, since possibly 98 per cent of the writings of Western antiquity are lost. However, Strabo was luckier with his second work, for it did survive. It is justly famous amongst scholars, despite the fact that barely a soul amongst the general public has ever heard of it or of its author.

But he should not be so little known, for his great work, *The Geography*, makes compelling reading for anyone of a nosy disposition who has ever been anywhere described in it, or who hopes to go there. And he discusses places as far apart as Morocco and the Crimea, Britain and Africa, along with everything in between, telling exactly what could be seen and who was living in each town in the first century AD. For people who are curious and like historical gossip, it is highly recommended. It fills eight volumes in its Loeb Library edition where the translation is on facing pages to the text, but you can buy the individual volume about the country that interests you, and the books are small enough to fit in your pocket.

In Book III, in the section discussing Spain, Strabo is discussing what he calls 'the Sacred Promontory', which we call today Cape St Vincent. He says of it:

> This is the most western point not only of Europe, but of the whole habitable earth.

He mentions the megalithic remains and dolmens to be found there, gives anecdotes about them, and says that it was forbidden to approach them at night 'because the gods take up their abode at that place' after dark. Such titbits of local lore are typical of Strabo's work. This leads him to consider the sunset as viewed over the Atlantic Ocean from the Spanish coast. At first he comments on what the famous Roman philosopher Posidonius (whose name would have been familiar to all of his readers, though most of his works are lost today) had to say about this dramatic sight. Here is what Strabo says:

> Posidonius tells us the sun appears larger as he sets, and makes a noise resembling the sound of hot metal in cold water, as though the sea were hissing as the sun was submerged in its depths. The statement of Artemidorus ([of Ephesus, fl. 104–101 BC, writer of 11 geographical

books] who states that he has himself been at the place) is also false, that night follows immediately on the setting of the sun: it does not follow immediately, although certainly the interval is short, as in other great seas. For when he sets behind mountains the agency of the false light prolongs the day for a long period; over the sea the twilight is shorter, but still darkness does not immediately supervene. The same thing may be remarked in large plains. The image of the sun is enlarged on the seas at its rising as well as at its setting, because at these times a larger mass of exhalations [mist] rises from the humid element; and the eye looking through these exhalations, sees images refracted into larger forms, as observed through tubes. The same thing happens when the setting sun or moon is seen through a dry and thin cloud, when those bodies appear reddish. Posidonius tells us that, having himself passed 30 days at Cadiz [then called Gades], during which time he carefully observed the setting of the sun, he is convinced of the falsity of Artemidorus's account. This latter writer tells us, that at the time of its setting the sun appears a hundred times larger than its ordinary size, and that night immediately succeeds. If we attend to his account, we cannot believe that he himself observed this phenomenon at the Sacred Promontory [Cape St Vincent], for he tells us that no one can approach during the night; therefore they cannot approach at sunset, since night immediately follows. Neither did he observe it from any other part of the coast washed by the ocean, for Cadiz is upon the ocean, and both Posidonius and many others testify that this is not the case there.

The alert reader may have noticed what was peculiar about the passage which I have just quoted. It is the mention of *tubes*: what does he mean by his phrase '*as observed through tubes*'?

The Greek text is explicit: it says *di 'aulōn*. The word *aulos* means 'tube', and was also applied to a kind of flute. And the expression given means 'through tubes' (the noun is plural). There is no way to get around this other than to change the text, and many attempts to do so have been made!

This passage gave rise to a classic case of the circularity of some scholarly changes in Greek and Latin texts: you read something which you don't believe, you then change it, and because it no longer says what it once said, it is then produced as evidence against the existence of the thing that you didn't believe existed and which led you to remove all mention of it from the text in the first place. In other words, you yourself create the absence of evidence by simply erasing or changing the words!

I shall give a simple nonsense example. Let us say that I wrote the following:

From the road I could clearly see an owl.

Let us assume that some future scholar, 200 years from now, was convinced that owls were extinct in my lifetime and I could not possibly have seen one. He would propose an 'editing change' in my text, and would suggest that as the result of a typographical error, the mistake 'owl' had crept into my sentence. I must have written something very similar, and so he suggests that my statement originally was:

From the road I could clearly see a pool.

The scholar would point out that two 'o's if written by a scribe can easily become distorted and resemble a 'w'. He would also suggest that the 'p' had lost its tail and had come to look like an 'o'. The copyist had then added an 'n' to my 'a' to read mistakenly: 'an owl'. He would then claim that he had proved that I had never seen an owl, but only a pool, as it was well known that I often walked in marshy areas with lots of pools, and there is no other evidence that I was interested in bird-watching.

And that is how history is made and texts are changed.

I believe that the first translation of Strabo into English was the three-volume *The Geography of Strabo* for George Bell and Sons, London, in 1887 (later absorbed into the famous Bohn's Library series). Although the whole work was translated jointly by W. C. Hamilton and W. Falconer, it was Hamilton who was responsible for the part containing the passage about the 'tubes', and it was his translation which I gave above. Here is how he dealt with the matter of the 'tubes' in his footnote:[1]

We extract the following notice on this passage from [Baron von] Humboldt (*Cosmos*, Vol. III, p. 54, Bohn's [English translation] edition): 'This passage has recently been pronounced corrupt ([by G.] Kramer [German editor of Strabo edition of 1844–52, Berlin], Vol. I, p. 211), and *di hyalōn* through glass spheres) substituted for *di áulōn* (see [Johann Gottlob] Schneider, *Eclog. Phys.* [*Eclogae Physicae Historium*, 1801], Vol. II, p. 273). The magnifying power of hollow glass spheres, filled with water (see Seneca [*Natural Questions*], I, 6) was, indeed, as familiar to the ancients as the action of burning glasses or crystals (see Aristophanes, *The Clouds*, V, 765) and that of Nero's emerald (see Pliny [*Natural History*], XXXVII, 5); but these spheres most assuredly could not have been employed as astronomical measuring instruments. (Compare [von Humboldt's] *Cosmos*, Vol. I, p. 619). Solar altitudes taken through thin light clouds, or through volcanic vapours, exhibit no trace of the influence of refraction.'

Notice how seriously it is taken that G. Kramer pronounces something to be corrupt. And consider the language: *pronounces*. G. Kramer does not suspect or think, he *pronounces*. He does not speculate or tentatively suggest, he *pronounces*.

Ever since the work of Strabo began to be studied seriously in the 16th century, an industry has existed for the purpose of getting rid of his mention of magnifying tubes, lest we be forced to admit the existence in antiquity of telescopes. At all costs, the ancient telescopes must be made to disappear. As we shall see, the various attempts were often desperate and comic. And the attempt of Kramer in 1801 to substitute 'through glass spheres' by altering the Greek letters is extraordinarily ironical, for as we have seen in an earlier chapter, the word *hyalos* which Kramer wished to insert is the very word which Aristophanes used to describe a burning-lens in his play, *The Clouds*. Kramer thus unwittingly deleted one optical reference only to replace it with another!

I believe it was originally the French aristocratic scholar, and Fellow of the Royal Academy of Sciences in Paris, the Count de Caylus, who in 1756 was the first general enquirer (other than an editor of the Greek text) to notice that Strabo had made a passing remark which was of profound optical interest.

Let us see what he had to say about the Strabo passage in part of a discussion of ancient optics. The account of his remarks in December 1756 to the French Royal Academy of Inscriptions and *Belles Lettres* was not actually published until 1761:

It is not only Monsieur le Comte de Caylus who wonders whether the ancients had the use of spectacles; a passage of Strabo (III, p. 138) gave birth to this notion. This geographer wished to explain why the disc of the sun seemed bigger on the sea when it rose or set, in attributing the cause to the vapours which rise up from the waters; and he explained this physical effect in these terms: . . . [Greek text quoted] . . . One cannot render this aspect: 'The vapours have the same effect as tubes, – they enlarge the appearances of objects.' The word *aulos* signifies very well and very properly 'a tube' [This is correct: *aulos* means 'hollow tube' according to the Liddell and Scott *Lexikon*.]; one cannot give to it any other sense in this passage than to suspect that the ancients had knowledge of the use of this instrument. Monsieur le Comte de Caylus after all did not give this opinion as simple conjecture; but he observed that Père [Father Jean] Mabillon had seen, in a manuscript from the beginning of the 13th century, Ptolemy [Claudius Ptolemy, second century AD] represented observing the stars with a telescope, or rather a tube. This manuscript was 300 years older than Galileo and Jacques Métius, inventor of telescopic glasses; the figure from the frontispiece had been handed down from copy to copy since the time of Ptolemy.[2]

After this, the knowledge that Strabo had apparently mentioned telescopes entered into the discussions of ancient optics as an occasionally recurring theme, though the scholarship required to appreciate who Strabo was, much less to consider his text, meant that the references were never common. It is to the credit of the aristocratic amateur de Caylus that he launched this theme into the thread of scholarly discourse, where we continue to discuss it here a century and a half later.

The hatchet-jobs done on Strabo's text to hack out the offending words commenced as early as Isaac Vossius, the first editor of Strabo's Greek text in the 16th century. He attempted to edit out the telescopes, and so did a succession of other continental editors. Unfortunately, not all of these editions are represented in the British Library and it is necessary to consult them in French or German libraries, so that I have not compiled the definitive list which I would have preferred to do if the circumstances had not meant that it was so inconvenient.

H. L. Jones, the Loeb Library editor and translator, published the text in its altered form as *di ᶜyalōn* rather than as *di 'aulōn*. This meant there were no tubes, but ironically, led Jones into even murkier optical territory. Hamilton had spoken of the rays as being 'refracted'. Jones is nervous of this, and translates 'the visual rays . . . are broken', but adds a footnote by way of clarification: 'We should say "refracted".'

However, Jones's translation of what should be describing the rays as seen through tubes reads: '. . . the visual rays, in passing through this vapour as through a lens . . .', and he adds a footnote which says: 'A globe filled with water, apparently.'[3]

We can readily see that Jones has decided to rely upon the *pronouncement* of G. Kramer for his own edition and translation.

When did the modern discussion of ancient telescopes begin? It was at least five centuries before the Count de Caylus noticed the passage in Strabo in 1756. The earliest reference to ancient telescopes which I have so far managed to locate in the literature is a puzzling one, which comes from the writings of Roger Bacon in the 13th century. It is not surprising to find Bacon discussing the subject, since he built a telescope himself when he was at Oxford, and that in itself was a subject for much later discussion – since he lived so long before Galileo. The puzzling comments of Bacon are ones where he claims that Julius Caesar had a telescope with which he viewed the coast of England from the coast of France before invading Britain. The trouble is, there is no surviving mention of this in any Roman historian, so where did Bacon get this strange story? Perhaps it is best to follow some of the discussions of both subjects – Bacon's telescope and Caesar's telescope – which commenced as far as I can determine in 1551, to see how these matters were understood by a variety of earlier writers.

In 1551, the amazing English polymath Robert Recorde (or Record) wrote in his book *The Path-way to Knowledg, Containing the First Principles of Geometrie* (in his quaint Tudor English, where I have had to clarify some of his spellings in brackets for modern readers):

... I should also speake of suche thynges as can not well be understande [understood] in talke, without somme knowledge in the principles of geometrie. But this will I promyse, that if I may perceave my paynes to be thankfully taken [that is, if his book meets with a good reception, so that he is encouraged to continue such efforts], I wyll not onely [only] write of suche pleasant inventions, declaryng what they were, but also wil teache howe a great numbre of them were wrought, that they may be practised in this tyme also. Wherby shalbe plainly perceaved, that many thynges seme [seem] imposible to be done, whiche by arte may very well be wrought. And whan [when] they be wrought, and the reason thereof not understande [understood], than [then] say the vulgare people, that those thynges are done by negromancy [necromancy, i.e. black magic]. And hereof came it that fryer [Friar] Bakon [Roger Bacon] was accompted [accounted, i.e. accused of being] so greate a negromancier [necromancer, i.e. black magician], whiche [who] never used that arte [i.e., Recorde says that Bacon never used the black magical arts] (by any conjecture that I can fynde) but was in geometrie and other mathematicall sciences so experte, that he coulde dooe by them such thynges as were wonderfull [i.e. incredible] in the syght of most people. Greate talke there is of a glasse [old-fashioned word for telescope] that he made in Óxforde, in whiche men myght see thynges that were doon [done] in other places [i.e. at a great distance], and that was judged to be done by the power of evyll spirites [evil spirits]. But I knowe the reason of it to bee good and naturall, and to be wrought by geometrie (sythe [since] perspective [the old-fashioned name for the geometry of optics] is a parte of it) and to stand as well with reason as to see your face in comon glasse [in a common mirror]. But this conclusion and other dyvers [diverse] of lyke sorte, are more mete [meet] for princes, for sundry causes, than for other men, and ought not to bee taught commonly [i.e. should not be revealed to common men]. Yet to repete it, I thought good for this cause, that the worthynes [worthiness] of geometry myght be the better knowen [known], & partly understanding geven [given], what wonderfull thynges may be wrought by it, and so consequently how pleasant it is, and how necessary also.[4]

Although he wrote several other books and is famous as the inventor of the modern equals sign (=) in mathematics, Robert Recorde never wrote the book about 'strange inventions' which he promised, in which he would have revealed the principles of the telescope and much more. He had a hard life, and he died young. Like most geniuses, he received a great deal of opposition and discouragement. In *The Path-way to Knowledg* he also referred to the burning-mirror of Archimedes, and burning-mirrors are another device which he would have explained to the public 'if his pains had been thankfully taken'. But the burning-mirror of Archimedes is something for us to discuss in the next chapter.

In 1558, the Italian genius and polymath Giambattista (i.e. Giovanni Battista) della Porta in the first edition of his famous book *Magia Naturalis* (*Natural Magic*) discussed, apparently for the first time in 'modern' times, the 'telescope of Ptolemy'. He was referring to the strange optical object which once stood on the top of the Pharos Lighthouse at Alexandria in Egypt, and the Ptolemy to whom he refers is not the astronomer Claudius Ptolemy but the Egyptian Pharaoh Ptolemy III Euergetes (born between 288 and 280 BC and died 221 BC). I mention this here for chronological purposes as we examine the sequence of writings, but in order to focus our discussion, we have to leave Ptolemy's 'telescope' till later in the chapter, and for the moment keep on the trail of the telescopes of Roger Bacon and Julius Caesar.

At this point I should give the actual passage plus the modern translation of what Roger Bacon actually says in his *Opus Majus* about Julius Caesar's optical exploits. What Bacon says is in Latin, and hence is not as precise as it would be if he were writing in Greek. The word he uses for the optical device of Julius Caesar is *specula*. The usual meaning for *specula* is 'mirror'. However, in the sense of 'a glass', *specula* can sometimes refer to a lens. If Bacon were writing in Greek and used the word *katoptron*, there would be no possible ambiguity, since that word in Greek means 'mirror' and *only* 'mirror'. The Greeks had a scientific bent which the Romans lacked, and the Greek language has a scientific precision wholly lacking in Latin.

But if we take the entire context of Bacon's comments – which was ignored by William Camden and Anthony à Wood, as we shall see in a moment – we see that it is one of the use of mirrors rather than lenses. Bacon says he will discuss both reflection and refraction, and the mention of Caesar occurs during the discussion of reflection in Chapter 3 of the section on Optical Science, and before he commences his discussion of refraction in Chapter 4. I give the relevant Latin text in a note,[5] and the modern translation by Burke is as follows:

As the wisdom of God is ordained for the direction of the universe, so is this science of vision evidently and beneficially ordained for its beauty. I shall give some examples both of refraction and reflection. . . . Similarly mirrors might be erected on an elevation opposite hostile cities and armies, so that all that was being done by the enemy might be visible. This can be done at any distance we desire, since, according to the book on Mirrors [he presumably means the *Catoptrica* attributed to Euclid; see Propositions 13–15], one and the same object can be seen by means of as many mirrors as we wish, if they are placed in the manner required. Therefore they can be placed more closely and more remotely, so that we might see an object as far off as we pleased. For in this way Julius Caesar, when he wished to subdue England, is said to have erected very large mirrors, in order that he might see in advance from the shore of Gaul the arrangement of the cities and camps of England.[6]

Later in this chapter when we come to our discussion of the Pharos Lighthouse at Alexandria, we shall see that in ancient lighthouses large mirrors were necessary to reflect the lamplight out to sea at night for mariners, but that in the daytime these huge optical instruments could be turned to another use – the ancient form of remote-viewing, so that ships could be seen in the distance which were invisible to the naked eye. It seems, therefore, that one of the Roman lighthouses which we know existed on the northern coast of France (see Figure 13) made its great mirror available to Caesar, from a high vantage point, and that he may even have enhanced its function by a combination of mirrors. This is the most likely explanation of the 'Julius Caesar telescope'; it was a reflective rather than a refractive telescope.

But this should not dissuade us from realizing with what ease Caesar could have had a refractive telescope as well, whether a portable one which he used on all his campaigns, or a supplementary refractive viewer which was routinely used on Roman lighthouses in the manner of the Carthaginian telescopes to be described in a moment, which were also based on military towers.

The next person after Robert Recorde to refer to Roger Bacon in the context of telescopes, in the course of citing Bacon's account of Julius Caesar's telescope, was the great Elizabethan historian William Camden. His famous historical and topographical work *Britannia* was published in Latin at London in 1586. The book is nearly always called today 'Camden's Britannia'. In the chapter on 'Cantium' (i.e. the County of Kent), Camden refers to Roger Bacon's account of Julius Caesar using a telescope to view the coast of Kent from the beach at Normandy. Here is what he said, which I give in my modernization from the translation by Philemon Holland done under Camden's supervision and published in 1610:

> (Julius Caesar) in the year before Christ's nativity fifty-four [that is, in 54 BC], and once again in the year ensuing, entered into Britain: having found havens [for ships] by his espyals [i.e. by means of spies], as Suetonius, and himself [Caesar himself] doth testify; and not, as Roger Bacon fableth [i.e. writes, but his report is really only a fable], by setting certain looking-glasses upon the coast of Gaul, and by art perspective [optical science], which by reflection multiplieth hidden forms.[7]

From this we may see that Camden hotly denied Bacon's account, for he knew that Caesar in his own writings and the Roman historian Suetonius (first century AD) said that it was by sending spies that Caesar was able to learn the dispositions of the harbours and 'havens' on the Kentish coast, in preparation for his military invasion across the English Channel. But this still leaves the question: *where did Bacon get his account?*

This is unknown. Bacon wrote 350 years before Camden, when all the monastic manuscript libraries in England were intact, and before those collections were dispersed and largely destroyed by the confiscation of the monasteries under King Henry VIII. Bacon would not simply have invented such a story. He must have read it in an old chronicle which no longer survives. That is not to say that the story is true, merely that we can be confident that Bacon did not make it up. However, we shall see as we go on that there is no reason at all why the account need be entirely fictitious. The Romans had several lighthouses on the coast of France, and Trajan's Column at Rome portrays a Roman lighthouse, which is reproduced in Figure 13. Indeed, a Roman lighthouse actually survives today within the precincts of Dover Castle on the English coast. The Roman lighthouses can be presumed to have contained optical aids at the top similar to the one which surmounted the Pharos Lighthouse at Alexandria under Pharaoh Ptolemy III, which we will consider in a moment. Whether essentially reflective and hence a mirror, or refractive and hence a lens, these optical aids to the nightly fires at the tops of the lighthouses could in the daytime readily be turned to use for inspecting ships or coasts at a distance. The reader will feel more comfortable with this notion once I have given the

Figure 13. A Roman lighthouse of the first century AD is shown here in this engraving of a carving on the famous Column of the Emperor Trajan (reigned 98–117 AD) which still stands in Rome, where it is a major tourist attraction. It was just such a lighthouse on the coast of Normandy in France that Julius Caesar was said by Roger Bacon to have studied the English coast prior to his invasion with either a telescope or a large telescopic mirror.
(From Bernard de Montfaucon, *l'Antiquité Expliquée et Présentée en Figures*, Paris, 1722, Vol. IV, Plate CXXXVIII. Collection of Robert Temple)

evidence for the Carthaginian military telescopes used in Roman times from watch-towers, and also the account of the 'Archimedes telescope' on the coast of Croatia which survived until only a few centuries ago.

In considering the nature of the simplest possible telescope, let us turn to a Greek lens. If you take a look at Plate X, which is a photograph of an ancient plano-convex Greek crystal lens of the sixth century BC (magnification between 1.5X and 1.75X) which I am fortunate enough to own, you can see the carving on its flat surface of someone flying through the air holding something in each hand. This figure would normally be interpreted by a classical archaeologist as a 'flying Eros'. However, I believe some of the adult flying Eros designs are not necessarily really of Eros at all. And in this case, I am inclined to the opinion that the figure is really meant to represent Prometheus, not Eros. Of course, it doesn't really matter one way or the other, as nothing much hangs on the choice of identity of the figure.

The flying figure is holding those two objects – what are they? They are clearly round. Are they discs or spheres? They could be either. I suggest that they are lenses, whether round or spherical, for either magnifying or burning – or both. After all, the figure itself *is carved upon a lens*. (The crude borehole through the crystal was made at a later date when it was recycled to be mounted on a swivel-ring.)

So why would somebody fly through the air, engraved upon a lens, holding two round things, one in each hand? I believe that the figure is holding two lenses, and that the intention is to signify to the initiated that if you hold one close in one hand and one further in the other, and peer through them, you have a rudimentary telescope. Prometheus brought fire from heaven – *by means of a lens*. But there was more to him than that. And this ancient lens is trying to tell us something.

I took my lens to the British Museum's Greek and Roman Antiquities Department for an opinion about the date of the carving, which I suspected was 'Archaic'. I met a woman who glanced at my lens, felt it with her hand, and said: 'This is a fake because it isn't rock crystal, it's glass. And they weren't making these of glass at that time.' 'At what time?' I asked. She replied: 'There's no point even talking about it. It's glass, just a cheap modern copy to fool the tourists. Did you get it in Greece in the past year or so?' I said that it had been in Britain for at least 50 years as far as I knew. 'Well, it's worthless. Just glass.'

I pressed her, asking how she could be sure it was really glass, as I thought it was rock crystal. 'I ought to know glass when I see it,' she said. I tried several times tactfully to pose a hypothetical question: 'But what if it were crystal, then what date would it be?' Several times she rebuffed this question. Finally, she said:

'If it were rock crystal – *which it most certainly isn't* – then of course it would be seventh or sixth century BC, Archaic, on the basis of the style of the carving – but more probably sixth century BC. In any case, it is just a glass fake so there isn't any point even mentioning it. And I am extremely busy, if you don't mind.'

I took my lens to the Natural History Museum for an X-Ray diffraction test, and the result came back that the lens was made of rock crystal. I dread to think of all the members of the public who go away with their tails between their legs when faced with withering dismissal by 'experts'.

Now to return to Julius Caesar and his telescope. It gets a bit tiring holding two lenses up in front of oneself, and getting their respective distances right so that they remain in focus. So naturally it is easier to fix them at the right distance from each other in mounts in a common object, hollow and long – a tube, or in Greek an *aulos*. This is the notorious *aulos* mentioned by Strabo which got edited out because it 'couldn't be true'. Remember?

In a moment we shall see *what kind* of tubes. But let us just follow the small amount of remaining discussion about Caesar. We can now appreci- ate that if Caesar had wanted to view the coast of Kent with a telescope it would not have been at all difficult, as magnifying lenses were extraordi- narily common, and all that was needed was for someone to have enough brains to put two together in a tube and hand it to the Commander. In any case, as I said a moment ago, we shall be examining proof that such telescopes were being used militarily before Caesar's time by the Carthaginians. And we shall also be examining what kind of optical aids existed on top of lighthouses, of which plenty existed opposite Britain during Roman times. So we may consider the story about Julius Caesar viewing the coast of Kent under magnification by one of these means as highly likely, and we may equally consider that Roger Bacon had access to a historical source mentioning this which is now lost to us.[8]

Let us return now to the question of *what kind of tubes* would have been used in antiquity for simple telescopes. For this is a subject of unexpected interest, with some bizarre twists to it.

If we think once again of the legendary figure of Prometheus, we may recall that according to the myths, he carried fire to earth in a special tube. It was called a *narthex*. What actually was a *narthex*? The answer to this question is very peculiar. It turns out that it is actually an extinct plant known as the true Giant Fennel. I came across the definite information about it by chance. Because I had written a number of articles about the history of medicine for two international medical magazines, and had reviewed occasional books for them, out of the blue they sent me for review a book with the extraordinary title, *Contraception and Abortion from the Ancient World to the Renaissance* by John M. Riddle.[9] I was as amazed to come across such a book as anyone would be, as I had not suspected that contraception was such a developed science in ancient times.

The most interesting section of the book concerned the Giant Fennel plant which had been known to the ancient Greek botanists as *narthex*. It

‍

produced a drug known both as Cyrenaic Juice and *silphion* or *silphium* (the name for it by Dioscorides the ancient herbalist). Riddle says of it:

> ... Cyrenaic juice is a species of *Ferula* (English, giant fennel), called by Dioscorides and others *silphion* or *silphium*, now extinct. Once the plant grew near the Greek city-state of Cyrene in North Africa. In fact, *silphium* made Cyrene famous. Herodotus spoke of the harvesting of the wild plant, and other Greek sources said that attempts to cultivate the plant failed. In 424 BC, Aristophanes spoke of its high price, and by the first century AD, Pliny said that it could scarcely be found. For centuries the city's coins had carried the image of the plant, which was its distinctive symbol. One may wonder why a plant would make a city famous. Soranus told us: it was a contraceptive – one of the best in the ancient world. Its popularity, however, drove it to extinction probably soon after Soranus' time.[10]

There is no use going into further detail about ancient contraception, but the importance of this Giant Fennel may now be understood, and the reasons why it no longer exists. The true Giant Fennel was evidently a really huge plant, on a par with the Giant Hogweed (*Heracleum giganteum*), which can grow fifteen feet or five metres high and is an umbelliferate resembling fennel. See Plate 12.

The historian David Rohl in his book *Legend: The Genesis of Civilisation* based part of his argument for a Caucasian origin of the ancient Egyptians upon the fact that in the Third Dynasty at Saqqara there were representations in stone of a mysterious umbelliferate plant which had been called *silphium* by the Greeks. Rohl concludes that because this plant must have been the Giant Hogweed, which does not grow in Egypt, the Egyptians came from somewhere where it did grow.[11] Rohl is completely unaware of the fact that *silphium* was an extinct plant which grew profusely at Cyrene in Libya, not far from Egypt, and was readily available in ancient Egypt.

So the plant which appears in Old Kingdom sculpture in Egypt, which was a major oral contraceptive in antiquity (and culled to extinction for that reason), and was the tube carried by Prometheus are all the same – the now-vanished Giant Fennel.

I am indebted to my friend Tony Anderson, who has travelled in the Caucasus and has considerable local knowledge, for informing me that in the Caucasus there is another tall, although not giant, umbelliferate which is believed to be a large form of 'Hog's Fennel', 'Masterwort', or 'Milk Parsley'; its Latin name is *Peucedanum*. It resembles Angelica, is a highly aromatic herb, and grows at least two metres high. Vast quantities of it grow on the Caucasian slopes. It is by no means impossible that a giant form of this or another umbelliferate may have had Promethean associations. Further botanical investigation would be worthwhile.

The Caucasian name for Prometheus is Amiran, or Amirani. It is interesting that he is associated in folklore with the *two* highest mountains: (1) Mount Elbrus/ Elbruz, the higher of the two whose peak is in southern Russia, and (2) Mount Kasbek/ Kazbek/ Kasbegi/ Kazbeg etc., in northern Georgia, technically in the autonomous region of Ossetia. (Later we shall find that the classical author Philostratus had something crucial to say about the connection of Prometheus with *two* mountains; the modern folkloric information and the classical source thus strikingly confirm one another.) There is an entire book in French about Prometheus and the Caucasus: G. Charachidzé, *Prométhée ou le Caucase* (*Prometheus, or the Caucasus*), Flammarion, Paris, 1986. But we do not have space for an extended discussion of this interesting subject.

Now, what sort of properties did this Giant Fennel have which could possibly be of interest to Prometheus? The nature of Prometheus's tube of *narthex* has come up before. The great scholar Sir James Frazer, whose many-volumed *Golden Bough* I have myself abridged,[12] wrote in one of his more obscure books, *Myths of the Origin of Fire*:

> The plant (*narthex*) in which Prometheus carried the stolen fire [from Heaven to Earth] is commonly identified with the giant fennel (*Ferula communis*) . . .[13]

In this, Frazer's identification of the ancient Giant Fennel with what is today called 'giant' fennel, profuse throughout the Greek region, is mistaken. For Frazer, like Rohl, was unaware of the existence of a much larger fennel which had become extinct. However, one echo of the Prometheus tradition may be found in Frazer's description of the smaller 'giant' fennel of today as a fire-container:

> The French traveller Tournefort found this fennel growing rank in Skinosa, the ancient Schinussa, a small deserted island south of Naxos. He describes the stalk as about five feet high [less than one third the height of the original Giant Fennel] and three inches thick, with knots and branches at intervals of about ten inches, the whole being covered with a tolerably hard rind. 'This stalk is filled with a white pith, which, being very dry, catches fire just like a wick; the fire keeps alight perfectly in the stalk and consumes the pith only gradually, without damaging the rind; hence people use this plant to carry fire from one place to another; our sailors laid in a supply of it. This custom is of great antiquity, and may serve to explain a passage in Hesiod, who, speaking of the fire which Prometheus stole from heaven, says that he carried it away in a stalk of fennel.' In Naxos the English traveller J. T. Bent saw orange gardens divided by hedges of tall reeds, and he adds: 'In Lesbos this reed is still called *narthēka* (*narthēx*), a survival of the old word for the reed by which Prometheus brought down fire from heaven. One can

understand the idea well: a peasant today who wishes to carry a light from one house to another will put it into one of these reeds to prevent its being blown out.' Apparently Mr Bent mistook the giant fennel for a reed.[14]

This is an excellent discovery, and gives us one of the layers of meaning of the carrying of fire from heaven to earth by Prometheus in a fennel-tube. But I believe that the *other* level of meaning is that the stalk of the true Giant Fennel was used as a telescope tube. For until its extinction, Giant Fennel stalks were able in many ways to serve functions which bamboo still serves in China. Although less strong than bamboo, and hardly capable of supporting building scaffoldings (as bamboo does all over China even at the present time), the Giant Fennel stalks were relatively strong, straight, easily hollowed, and of sufficient length to mount two simple lenses, one at the front and one at the back, to form a rudimentary telescope.

Plate 13 shows an Egyptian Fourth Dynasty depiction of what may have been the stalk of this plant.

If you look at Plate 10, which shows a Greek of the fifth to fourth century BC looking through a tube – I believe you are seeing a Greek using a telescope tube made of a small upper stem of Giant Fennel. This fragment of a broken pot has been on public display in Vitrine [Case] 6, of Room Five (in an alcove) of the Acropolis Museum at Athens for some years now, having been excavated between 1955 and 1960. It is Object NA.55.Aa.4, a fragment of black and red-painted pottery which is, according to the official description:

> Part of New Findings from the Sanctuary of the Nymph on the south slope of the Acropolis. Excavated as a result of the construction of Areopogitou Boulevard, south of the Theatre of Herodes Atticus. The Shrine of the Nymph was an open-air shrine destroyed by the Roman general Sulla in 86 BC. It was devoted to a female chthonic [underworld] deity of unknown name but who was called 'the Nymph' on a boundary stone and in the grafitti on several vase fragments. Votive offerings were made to her and she was especially associated with marriage and fertility.

It seems to me remarkable that a pottery fragment which appears to show a person looking through a telescope has been on view in such an intensely public place as the Acropolis Museum, which is visited by millions of people every year, and nobody seems ever to have 'noticed' it.

But it is not only the person with the telescope which has not been 'noticed' at Athens. The Athens Archaeological Museum has several rock crystal lenses on public display in one of the most commonly visited rooms, the Mycenaean Room (Room 4), and yet nobody has 'noticed' them either. See Plate 43. Yet in the Mycenaean Room there are the following:

In Case 1, Object number 4910. Two lenses; the larger I call A and the smaller I call B. Both are round and plano-convex. A is of perfectly clear crystal and B would be if cleaned but for a ghostly flaw in the centre along the superior surface. The magnification of A is 2.5X and of B is 2X.

In Case 5 is Object number 8652. It is an eye-shaped crystal, plano-convex, which was presumably meant to act as a magnifying eye in a statue; its magnification is 1.5X.

In Case 8 is Object number 5662. This is a slightly oval, plano-convex crystal with an unusual feature: its rim is effectively a regular sine curve with two maxima and two minima. It magnifies 2X with the minor axis horizontal and 1.5X with the major axis horizontal (assuming horizontal lines of type being viewed). Modern glue, due to an earlier attempt to mount this object for public display, considerably impairs the transparency of this lens. The superior surface has suffered very severe abrasion, which is deeply ingrained with microscopic dirt, rendering what was once a perfectly transparent lens slightly opaque and making visibility through it difficult today.

In Case 1 there is Object number 3192, a bored oblate spheroid crystal which still magnifies 2X despite much dirt and the later borehole.

In Case 23 there is Object number 104, another bored oblate spheroid crystal which magnifies 2X when resting on a surface and 2.5X when raised despite being hopelessly clumsily bored where two late boring attempts have barely met, whereas the crystal itself is smoothly and expertly polished by a proper artisan at a much earlier date.

In Case 14 there is Object number T51/6571–2. The clear one I name A and the smoky one I name B. Both are slightly oblate crystal spheroids, the former magnifying 2X in the one small portion where this is still visible, as the object is extremely severely pressure-shattered; the latter which is also extensively damaged still is partially transparent and magnifies 2X when resting (magnification when raised can be no longer be discerned).

These objects date from the 16th to the 13th century BC.

But it is not only Greece where there are 'invisible lenses' on prominent public display. In Room 69, Case Number 9, just outside the door leading to the Greek and Roman Antiquities Department in the British Museum, which contains some people who do not believe in the existence of ancient lenses, are some 'invisible' ancient lenses made of rock crystal. These have been subsequently engraved as counters. Object GR 1923–4.4–1.47 (round, biconvex) magnifies by 3X. Object GR 1923. 4–1.22 (round, biconvex) magnifies 3X. The very badly damaged GR 1890. 9–21.16 (round, biconvex) nevertheless still magnifies 2X. Object BM GEM CAT. 3990=1923.4–1.157 (round, biconvex) is perfectly clear, beautifully ground and polished, and magnifies 2X. The slightly oval and pronouncedly biconvex Object number BR GEM CAT. 3991 =

1923.4–1.238 magnifies 2X. There are five more crystal lenses in the Department, magnifying between 3X and 1.5X. (Some of the above-mentioned lenses are not in the display cabinet but in store.) But until now, these lenses have all been quite 'invisible' in the British Museum, which also has various other ancient lenses in different departments, including the Egyptian, besides the Layard Lens. It must only be that people see what they expect to see and are blind to what they are convinced cannot exist it is what I call 'consensus blindness'.

I promised to explain the military uses of telescopes by the Carthaginians during the Roman period, and that is what I shall now do. I came across this extremely obscure information in a very unexpected way. A German ophthalmologist who wrote about ancient optics had mentioned a Greek named Andreas Anagnostakis having written a work in modern Greek the translated title of which is *Studies Concerning the Optics of the Ancients*. No copy of this exists in Britain (except my own photocopy now), and I was finally able to locate this extremely rare booklet of 28 pages in the Bibliothèque Nationale in Paris. It took a very long time for the microfilm to reach me, and then I had to print that out, and then I couldn't read it anyway. Nor could most of my Greek friends because it is not in the demotic Greek spoken today but, having been published in 1878 by an intellectual who was Rector of the University of Athens, it was in the 19th-century form of Greek which few people today can read. Struggling, there-fore, at least with the footnotes, I found one in French referring to a book by a man named Daux of whom I had never heard. My friend Professor Ioannis Liritzis, who does read the formal modern Greek, has since trans-lated Anagnostakis's only two sentences referring to Daux:

> The hypothesis of Mr Daux is improbable that ancient people had some form of elementary telescopes, because according to Polyaenus and Polybius, upon whom Mr Daux's idea is based, it is simply telegraphy through torches. Surely it was no use of complicated *dioptra*.[15]

The Greek word *dioptra* is one which several people have thought was used by Greek authors for telescopes. And it was so used by Polybius (second century BC), as well as others, as we shall see.

Who, then, is Mr Daux? He is only known as 'A. Daux' on the title page of his book, and I can discover no first name for him, only the initial. He was a Carthaginian archaeologist, and in 1869 he published a remarkable book in French describing the Carthaginian ruins and in the course of doing so, he described the use of telescopes by the ancient Carthaginian military.[16] Daux found this strange information in a book called *Stratagems* by a completely obscure Greek military historian of the second century AD named Polyaenus. Hardly any classicist will ever have heard of him. His works are practically unknown, as few people want to read ancient military works of that sort. Further confirmation of Polyaenus's account can be gained from the historical works of Polybius (second century BC), and from other sources, such as Aelian (second/third century AD), which I have discovered and which were unknown to Daux.

What drove Daux to make his textual discovery was his passion to understand the Carthaginian ruins he was studying as a working archaeologist. He ransacked classical literature for clues. Daux is in the middle of describing a curious old Carthaginian tower, when he says of it: '. . . (it) has a particular shape . . . which makes me suspect that it could have been a signal station.'

He then goes on to add:

One of these towers seems to have been used for signalling, erected on the coastline four or five centuries BC for the purpose of telegraphy transmission by the Phoenicians in Sicily and in Africa. That expression, 'telegraphic transmissions', in speaking of an epoch so far from us, about 2,300 years ago [he was writing in 1867], seems at first sight somewhat strange, for it would appear that the sense of the phrase is wholly modern. However, I must be careful not to make assertions without proof unless it be by quoting an ancient writer whose authority I can invoke. This ingenious method of communication across very great distances is, I think, little known. And if we are to believe the [ancient] author in question, it is nevertheless remarkable enough to give us an idea of the inventive genius of a people of whom the Romans have left little for us to know. I cite in its entirety the passage of Polyaenus [second-century AD Greek author of the military and historical work, *Stratagems*].

Around the beginning of the fourth century BC, the Carthaginians, then at the height of their power, wished to achieve the conquest of the whole of Sicily, of which they possessed almost four-fifths. Syracuse was almost the last to resist, and Denys its Chief hung on with difficulty in the struggle against the Carthaginians. This long war, full of surprises, of ruses, and unforeseen events, wore out the Carthaginians owing to its distance from Africa, from where they got their supplies by sea, and through the uncertainty at Carthage concerning the needs of the army at Sicily, the nature of which needs often varied unexpectedly. To remedy these inconveniences, and in the hope of ending the war promptly, the Phoenicians did the following:

'While they were at war in Sicily,' says Polyaenus, Book VI, Chapter 16, 'the Carthaginians, in order to get various kinds of help from Libya more quickly, decided to make two water clocks of the same construction. Each was divided vertically into several circles. On one [circle] they had written: "We need ships", on others: "We need gold" . . . "[siege] engines" . . . "food supplies" . . . "beasts of burden", . . . "some infantry" . . . "some cavalry" . . . etc., etc. Of these two water clocks thus marked, they kept one in Sicily and sent the other to Carthage with orders that when someone went to light a [signal] fire, to look out for the dial where the water would stop, when one would light the second [signal] fire. By this means, one knew in an instant at Carthage what was being asked for in Sicily, and dispatched it to the field of action. It is thus that the Phoenicians came to have all the help promptly of which they had need to sustain the war.'

Such is the account of Polyaenus. These details, which throw a completely new light on the means of transmission which the ancients had at their disposal, suggest to us concerning their means of application some brief observations. From the extreme point of the *Promontorium Hermaeum* (the headland of Cape Bon) to the point opposite in Sicily, the distance is 134 kilometres. The island of Pantelleria cuts this distance between the two capes almost in two; it is very elevated above sea level, and according to this account, could have been an intermediary point for the fires. Thus one ought to be able, it seems, on a clear night to see the signals from one side and from the other. From there one quickly transmitted the news, even to Carthage itself. The tower in question, near Utica, beside the sea, could have been a tower used for this purpose. Utica was for a long time a town of some importance, for having had means of this kind at her disposal. Some precision instruments, besides, seem to have been familiar to the Phoenicians, judging from the sun dial which they established in the town of Catane, and, even more anciently, by that which they made for Achaz, the King of Judea.

That is the end of Daux's main passage, and he continues in his Notes section, pp. 281–9, where he cites the additional evidence given by Polybius (second century BC):

This method of telegraphic transmission had before long a number of imitators in other nations. Above all, the Greeks went on to invent and more or less perfect other methods. Polybius cites several, which were in use 250 years after the Phoenician invention. Perhaps it will not be without interest in our time, when the telegraphic art seems to have arrived at the height of its perfection, to read the details of these ancient methods which seemed in the time of Polybius to bring about the best results. I leave the historian to speak [Book 10, Fragments xlv and xlvi]:

'The last system had for its authors Cleoxenus and Democlitus ['Cléoxène' and 'Démoclite' – unknown names!]; but we Romans have perfected it. The method is certain and follows fixed rules, and by its means one can signal all that is happening. It only demands much vigilance and attention. Here is what it consists of: One takes all the letters of the alphabet, and makes five divisions, putting five letters into each; there will be one group having only four letters, but that is of no consequence to the objective proposed; those who will be designated to give and receive the signals write on five tablets these five groups of letters, and then agree between them that he who will send the signal must first lift up two signalling-lanterns at once and that he will hold them up until the man who is on the other side has also raised two of them, so that they can warn each other when they are ready; the signalling-lanterns being lowered, he who will send the signal lifts up his lantern in his left hand to make known which tablet ought to be looked at; such that, if it is the first, he lifts up only one, if it is the second, he lifts up two, and so forth. And he does the same with his right hand, to indicate to him who receives the signal which letter on the tablet he ought to observe and ought to write down. Consequent to these rules, each one being positioned at his post, it is necessary that the two men charged with signalling each possesses a telescope [*dioptran*] fitted with two tubes [*duo aulischous*] so that the person who gives the signals sees through one to the right and through the other to the left of the person who must respond to him. Near this telescope those tablets of which we are going to speak should be set upright in the ground, and to the right and the left one raises a palisade of ten feet in length, and about the height of a man, so that the signalling lanterns raised up give by their light an unmistakable signal, but upon being lowered, they will be completely hidden. All this process carried out with care on the part of both men, supposing for example that one wishes to announce that some auxiliary troops to the number of about a hundred men had passed over to the enemy, one would choose the words which indicate this with the least letters possible, such as "100 Cretans have deserted". One would write this on a small tablet and then announce it in this way: the first letter is a "K" [*Krētes* is Greek for 'Cretans'] which is in the second series of the alphabet and on the second tablet. Then one would lift up with the left hand two lanterns to mark to the man receiving the signal that it was the second tablet which he should examine; and to the right, five, which make known to him that it is a "K", the fifth letter of the second series which he should write on his small tablet. Then, four lanterns would be lifted in the left hand to describe the letter "R" which is in the fourth series; then two in the right to indicate that that letter is the second of this fourth series. He who observes these signals should then write an "R" on his tablet, etc. By this method, he cannot arrive at anything that does not specify a message in a fixed and determined manner. If one makes use of various lanterns, it is because each letter demands to be indicated twice, but on the other hand, if one takes the necessary precautions, all will be satisfactory. However, whether one makes use of one method or another, it is necessary to be experienced in it before making use of the system, so that when one does use it, one can avoid making mistakes or lacking in mutual communication.'

A propos of this descriptive passage of Polybius there is an observation to make, regardless of the mode of transmission itself: it is that this passage establishes that one then made use of distant vision, of double-lenses, parallel or [slightly] divergent lenses, at each telegraphic post. The notion of this instrument is most certainly that which gives most surprise in this account. However extraordinary this assertion may appear, it must nevertheless be taken in the sense that Polybius gives it; and let us remember that this historian justly enjoys the confidence of all modern scholars. I would further observe that he did not speak of it as an invention new to his time, but that the sense of his phrase, to the contrary, leads one to believe that this optical instrument was in use at that time and well known.[17]

Daux also says: "Two columns," [Polyaenus] says, "divided by circles each indicating the nature of the things which one had need of, were placed, one on the extreme point of Sicily, and the other on the opposite coastal point in Africa." Now, the distance between these two points is 134 kilometres (a little more than 24 marine leagues.) It was *physically impossible* that natural sight could penetrate to such a distance, especially to be able to count the raising and extinction of the signal lanterns at the two extremities of the distance. It must then be admitted that the Phoenicians, inventors of this system of telegraphy two thousand two hundred and sixty-eight years ago [he is writing in 1868/9], founded it on the perception of two coasts, of two headlands, by the means of telescopes. The effect of the curvature of the waters was ruled out by the choice of two headlands which were both very elevated. I have had the occasion to climb one of them, the ancient Promontory of Hermes (Cape Bon), and on a good day with very clear weather, I could not see the coast of Sicily except with the use of a powerful telescope which I had with me. Finally, the expressions which Polybius used without much doubt refer to the use of telescopes: . . . *deēsei ōsōton men dioptran echein, duo aulischous echousan* . . . the instrument by which one sees is a *dioptran*, and the two little tubes (the word also means "flutes") are *duo aulischous*. That is, according to all appearances, it indicates two telescopes. And the rest of the passage tells us that they were parallel or [slightly] divergent, but paired [i.e. binocular] in their use.'[18]

One should note especially the description by Polybius that a *dioptra* was 'fitted with' tubes. In other words, the *dioptra* was the optical part of the telescope and the tubes were the lens-holders – just as we were discussing in connection with Prometheus – that the tube was the container for his lenses.

Daux did not give the full picture from Polybius. He cited only sections 45 and 46 of Book Ten, but the discussion really commenced in Section 43, where Polybius explains why he is talking about these things in the first place:

The method of signalling by fire, which is of the highest utility in the operations of war, has never before been clearly expounded; and I think I shall be doing a service if I do not pass it over, but give an account of it adequate to its importance. . . . nothing is more efficacious than fire signals. For they convey intelligence sometimes of what has just happened, sometimes of what is actually going on; and by paying proper attention to them one can get this information at three or four days' journey off, and even more . . . Now, formerly, as the art of signalling by fire was confined to a single method, it proved in very many cases unserviceable to those employing it. . . .[19]

He then describes various improvements, including the adoption of telescopes in connection with the fire-signalling. The first complete translation of Polybius into English was that of Shuckburgh, in 1889. He tackles the *dioptran* and its tubes by using an English expression which I fear I do not understand, as it uses some sort of Victorian word. He says of the observing and signalling parties that 'each must have, to begin with, a stenoscope with two funnels . . .'[20] I have no idea what a stenoscope is; doubtless in 1889 this word meant something now long forgotten. Shuckburgh clearly had a bit of a struggle over this, and could not bring himself simply to say 'a telescope with two tubes' because he thought they didn't exist at that time.

Another source which I have found referring to the Carthaginians and their telescopic capability is the *Historical Miscellany* of Aelian (second/third centuries AD). It is amusing to see how Aelian has received a garbled account:

They say that in Sicily there was an islander with eyesight so sharp that if he directed his gaze from Lilybaeum to Carthage nothing escaped his eye. They say he could specify the number of ships leaving Carthage, and never made a mistake.[21]

In the 400 years which had elapsed between Polybius and Aelian, the story had lost its technological explanation and survived merely as an amazing tale. The edition and translation of Aelian was only published in 1997/8, and the scholar who prepared it, Nigel Wilson, adds a footnote to the quote which I have just given:

Other writers who tell this story give the name of the man as Strabo and set it in the time of the Punic Wars. But they leave a puzzle unexplained: even from the top of a mountain – and there is no high ground near Lilybaeum – the man could hardly have seen the nearest point on the African coast, 140 km distant, let alone Carthage, 215 km away. Strabo 6.2.1 (267) says the man watched from a lookout post, as if this could have given him sufficient altitude.[22]

This is very sharp of Wilson, who although unaware of Polyaenus, Polybius, or Daux, has intuited that there is more to this than meets the eye (pun intended). And although he doesn't identify more than one of the 'other writers', Wilson very helpfully gives the reference to *The Geography* of Strabo (first centuries BC/AD), which Daux had also not known. The passage in Strabo is as follows:

> The shortest run is 1500 stadia from Lilybaeum [in Sicily] to the coast of Africa about Carthage; and, according to report, a certain very sharp-sighted person, placed on a watch-tower, announced to the Carthaginians besieged in Lilybaeum the number of the ships which were leaving Carthage.[23]

The first translators of Strabo in 1887 helpfully added a footnote giving us yet another reference:

> This person, according to Varro, was named Strabo.[24]

And he refers us to a passage where Pliny quotes a lost work by Varro. This quotation, in Pliny's *Natural History* (VII, 21), in turn says:

> Cicero . . . records a case of a man who could see 123 miles. Marcus Varro [first century BC] also gives this man's name, which was Strabo, and states that in the Punic wars he was in the habit of telling from the promontory of Lilybaeum in Sicily the actual number of ships in a fleet that was passing out from the harbour of Carthage.[25]

Knowing what we do, we can appreciate the joke of the man in the garbled account being called Strabo. For, as I stated near the opening of this chapter, it is a word meaning 'squinter' or 'cross-eyed'. And that name was a punning reference to the binocular telescope!

Finally, our good friend Solinus (*circa* 200 AD) preserves some information as well. He says, quoting Arthur Golding's charming 1587 translation (for there is none more modern):

> The quickest of sight was one Strabo, whom Varro avoucheth to have overlooked a hundred thirty & five miles, and that hee was wont exactlie to viewe from the watch Towre of Lyliby in Sicill, ye Punicke fleete setting out of the Haven of Carthage, and to reporte the just number of their Shippes.[26]

We thus see that there are many references in classical literature to the telescopes used by the Carthaginians, but only Polyaenus and Polybius got it right. The other accounts, which had degenerated into Fortean hearsay, were garbled and had lost their technological facts.

Having examined all this evidence of the supposed use of lenses by the Carthaginians, the question naturally poses itself: 'Did the Carthaginians ever actually possess any lenses which have been discovered by archaeologists?'

The reader will not be surprised to discover that the answer is: 'Yes!' They may be seen in Plate 3. Sixteen polished glass and crystal plano-convex lenses have been excavated at Carthage, in addition to many round or oval plano-convex pieces of glass which had not yet been polished. Of the sixteen, two are still transparent and will both magnify and start fires. These lenses are all preserved in the Carthage Museum (formerly called the Lavigerie Museum), although they are not on display but are kept in a box in storage. They were all excavated by the White Fathers, a French religious order who doubled as archaeologists during the time when Tunisia (where the site of Carthage is to be found) was still a French colony. No records are preserved about these lenses today at Carthage, and the French excavation records are presumably somewhere in Paris.[27]

The first publication mentioning some of the Carthaginian lenses as far as I know was an article by the ophthalmological historian Harry L. Taylor in 1924, although at that time he reported that he had originally examined them in April 1914, at which time the surfaces were all clear; but by 1930 the surfaces had gone opaque due to exposure to air. (See his two 1930 articles mentioned in a moment.) The most interesting of the Carthaginian lenses (especially keeping in mind the binocular tradition of the Carthaginians) was a pair of round convex lenses of the same size which I have named the Sarcophagus Pair. Taylor reports that they were excavated by the Rev. Delattre of the White Fathers in 1902, who found them in a stone sarcophagus which he dated to the fourth century BC.[28] This was two centuries prior to the date of Polybius. The lenses were discovered embedded in the remains of resin used to preserve the body. Beck referred to the Carthaginian lenses in 1928.[29] Taylor discussed them again in two articles in 1930. Taylor also says that the Carthaginian lenses appear to be the earliest surviving *glass* ones. Indeed, perhaps the Romans learned the art of their manufacture from the Carthaginians. Taylor gives further details and says that there were three small and oval lenses. The Sarcophagus Pair were about one-and-a-half inches in diameter, and of 5.5D (dioptres) in magnifying power. (He measured this with a spherometer.)[30] It will surprise no one that an anonymous writer in *Nature* speculated in 1930 that the man in the sarcophagus was presbyopic (long-sighted) and wished to aid his sight in the afterlife with these spectacles, the mounting of which had perished. This pair may be seen in Plate 2, which is the amusing photo taken by William Graham showing them placed over the eye sockets (which they perfectly fit) of an ancient face.

The last person apparently to mention the Carthaginian lenses in print was R. J. Forbes, who in 1957 mentioned that there were nine altogether which were all magnifying glasses 'excellent for engraving work', three of them of rock crystal and six of glass.[31] Forbes was unaware of the existence of a further seven Carthaginian lenses.

There is plenty of archaeological evidence, therefore, to back up the stories in Polyaenus and Polybius, and to explain the later legends of the keen-sighted Carthaginians.

So much for the Carthaginians. Let us now see who else used the word *dioptra* to refer to a telescope. First of all, there is Iamblichus, the Neoplatonist philosopher and tutor of the Emperor Julian the Apostate, who lived in the second century AD and referred to telescopes in his *Life of Pythagoras*.

There is no Loeb Library translation of any of the works of Iamblichus, in line with the apparent bias of that Library against the Neoplatonist philosophers. And I know of no edition of text and facing translation. So for the text, one has to go to a separate volume, and often an old one. I am afraid my text is very old-fashioned indeed, and is from a book published in 1598, but as that is the one I happen to have, that is the one I use; it has a Latin translation facing the Greek text.[32] The passage comes from Chapter 26, where Pythagoras is described as brooding on music and harmony. He wonders whether some device might be invented which could improve the hearing in the same way that the compass, the rule, and the telescope (*dioptra*) improve the sight! There are two English translations. First I give that of Kenneth Sylvan Guthrie of 1919:

> While describing Pythagoras's wisdom in instructing his disciples, we must not fail to note that he invented the harmonic science and ratios. But to explain this we must go a little backwards in time. Once as he was intently considering music, and reasoning with himself whether it would be possible to devise some instrumental assistance to the sense of hearing, so as to systematize it, as sight is made precise by the compass, the rule, and telescope, or touch is made reckonable by balance and measures, . . .[33]

A more old-fashioned translation was done by Thomas Taylor in 1818:

> Since, however, we are narrating the wisdom employed by Pythagoras in instructing his disciples, it will not be unappropriate to relate that which is proximate in a following order to this, viz. how he invented the harmonic science, and harmonic ratios. But for this purpose we must begin a little higher [earlier]. Intently considering once, and reasoning with himself, whether it would be possible to devise a certain instrumental assistance to the hearing, which should be firm and unerring, such as the sight obtains through the compass and the rule, or, by Jupiter,

through a dioptric instrument; or such as the touch obtains through the balance, or the contrivance of measures; . . .'[34]

Taylor took care not to omit translation of the expression *nē Dia*, which the Greeks used constantly and means 'by God', although technically it meant 'by Zeus', and Taylor has translated it with the Latin name of Zeus as 'by Jupiter'. Guthrie had omitted this phrase as superfluous. But it is a rather interesting touch that it is there, for it shows that Iamblichus was prefacing his mention of the telescope with a mild blurted imprecation, indicating that he drew his breath in and 'by jimminy, by Jove, by Jumpin' Jupiter' was going to go ahead and mention that thing even though one was meant to keep quiet about it.

Taylor's use of the phrase 'dioptric instrument' manages to be accurate without being a genuine translation. 'Dioptric instrument' doesn't really mean anything, but merely keeps the Greek word and makes clear that an instrument is intended by it. Guthrie simply went ahead and translated *dioptra* as 'telescope', without appearing to experience any ill effects or indigestion as a result.

Imagine my surprise when I came across the Iamblichus passage, word for word, in another ancient work quite by chance during the editing of this book! I had taken a break after Chapter Four and before commencing the final editing of this chapter, I read a book purely for relaxation and not for any research purpose. It was *The Manual of Harmonics* by Nicomachus of Gerasa (second century AD). In Chapter 6 of that work, the original passage occurs which Iamblichus, who was a contemporary of Nicomachus, simply 'lifted' and used without citation. In the translation by Flora Levin, it reads:

> One day he [Pythagoras] was deep in thought and seriously considering whether it could be possible to devise some kind of instrumental aid for the ears which would be firm and unerring, such as vision obtains through the compass and the ruler or the *dioptra*; or touch obtains with the balance-beam or the system of measures.[35]

In her footnote, Flora Levin says:

> The account offered by Iamblichus in his *De vita Pyth.* [*On the Life of Pythagoras*] 115–120 [Deubner, 66–69] is taken verbatim from that of Nicomachus.[36]

Another ancient Greek author who appears to have mentioned a telescope, using the term *dioptra*, is Geminus (first century BC), author of an *Introduction to Astronomy*. The Greek text was published with a Latin translation in 1630 in a collection of old astronomical texts edited and gathered together by the Jesuit Dionysius Petavius.[37] The famous French historian of astronomy, Jean Sylvain Bailly, discussed this in 1779 in his

Histoire de l'Astronomie Moderne depuis la Fondation de l'École d'Alexandrie (History of Modern Astronomy since the Foundation of the School of Alexandria). Bailly was confused about Roger Bacon's telescope, at first denying it and then appearing almost to accept it later in his treatise. From Bacon he takes the story of Julius Caesar's telescope and speaks of Caesar viewing the ports and maritime towns of England through an optical tube from the coast of France. Bailly mentions Bacon's contention that convex glasses can bring the surfaces of the sun and moon closer to us, and that the construction of such astronomical instruments required a knowledge of optics. He then says:

> These passages are very strange, especially when it is remembered that one comes across these tubes from time to time in history, like the traces of a more ancient invention preserved. These tubes seem to have been known from Hipparchus [second century BC] and from [Claudius] Ptolemy [second century AD]. One encounters them from China at various times. One also has a citation from the time of Caesar. Gerbert [a great mathematician and philosopher who became Pope Sylvester II, and died 999 AD] made use of them in the tenth century for the construction of his clock at Magdeburg. Perhaps the knowledge of these tubes was to be found in the *Optics* of Ptolemy, which still existed in the time of Bacon [13th century, the manuscripts since having disappeared]. The conjecture of Monsieur [le Comte] de Caylus [whom we encountered earlier] that the ancients had knowledge of the telescope reconciled all of this. The tradition could have been passed on until the time of Bacon, via the *Optics* of Ptolemy or by some other lost work, and it would have made its way to Bacon as it would to all men endowed with much imagination who write concerning the accounts of others, who speak of things which they have not themselves seen.[38]

By this strange remark, Bailly makes known his theory that Bacon described the uses of telescopes which he himself had not seen but only read about in the lost *Optics* of Ptolemy. The evidence seems to be rather that Bacon actually constructed a telescope at Oxford, as we have already seen, which led to his being accused of witchcraft, and possibly led to the destruction of any copy of Ptolemy's *Optics* which he was using (perhaps the last existing?) as a 'work of the Devil'.

In his Notes section, Bailly goes on to say that Father Jean Mabillon had seen a 13th-century manuscript by a monk called Conrad stating that he in turn had come across an ancient manuscript which contained an illustration of Claudius Ptolemy (second century AD) looking at the stars through a long tube. Bailly says that he thinks the star catalogues compiled by Hipparchus and Ptolemy were done with individual star observations made through such long tubes. These were the classic attempts by those early Greek astronomers to make comprehensive lists of all stars which could be seen in the sky. He says: 'One knows by experience that these tubes, made of paper, facilitated vision. (Bailly was unaware that paper, a Chinese invention, did not exist in Europe prior to the eleventh century as an Arab import and was not manufactured in Europe until the twelfth century.)' He is here speaking of astronomical sighting-tubes without lenses. However, he then goes on to say that some sighting-tubes actually contained lenses, and he is convinced that those used by Gerbert in the tenth century did:

> This tube was very remarkable. One can safely believe that it made use of glasses. Since we came across this idea of using tubes, we have found a passage of Geminus which seems to confirm it . . .[39]

Bailly then attempts to clarify his thoughts further, having implied that Geminus was using a *dioptra* with lenses for astronomical observations in the first century BC. Geminus may have used lenses in his *dioptra* but the *dioptra* invented by Hipparchus the century before was a different instrument – it was a long sighting-tube, taking its name from the Greek meaning 'to see across', and used for observing and counting stars and for observing the eclipses of the Moon. Bailly does not actually rule out the use of lenses by Hipparchus in his instrument, although he appears to think they were not used. However, he believes that Geminus *did* use lenses and had an actual telescope.

Subsequent French scholars, always dutiful in their respect for Bailly, mentioned the Geminus reference which he had discovered. In 1853, Félix Pouchet wrote:

> Some scholars went even further and unreservedly attributed to Roger Bacon the invention of the telescope and of astronomical lenses. According to them, these instruments are referred to in his work so precisely that it would seem he had himself frequently made use of them. . . . Cuvier himself considered it as certain that it was the reflecting telescope of which Bacon spoke, and that he made use of that instrument for his astronomical observations. He said the use he made of it was to observe the sky, which led him to recognize the inaccuracy of the calendar. . . . It is generally thought that Hipparchus and Ptolemy used some instrument to make their observations of the stars, but one passes over what the nature of this instrument was. Father Mabillon [in his *Voyage d'Allemagne*, which is not in the British Library] said that he had found in a manuscript of the 13th century a figure which represented Ptolemy looking at the stars with the aid of a long tube. This manuscript, the work of a monk called Conrad, and which one supposes to have been copied from an earlier original manuscript, has led some people to presume that telescopes were known at a time more remote. . . . And from the tenth century Gerbert used a similar apparatus at Magdeburg to observe the polar star and regulate the clock which he had constructed in that town.

But since Bailly it has been falsely believed that these optical tubes were fitted with glass: according to him, they consisted only of a cylinder intended to make the sighting of objects clearer. . . . A passage from Geminus in which this instrument is called *dioptra* (a word derived from the Greek which signifies 'to see through something') appears decisive to French astronomy. It concludes that the ancients made use simply of long tubes of that name to observe the stars.[40]

Pouchet, then, seems to have increased the muddle about the *dioptra*, not grasping that Bailly had believed the Geminus instrument *did* contain lenses. The subject was raised again by François Arago the following year:

Geminus, the contemporary of Cicero, alludes to an instrument called the dioptra, turning about an axis parallel to the celestial sphere, as affording the means of proving that the stars describe circles in virtue of the diurnal motion. The means employed were excellent. It is the instrument known at the present day by the name of the equatorial; Geminus does not assert that he [personally] used it.[41]

Arago also mentions the manuscript seen by Father Mabillon, but concludes 'that the ancients were in the habit of occasionally examining the heavenly bodies through long tubes'. And then he refers to a curious passage in Aristotle's *Generation of Animals*,[42] which we will examine next ourselves.

Aristotle (died 322 BC) was the greatest philosopher of antiquity. I have a particular fondness for his zoological works. In his long treatise *Generation of Animals*, Aristotle tries to get to the bottom of fertility, a subject with which he also deals elsewhere, and which he clearly felt was a critical mystery of life. (His other treatise *On Failure to Generate*, thought to have been lost, has now been identified as the so-called Book Ten of the *History of Animals*.) His *Generation of Animals* is not for the squeamish, and Aristotle did not flinch from the most extraordinary details of the genitalia of all creatures, their fluids, their semen, their eggs, and their menstrual discharges. Many classicists do not realize just how far Aristotle went in his passionate pursuit of natural science, because these matters are not of great interest to most classical scholars, who are not themselves scientists. I managed to work out from his zoological writings that Aristotle must have personally dissected no less than 300 species of animals, and of course he would have studied the genitalia of the same number. I was able to discover that the only full dissection report of his which survives is the one of the chameleon, which he quoted elsewhere as a specimen (it now constitutes Chapter Eleven of Book Two of the *History of Animals*). The other 299-plus reports are lost.

In *Generation of Animals*, Aristotle becomes involved in a long digression about his theories of sight, and of different types of eyes, as a result of discussing infants, and pointing out that 'The eyes of all infants are bluish immediately after birth; later on they change over to the colour which is going to be their natural colour for life.'[43] This sets him going and he spends many pages elaborating on various aspects of vision. This brings him to the subject of 'keenness of vision', and it is here where he makes various curious comments about *tubes*.

Here are some of his remarks, first in the translation by A. L. Peck:

The fact that some animals are keen-sighted and others not is due to two sets of causes, for 'keen' here has practically two meanings (so it has when applied to hearing and smelling). Thus, keen sight means (a) ability to see from a distance, (b) distinguishing as accurately as possible the differences of the objects which are seen; and these faculties do not occur together in the same persons. The man who shades his eye with his hand or looks through a tube [*aulos*] will not distinguish any more or less the differences of colours, but he will see further; at any rate, people in pits and wells sometimes see the stars. So, that if any animal has a considerable projection over his eyes . . . he will be able to see from a distance (just as he would from close quarters) better than animals which . . . have no projecting brow at all in front of their eyes.[44]

Arthur Platt did an earlier translation of this passage:

The cause of some animals being keen-sighted and others not so is not simple but double. For the word 'keen' has a double sense (and this is the case in like manner with hearing and smelling). In one sense keen sight means the power of seeing at a distance, in another it means the power of distinguishing as accurately as possible the objects seen. These two faculties are not necessarily contained in the same individual. For the same person, if he shade his eyes with his hand or look through a tube [*aulos*], does not distinguish the differences of colour either more or less in any way, but he will see further; in fact, men in pits or wells sometimes see the stars [the translator adds in a footnote: '"In the daytime" is of course meant.']. Therefore, if any animal's brows project far over the eye, . . . this animal . . . will be able to see from a long distance (just as it can from a short one) better than those . . . which have no brows projecting over the eyes.[45]

It seems clear that Aristotle is not referring to telescopes here. However, that is different from saying that Aristotle was not familiar with telescopes. Aristotle was extremely careful in excluding subjects of a different category from his discussions; no one in history has been so particular about trying to avoid confusion of subject-matter in his discourses. Let us see what his further comments about tubes were, since they are even more remarkable. First, he points out that there are two basic theories of sight, one that light is emitted by the eye, and the other that light is received by the eye. He then says:

> It makes no difference to this which of the two theories of sight we adopt. Thus, if we say, as some people [such as Plato] do, that seeing is effected 'by the sight issuing forth' [from the eye to the object], then on this theory, unless there is something projecting in front of the eyes, the 'sight' of necessity gets scattered and so less of it strikes the object, with the result that distant objects are less well seen. If we say that seeing is effected 'by a movement derived from the visible object' [i.e. by light coming from the object to the eye], then on this theory, the clarity with which the sight sees will of necessity vary with the clarity of the movement [i.e. the emission of light from the object]: distant objects would be seen best of all if there were a sort of continuous tube [*aulos*] extending straight from the sight to what is seen, for then the movement [light emission] which proceeds from the visible objects would not get dissipated; failing that, the further the tube extends, the greater is bound to be the accuracy with which distant objects are seen.[46]

The Platt translation of this last sentence is:

> Things at a distance, then, would be seen best if there were, so to say, a continuous tube straight from the sight to its object, for the movement from the object would not then be dissipated; but, if that is impossible, still the further the tube extends the more accurately most distant objects will be seen.[47]

Platt reveals in a footnote[48] that the word which he translates 'extends' required an alteration by him of the Greek text. As transmitted, the text used instead the verb *apechō*, which means something quite different: 'to be far away from'. So what the actual manuscripts of Aristotle say is really: 'the further away the tube is, the more accurately most distant objects will be seen'. Platt therefore edited the text by a single letter to read instead 'the further the tube extends', by substituting the verb *epechō*, meaning among many other things 'to extend over a space'. Once again, we see a crucial ancient text relating to viewing through tubes which has had the text edited by a modern translator. Peck adopted the new text, citing Platt in his own footnote for this change. But there is even more to it than that. Peck tersely notes in his footnote that there are other variations at this crucial point in different manuscripts. Peck points out a variant reading in the Corpus Christi, Oxford, manuscript known as Z, but then goes on to point out a further variant.[49] It seems that the scribe had originally written *eonapachēi* but had erased it and put *pleonapachēi* but the latter part of that verb was then changed by the modern editors from 'be far away' to 'extend', so that the two versions of the original verb then gave four versions in all, considering the now-changed verb: *eonapechēi* and *pleonapechēi*. Four verbs seems too many to me! What is going on here? My Greek comes close to collapse at this point, but it seems to me that the scribe's corrected verb is referring to 'multiplication-by-distance', which when dealing with looking down tubes would have to be a reference to magnified images as seen through lenses in that tube.

In the first part of his statement, Aristotle seems to be speaking of the prevention of the dissipation of light rays by one simple – albeit imaginary and entirely hypothetical – method, namely by running a tube between the eye and the object, to exclude dissipation of rays. I think we can be quite clear on that. But in the second part of his statement, the translations and textual editings *merely presume* that he is still talking of that idea, which I think is *not* a safe assumption at all. In line with his usual habit of positing distinct alternatives, I believe that it was the intention of Aristotle at this point to offer another and more realistic possibility – one which was not hypothetical in any way: that the most distant objects will *in actuality* be seen most accurately if we use a tube which when we look through it 'multiplies by distance' – i.e., a telescope.

Platt and Peck, not having the slightest idea that a telescope could have existed in antiquity, tried to bring the text into some kind of sense by changing the words so that Aristotle appeared to be continuing to speak of the imaginary endless tube, by saying that it should be as long as possible. But I believe his intention was quite different, and that he was changing the subject from an imaginary and purely hypothetical tube, which was physically impossible, to one of those real tubes which people used which combined the two functions of the excluding of the dissipation of rays (the tube function) with the magnifying of images (the lens function). In other words, I am suggesting that the verb *apechō*, far from being a presumed mistake which needs to be corrected, is crucial to what Aristotle really meant to say; it was essential to his meaning that the concept of 'being far away from' be retained in his statement.

Another Greek word which needs a look is the one which has been thought to be used for a telescope, *dioptra*. This word comes from the basic verb *diopteuō*, which means 'to watch accurately, to spy about', as used by Homer in the *Iliad* (10.451), and which gave birth to the noun *dioptēr*, 'a spy or scout', also used in the *Iliad* (10.562). As time went on, however, the meaning of this word spread to related areas of meaning. By the time of Sophocles (in 441 BC, several centuries after Homer), the verb *diopteuō* had acquired the broader meaning of 'to look into' (his play *Ajax*, 307), and by 425 BC in the *Acharnians* (435) by the playwright Aristophanes, the noun *dioptēs* was already being applied for the first time on record to a concept of transparency, used in fact with regard to a ragged garment held up to the light, which could be 'seen through'.

By the second century BC, Polybius as we have seen was already using the word *dioptra* to describe the lens components of the Carthaginian telescopes. And by the first century AD, Strabo (54) was using *dioptra* specifically to describe a transparent stone, in this case a window pane, and Plutarch (2.1093E) was using *dioptrikos* to refer to 'the science of dioptrics'. However, the word *dioptron* repeated by Horace for 'spying-glass' is drawn from the Greek poet Alcaeus (seventh century BC; see his Fragment 53), the friend of Sappho, and it may therefore be that the disappearance of so large a portion of ancient Greek literature has obscured the fact that this word was being technically applied to telescopes at least three centuries before Polybius, and that *dioptra* is merely a later variation of *dioptron*. The related verb *dioraō* means 'to see through' (as used by Plato for instance in the fourth century BC).

It is very unlikely, considering the pedigrees of these word-forms, that the word *dioptra* would be applied to *empty* sighting-tubes placed on astronomical instruments, except perhaps in a much later phase of usage, and only then by extension. The fact that these words were being applied specifically to transparent stones (for in the time of Alcaeus a 'spying-glass' would have had to be rock crystal rather than glass), whether as optical aids or as window panes, and being used in the technical sense of telescopic lenses by Polybius as early as the second century BC, links the conceptual penumbra of the word-forms firmly to ideas of *transparency*. There is no hint of peering through tubes here. And Polybius is at pains to differentiate the two tubes of the Carthaginian instruments from the *dioptra*, which were clearly the mounted lenses within them. If, as astronomical instruments developed, empty sighting-tubes came to take on the name of *dioptra*, it must have been a late development. An empty tube was for many hundreds of years an *aulos*, not a *dioptra*.

Therefore, mentions of the *dioptra* such as that by Nicomachus of Gerasa and repeated by Iamblichus in his *Life of Pythagoras* are almost certainly of *tubes containing lenses, not of empty tubes*. But even when a person was discussing just an *aulos* – as in the last part of Aristotle's comments – it is possible that by adding certain qualifying remarks, he is speaking of a tube *modified* in such a way that it has effectively become a *dioptra*. The Aristotelian passage, however, will remain a 'grey area' of philological dispute for the moment, until a variety of manuscripts in several countries can be consulted by some scholar suitable to the task and a proper and unbiased survey made of the precise meanings of the four verbs, of whether additional variations may even exist, and a view can be taken as to what it was that Aristotle was actually saying. Until that is done, it seems that all we can do is raise a fluttering marker above the passage to signal that it is under investigation.

It is now time to turn our attention to a further use of telescopic tubes in the ancient world. We will do this by returning to the myth of Prometheus, who keeps coming up in optical contexts, but this time in a most unexpected way and from a rather bizarre source. The classic myth of Prometheus has several variations. Much of what is known of the myth comes from the surviving short play attributed to Aeschylus (sixth/fifth centuries BC), *Prometheus Bound*. I say 'attributed to' Aeschylus, because there is a considerable controversy over its true authorship, which we do not need to worry about. The subject of Prometheus is a vast one, and I have referred to some aspects of it in some footnotes in the Penguin translation my wife and I have published of the *Fables of Aesop*, in which Prometheus occasionally appears as a character.[50] The variant tradition which makes Prometheus the creator of mankind first appears in the Aesopic Fable 322, 'Prometheus and Men', and is next mentioned by the comic poet Philemon in the fourth century BC.

In the course of research carried out for a much earlier book entitled *Conversations with Eternity* (which I published in 1984, only in Britain, and of which I am currently undertaking a very extensive revision, with expanded text, to be published in early 2001), I undertook to study the most important divination techniques of ancient cultures, with the intention of giving an account of this crucial but neglected 'underside of history'. I discovered in my research that the most important divination technique in the history of the world had without question been divination by the entrails of animals, often called by its technical name of *extispicy*. Extispicy had been conducted for thousands of years, going back well into the Stone Age, and it had a huge geographical spread across most of the world. I had no choice but to follow this up in detail, an area of research which had understandably been given a wide berth by previous scholars frightened of the sight of blood.

My first results were published in that esoteric periodical, *The Journal of Cuneiform Studies*, where I was able to clear up a dispute about Babylonian/ Assyrian terminology and lambs' intestines which had been going on for a century amongst scholars too timid to settle it in an abattoir as I did.[51]

One of my most surprising discoveries came about when I was allowed to study freshly slaughtered lambs by lifting out their livers as the carcasses lay on their backs and their stomachs had been cut open. I had not antici- pated what I was going to see. I was merely lifting out the livers with the intention of setting them down for inspection of their various shapes and so forth. To my astonishment, I realized that I could see my face quite clearly in the livers. They were perfect shiny black reflecting-mirrors which steamed slightly. After 15 or 20 minutes' exposure to the air, these liver- mirrors go dull and nothing can be reflected in them anymore. It became clear to me that only people who work in abattoirs (and they presumably don't have time or interest) have access to livers lifted from freshly slaugh- tered animals, and can therefore know that they act as mirrors. This was a bit of knowledge which had been lost because of social developments. But it was a crucial bit of knowledge to our ancestors.

Ancient men tended to be very literal-minded when it came to natural phenomena, in contrast to their many superstitions in other areas of thought and experience. And because everyone who lived in the ancient world frequently saw animals being slaughtered and cut up, everyone had opportunity to see that the livers extracted from the carcasses were obviously mirrors.

The point of all this is to stress that things have changed, and that there was a time – not very long ago, and in many parts of the world still in full swing – when everybody knew the simple and obvious fact that livers lifted from freshly slaughtered beasts acted as reflecting mirrors.

Armed with this surprising discovery, I made a search of the ancient Greek literature and found that it was full of accounts of human livers acting as mirrors which reflect the divine rays with which the gods are always irradiating us. The imprints of these divine rays were thought to leave traces on animal livers, hence the intensity with which they were scrutinized for thousands of years as clues to the future; the gods, of course, having knowledge of the future so that the imprints of their rays might reveal some. Hence the subject of extispicy, and the fanatical liver-science of the Babylonians; in my 1984 book I reproduced a photo of a Babylonian clay liver model dating from 2000 BC, which showed the 55 zones of the liver where the diviner was meant to look for signs.[52]

In this context, here is an interesting passage by the Jewish writer Philo Judaeus of Alexandria (first century BC/first century AD):

> . . . the nature of the liver being of a lofty character and very smooth, by reason of its smoothness is looked upon as a very transparent mirror, so that when the mind, retreating from the cares of the day (while the body is relaxed in sleep, and while no one of the outward senses is any hindrance or impediment), begins to roll itself about, and to consider the objects of its thought by itself without interruption, looking into the liver as into a mirror, it then sees, very clearly and without any alloy, every one of the proper objects of the intellect, and looking round upon all vain idols, and seeing that no disgrace can accrue to it, but taking care to avoid that and to choose the contrary, and being contented and pleased with all that it sees, it by dreams obtains a prophetic sight of the future.[53]

This single passage must suffice to give the idea, as I do not wish to enter here into long discussions of liver lore, as I have already done that in my earlier book. But note two things: (a) Prometheus was supposed to have an ability to prophesy and see into the future, since his name comes from *promētheia*, meaning in Greek 'foresight, forethought'; and (b) his liver was one of the most prominent things about him. There can be no doubt whatever that Prometheus's liver was connected with divination, foreknowledge, and its mirror-function of reflection of the divine rays. Hence he has yet another optical aspect to him. In the standard myth,

Prometheus is chained to a mountain peak in punishment for giving heavenly fire to men. Every day a bird comes and eats part of his liver, which regenerates and grows back at night. Finally, after ages of this torture, Hercules comes along and unbinds Prometheus and sets him free at last. All of this was said to take place in the region of the Caucasus Mountains, where the Promethean myth is still strong among the locals.

Figure 14. A design from the back of an Etruscan mirror (probably dating to *circa* 500 BC) showing Prometheus (*Prumathe* in Etruscan) chained to the rock in the Caucasus. He is bearded and the lower part of his body is clothed. He is looking at Hercules (*Hercle*), who leans on a large club which he holds in his right hand and who has a lion skin over his left shoulder. On the other side of Prometheus is the god Apollo (*Aplu*), leaning on a staff of laurel. Hercules has arrived to free Prometheus from his bonds. He will shortly invoke the aid of Apollo and shoot the eagle which has been eating Prometheus's liver, using an arrow which is later placed in the sky as the constellation Sagitta. Then Hercules is at last freed, on condition that he always wear a ring made of his metal bonds and bearing a fragment of the stone to which he has been chained – in other words, a rock crystal lens like that seen in Plate 11; the Caucasus was a noted source of rock crystal, and that is why crystal could be considered a fragment of the mountain. (From Eduard Gerhard, *Etruskische Spiegel (Etruscan Mirrors)*, Berlin, 1863; reprinted, Rome, 1966, Figure CXXXIX; description appears in Vol. III, pp. 133–4. This mirror was in Gerhard's private collection at the time of publication of his books.)

We should note in the myth that Prometheus's liver is *exposed to the sun on a mountain top*. The reflection of this mirror takes place all during the day, during which time the reflection is devoured, resting only at night when no reflection is possible. Prometheus is also associated with bringing heavenly fire to earth by means of lenses or mirrors, and with a long tube of the now-extinct plant whose stalks were the tubes used for telescopes. But why is Prometheus on a mountain top?

The answer to this seems to be connected with geodetical surveying, which must be done with telescopes. It would lead us too far astray in our discussions to review all the evidence of the importance of mountain peaks in the ancient religious lore, especially as it is connected with the oracle centres. I have pointed out in no less than three previous books that the major Greek oracle centres of Dodona, Delphi, and Delos, in the archaic and prehistoric periods (i.e. long before classical times) were laid out on latitude lines and spaced precisely one degree of latitude apart. Since Delos ceased to have a functioning oracle by the seventh century BC,[54] it is clear that any scheme incorporating it had to be much earlier. Indeed, the excavation of Minoan remains at Delphi makes it clear that Delphi was of importance at least by the 12th century BC. My friend Professor Ioannis Liritzis and I have discovered a significant prehistoric structure in the immediate vicinity of Delphi (though not at the eighth-century site of Pytho, where the tourist buses go) which remains unpublished, so that I cannot give details, but there seems little doubt that Delphi's importance goes back long before the Minoans. Dating problems of prehistoric Greece are too complex for us to enter into here. Suffice it to say that the scheme of Dodona/Delphi/Delos is geodetically laid out and must be of prehistoric date, from before the time that any people who could recognizably be called Greeks inhabited Greece. There was an intense preoccupation with surveying in pre-classical times, and establishing sacred points on the Earth by this means. I believe that ultimately the Prometheus myth relates to this.

I promised a little while ago that I had found some new evidence from a rather bizarre source, and now we must consider it. The source is *The Life of Apollonius of Tyana* by Philostratus (second century AD).[55]

Much of this work is dedicated to recording information about unusual localities visited by the same Apollonius and his friend Damis on their extensive travels. In Chapter 3 of Book II, some interesting information gleaned from the natives of the Southern Caucasus is recorded:

And legends are told of this mountain [Mount Mycale] by the barbarians, which also have an echo in the poems of the Greeks about it, to the effect that Prometheus, because of his love of man, was bound there, and that Hercules – another Hercules, for of course the Theban is not meant – could not brook the ill-treatment of Prometheus, and shot the bird which was feeding upon his entrails. And some say that he was bound in a cave, which as a matter of fact is shown in a foot-hill of the mountain; and Damis says that his chains still hung from the rocks, though you could not easily guess at the material of which they were made, but others say that they bound him on the peak of the mountain; and it has two summits, and they say that his hands were lashed to them, although they are distant from one another not less than a stade [606 English feet], so great was his bulk. But the inhabitants of the Caucasus regard the

157

eagle of the tale as a hostile bird, and burn out the nests which they build among the rocks by hurling into them fiery darts, and they also set snares for them, declaring that they are avenging Prometheus; to such an extent are their imaginations dominated by the fable.[56]

This is a very unexpected but priceless survival of some specific information about the Prometheus myth which helps us make sense of it. The key element is the statement that Prometheus was *stretched between two peaks.* I take this to be an unambiguous reference to the use of an optical surveying instrument for sighting between two peaks. The tube of Prometheus would have provided the necessary telescope portion of what today we would call a theodolite – the basic instrument of optical surveying. It is impossible to achieve a reasonable accuracy in surveying without an optical instrument. But the telescope part of it can be rudimentary, and it is not necessary for the optical portion of the instrument to be highly sophisticated. The kind of simple telescopes which the ancients had would have sufficed. As for the chains, what with the heavy winds blowing on mountain tops, it is evident that ancient surveyors would have needed to secure their devices very firmly indeed to the rocks by means of chains in order to achieve unwobbly sightings and measurements. So 'Prometheus' *must* be chained. And the devouring of the reflection of the mirror during the daytime may refer to the light signal from the mirror of one team on one peak being observed by the telescope tube of the observers of the other team on the other peak.

The fundamental requirement for any act of surveying is to achieve a level. Today every builder and handyman has his spirit level, or bubble level. The little air bubble floats to the right place in the fluid trapped in a glass tube, and then a true horizontal level is demonstrated. I doubt that ancient men ever invented this handy device. The only reason I am not absolutely certain of that is that they do on rare occasions actually occur in nature, and I have many of these in my collection: I refer to water bubbles trapped inside pieces of quartz. In my specimens, little water bubbles slide around inside the quartz when it is moved, but they do so in a way which would not really be very useful for finding a level. Nonetheless, it is worth mentioning that this phenomenon does exist, as we should never ignore any detail in a complex subject. (Bubbles in quartz are discussed again in the chapter on 'Thunderstones'; see one in Plate 9.)

However, I believe that the way a level was found in ancient times was by weights and balance, using the force of gravity in a different way from that which settles the bubble in its correct place. In Plate 58 I reproduce a photo I took of a carving on a temple in Upper Egypt. This shows the *ankh* (sign of life) with two arms projecting from it, and a heavy weight suspended from each elbow. I believe this represents the ancient Egyptian method of achieving a level. In surveying for a building, the other thing you need to do is get your base line measurement, and the 'stretching of the cord' at the foundation of every temple and palace is celebrated in so many Egyptian wall carvings and texts that evidence of this practice is everywhere. Its other use, of course, was in connection with orientation alignments – to sunrise, or star-rise, or whatever was appropriate to the building in question.

So if we consider surveying on mountain peaks in ancient times, I believe that the achieving of a level was not done by any form of bubble level, but was instead accomplished by weights. And in order to do this properly, the entire apparatus would have had to be chained to the rock so that it was absolutely rigid apart from the balance. I believe that this is the real meaning of 'Prometheus' being chained to the mountain peak. And as for 'Prometheus', the name in this instance is a pun, and 'Foresight' or 'Looking Ahead' refers to the actual act of sighting by the surveyors.

Before we leave Prometheus, there is one other detail I should mention. In his *Natural History*, Book 37, Chapter 1, Pliny relates another tradition of the Caucasus region that stated that Prometheus was the first person in history to wear a ring with a fastened gemstone. I take this to be yet another esoteric reference to crystal burning and magnifying lenses – so many of which were later bored and mounted on swivel rings in antiquity, such as the Greek one I have. (I have examined several other excellent crystal lenses which were subsequently bored and mounted in rings, in museums including the British Museum, but to list them all is too tedious. They can be found in most major museums containing collections of classical antiquities.) In my exhaustive studies of approximately 100 crystal lenses in Scandinavia, I was sometimes able to demonstrate by clear evidence three successive stages of use by such means as microscopic examination of the surfaces, patterns of wear, etc., etc. I am publishing three technical papers in Sweden about all of this, so shall omit most of it here, as there is no room in this book for such lengthy studies and reports. In Appendix 8, however, I publish one paper in full because its only other publication will be in Swedish translation, and I wanted to make my original text available in English. But it can be shown from undeniable physical evidence sometimes that crystals were ground and polished as lenses, and later recycled for jewellery, sometimes in two phases of reuse.

With the Greek ring gems, they may have started life in Minoan or Mycenaean times as simple polished lenses (of which such a large number survive from excavations), then have been engraved in archaic times (such as my lens with its quaint carving of the flying figure), and finally have been bored – often incredibly clumsily by people who didn't know how to handle crystal, in clear contrast to the original fabricators of the lenses and gems – for mounting on gold swivel-rings. Having inspected a number of these, and attempted to fit several of these rings onto my fingers, I have come to the conclusion that they were rarely worn in that way. I think they must have been suspended from belts or kept in purses, or something of that kind. Their physical specifications are unsuited in many cases to actual fingers and hands, and I am convinced that many of them were never designed actually to go onto a human finger at all. Hence they were not really 'rings'.

I believe moderns have been misled into assuming that these objects are rings just because the crystals are swivel-mounted on gold loops. Perhaps these loops were suspended from ribbons or chains around the neck. But still, we can call them 'rings' if it pleases us to do so, and there were some which appear actually to have been worn on fingers. We must also remember that anyone rich enough to own one of these ancient rings would have had slaves doing all his work for him, and there was no need for him to have his fingers free for grasping much more than a goblet of wine at a banquet, so that the cumbersome aspect of these objects would have been less of an impediment to him than it would be to us today.

And there is one final point to be made from Pliny's Caucasian tradition: it encourages me further to believe that some of the adult 'flying Eros' figures of archaic times in Greece are really meant to represent Prometheus, in celebration of his being the 'first person to wear a ring' as well as of more esoteric matters such as his connection with fire from heaven. And I thus further justify my belief that my ancient crystal shows Prometheus rather than Eros flying with a lens in each hand.

Also, before leaving behind *The Life of Apollonius of Tyana*, I should just mention that it contains at Book III, Chapter 14, a specific mention of sacrificial fire being produced by burning-lenses or burning-mirrors in the first century by the Brahmans of India, who were visited by Apollonius in his extensive travels:

> And they say that they are inhabiting the heart of India, and they regard the mound as the navel of this hill, and on it they worship fire with mysterious rites, deriving the fire, according to their own account, from the rays of the sun; and to the Sun they sing a hymn every day at midday.[57]

We shall return to the subject of ancient optical surveying when we consider the ancient Egyptians at some length in our final chapter. So, for the moment we leave it.

Now we come to some surprising evidence of the existence, up until the 17th century AD, of an old telescope which was said to have been made by Archimedes in the third century BC. Can the instrument really have been 2,000 years old? Or did the name of Archimedes merely attach to it because of his fame? It does seem that the telescope in question was genuinely ancient, but that is about all we can safely conclude. The evidence comes from a very obscure source indeed: a private letter, written in 1672 in Italian, to a French astronomer named Ismaël Boulliau by an Italian lens-grinder named Tito Livio Burattini. This letter was translated into French and published in 1835 by an Italian scientist of note who lived in Paris and wrote in French under the name of Guillaume Libri, but whose real name and title were Guglielmo Bruto Icilio Timoleone, il Conte Libri Carrucci dalla Sommaia. He wrote, in French, a *History of Mathematical Sciences in Italy since the Renaissance, to the Close of the Seventeenth Century*, a considerable work of erudition which appeared in a second edition in 1838.

Here is how Count Libri introduces the matter and describes his discovery of the information:

> Now, an original document which we have discovered in the correspondence of [Ismaël] Boulliau, seems to demonstrate that several centuries before [Isaac] Newton and [Nikolai] Zucchi there was knowledge of a type of reflecting telescope which was used to see ships afar off.
>
> This document is an unpublished letter from [Tito Livio] Burattini (author of *La Mesure Universelle* [*The Universal Measure*] and a very able mechanic) written in 1672 and addressed by him to Boulliau. Burattini, replying to the French astronomer, who wrote to announce to him the discovery of the reflecting telescope of Newton, told him that there was at Raguse [not the Ragusa in Sicily but modern Cavtat on the coast of Croatia], on a tower, an instrument of the same kind, to help those of the inhabitants of this village to see ships from a distance of 25 or 30 miles, and that they had there a guardian of this instrument who attributed its construction to Archimedes. This fact, attested by several people (among others, by Gisgoni, the first doctor of the Empress Eleonora) to Burattini, and to Paul of Buono, a Member of the Academy of Cimento, proves in our opinion in an incontestable manner the ancient existence of instruments made for bringing objects nearer. . . . Here is the letter of Burattini, the original of which is preserved in the Bibliothèque du Roi (*Correspondance de Boulliau*, Vol. XVI, *Supplément Français*, Number 987), and which we reproduce with the translation.[58]

I presume that this manuscript is now in the Bibliothèque Nationale in Paris:

Varsavia [Italy], October 7, 1672

Monsieur,

> I have received the design which you had the kindness to send me, with the explanation of the catoptric tube invented by Signore Newton, and I thank you kindly. The invention is very beautiful and much honours its author. At Raguse (which was ancient Epidaurus, a very famous town of Illyria [Dalmatia] and the country of Aesculapius), is still preserved – if it has not perished in the last earthquake – an instrument of the same kind, with which one watched the ships in the Adriatic Sea at a distance of 25 and 30 miles from Italy, as if they were in the same port of Raguse. While I was in Vienna in 1656, I heard mention of that instrument by someone from Raguse.

Signore Paulo del Buono, whom you know, Monsieur, was present at that conversation. After which it was said of it that the instrument had the shape of a measure [*misura/ boisseau*] for measuring grain; but, like him I did not know more about it. We believed then, Signore Paulo and I, that it was a yarn and I thought no more of it. It is now two years ago that Signore Dottore Aurelio Gisgoni, the leading doctor of Her Majesty the Empress Leonora, came here to Varsavia: this doctor practised medicine in Ragusc for eight or ten years. One day, when he was conversing with me, a terrible earth tremor came to this village. He added after a long conversation these very words: 'God knows, of so many curiosities that there are at Raguse, one would not want to lose that admirable instrument, which tradition attributes to Archimedes, and which has aided people to see ships at a distance of 20 or 30 miles as distinctly as if they had been in the port.' I asked him how this instrument was made; he replied that its shape was that of a drum [*tamburo/ tambour*] which had only one bottom: which one looked at sideways, and it was believed by tradition that this instrument had been made by Archimedes. I remember what was said to me in Vienna in 1656, for the difference between a vessel to measure the wheat and a drum with one bottom lies only in the words. Signore Gisgoni is still alive and is still in the service of Her Majesty, Her Imperial Highness. What astonished me greatly is that one could never imagine how to make such a stupendous instrument, while Raguse did not lack illustrious mathematicians: formerly there were Marino Ghettaldo, and several other geometers, and in our day, Signore Gio-Batta Hodierna [*Burattini is mistaken here; for Hodierna was of Ragusa in Sicily and not from the Dalmatian coast.*], who as far as I know is still living and established at Palermo in Sicily. None of them, to my knowledge, has made mention of such an instrument. Yet Signore Hodierna has written on Archimedes and on telescopes and microscopes. I do not make this account to you to diminish the glory of Signore Newton, but I am very surprised that such an admirable invention could have remained unknown for such a long time. As for myself, I continue to believe that it was the same instrument which is in question in several authors and which was on the lighthouse of Alexandria at the time of the Ptolemies, who used it to see the ships 50 or 60 miles away. Lost perhaps through the decadence of the Roman Empire, it was hidden and kept in the town of Raguse [south of Dubrovnik] where Signore Dottore Gisgoni tells me that it was placed on a tower and kept by a magistrate.

The instrument [a reflecting telescope containing a mirror] made in England [by Newton] has a narrower proportion than that which is – or was – at Raguse, and as we know by experience, the metallic burning-mirrors are much better the bigger they are (as one sees from that made by Monsieur Villette at Lyons, and which is now, from what

I hear, in the hands of Her Very Christian Majesty). Similarly, I believe that an objective mirror ['objective mirror' and 'objective lens' are terms used in optics to describe the fact that it is the nearest to the object being observed] is much better because it receives more rays. I have communicated this idea to Monsieur Hevelius, who is now in the process of making one; and he shares my opinion. He wants to make hyperbolic and parabolic ones; but I think that the spherical ones are always better. Monsieur Hevelius has even undertaken to make the sonorous trumpet, which is also an English invention: I await the results of it, for I know very well that Monsieur Hevelius will make an excellent thing. . . .

No other discussion of this matter is known to me in print, although it may well be that subsequent to the publication of Libri's work, various Italian authors pursued it – something which an Italian scholar would have to investigate in the libraries of Italy. Nor have I gone to Cavtat to see whether any local antiquaries have ever heard of this telescope or have any knowledge of what happened to it. Nor do I have the slightest idea where the papers of Burattini have ended up, which might well contain further information.

Here surely is a job for a Croatian well-wisher. In the meantime, all we have to go on is what we have just seen. What seems certain is that the news of Newton's invention precipitated this report of the pre-existence of a similar device, and that the report is probably genuine. It is also likely that the telescope at Raguse was very old indeed, going back at least to the Middle Ages. Otherwise it could not have been considered to be so ancient. This is the conservative standpoint. But it is equally possible that the telescope did actually survive from at least late Roman antiquity, and it is not completely impossible that it really did go back to the time of Archimedes. Without more evidence, there is little more we can say. So I hope that some more evidence one day will turn up.

On another subject, notice that Burattini mentions the possibility that this telescope at Cavtat, just south of Dubrovnik in Croatia, might be the one salvaged from the Pharos Lighthouse at Alexandria, which collapsed into the sea as the result of an earthquake in ancient times, and pieces of which have recently been identified by divers on the seabed. Although this suggestion of Burattini is perhaps far-fetched, what is not so unlikely is that the two instruments resembled one another to a certain extent. As a matter of fact, how did Burattini know about the Pharos optical instrument? When did public discussion of it commence in modern times?

The first modern to mention the Pharos instrument appears to have been the brilliant Renaissance compatriot of Burattini, Giambattista [Giovanni Battista] della Porta, one of those great unruly geniuses of that age in Italy. In 1558, della Porta published the first edition of his famous work *Magia Naturalis* (*Natural Magic*) at Naples. Very few copies of this edition survive in the world, I have not seen it. The contents of this youthful version extended to only Four Books, and although I know that some material about optics was included, the full treatment of the subject of optics by della Porta did not appear until 31 years later, when he brought out the revised and very greatly expanded edition of *Magia Naturalis* in Twenty Books, also at Naples, in 1589. It was translated anonymously into English as *Natural Magick* by 'John Baptista Porta' and published at London in 1658. This edition has been photographically reprinted by Basic Books, New York, 1957, edited and with an introduction by Derek Price. In other words, we come full circle, back to Derek de Solla Price whom I described in Chapter One as being interested in the Layard Lens in the 1960s and encouraging me to take an interest. Having edited della Porta in the mid-1950s, his interest in ancient optics must have been aroused as a result, although he never mentioned della Porta to me in our conversations, and I only discovered his connection with *Natural Magick* in the 1980s when I was able to buy my own copy of the reprint.

I don't know whether he mentioned it in his first edition, but in Book 17, Chapter 11, of his full edition, under the subject 'Of Spectacles whereby one may see very far, beyond imagination', della Porta mentions the Pharos instrument (I have modernized the spelling of the 1658 translation, and the passage comes from p. 369):

> I will not omit a thing admirable and exceedingly useful; how bleary-eyed people may see very far, and beyond what one would believe. I speak of Ptolemy's glass, or rather telescope [I have rectified a translated term here, which had been translated 'spectacle'], whereby for 600 miles he saw the enemy's ships coming; and I shall attempt to show how that might be done, that we may know our friends some miles off, and read the smallest letters at a great distance, which can hardly be seen. A thing needful for man's use, and grounded upon Optics.

Porta then goes on to describe the construction of a telescope, many years before Galileo, though he does not give any source for his information. He is such an enthusiast for optics that he suggests that a suitably constructed mirror could project a written message upon the surface of the Moon!

Ten years later, Guido Pancirollo and his editor Heinrich Salmuth, who have already been discussed in an earlier chapter, cite della Porta's account of the Pharos instrument:

> . . . the [Latin] word *Conspicilium* . . . (sometimes) signifies an Instrument which magnifies Objects and makes them bigger . . . so that 'tis probable . . . that they were anciently in use, as it also may appear from Ptolemy's Glass (mentioned by Baptista Porta) by which he saw Ships coming 600 Miles off, and whereby we might discern our Friends for some Miles, and read at a vast distance the smallest Characters.[59]

It is evident that these remarks are directly taken from Porta, with no further information added. Father L. P. Pezenas, the French translator of Robert Smith's *A Compleat System of Opticks*, published in 1767 as *Cours Complet d'Optique*, mentions a telescope on the top of the Pharos Lighthouse at Alexandria in passing, and gives Porta as a reference, adding nothing.[60] But it was Bonaventure Abat in 1763, four years before this, who in his book (in French) *Philosophical Diversions* offered a very extended discussion of the matter. Abat concludes that the object was a mirror, not a lens. And he says of it:

One reads in several authors that Ptolemy Euergetes set a mirror on the tower of the lighthouse of Alexandria which represented clearly all that was done in the whole of Egypt, both on the sea and on the land. Some authors say that with this mirror one could see the enemy's fleet coming from 600 miles away: others say from 500 parasangs, which is more than 100 leagues [400 kilometres]. Almost all of those whom I have heard speak of this fact have regarded it as an idle tale and as something impossible. There are even famous opticians who think that if this fact be true, it can only be an effect of magic and a marvel of the Devil. Amongst others, such is the view of Father [Athanasius] Kircher, who speaking of several superstitious facts, puts this one in the same category . . . in his *Ars Magna Lucis & Umbrae* [Kircher was a 17th-century Jesuit author] . . . Experience has taught me that a great number of things which have been regarded as fanciful by several scholars, having been better examined by other scholars, have been found to be not only possible but even shown to have existed. I suspect that this mirror of Ptolemy could well be in the same category . . . The evidence which testifies that the mirror of Ptolemy mounted on the lighthouse tower actually existed is not normally considered as having the necessary authenticity to establish solidly its truth as a historical fact. One can give two reasons why it seems plausible to challenge those evidences.

The first is that some authors attribute this mirror to Ptolemy and others to Alexander the Great. Giambattista della Porta, in his *Natural Magic*, Father [Athanasius] Kircher, and Father Gaspar Schott [in *Magia Optica*, 1657] are among those who place the manufacture of this mirror in the time of Ptolemy. Monsieur de la Martiniere, in his *Dictionnaire Géographique* (*Geographical Dictionary*), quotes Martin Crusius, who in his *Turko-Grèce* [Turko-Grecia, his entry for Turkey-Greece, p. 231] says on the evidence of the Arabs that: 'Alexander the Great placed on the top of the lighthouse a mirror made with such art that one could discern from there at a distance of 500 parasangs, that is to say, more than 100 leagues [400 kilometres], the enemies' fleets which came against Alexandria or against Egypt; and after the death of Alexander this mirror was broken by a Greek named Sodore, who stole up and did this at a time when the soldiers guarding it were asleep.'

But this diversity of opinions on the originator of this mirror cannot cast any doubt on the truth of the fact itself. For it is quite a frequent matter in history that different authors attribute to different people the same thing, without our needing thereby to regard the fact itself as fabulous. The construction of the lighthouse attributed by some people to Alexander and by others to Ptolemy is just such an example. It appears that those who have spoken of this mirror have judged its *construction* by the *constructor* of this marvellous edifice.

The second reason, which is also seemingly the stronger in opposing its actual existence, concerns the circumstances and the impossible properties which the historians have ascribed to it. Paul Arese, Bishop of Tortonne, in his book entitled *Imprese Sacre*, Impress 54, Numbers 1 and 2, quoted by Monsieur Scarabelli in his *Museo Settaliano*, says that he knew that 'Ptolemy had seen from a distance of 600 miles the ships which came to the port of Alexandria; not by the strength of his sight but by virtue of a crystal or a glass.' Meanwhile, he adds that: 'the truth of this fact is suspect because of the roundness of the Earth, which renders it impossible.'

But I suspect that this circumstance of seeing 600 miles away or 500 parasangs away is so impossible that it does not derogate at all from the possibility of the mirror's existence. For if this mirror had existed, it is probable that it was unique of its kind; that there was no other like it which had the same properties, and that one could find no other means to see distinctly such faraway objects. It ought thus to be regarded as a marvel of its times, and all those who saw its effects would be filled with astonishment and surprise. . . . From which it is only natural to assume that these effects were exaggerated quite beyond reasonableness and even beyond the bounds of possibility. For as happens with ordinary machines and rare and admirable inventions, they often have attributed to them capabilities which they do not have, and even impossible capabilities. Thus, if we take away from the account of the mirror of Ptolemy that which is obviously exaggerated through ignorance, what is removed relates only to the distance at which the objects viewed were situated. Providing that there was nothing interposed between the objects and the mirror, one could still see them more distinctly than with the naked eye, and by this means, one could see many objects which were normally imperceptible because of their distance. And then the account contains nothing other than what is possible and reasonable. . . . As regards catoptrics and dioptrics [the sciences of mirrors and lenses], I say that the knowledge of the ancients goes back a bit further than it is normally believed to have done . . . (and this helps in) rendering believable the existence of the mirror of Ptolemy.[61]

Count Guillaume Libri (whom we quoted not long ago in connection with the telescope at Raguse, since he published the letter by Burattini) also discussed the Pharos Lighthouse in 1835:

> It now remains for us to discuss a very interesting point in the history of astronomy, to know whether the Orientals were familiar with some instrument to improve the visibility of objects far away. From a Muslim tradition of long ago, there was at the lighthouse of Alexandria a huge mirror by the means of which one would be able to see boats leaving the ports of Greece. This mirror, cited by Hafez, described by Abd-allatif (*Relation de l'Égypte*, p. 240), by Masoudi (*Notices des Manuscrits de la Bibliothèque du Roi* [*Notices of the Manuscripts in the Royal Library*], Vol. I, pp. 25–6), and by Benjamin of Tudela (*Itinerarium*, p. 121), in quite a detailed way, is met again in the *Adjaïb-Alboldan* of Kazwini, which exists in manuscript in the Bibliothèque du Roi (*MSS. Arabes*, Number 19, p. 89). More recently, [Gaspar] Schott (*Magia Naturalis*, Bamberg, 1677, quarto, p. 443) [this reference is to the second German edition rather than the Latin edition (1657) of this work], [Athanasius] Kircher (*Ars Magna Lucis et Umbrae*, Amsterdam, 1671, folio, p. 790). Montfaucon . . . Buffon . . . Herbelot . . . the *Aïneh-Iskanderi* . . . Langlès . . . Reinaud . . . are occupied with the same subject . . . It has been remarked on this subject that Abulféda, speaking of the mirror of Alexandria, says that it was made of Chinese metal – see his *Descriptio Aegypti*, Göttingen, 1776, quarto, p. 7 of the Arab text.[62,63]

What this all adds up to is that the Pharos Lighthouse almost certainly had a large mirror or lens on top, which during the daytime when it wasn't magnifying the light for sailors at sea, could be used to see great distances, acting therefore as a very powerful telescope. The astronomer François Arago made some sensible remarks about it in 1854:

> It is related in history that Ptolemy Euergetes had caused to be established on the summit of the lighthouse at Alexandria an instrument for discovering vessels at a great distance off. Leaving out of consideration the exaggerated statements respecting the distance contained in these accounts, it has been maintained that the instrument in question could not have been any other than a concave reflecting mirror. Father [Bonaventure] Abat remarked, as many of his predecessors had already done, that it is possible to observe with the naked eye the images of distant objects formed in the focus of a concave reflecting mirror, and that such images are very bright. In the experiments of Father Abat, as well as those of a similar kind, the reflecting telescope is reduced to its most simple form; that is to say, the eye-lens is suppressed. Such must have been the construction employed at the lighthouse of Alexandria, if it be really true that a mirror ever was employed there in observing distant objects.

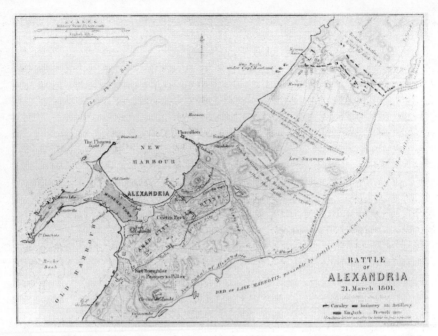

Figure 15. This map of the Battle of Alexandria in 1801 gives a good bird's-eye view of the topography of Alexandria, and to the left the location of the site of the ancient Pharos Lighthouse is clearly indicated.

And we should not forget that the Pharos Lighthouse was one of the 'Seven Wonders of the World' in ancient times. Now that its ruins are being explored underwater, I hope the impetus can be aroused to bring some of the stones up and reconstruct at least the base of the edifice. And in connection with that, an attempt might be made to demonstrate the miraculous optical instrument which once sat on top of it.

I am inclined to think that the Pharos mirror was a glass mirror backed in silver, of the type which we know existed at that time, and which had maximum reflectivity. I have shown in this book that the optical technology certainly existed for its construction. I go on in the next chapter to give an account of the fantastic burning-mirrors of the ancient world, beginning with that constructed by Archimedes himself in the third century BC, prior to the construction of the Pharos by Ptolemy III. (The confusion with Alexander the Great is obviously a case of garbling of the tradition, since he was the original founder of Alexandria, not the builder of the Pharos.) My friend Ioannis Sakas carried out a famous experiment in the 1970s to show that burning-mirrors could indeed burn boats in the water within seconds (see Plate 47, and the next chapter). These ancient optical experiments can be successfully and dramatically reproduced. So perhaps it is time to consider re-erecting the mirror and the Pharos in Egypt.[64]

Figure 16. A 19th-century scenic steel engraving of Alexandria. The tower in the foreground is not the ancient Pharos Lighthouse; that stood at the far left, where a smaller structure is visible at the other tip of the peninsula.

Turning now to another record of astronomical observations which seem to have taken place using telescopes with lenses in antiquity, we are faced with an even more unusual tradition recorded by the Greek historian Diodorus Siculus (first century BC). He drew his account from the earlier traveller and writer Hecataeus of Miletus (sixth/fifth centuries BC), who was a historical writer even earlier than Herodotus (fifth century BC), and from whom Herodotus took a lot of his material. Unfortunately the writings of Hecataeus are lost except for numerous fragments.

The temple in question is described as being a great round temple in the country which we know to have been Britain, and thus must have been Avebury, Stonehenge, or Stanton Drew, unless it was a now-vanished woodhenge. I am inclined to favour Stonehenge as the site because of its strong astronomical associations. Diodorus mentions this matter in Book II (47) of his *Library of History*.

The subject appears to have been first raised in modern times by Godfrey Higgins in his magnificently illustrated book *The Celtic Druids*, London, 1827, of which I am fortunate to have a copy, and from which Figures 17, 18, 19, 20 and 21 are taken. Higgins says:

Many persons have thought that the Druids and the ancients generally had the use of telescopes.

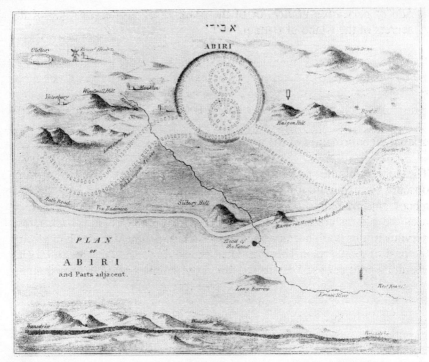

Figure 17. A reconstruction published in 1827 of the layout of the ancient British site of Avebury (here called 'Abiri', in old local pronunciation) as it was before it was largely destroyed by the local farmers. It is unlikely that this site is the one referred to by Hecataeus, because although round, it is a complex structure involving rings within a ring. (From Godfrey Higgins, *The Celtic Druids*, London, 1827. This is Plate 13 following p. xviii. Collection of Robert Temple.)

According to Strabo [Book 17], a large mirror was elevated on the summit of the temple of the sun at Heliopolis, to reflect into that temple the full splendour of its meridian beam, whilst another of still larger dimensions was placed on the Pharos at Alexandria, in such a manner as to reflect ships approaching Egypt at a great distance, and imperceptible to the eye. . . . Diodorus Siculus says, that in an island west of the Celtae [Celts], the Druids brought the sun and moon near them, whence some have suspected telescopes were known to them.

The ancients knew that the milky way consisted of small stars [he is referring to Democritus but does not name him]; this, it is thought, they could not have known without telescopes.

The expression in one of the Triads, of the moon appearing to be near the earth, is curious, and Mr. Davies suspects from this, that the Druids knew the use of the telescope. These Triads *every one* must allow to have existed long prior to the discovery of telescopes in modern times. In one of them it is written: *Drych ab*, Cibddar or Cilidawr, the speculum of the

Son of pervading glance, or of the searcher of mystery, as one of the secrets of the island of Britain.[65]

Being rather ignorant of ancient British and Welsh manuscripts and lore, I cannot intelligently discuss the Triads and what they say. But the fact that there is an ancient British reference confirming the statement of Diodorus (which is taken from the earlier writer Hecataeus) about the moon being 'brought nearer', apparently by means of a rudimentary telescope, seems dramatic confirmation of the accuracy of the Greek report.

The subject of the ancient British telescope was next raised by a truly obscure German author named Christian Karl Barth. In 1818 he published a book entitled *Teutschlands Urgeschichte* (*Germany's Pre-History*), which uses the old-fashioned 'T' instead of a 'D' for Deutschland. I am rather nervous of this book because the enthusiasm of people like Barth to glorify the past of the German *Volk* was later hijacked by the Nazis and turned to insidious political uses. Barth was an early member of what turned into a gigantic tidal wave of German fervour for the magnificent past of the Fatherland. However, one cannot blame Barth for what happened a hundred years later, for that is taking hindsight too far.

In the first edition of his book in 1818, Barth expounded the wonders of the ancient land of the 'Hyperboreans', which had been mentioned by such classical writers as Diodorus. 'Hyperborean' means 'beyond Boreas', and as Boreas was the Greek name of the North Wind, it meant a northerly land noted for its high civilization and which was also specifically described as being a substantial island larger than Sicily. Most scholars are inclined to accept the 'Hyperboreans' mentioned by the ancient Greeks as the British. We cannot take the space here to go into a full account of this fascinating subject, but it should be pointed out that the Hyperboreans had extremely ancient contacts with the Greeks going back well before the classical period. They regularly sent special gifts to the Island of Delos because they worshipped Apollo (under a different name, of course, probably the British god Bran), and Delos was reputed to have been his birthplace. We can do no more than hint at this huge subject here. But it should be pointed out that Delos ceased to be a major oracle centre by the seventh century BC, and that the famous 'Hyperborean Gifts' sent there originated well before that time.

Barth in his first edition did not mention any optical phenomena, but he drew upon the passage in Diodorus which contains it, and wrote:

The [Hyperborean] land was fruitful and gave two harvests annually. Latona [mother of Apollo and Artemis] was reputed to have been born there, where in the form of a she-wolf she bore the sun god [Apollo]. Therefore he was called Lykogenos, and a statue of a wolf stood in the temple at Delphi. He was honoured above all the gods in that country [it is true that Bran was the chief god of the ancient Britons], a sacred grove was consecrated to him, and a circular temple adorned with offerings . . .⁶⁶

In 1840, 22 years later, calling himself simply Karl Barth (perhaps he dropped the Christian because it wasn't pagan enough?), Barth issued a vastly expanded, and in the author's words 'entirely rewritten', second edition of *Teutschlands Urgeschichte*. By this time he is described on the title page as a Royal Bavarian Councillor. In this edition he tells more about the circular temple of the Hyperboreans. Drawing upon Diodorus Siculus (II, 47), Barth specifically states that the ancient Hyperboreans observed the Moon from their circular temple through magnifying lenses, which made the Moon appear nearer, and they therefore used rudimentary telescopes. This was the second time this was overtly stated in modern times.⁶⁷,⁶⁸ (Higgins was the first, as we have just seen.)

It is important for us to remember, as we read Diodorus's comments, that it is thus considered likely by most scholars that the Hyperboreans are the British and that their circular temple is Stonehenge. Here are the actual remarks of Diodorus in Oldfather's translation:

> . . . we feel that it will not be foreign to our purpose to discuss the legendary accounts of the Hyperboreans. Of those who have written about the ancient myths, Hecataeus and certain others say that in the regions beyond the land of the Celts [i.e. Gaul – modern France] there lies in the ocean an island no smaller than Sicily. This island, the account continues, is situated in the north and is inhabited by the Hyperboreans, who are called by that name because their home is beyond the point whence the north wind (Boreas) blows; and the island is both fertile and productive of every crop, and since it has an unusually temperate climate [because of the Gulf Stream, as we now know] it produces two harvests each year. Moreover, the following legend is told concerning it: Leto [the mother of Apollo and Artemis] was born on this island, and for that reason Apollo [as sun god] is honoured among them above all other gods; and the inhabitants are looked upon as priests of Apollo, after a manner, since daily they praise this god continuously in song and honour him exceedingly. And there is also on the island both a magnificent sacred precinct of Apollo and a notable temple which is adorned with many votive offerings and is spherical in shape [*sphairoeidē tō schēmati*]. Furthermore, a city is there which is sacred to this god, and the majority of its inhabitants are players on the cithara [an ancient stringed instrument]; and these continually play on this instrument in the temple and sing hymns of praise to the god, glorifying his deeds.
>
> The Hyperboreans also have a language, we are informed, which is peculiar to them, and are most friendly disposed towards the Greeks, and especially towards the Athenians and the Delians [of the island of Delos, birthplace of Apollo and Artemis], who have inherited this good-will

from most ancient times. The myth also relates that certain Greeks visited the Hyperboreans and left behind them there costly votive offerings bearing inscriptions in Greek letters. And in the same way Abaris, a Hyperborean, came to Greece in ancient times and renewed the goodwill and kinship of his people to the Delians. They say also that the moon, as viewed from this island, appears to be but a little distance from the earth and to have upon it prominences, like those of the earth, which are visible to the eye. The account is also given that the god visits the island every 19 years, the period in which the return of the stars to the same place in the heavens is accomplished; and for this reason the nineteen-year period is called by the Greeks the 'year of Meton' [the Metonic Cycle, introduced in Athens in 432 BC, designed to reconcile the lunar and solar years, with the latter being reckoned at 365.2632 days]. At the time of this appearance of the god he both plays on the cithara and dances continuously the night through from the vernal equinox until the rising of the Pleiades, expressing in this manner his delight in his successes. And the kings of this city and the supervisors of the sacred precinct are called Boreadae, since they are descendants of Boreas, and the succession to these positions is always kept in their family.[69]

The description of the Moon being 'visible to the eye' in such a way that its mountains can be made out clearly, and so that 'it appears to be but a little distance from the earth', can only be satisfactorily explained on the basis of this being a description of a telescopic examination of the Moon. (And as I mentioned before, examining the Moon with only two lenses does not matter, for an inverted image of a heavenly body is just as good as one right way up, though of course they may have had a third lens to flip the image right way up – but we do not need to assume that.)[70]

If one relied on some of the books now available about British megalithic culture, one would not get very far in discovering this information. An example is the large and generally impressive book about megalithic science, *Sun, Moon and Standing Stones*, by John Wood. One would think that if anybody had an interest in the evidence of the use of telescopes in ancient Britain, Wood would, since his book deals with megalithic astronomy. But he behaves in a quite incomprehensible manner right at the beginning of his book. On page four he quotes part of the passage from Diodorus, but he *removes* all mention of the Moon being brought nearer to view, and substitutes dots! He makes the situation far worse by giving no textual reference to Diodorus. Since Diodorus Siculus in the Loeb Library runs to 12 volumes, this is far from helpful. He also gives no reference whatever to the source of his translation, which contains two errors, one being a reference to a stellar constellation which is not in the Greek, and the other mistranslating the description of the temple as 'circular', when the Greek really says 'spherical'. Wood also gets the dates of Hecataeus wrong, believing him to have lived two centuries later than he did, and says he was from Thrace in Greece, whereas he was really from Miletus in Turkey.[71]

In the book by Douglas Heggie, *Megalithic Science*, Diodorus is not quoted and is only referred to in passing twice, once as 'a well-known quotation from the classical writer Diodorus Siculus about a race known as the Hyperboreans'.[72] Heggie does not give any kind of reference indicating where this 'quotation' may be consulted. But he does at least correctly refer to the temple as 'spherical'. He only refers to other modern authors, and apparently did not consult Diodorus himself. Heggie seems blissfully unaware of the passage containing evidence of the use of the telescope in ancient Britain – something one would have thought of concern to him since he bothered to write an entire book about megalithic science!

The many years it took me to locate the ancient British lenses is a saga so vast that there is no room for it in this book. There is also a huge literature relating to them. When I finally found the British lenses, in two unexpected museums which have no connection whatever with archaeology, I discovered that they were ground and polished to a high degree of perfection. It is likely that Britain was the centre of a superb crystal lens industry, though no workshop has apparently ever been found, and it is possible that the lenses may all have been imported. Archaeologists are very familiar with numerous crystal balls which have been excavated in Britain, but they never think of them in optical terms, generally regarding them as 'magical apparatus'. But those crystal balls all magnify and burn, and are generally very professionally manufactured. They should therefore be added to the various British lenses as optical artifacts native to Britain, and judged as such. In Plate 53 may be seen one of the British lenses which I analysed.

The reader may be assured that the textual evidence of the use of a telescope in ancient Britain is fully substantiated by the existence of crystal lenses in ancient Britain, any two of which held together would have been sufficient to perform the action described by Diodorus with the greatest of ease. Furthermore, the British lenses were among the most advanced technologically of any ancient lenses I ever examined; one has already been mentioned in connection with its ability to illuminate what it magnified. The invention of 'resting-points' – strange protrusions from the lenses the use of which is not immediately evident – enabled them to be raised above the surface of what they were magnifying, for the insertion of tools beneath, while not requiring to be held. This was sheer genius! Another appears to be a disc, but a spherometer revealed a minute curvature, and if held to the eye when seated, this lens acts as a splendid spectacle lens to correct for presbyopia and enables one to read something on the table in front of one. I must stress, however, that none of the actual lenses (as opposed to crystal balls) has a modern excavation source, so precise dating for them is unavailable. The last-mentioned lens worries me, and I suspect it is more recent than the others. It may have been interpolated into the collection and be only a few hundred years old. It does not 'feel' ancient to me at all.

The passage of Hecataeus contained some unexpected and very specific information about the importance among the Hyperboreans of a 19-year astronomical cycle. This has been amply confirmed by research since the 1960s. In other words, a millennium-and-a-half after the death of Hecataeus, the most specific information in his account has been proved to be correct. Such verification means that we should give the highest rating to him for accuracy. (And it is also easy to overlook the fact that he correctly stated that there were round temples among the Hyperboreans, as it is so obvious to us today – but that was by no means an obvious thing for a Greek of the sixth/fifth centuries BC to say.)

The proof of the importance of the Metonic Cycle in ancient Britain came about as a result of the pioneering work of Professor Alexander Thom, and was amply demonstrated in his two books *Megalithic Sites in Britain* (1967)[73] and *Megalithic Lunar Observatories* (1971),[74] as well as in numerous articles commencing from at least 1966. I knew Alexander Thom, and had immense respect for him. A thin, almost gaunt man with an exceedingly dry sense of humour, he had enough of a Scottish accent to make him exotic, and enough integrity for ten men. He had been Professor of Engineering at Oxford, but was retired by the time I met him. Since the 1930s he had spent his spare time visiting megalithic sites all over Britain and surveying them; it was his private passion, but when he made his private passion public and started publishing his results, the reception was often vitriolic among orthodox archaeologists. There is nothing an archaeologist less wants to do than to have to learn astronomy, so he or she will fight tooth and nail, scratch, claw, and bite, to get out of this situation. They don't want to know anything about proof that monuments were astronomical, they just want an easy life and not to have to worry about it.

Thom was vilified and an attempt was made to classify him as a dangerous nut. What a pity – he had once been a dignified Oxford professor who knew how to behave, but he had gone mad after his retirement. That was why he came up with this nonsense that the megalithic monuments were oriented to astronomical phenomena. In fact a less likely candidate for a mad professor than Alexander Thom could not be imagined. He exuded good Scottish common sense from every pore. To try to portray him as having become a lunatic was as ridiculous an attempt at character assassination as I have ever witnessed. But when people are desperate, they will try anything.

After Thom's death, his son Archie asked me to help him preserve the survey documents of the 600 megalithic sites in Britain which he and his father had surveyed (for Archie was a partner with his father in much of that work). The documents were very bulky and Archie had nowhere to keep them. Also, I think he may have known he was on the way out, for he did not live long, and his son was not 'into megaliths' as Archie and Alexander had been. Fired by the need to preserve these priceless documents, I went around to various learned societies, libraries, and so on, trying to persuade them to accept the documents and preserve them. I remember approaching the silly folk at the Royal Institution, who were amazed at the suggestion that they should sully their hands with megaliths – what was that to them? And as for the rest of the august bodies whom I approached, they behaved like outraged virgins being menaced by a satyr. Megalithic surveys? What nonsense! Who did I think they were? Members of the lunatic fringe or something of that sort?

I tried in vain to dispute with these people and stress the priceless importance of Britain's megalithic heritage. I pointed out that many of the sites surveyed by Thom no longer even existed, had been bulldozed by farmers or removed for road construction, etc. I said there were over 600 monuments recorded, with full plans and orientations – material which could never be obtained again about early British civilization – plans which had been compiled from the 1930s to the 1970s, representing a whole lifetime's work. None of this made the slightest impression; universal arrogance prevailed. Then Archie Thom died and I have no idea what happened to all this material. Was it thrown on a bonfire? I hope not. But the situation was infinitely depressing.

What was it that Alexander Thom had done, to make the lives of so many people so uncomfortable? He had proved conclusively that it was impossible to be a responsible British archaeologist dealing with the megalithic period and to be ignorant of astronomy. For he had shown that the megalithic monuments of Britain were astronomical monuments, and can only be comprehended as such. The message to megalithic astronomers was simple – go back to school and learn a new subject, or resign!

When *Megalithic Sites in Britain* was published in 1967, it could not have been a drier, more technical book, full of numbers and formulae, and yet it was only really welcomed by 'fringey people', who had suspected all along that the megaliths were more than just a lot of stones stuck here and there, and that they must have some meaning behind them. But in between the technical details, expressed in the tersest economy of measured Scottish thrift for words, Thom had made such statements as these:

Scattered throughout Britain there are thousands of Megalithic sites. A few of these are well known but the great majority lie off the beaten track in the fields and on the moors. Many are not even recognized (or obviously recognizable) as being Megalithic at all . . . the erection of 5000 to 10,000 megaliths must have made demands on its [Megalithic Britain's] engineers. . . . One has only to think of the tremendous organizing effort which would be necessary to transport and erect numbers of stones some weighing up to 30 tons. Swampy ground might make it necessary to operate in winter when the ground was frozen. Think of feeding hundreds of men and the necessity of starting before dawn in the short winter day. The hour was important. Thus methods of obtaining time from the stars must have been well understood. To obtain time from the stars the date must be known and this as we shall see came from the sun at the calendar sites. . . . It is remarkable that 1000 years before the earliest mathematicians of classical Greece, people in these islands not only had a practical knowledge of geometry and were capable of setting out elaborate geometrical designs but could also set out ellipses based on Pythagorean triangles. We need not be surprised to find that their calendar was a highly developed arrangement involving an exact knowledge of the length of the year or that they had set up many stations for observing the 18-year cycle of the revolution of the lunar nodes . . . (called) the *line of nodes*. This line . . . completes a circuit in 18.6 years. This rotation of the line of nodes has an important effect on the position of the full moon in the sky. . . . One may ask in what way these changes in the position of the moon's orbit throughout the 19-year cycle would make themselves apparent. For a community whose only effective illumination during the long winter nights was the moon perhaps the most important apparent change would be that the midwinter full moon's altitude on the meridian varied from about 57° to 67° . . . But transcending these phenomena in importance lay the challenge of the eclipse. To early man the eclipse of the sun or of the moon must have been an impressive spectacle and a desire to master eclipse prediction probably motivated Megalithic man's preoccupation with lunar phenomena. Since eclipses happen only when a moon is at a node it would soon have become apparent that no eclipse occurred near the solstices when the full moon was in either of its extreme positions but only in the years which lay midway between these.

To understand some of the lunar sites dealt with [by Thom] . . . it is necessary to examine the moon's motion in greater detail . . .[75]

Something no archaeologist wished to do!

We see here that the '19-year cycle', sometimes called the '18-year cycle', but really of 18.6 years – in other words, the Metonic Cycle – mentioned by Diodorus as being of crucial importance to the Hyperboreans was indeed fundamental to British culture in the megalithic period, and probably remained so right through the Druid period up until the invasion by the Romans. This fundamental confirmation of the most specific information conveyed by Diodorus shows us just how reliable his source, Hecataeus, really was, and strengthens our confidence in his report of the use of a telescope. And the fact that the telescope was used *to observe the Moon* makes even more sense, since we see that the ancient British spent a very great deal of their time doing just that.

However, the importance of telescopes in ancient Britain is likely to have been much greater than merely looking at the moon. Thom stresses the extraordinary accuracy of the ancient British astronomical observations and their even more extraordinary accuracy of surveying. In fact, he says:

It is fortunate for us that Megalithic man liked, for some reason or another, to get as many as possible of the dimensions of his constructions to be multiples of his basic unit. We are thereby enabled to determine unequivocally the exact size of this unit. In fact probably no linear unit of antiquity is at present known with a precision approaching our knowledge of the Megalithic yard [of 2.72 feet]. . . . [The ancient Britons were a] civilization which could carry a unit of length [the Megalithic yard] from one end of Britain to the other, and perhaps much further afield, with an accuracy of 0.1 per cent . . . [our] study shows us that Megalithic man was well acquainted with the small amplitude ripple on the moon's declination and has left such definite indicators that we can, with their help alone, determine its magnitude. *We do not know of any technique which could have been used to examine this oscillation with the moon at the nodes*, [italics mine] . . . [Thom's surveys had to] be made with the same accuracy as was used in the original setting out and it will be shown that some sites, for example Avebury, were set out with an accuracy approaching 1 in 1,000. Only an experienced surveyor with good equipment is likely to attain this kind of accuracy. The differences in tension applied to an ordinary measuring tape by different individuals can produce variations in length of this amount or more. The necessity for this kind of accuracy has not in the past been appreciated and has in fact only become apparent as the work recorded here progressed.[76]

We see here that by 1967, Thom had already established the *implied necessity* of telescopes in ancient Britain, if only to measure small lunar oscillations in the sky and for use in some form of theodolite to survey with an accuracy which was physically impossible without optical instruments. When Thom says that the surveying accuracy was so great that the variation in muscle tension in the arm of the assistant surveyor holding the tape was sufficient to throw it off, then we know that this fanatical accuracy of the ancient British must have relied upon theodolites, for once again, as with the Egyptian pyramids (see Chapter Nine), no other explanation is possible other than magic!

There is no need to go through the subsequent publications by others, and to review the use of the Metonic Cycle in ancient Britain, as we have gone into that subject sufficiently for our purposes here. But let us just consider one last detail of the report of Diodorus before leaving him. What did he mean exactly by the 'spherical temple'? Round, yes, but *spherical*? Diodorus differentiates clearly between three things:

(a) a magnificent sacred precinct of Apollo

(b) a notable temple which is adorned with many votive offerings and is spherical in shape

Figure 18. An 1827 engraving of Avebury (here called by its local pronunciation at that time of 'Abury'). It is a redrawing by W. Day of a drawing by Philip Crocker published six years earlier in Sir Richard Colt Hoare's *The Ancient History of North Wiltshire*, London, 1821. Of it Aubrey Burl says (*Prehistoric Avebury*, Yale University Press, 1979, p. 54): 'Despite the absence of causeways across the ditch and the incorrect concentric ring inside the South Circle, Crocker's reconstruction does have a good likeness to the original site.' This view thus 'restores' to their place many stones which were missing already. Of the 650 stones which originally constituted Avebury, 317 had been taken away by the locals by 1815 and broken up and used as building materials. (The last stone to be destroyed is thought to have met its fate in 1828.) Farmer Griffin destroyed twenty stones, farmer John Fowler destroyed five to build an ale house, Farmer Green destroyed an entire subsidiary megalithic ring to build his house and walls at Beckhampton, etc. Despite these and many other such acts of wanton destruction by the small-minded locals, much still remains, which enables us to come to certain conclusions. Professor Alexander Thom demonstrated by his survey that the site of Avebury was laid out with such precision that its accuracy was one part in a thousand. This is impossible without optical surveying techniques. The very existence of Avebury thus constitutes evidence of the use of rudimentary telescopes in ancient Britain, for surveying purposes, in addition to the astronomical purposes recorded by Hecataeus.
(From Godfrey Higgins, *The Celtic Druids*, London, 1827, plate following p. xviii. Collection of Robert Temple.)

(c) a city which is sacred to this god, and which is near the said (spherical) temple, because the inhabitants of the city play their citharas and
sing their hymns in the temple, which must be within walking distance

I think we are safe in assuming that Stonehenge is the 'spherical' temple, because such a large number of ancient dwellings have now been found near it, that they presumably constitute 'the city'. As for the sacred precinct of Apollo, there is no need to situate it near Stonehenge. It could be Avebury, or even Stanton Drew.

Figure 19. Stonehenge seen from the north-east in 1827. Why did Stonehenge have 'trilithons' – formed by a succession of stones lying horizontally along the tops of pairs of uprights? Although not an original feature of the earliest structure, why were they added? It is true that they are an attractive feature, but did they have a use?
(From Godfrey Higgins, *The Celtic Druids*, London, 1827. The figure is Plate 6 following page xiv. Collection of Robert Temple.)

This leaves us with one mystery – what is meant by the description *spherical*?

In order to try and answer this question, I call attention to a curious and unique feature of Stonehenge: it is the only megalithic ring in Britain which has trilithons. We know that these were erected later than the earliest Stonehenge, and are of a subsequent cultural phase. Could these trilithons – two columns with a flat stone laid on top – have been erected simply because they were aesthetically pleasing? I don't think so.

I suspect that the point of having those elevated horizontal stone slabs was to provide the base for a dome of perishable materials to arch over the precinct. This would have made the round temple into a spherical temple. The central portions of the horizontal slabs could have been lashed round with rope or withies to fasten a dome of wicker, or withy, or wood, or a frame covered in hides. Planks could have been laid across the top of the stone structure from horizontal slab to horizontal slab to give an elevated floor to the dome. There was plenty of wood available – even now tall trees stand not far away in scattered copses.

A spherical dome over the trilithoned portion of Stonehenge would have converted what was originally a temple open to the elements to one which was covered; the votive offerings could have been suspended from the dome, as it is hard to hang things on giant stones. The platform of the dome

Figure 20. An attempt to reconstruct the appearance of Stonehenge as it was originally, published in 1827. This reconstruction was devised by William Cunnington, a wool merchant of Heytesbury, Wiltshire, who during the 18th century took an interest in Stonehenge owing to the necessity of riding every day for the sake of his health. It was Cunnington who seems to have been the first person to notice that Stonehenge was built in at least two stages at different periods and of different stone. He pointed out that the trilithons 'are of that species of stone called *sarsen*', whereas the older parts of Stonehenge are not; the minor stones of Stonehenge are here omitted from the drawing in order to call attention to the remarkable nature of the trilithons as they would once have appeared. Cunnington was still excavating at Stonehenge in 1803, when he found human remains, amber beads and rings, beads of jet, ivory tweezers, 'a curious whetstone', and a brass dart in nearby barrows.
(From Godfrey Higgins, *The Celtic Druids*, London, 1827, Plate 7, following p. xiv. Collection of Robert Temple.)

suspended in the air would have provided an excellent observatory in the cold night air, for keen priests to use their telescope. The advantage of a dome made of soft materials is that they could poke a hole in it anywhere they liked to look at any part of the sky that took their fancy, leave slits, even insert markers. Furthermore, they could not be observed by the uninitiated as they pursued these esoteric purposes. But perhaps what was more likely was a kind of covered horseshoe wooden gallery open to the summer solstice sunrise, so that at the centre of the arc the chief priests would have stood observing the sunrise, which they could see seconds before people standing lower down on the ground. Imagine them raising their arms and singing a hymn, with their cithara players and choir ranged to either side of them, so that everyone else who was at ground level would hear the swelling music at the precise instant that the golden globe of the sun rolled up over the heelstone, rather than having the music delayed by a few seconds, as it would otherwise have been. The chief priest could thus have the advantage of being the first to see the sun, and all eyes would be on him to raise his arms as an advance signal accompanied by the onset of music, in the same way that the ancient Egyptians observed the golden-tipped obelisks to see the pre-sunrise 'flash' at the obelisk-tip – for all we know, also accompanied by music – as advance notice to turn around and witness the glorious sight of the sunrise itself. (This is described in our final chapter.)

At least this gives a rational reason for the lintels being laid along the tops of the trilithons, as the base for a further perishable structure which would have had a sensible use. And this has the further advantage of

Figure 21. A fuller reconstruction view of Stonehenge, according to the model built by Mr Waltire, 'a very respectable old philosopher and astronomer ... who travelled the country many years as a lecturer in natural philosophy. He encamped and remained on the ground two months, in order to make himself master of the subject; and a model which is now in the possession of Mr Dalton of York, was the fruit of his labour.' This engraving of 1827 is of the late Mr Waltire's model. Waltire was convinced that 'this structure has been erected (for) making astronomical observations on the heavenly bodies. By careful observations made on the spot, Mr W. found, that the barrows or tumuli surrounding this temple accurately represented the situation and magnitude of the fixed stars, forming a correct and complete planisphere ... (and) that the trilithons are registers of the transits of Mercury and Venus ...' Unfortunately, all of Waltire's writings on the subject of Stonehenge had already been lost by his friend before the time of Godfrey Higgins, so that Higgins could merely glean verbal summaries. It may be seen from this model how neatly a dome could have been supported over the structure from the horizontal ring of stones, and that the five great central trilithons could have supported a central solar and astronomical observation platform.
(From Godfrey Higgins, *The Celtic Druids*, London, 1827, Plate 7a, following p. xiv. Collection of Robert Temple.)

explaining the only surviving eye-witness description of the temple which we think was Stonehenge, as being 'spherical' rather than merely circular. But of course I do not insist on this, and must stress that I am engaging only in speculation intended to reconcile anomalies of evidence.

Shortly before going to press I was browsing in a secondhand bookshop and looking through some old issues of the archaeological journal *Antiquity*. In the issue for March 1937, I found a surprising article. A man named A. Vayson de Pradenne had written about 'The Use of Wood in Megalithic Structures', and in his Figure I, which I reproduce here as Figure 22, he published a drawing of the 'Suggested Reconstruction of Stonehenge' which showed it with a wooden dome! The extraordinary thing about de Pradenne's article was that he had come to the conclusion that Stonehenge had had a wooden covering seemingly without any knowledge of the text of Diodorus Siculus. His notion was thus independent of the apparent ancient description of Stonehenge as being 'spherical'. De Pradenne's conclusions were based upon the existence of other domed structures in different cultures, upon his investigations of the importance of wood in association with the megaliths and especially the nature of Woodhenge, and also the following considerations:

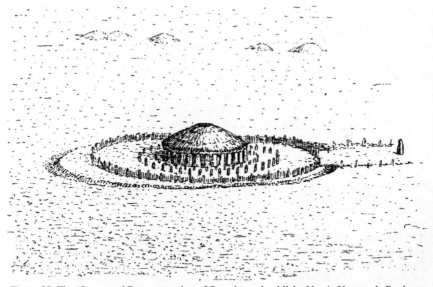

Figure 22. The 'Suggested Reconstruction of Stonehenge' published by A. Vayson de Pradenne in 1937 in the British archaeological journal *Antiquity* (Gloucester, Vol. XI, No. 41, March 1937, Figure 1, p. 89). After I had concluded from the ancient text of the Greek traveller Hecataeus that the 'spherical' temple used for astronomical observation which he described might have been Stonehenge with a domed roof of wood resting on its lintels, I came across this article and illustration by de Pradenne suggesting a domed Stonehenge for entirely different reasons. He was unaware of the text of Hecataeus. The case for Stonehenge having been roofed is a strong one, but it is rarely discussed.

The colonnade with architrave which forms the façade of the monument is a very characteristic architectural feature, and one which seems hardly intended merely to delimit an open space. The junction of the stones has been effected by mortise and tenon and these are features associated with the technique of woodwork; it seems to indicate that the makers were more carpenters than masons, which is a good reason for supposing that they might have thought of a wooden roof. Finally, on the lintel-stone joining the two highest uprights of the horseshoe, two unexplained mortises have been observed; they could be easily explained as supports for the roof-beams. If such mortises do not occur on the other trilithons, one might suppose that it was due to the particular situation of the former, which is not on the same level and situated in the vicinity of the central opening. It would need special *points d'appui*, whereas on the others, which are all of the same level, one could ultimately place horizontal sleepers to support the rafters.

Would the imposition of a roof over Stonehenge appear to be technically impossible? It must have seemed so in the eyes of certain persons, for Fergusson rejected the idea on *a priori* grounds without even discussing it. In actual fact, the space between the two successive circles of supporting-stones being 7.5 metres, if one assumes an inclination of 30 to 40 per cent for the roof, which appears to be that of the earth-lodge [of the Omaha Indians in America] figured by A. C. Fletcher, the beams should be between 8 and 9 metres long, which is by no means prohibitive for people who raised stones of a weight of 40 tons, and placed them on lintel-stones weighing 7 tons. One could still find such beams in the fine forests of England without the slightest difficulty. The covering of the whole roof with turf was quite possible in view of the existing climate. Moreover a similar procedure is still adopted in Scandinavia [and in the Hebrides Islands off the coast of Scotland].

Thus a series of facts combine to show that the monument of Stonehenge, whether it was a tomb or a dwelling-place [or a temple], must have been constructed in a manner comparable with the great wooden houses which were used by certain North American tribes. There seems to be no serious objection to this hypothesis.[77]

It is certainly most interesting that de Pradenne came to the same conclusions as myself about Stonehenge, but for entirely different reasons. The evidence which he and I separately bring forward should be taken seriously, especially in combination.

Another curious fact fell into my lap just before going to press. A book I had acquired but not yet read on the antiquities of Malta fell open as I was rearranging some of my piles of books, and I couldn't help but read the caption to a photo of the Middle Temple at Tarxien, Malta, which looks like a 'squashed-together Stonehenge', with uprights pressed right together and horizontal stones across them, and together forming a horseshoe as if a giant had taken smaller Stonehenge-like trilithons and squeezed them tightly into a solid ring with an opening. This structure was completely buried under the soil until 1914 and forms one of a complex of structures, since there are four distinct temple units at Tarxien. I do not wish to digress into the archaeology of Malta here, but the following remarks from the caption I mentioned are of more than passing interest in the light of my suggestion of a dome over Stonehenge: 'Left apse at the rear end of the Middle Temple at Tarxien. Remarkable is the perfect fit between the upright slabs. Above them the only surviving block of the first horizontal course has an inclined upper surface suggesting the spring of an arched dome. Could it be that by the end of the Temple period this culture had come to grips with the arch principle? Several prehistorians have expressed doubts on this possibility.' (Taken from p. 43, Anthony Bonanno, *Malta: An Archaeological Paradise*, Valetta, 1997.) Perhaps it was not the arch principle in stone that these remains really indicate, but rather the base of a dome made of perishable materials. In any case, the echo of the Stonehenge idea seemed too suggestive to leave unmentioned here.

So with that, we leave the ancient Britons. In the course of this chapter we have seen many 'disappearing telescopes'. Sometimes they are just omitted and replaced by dots, sometimes the words get changed or even erased, sometimes whole manuscripts (such as Ptolemy's *Optics*) seem to get burned, and the people like Roger Bacon who dared to read them and follow their principles are declared agents of the Devil. Classical scholars alter texts, translators fudge the translations, and so on and so on. People, it seems, will go to any lengths to avoid having to confront the unthinkable.

It has always been obvious from the surviving fragments of Democritus (fifth century BC), with whom we open Chapter Six, that rudimentary telescopes must have been available in antiquity. He expressed numerous views which indicate that he had been observing both the Moon and the stars through a telescope. He said, like the Hyperboreans (and perhaps he read this in Hecataeus and checked it out), that the Moon was like the Earth, that it had mountains which cast shadows, as well as valleys. How did he know that there were mountains which cast shadows on the Moon unless he had looked at it through a telescope? He also maintained that there were infinite worlds, differing in size, and that the Milky Way was not just a mass of light but was composed of innumerable small stars; and how could he make them out so surely, unless he had used a telescope to look more closely?

Possibly the best description of Democritus's views on the Milky Way is found in the somewhat obscure work *Commentary on the Dream of Scipio* by Macrobius (fourth/fifth centuries AD). Evidently, some of the writings of Democritus were still extant at that time:

Concerning this Milky Way many men have expressed different views, some offering fabulous explanations of its existence, others natural ones; we shall say nothing about the fabulous explanations and shall take up only those that seem essential to its nature. . . . Democritus's explanation was that countless stars, all of them small, had been compressed into a mass by their narrow confines, so that the scanty spaces lying between them were concealed; being thus close-set, they scattered light in all directions and consequently gave the appearance of a continuous beam of light.[78]

This has been realized since 1796, when Louis Dutens published the third and revised edition of his book (in French) *Origin of the Discoveries Attributed to the Moderns*. Dutens comments on the passage of Strabo with which we opened this chapter, and then relates it to the observations of Democritus:

In the first edition of this work I omitted to treat of the subject of telescopes. Aristotle is the first writer with whom I have found traces of the knowledge of the means that the ancients had of assisting sight or vision . . . The tube of which he speaks is the infant telescope . . . But I cannot refrain from being struck by a passage of Strabo (III, 1, 5) which is so clearly an explanation of the cause of the effects of the telescope, that I don't know how one can understand it otherwise . . . In comparing this passage of Strabo with the astronomical knowledge that Democritus seems to have acquired, and which seems to have depended upon the telescope, it is difficult to refrain from believing that the ancients had the use of the telescope . . .[79]

It is now more than 200 years since Dutens said that, and let us hope that at last the idea can find the acceptance which it deserves.

Notes

1. *The Geography of Strabo*, translated by H. C. Hamilton and W. Falconer, 3 vols, London, 1887, Volume I, p. 208, Note 1.
2. Caylus, Anne-Claude-Philippe de Thubières de Grimoard de Pestel de Lévy, Comte de, 'Sur les Connoissances Physiques des Anciens' ('On the Ancients' Knowledge of Physics'), in 'Réflexions Sommaires' ('Abstracts of Reflections') section in the *Histoire de l'Académie Royale des Inscriptions et Belles-Lettres* (*History of the Royal Academy of Inscriptions and Belles Lettres*), Paris, Vol. 27, published in 1761 (covering the years 1755–57); the contribution of de Caylus took place in December 1756.
3. *The Geography of Strabo*, translated by H. L. Jones, Loeb Classical Library, Harvard University Press, USA, Vol. II, 1988, pp. 10–11.
4. Recorde (Record), Robert, *The Path-way to Knowledg, Containing the First Principles of Geometrie*, London, 1551, unpaginated, but these comments are near the end of The Preface. A modern photographic reprint of this book was published in 1974 by Walter J. Johnson Inc., of Norwood, New Jersey, USA.

5. Bacon, Roger, *The 'Opus Majus' of Roger Bacon*, edited and with an introduction and analytical table by John Henry Bridges, Oxford Press, 2 vols 1897; Vol. II, Part 3, Chapter 3, pp. 164–5. The relevant parts of the Latin are: 'Et ponam aliqua exempla tam de fractione [refraction] quam de reflexione [reflection]. . . . Similiter possent specula [mirrors] erigi in alto contra civitates contrarias et exercitus, ut omnia quae fierent ab inimicis viderentur; et hoc potest fieri in omni distantia quam desideramus; quia secundum librum de speculis [Bridges gives a footnote saying see Propositions 13, 14, and 15 of the *Catoptrica* attributed to Euclid] potest una et eadem res videri per quotcunque specula volumnus, si debito modo situentur. Et ideo possunt propinquius et remotius situari, ut videremus rem quantum a longe vellemus. Sic enim Julius Caesar, quando voluit Angliam expugnare, refertur maxima specula erexisse, ut a Gallicano littore dispositionem civitatum et castrorum Angliae praevideret.'

6. Bacon, Roger, *The Opus Majus of*, translated by Robert Belle Burke, University of Pennsylvania Press, Philadelphia, 2 vols, 1928, Vol. II, pp. 580–2.

7. Camden, William, *Britannia* (in Latin), London, 1586, pp. 179–80, gives the original text in Latin as follows: '. . . vel gloriae cupiditate ut alii tradunt, inflammatus, anno ante Christim natum LIIII. & rursus sequenti, Britannium ingressus est. Cum antea, non ut fabulator Rog. Bachonus [Roger Bacon] speculis in ora Gallica dispositis, & arte Catoptrica [he refers to mirrors rather than lenses by this] quae latentes species multiplicat; sed per speculatores, ut ipse, & Suetonius contestantur, portus & navigationem exploras-set.' Twenty-four years later, the work was published in its English translation: Camden, William, *Britannia* (in English translated by Philemon Holland under the supervision of Camden), London, 1610, p. 343: '[Julius Caesar] in the yeare before Christs nativitie fiftie foure [that is, in 54 BC], and once againe in the yeare ensuing, entred into Britan: having found the havens [for ships] by his espialles [espyals – i.e. by means of spies], as Suetonius, and himselfe [Caesar himself] doth testifie; and not, as Roger Bachon [Bacon] fableth [i.e. writes, but his report is really only a fable], by setting certaine looking glasses upon the coast of Gaule, and by Art perspective, which by reflexion multiplieth hidden formes.'

8. The 'telescope of Caesar' was not discussed much further. Its next mention in print after the English translation of Camden's *Britannia* appeared in 1610 was in 1674. In that year, Anthony à Wood published his magnificent *Historia et Antiquitates Universitatis Oxoniensis* (*The History and Antiquities of the University of Oxford*) in its original Latin edition. Under his account of the year 1267, he says (I quote from the English translation by John Gutch which only appeared in 1792):

> Also Archimedes by his art perspective [optics] devised such Glasses within the Town of Syracusa [Syracuse, Sicily], commonly called Saragossa, that with them he could burn the enemies ships that came against it a great way from the Town, with other strange matters attributed to it. From this Science certainly, and other secrets in learning, it was that our famous Fryer [Friar] R. Bacon was esteemed by the vulgar Scholars so great a Necromancer [black magician]; but others since have so much vindicated his memory as to say that he never used that art any further than his Geometry permitted: By which and other Mathematical knowledge he performed such things that were most wonderful not only to the ordinary sort of Scholars, but to those that were accounted wise. There was also a great discourse in this and following ages that he had made a Glass in the Franciscan Frierie [Friary] in Oxford, in which men might see things that were done in other places [a telescope]; and thereupon it was judged to be done by the power of evil spirits, but certainly judicious men knew the reason of it to be natural, and to be wrought by Geometry (seeing that perspectives [optics] are a part of it) and to consist as well with reason as to the appearance of a face in a common glass [a reflection of a face in a common mirror]. . . . The chiefest person beyond seas [outside of Britain] for this art (for few there were, either in England or elsewhere famous for it, because it required great labour and expense) was Peter de Maharncourt, or Peter Peregrine as he is sometimes

called, who laboured so zealously in it, that he cared not for the words or blows of imper- tinent contradictors, but prosecuted what he had began [*sic*, = begun], taking a resolution to himself to abide in that Study till he had reaped some satisfaction. A little before this time [not long prior to 1267], he spent three years and above in making a Glass that should burn at a great distance, which none of the Latins [i.e. the French, Spanish, and Italians of the time] knew, or was ever attempted to be done among them. It is reported that Julius Caesar when he came to conquer Britain stood on the French shore, and viewed the whole Region with the Cities and Castles therein, that he might better inform himself of the place. (à Wood, Anthony, *Historia et Antiquitates Universitatis Oxoniensis*, 2 vols, Oxford, 1674, Vol. I, pp. 122b–123a. I have quoted from the English translation: à Wood, Anthony, *The History and Antiquities of the University of Oxford*, translated by John Gutch, 2 vols, Oxford, Vol. I, pp. 290–3.)

Even though à Wood wrote in Latin, the reference he gives is to the English, not the Latin, edition of Camden's *Britannia* for this information. And he clearly disregards Camden's dismissal of Bacon's report and, having a higher opinion of Bacon than Camden evidently did, he accepts the story as true.

No further mention of Caesar's telescope seems to have been made in print until 1767, when it is cited by a Frenchman. The English scientist Robert Smith published a very extensive textbook about optics in 1738 entitled *A Compleat System of Opticks*, in which he made a few comments about the history of optics, but not many. (Smith, Robert, *A Compleat System of Opticks*, 2 vols, Cambridge, 1738. Smith's comments relevant to the history of optics are to be found on pp. 30–1 of Vol. I and at the back of Vol. II where a fresh pagination commences, on pp. 11–16.) In 1755 a German translation of his work by Abraham Kästner appeared, with voluminous additions by Kästner himself. (Smith, Robert, *Vollständiger Lehrbegriff der Optik, nach Herrn Robert Smiths Englischen mit Änderungen und Zusätzen ausgearbeitet von Abraham Gotthelf Kästner* (*Complete System of Optics prepared by Abraham Gotthelf Kästner from the English of Mr Robert Smith, with Corrections and Additions*), Altenburg, 1755.) For many years I tried fruitlessly to locate in libraries both in Britain and abroad a book called *Lehrbegriff der Optik* by Abraham Kästner which had been referred to by various German writers on optics, until in the 1980s a book dealer suddenly offered it for sale at a very high price in London and I was able to obtain a photocopy of the entire work from him. This revealed that it was in fact a transla- tion of Smith's work, and hence listed under Smith in library catalogues, but because the additions by Kästner were so substantial, the German writers of the 18th and 19th centuries such as Gotthold Ephraim Lessing never bothered to mention Smith's name in their refer- ences, but only Kästner's. Mystery solved!

But, sobered by this discovery, I decided to check out the French translation of Smith's work as well, suspecting that it too would reveal substantial additions by its translator, and in this I was not disappointed. The French translation, published in 1767, was by a scholar called Father L. P. Pezenas. (Smith, Robert, *Cours Complet d'Optique . . . Avec Additions Considérables* (*Complete Course of Optics . . . with Considerable Additions*), translated and with additions by Father L. P. Pezenas, 2 vols, Avignon, 1767. (This work is 48.c.9 in the British Library.) Pezenas, like Kästner before him, appended voluminous remarks of his own in this work, which appear at the back of his second volume. However, nothing relevant to the history of optics appears in the main body of his additions; I discovered by diligent search that Pezenas had also freely interpolated his own comments throughout the entire main text, and early in the first volume referred to Julius Caesar's telescope as well as the optical instrument at the top of the Pharos Lighthouse at Alexandria (*Ibid.*, Vol. I, p. 77; the Pharos references cite Giambattista della Porta, *Magia Naturalis*, Book 17, Chapter 11, which we shall ourselves consider shortly), neither of which subjects was at all mentioned by Robert Smith himself.

The brief reference by Pezenas to Julius Caesar's telescope is apparently the last original reference to be made in the literature, so that it has been a dormant subject since 1767 in

French and since 1792 in English, when the English translation of à Wood was published. More than two centuries have thus elapsed since it was referred to in any way.

9. Riddle, John M. *Contraception and Abortion from the Ancient World to the Renaissance*, Harvard University Press, USA, 1992.
10. *Ibid.*, p. 28.
11. Rohl, David, *Legend: The Genesis of Civilisation*, Century, London, 1998, pp. 374–7.
12. Frazer, Sir James, *The Illustrated Golden Bough*, abridged by Robert Temple, B.T. Batsford, London, 1996, and other editions in different countries.
13. Frazer, Sir James, *Myths of the Origin of Fire*, Macmillan and Co., London, 1930, p. 195.
14. *Ibid.*
15. Anagnostakis, Andreas, *Meletai peri tēs Optikēs tōn Archaiōn (Studies concerning the Optics of the Ancients)*, Athens, 1878, p. 13.
16. Daux, A., *Recherches sur l'Origine et l'Emplacement des Emporia Phéniciens dans le Zeugis et la Byzacium (Researches on the Origin and Location of the Phoenician Emporia in the Zeugis and the Byzacium)*, Paris, 1869. The relevant sections are pp. 230–4 and Notes, pp. 281–9.
17. Daux also says:

> Without permitting us any certainty on this subject, one can nevertheless, because of the strangeness of the matter, recall that glass as well as a large number of its applications to industry had already been invented for a long time – several centuries before this epoch – by the Phoenicians; that the Greeks had learnt the art of fabricating glass, and that we have for proof of this their use of magnifying glasses, or to say better, glass globes filled with water which they used like magnifying glasses to engrave infinitely small subjects on precious stones. We have some of these engraved gems in our museums. Today we have to have the aid of powerful magnifying lenses to discover certain details of these ancient engravings on gems, which were very common in ancient times. I have had occasion to admire one in [North] Africa found, according to my informant, in the ruins of Hadrumetum [the modern Sousse]. This marvel of antiquity is a red carnelian, ovoid, from 17 to 18 millimetres [carved in a depression], across a surface of 15 mm, so that on that tiny surface is represented, engraved in a hollow, a Neptune with an entourage of sea deities; the chariot is a harnessed shell with four sea horses; Neptune is crowned and carries a trident; Tritons are playing trumpets, and Naiads [sea nymphs] frolic in the waves round the chariot of their sovereign. Each figure, admirably proportioned and executed with finesse, is already microscopic, but still the Greek artist has found the opportunity to show under the shoes of the front feet of the horses the nails which attach them, perfectly distinguishable with the aid of a very highly enlarging magnifying-glass. On the back of the gem is an inscription or a Greek name of which I deeply regret to this day that I have lost my copy. That gem is in Tunis; I thus put forward a fact which one can verify. So the conclusion is that as no human eyesight is capable of attaining to such a degree of acuity, it would have been of absolute necessity that the ancients had the capability to use instruments equivalent to our magnifying glasses in order to be able to execute such masterpieces; that not only were these devices obviously optical instruments, but that if they had such instruments that could be used to engrave on fine stones, it is by no means improbable that they had other uses for them, namely to bring things seen at a distance closer, that is to say telescopes.
>
> This example, which I quote for the purpose of the delicate art of engraving on precious stones, has an equal analogy for the purpose of bringing far objects closer; it is provided to us by the passage from Polyaenus which I have quoted.

18. Daux also tells us:

> The existence of these instruments in such ancient times ought not to surprise us unduly. We already know that the use of glass and its applications existed well before the time

of which Polybius speaks, as I have said above; and I have as evidence quite a number of fragments of glass which are interesting from this point of view which I have found in the Phoenician ruins, and at quite a depth under the surface.

Finally, it is demonstrated by the quantity of ancient objects discovered that the arts and diverse manufactures were very greatly developed from remote times. The history of Archimedes proves that ingenious and extremely clever people existed, and that they had produced precision instruments very skilfully conceived and of very great power. The most serious objection that one can raise against the existence of telescopes with the ancients is that they don't seem to have known about the grinding of glass, and that it would not have been possible for them, consequently, to fully grind and polish lenticular glass. This objection, in effect, is not without a certain force, because one has not found anything up until now that attests that they had the art of grinding and polishing glass. (*Footnote:* Nevertheless it is certain that some ancient peoples had ground and fashioned materials just as hard, such as, for example, precious stones to decorate jewellery, jade, carnelian, jasper, etc. These materials are just as resistant to being ground and polished as glass. Furthermore, Monsieur the Abbé Brasseur de Bourbourg and other travellers have seen magnifying glasses or lenses of rock crystal *ground and polished*, found under the ruins of the most ancient buildings in Mexico. The use of these crystal lenses appears, one could say, to date well before the era when the Phoenicians were making glass at Tyre and at Sidon. Everyone has been able to see a half-moon in rock crystal from the Boban Collection at an Exhibition put on last year [1867/8] at the Ministry of Public Instruction [in Paris]. The oldest documents of Mexico speak of the cutting of rock crystal more than twenty centuries before our time.) But in the absence of this precious method which seems modern, they had another resource at their disposal which could take the place of it: that was the use of flasks in very, very thin glass, hollow and round, of which the sides were ground all round and the faces convex. They took the form of a lens, and one filled them with very pure water.

(*Footnote:* This form of lens was common in ancient vases. I have also seen them in terra cotta. Even today there are some still preserved amongst certain African peoples.) (Seneca, *Natural Questions*, Book I, Chapter 6, indicates the usual use of these glass globes filled with water, used to enlarge objects. Cited by Monsieur Arthur [should be Charles, not Arthur] Chevalier, an ingenious optician who has written a remarkable treatise on optics.) Even nowadays, this use is perpetuated in certain industries, and the artisans work in the evening with the aid of a light filtered through glass globes filled with water. In the distilled liquid is a calculated quantity of sulphate of copper, giving to the light projected through the globe which extends beyond the actual enlarged diameter of the globe the [blue] tint of coloured sunlight. There is thus the means of replacing ground glass lenses well attested by the ancients. It remains to examine whether it was possible to apply it to the construction of telescopes; so if we take two magnifying glasses or two lenticular globes full of water of different diameters, and if we place them at a suitable distance apart, the smaller near to the eye and the larger in front of it, as an optician of Middelburg [in the Netherlands, where an early 'modern' telescope was made] in 1600 would have done, we would have an ocular lens and an objective lens and we would see faraway objects brought closer at the same instant. There is no need to enclose the glasses or the lenticular globes in a tube, to isolate any optical effect produced by the surrounding objects. This is a telescope, whether it is is equipped with filled glasses or lenticular globes filled with water. This construction, of an extreme simplicity, has as a drawback the fact that it inverts the images of the objects which it brings near, but one quickly becomes used to this inconvenience, and at all times, even today, skilled people use glasses which invert images. This simplicity even leads us to conclude that antiquity, having produced so many physicians and celebrated inventors, is, we believe, not granted a great honour by admitting their knowledge of the telescope, seeing that they had the elements of them to hand. The passage from Polybius seems to attest to this as well. It is true that these instruments were invented around 1600 at Middleburg [in the Netherlands] by Zachariah Jans, spectacle-maker, and that almost immediately the illustrious Galileo perfected them. The truth of this assertion cannot be contested. But nothing under the sun is new; and we daily invent things which we really rediscover a bit late, described in some little-known fragment of narratives from the Middle Ages or from the ancients.

We could cite many examples, such as gunpowder, which was known to the Chinese well before us, lighting gas, mirrors, etc. It is even the same in our time, so productive of progress, which seems to derive from marvels, that there still remain things to rediscover. I will quote one of them because it has come to my attention while researching the manufacture of glass, the last word on which is far from being said, and with which subject we are concerned at the moment. Dion Cassius [historian of the third century AD] refers to the following anecdote, which took place in the year 23 AD: 'An architect in Rome was condemned to exile by Tiberius for having reerected [i.e., straightened] with admirable skill a large public building which had leaned to one side. Tiberius was supposed to give him money, but, jealous of his reputation, chased him out of Rome. Some time afterwards, the same architect, having returned despite the ban to obtain pardon from Tiberius, purposely dropped in the Emperor's presence a magnificent glass vase which he held in his hand. The vase broke, but collecting all the fragments and handling them a little, he showed everyone the vase whole again, without any breaks. Tiberius, instead of recompensing him, condemned him to death.' Pliny, in his *Natural History* (XXXVI, 26), also assures us that from the time of Tiberius the means had been found of making glass which had been broken mended again. Thus this is a matter of which the existence and the properties in ancient times are affirmed by two eyewitnesses. Was it really of glass or some transparent and colourless substance? Little matter. Nevertheless, despite the evident fact that it once existed, we presently have no notion of it, and it remains to be rediscovered. Cannot we equally admit that telescopes were used by the ancients; that their use, being lost with time like so many other things, it was but a happy chance that led us to find them again in the year 1600?

(This voluminous quotation, from Daux, *op. cit.*, together with all the French translated for my book, has been translated by my wife Olivia Temple.)

19. Polybius, *The Histories*, translated by Evelyn S. Shuckburgh, Macmillan and Co., London, 1889, 2 vols, Vol. II, pp. 41–2.
20. *Ibid.*, p. 44.
21. Aelian, *Historical Miscellany*, Book 11, Chapter 11, edited and translated by N. G. Wilson, Harvard University Press, USA, 1997, p. 339.
22. *Ibid.*, footnote b.
23. Strabo, *The Geography*, translated by H. C. Hamilton and W. Falconer, 3 vols, George Bell & Sons (but Bohn's Libraries appears on the spines, as Bohn bought out Bell), London, 1887, Vol. I, p. 403.
24. *Ibid.*, footnote 4.
25. Pliny, *Natural History*, Book VII, Chapter 21, translated by H. Rackham, Loeb Classical Library, Harvard University Press, USA, Vol. II, 1969, p. 561.
26. Solinus, Gaius Julius, *Collectanea Rerum Memorabilium*, Chapter 5, translated by Arthur Golding, London, 1587, photographically reprinted by Scholars' Facsimiles & Reprints, Gainesville, Florida, USA, 1955, unpaginated, at the top of the second page of Cap. V. It seems evident that this information has simply been taken from Pliny's *Natural History*.
27. A similar situation existed for the Rhodes lenses – it took me nearly a year to get the authorities in Rome to search for the catalogue numbers in the records of the Italian archaeologists to enable the authorities in Rhodes to locate the Rhodes lenses, which had been excavated from the necropolis at Rhodes by the Italians at the time when Rhodes was occupied by the Italians, who took their records with them when they left.
28. Taylor, Harry L., 'The Antiquity of Lenses', in *American Journal of Physiological Optics*, Vol. 5, No. 4, pp. 514–16.

29. Beck, H. C., 'Ancient Magnifying Glasses', in *The Antiquaries Journal*, The Society of Antiquaries, London, Vol. 8, pp. 328–30.

30. Taylor, Harry L., 'Lens Work of the Ancients', in *The British Journal of Physiological Optics*, Vol. IV, Number 1, January 1930, pp. 1–3. Taylor, Harry L., 'The Origin and Development of Lenses in Ancient Times', in *The British Journal of Physiological Optics*, Vol. IV, Number 2, July 1930, pp. 97–103.

31. Forbes, R. J., *Studies in Ancient Technology*, Leiden, Vol. V, 1957, pp. 186–7. His discussion of ancient lenses is extraordinarily brief for such a prolix historian of science.

32. Iamblichus, *De Vita Pythagorae, & Protrepticae orationes ad Philosophiam* (*The Life of Pythagoras & the Protrepticus*), translated into Latin by Ioanne Arcerio Theodoreto, In Bibliopolio Commeliniano [sorry, I don't know where this is], 1598, fourth line of the Greek from the top of p.112 (mispaginated 121) but opposite the correctly paginated p. 113. A contemporary marginal note by hand is to Censorinus, Chapter 13, which I have not bothered to check. The Latin translation reads *per dioptras*, so merely Latinizes the Greek word; it is in the fourth line of Latin from the top.

33. Iamblichus, *The Life of Pythagoras, English Version*, translated by Kenneth Sylvan Guthrie, Platonist Press, Box 42, Alpine, New Jersey, USA, 1919, p. 55. This is one of Guthrie's famous mimeographed volumes, of which so few copies exist. Although a line appears to be missing on p. 55 this was merely a fault of the mimeograph drum, and no text is actually omitted. Guthrie writes at the head of this chapter, Chapter 26, 'from Nicomachus'. It is probable, therefore, that somewhere in the works of Nicomachus of Gerasa, the Neopythagorean mathematician and harmonist who lived between 50 and 150 AD, this same evidence of early telescopes is to be found, and that Iamblichus took it from him. I have not troubled to look through the entire works to try and find this sentence, for which no further reference is available. However, it could be done if anyone thought it important. Probably the place to look is in his *Manual of Harmony*.
Postscript: I was right! I came across the passage in that book as described in the main text postscript: the references are in notes 35 and 36 below.

34. Iamblichus, *Life of Pythagoras or Pythagoric Life, accompanied by Fragments of the Ethical Writings of Certain Pythagoreans in the Doric Dialect and a Collection of Pythagoric Sentences from Stobaeus and Others, which are Omitted by Gale in his Opuscula Mythologica, and Have Not Been Noticed by Any Editor*, translated by Thomas Taylor, London, 1818, pp. 83–4. The modern reprint of this book in 1965 was not photographic, but had reset type, so that the pagination of the reference is therefore different: Iamblichus, *Life of Pythagoras*, etc., John M. Watkins, London, 1965, pp. 61–2. I am very fortunate to have in my possession copies of all four of the relevant Iamblichus volumes which I have cited here.

35. *The Manual of Harmonics of Nicomachus the Pythagorean*, translation and commentary by Flora R. Levin, Phanes Press, Grand Rapids, Michigan, USA, 1994, p. 83.

36. *Ibid.*, p. 95.

37. Geminus with several other authors printed in *Uranologion sive Systema Variorum Authorum qui de Sphaera, ac Sideribus, Eorumque Motibus Graece commentati sunt*, edited by Dionysius Petavius, S.J., Paris, 1630. Geminus is the first text in this 347-page collection: *Geminou Eisagōgē eis ta Phainomena; Gemini Elementa Astronomiae interprete Edone Hilderico D.*, pp. 1–70. The relevant passage (Chapter Ten) is on p. 42. The Latin translation reads: 'Quod vero circularem faciat motum, ex eo manifestum est, quod omnes stellae ex eodem loco oriantur, & in eundem locum occidant, praeterea etiam per dioptra omnes stellae spectatae videntur circularem motum facere in tota circunductione dioptrorum.' The call number of this in the British Library is 48.h.19.

38. Bailly, Jean Sylvain, *Histoire de l'Astronomie Moderne depuis la Fondation de l'École de l'Alexandrie* (*History of Modern Astronomy since the Foundation of the School of Alexandria*), Paris, 1779, Vol. I, pp. 303–5.

39. *Ibid.*, Notes section, pp. 555–6.

40. Pouchet, Félix Archimède, *Histoire des Sciences Naturelles au Moyen Age ou Albert le*

Grand et Son Époque Considérés comme Point de Départ de l'École Expérimentale (*History of the Natural Sciences in the Middle Ages, or, Albert the Great and His Age, Considered as a Starting-Point of the Experimental School*), Paris, 1853, pp. 342–7.

41. Arago, Dominique François Jean (generally called François Arago), *Astronomie Populaire* (*Popular Astronomy*), 4 vols, Paris, 1854–7. I have quoted from the contemporary English translation, *Popular Astronomy*, translated by Admiral W. H. Smyth and Robert Grant, 2 vols, London, 1855; Vol. II, Book VI, Chapter 9, pp. 158–9.

42. *Ibid.*, pp. 156–9.

43. Aristotle, *Generation of Animals*, Book Five, Chapter 1, translated by A. L. Peck, Loeb Classical Library, Harvard University Press, USA, 1990, p. 493.

44. *Ibid.*, pp. 503–5.

45. Aristotle, *De Generatione Animalium*, translated by Arthur Platt, in Volume Five of *The Works of Aristotle Translated into English*, edited by J. A. Smith and W. D. Ross, Oxford Press, 1958, 780b.

46. Aristotle, *Generation*, translated by Peck, *op. cit.*, p. 505.

47. Aristotle, *Generatione*, translated by Platt, *op. cit.*, 781a.

48. *Ibid.*

49. This is in Z², meaning I presume that this Corpus Christi manuscript itself has two versions of the same text (?). At this point I lose my way, as Peck seems to be referring to something as mystical as 'the Two in One', which might as well be a theological concept for all I can make of it. There is *no* manuscript called Z², so it must be that Peck is referring to a palimpsest (erased and written-over) word in the Corpus Christi manuscript, since he adds the cryptic comment 'in ras.', which I take to be a Latin abbreviation meaning 'shaved off'. But this is just my guess, and is the only sense I can make of all this.

50. Temple, Olivia, and Temple, Robert, *Aesop. The Complete Fables*, Penguin Books, UK, 1998, pp. 94, 158, 236.

51. Temple, Robert K.G., 'An Anatomical Verification of the Reading of a Term in Extispicy', *The Journal of Cuneiform Studies*, Vol. 34, 1982, Philadelphia, USA, pp. 19–27, including two photos by myself as Figures 1 and 2. The text alone was reprinted as Appendix 2 to my book *Conversations with Eternity*, Rider, London, 1984, pp. 179–84.

52. Temple, Robert K. G., *Conversations with Eternity*, Rider, London, 1984, Plate XI.

53. *Ibid.*, pp. 102–3. The quotation is from Philo's obscure work 'On Animals Fit for Sacrifice', also called 'On Victims'; translation by C. D. Yonge, in *The Works of Philo Judaeus*, Bohn's Library, London, 1855, Vol. III, p. 221.

54. Parke, H. W., *Greek Oracles*, Hutchinson (paperback), London, 1967, p. 94.

55. Philostratus, *The Life of Apollonius of Tyana*, translated by F. C. Conybeare, 2 vols, Loeb Classical Library, Harvard University Press, USA, 1969; the quote is from Conybeare's Introduction to Vol. I, pp. vii-ix.

56. *Ibid.*, Vol. I, p. 123.

57. *Ibid.*, Vol. I, p. 257.

58. Libri, Guillaume, *Histoire des Sciences Mathématiques en Italie depuis la Renaissance des Lettres, Jusqu'à la Fin du Dix-Septième Siècle* (*History of the Mathematical Sciences in Italy since the Renaissance, to the Close of the Seventeenth Century*), Paris, 1835. The second edition was published in 1838, and I use its page numbers: see pp. 46–9.

59. Pancirollo/Pancirollus, Guidone (Guido), *Rerum Memorabilium Iam Olim Deperditarum & contra Recens Atque Ingeniose Inventarum: Libri Duo* (*The History of Many Memorable Things Lost, Which Were in Use among the Ancients: and An Account of Many Excellent Things Found, Now in Use among the Moderns, Both Natural and Artificial*), Amberg, 1599, the quotation taken from the anonymous English translation, London, 1715, reprinted in 1727, pp. 373–3. These comments are from the Supplementary Notes of Heinrich (Henricus) Salmuth.

60. Smith, Robert, *Cours Complet d'Optique* (*A Compleat System of Opticks*), translated by Father L. P. Pezenas, Avignon, 2 vols, 1767, Vol. I, p. 77.

61. Abat, Bonaventure, *Amusemens Philosophiques sur Diverses Parties des Sciences, et*

Principalement de la Physique et des Mathématiques (*Philosophical Diversions concerning Various Types of Sciences, and Principally of Physics and Mathematics*), Amsterdam and Marseilles, 1763, Diversion VI, pp. 361–414.

62. Libri, *op. cit.*, pp. 214–230, with much more about ancient telescopes.

63. It is clearly impossible to give all that Libri says on this subject, and to quote all of these authors would be too lengthy a business. Many of them, of course, are to be found only in Arabic. In fact, it is clear that the information about the optical instrument atop the Lighthouse originates entirely from Arabic sources, and no classical sources mentioning it survive. A full investigation of this fascinating matter is something to be undertaken in company with a highly skilled Arabist, and I intend to do that. Some of the references casually given above by Libri are really very important and impressive. He refers, for instance, to 'Masoudi'. That would be Abu 'l-Ḥasan al-Mas ' ūdi, author of the great cosmological, historical and geographical encyclopaedia which rivals Pliny, *Prairies of Gold*. He is very much an author to be reckoned with, and his evidence should not be discounted. 'Abd-allatif' is 'Abd al-Laṭīf al-Baghdādi, whose book *The Eastern Key* is a classic, full of unique information about Egypt. 'Abulféda' is Abu 'l-Fidā, a famous Arab geographer. 'Kazwini' is typical misspelling which could be more than one person, but may be the famous mathematician and astronomer, Muhammad ibn Mūsā al-Khwārazmi, whose name is always muddled by Europeans. However, Libri is more probably referring to 'Abdal-Rahman al-Khāzinī, an equally distinguished astronomer and scientist, who drew heavily upon the writings of Archimedes, of Hero of Alexandria, and of Philo of Byzantium, including works which are now lost to us. In fact, if this is the man Libri means, then this is the simplest answer to where the entire story came from – for he had access to Greek scientific tests which would have given the specifications of the optical instrument at the top of the Pharos Lighthouse. In short, anyone who ignores this tradition does so out of pitiful ignorance and does less than justice to the great works of Arabic science of that period.

64. There is just one other point to make about the Pharos Mirror before leaving the subject. Libri pointed out that Abu 'l-Fidā stated that it was made of 'Chinese metal'. But what is 'Chinese metal'? Let us look at the chronological context: Ptolemy III Euergetes reigned as Pharaoh of Egypt from 246 to 221 BC. In my book on the history of Chinese science and technology, I describe the Chinese invention of cast iron no later than the fourth century BC, their invention of steel no later than the second century BC by what we call today the 'Bessemer Process' of removing carbon from cast iron, and their invention of steel manufactured by what we call the 'Siemens Process' of co-fusion much later, by the fifth century AD. (Temple, Robert K. G., *China: Land of Discovery and Invention*, also titled *The Genius of China,* originally published in 1986, printed by various publishers at various dates but with the same pagination – see pp. 42, 49, and 68.) The Pharos Mirror was probably too early to have been made from polished 'Bessemer Process' steel imported from China. But it may be that cast iron was obtained from China for the mounting of the mirror, enabling a truly vast mirror to be used, the weight and size of which only such 'Chinese metal' would have had the strength to sustain. However, I put that forward at this stage only as a possibility – every aspect of the Pharos Mirror requires further research.

65. Higgins, Godfrey, *The Celtic Druids*, London, 1827, p.114.

66. Barth, Christian Karl, *Teutschlands Urgeschichte* (*Germany's Pre-History*), first edition, Bayreuth, 1818, pp. 10–11.

67. Barth, Karl, *Teutschlands Urgeschichte* (*Germany's Pre-History*), second vastly expanded and rewritten edition, Erlangen, 1840, p. 12.

68. In a moment we shall see what Diodorus actually says, but first I want to call attention to the interesting footnote by his Loeb Library translator, C. H. Oldfather, commenting on the probable identity of the Hyperboreans as the ancient British, so that we can see this is the general view of scholars today:

> There seems good reason . . . [he gives a reference to a German author, R. Hennig] . . . to see in this people who live 'beyond the north wind,' as their name signifies, an early

acquaintance of the Greeks, through the medium of the Celts, with Britain and its inhabitants. In this chapter Apollo would be the Celtic sun-god Borvon [or Bran], and the 'sacred precinct' of Apollo would be the famous Stone Age remains of Stonehenge. (Diodorus Siculus – 'Diodorus of Sicily', *Library of History*, translated by C. H. Oldfather, Loeb Classical Library, Harvard University Press, USA, 12 vols, Vol. II, 1967, pp. 36–7, note 2.)

69. *Ibid.*, pp. 37–41. The passage constitutes Chapter 47 of Book II, lacking only a few words at the beginning.
70. This passage was first brought to my attention about 1968 by the anthropologist Francis Huxley, who loved the mystery involved in the suggestion that the ancient Britons had used telescopes. His mentioning this to me at that time was a major boost to my curiosity, and I wish to pay tribute to him for that here. Francis had no explanation for the passage, but merely savoured its enigma. Nor could he remember the reference exactly, so that I had to track it down page by page. But without him, I would only have discovered this many years later, to the great detriment of my research.
71. Wood, John Edwin, *Sun, Moon and Standing Stones*, Oxford Press, 1978, p. 4.
72. Heggie, Douglas C., *Megalithic Science: Ancient Mathematics and Astronomy in Northwest Europe*, Thames and Hudson, London, 1981, p. 212. See also p. 106.
73. Thom, Alexander, *Megalithic Sites in Britain*, Oxford Press, 1967. Subsequent reprints were slightly revised.
74. Thom, Alexander, *Megalithic Lunar Observations*, Oxford Press, 1971.
75. Thom, *Sites, op. cit.*, pp. 1–22.
76. *Ibid.*, pp. 2–5, 165, 1.
77. de Pradenne, A. Vayson, 'The Use of Wood in Megalithic Structures', *Antiquity*, Gloucester, England, Vol. XI, No. 41, March 1937, pp. 87–92.
78. Macrobius, *Commentary on the Dream of Scipio*, Chapter 15, Section 6, translated with an introduction and notes by William Harris Stahl, Number XL VIII of the Records of Civilization, Sources and Studies, Columbia University Press, New York, 1952, p. 149.
79. Dutens, Louis, *Origine des Découvertes Attribuées aux Modernes (Origin of the Discoveries Attributed to the Moderns)*, London, 1796, p. 12. The first and second French editions of this work and the only English translation, *An Inquiry into the Origin of the Discoveries Attributed to the Moderns* (1769), do not contain these remarks.

Chapter Five

The Quest for the Death-ray

Archimedes was one of the greatest scientists in the history of the world. He was born about 287 BC and died in 212 BC. He invented many astounding machines, and was as fertile a genius as Leonardo da Vinci. He was born at Syracuse (modern Siracusa), a Sicilian port, and is believed to have been related to its King Hieron II, who was in any case his close friend. From our point of view in this book, the chief importance of Archimedes is that he invented and constructed a very large and deadly weapon to defend his city against an attack by the Roman fleet. The weapon was a multiple-mirror capable of reflecting the rays of the Sun in concentrated form and creating the first 'Death Ray' in history. For Archimedes's Burning-Mirror succeeded in setting fire to many Roman ships as they were attacking Syracuse. It was therefore a direct ancestor of the laser-beam weapons of today.

After Archimedes, many other people made huge burning-mirrors. The ancient Greeks Proclus (not the same as the Platonic philosopher of that name) and Anthemius, who both lived in the sixth century AD, did so. And much later, Peter Peregrine and Roger Bacon constructed a small version in the Middle Ages. Burning-mirrors in more modern times have been constructed by Athanasius Kircher and Gaspar Schott in the 17th century and the Comte du Buffon in the 18th century. Finally, Ioannis Sakas has done so as recently as the 1970s, with spectacular results, as we shall see. In all these cases, and many others, the efficacy of the invention of Archimedes has been amply demonstrated. Various scholars have written about the Burning-Mirror of Archimedes, expressing fashionable scepticism that it ever existed, and even if it did, insisting that it could not have burnt any ships. However, the plain physical evidence and many texts are against such a view. It has been proved over and over again that huge burning-mirrors do create beams capable of igniting wood within seconds at a great distance, and even of melting metal within seconds. There can be no doubt whatsoever that Archimedes's Burning-Mirror could have worked, and I believe that there is not the slightest doubt either that it actually did so. And it set the world off on 'the Quest for the Death Ray' which continues to this day.

In 212 BC, the Roman consul Marcus Claudius Marcellus laid siege to

Syracuse with the Roman fleet. Syracuse was defended by numerous clever inventions of its distinguished scientist Archimedes, including some strange and remarkable devices which are said to have raised the Roman ships up and suddenly dropped them, hoping to shatter their timbers or swamp them with water. The surviving account of the siege of Syracuse was written by Polybius (VII, 5–7), whom we have encountered already for his account of the Carthaginian signalling telescopes. Although the siege is also described by Plutarch and Livy, it has been pointed out by a classical scholar that they drew their accounts from that of Polybius and added nothing original about the siege themselves.[1] Some scholars have made heavy weather out of the fact that Polybius – and hence also Plutarch and Livy who derive from him – does not mention the burning-mirrors at all. A number of them have taken this to mean that they never existed. But we have already seen that the text of Polybius does not survive in its entirety, and we are very lucky indeed that the description of the Carthaginian telescopes does survive in two of the fragments that remain of an otherwise lost book. For all we know, the burning-mirrors were described in a lost fragment of that same book, which dealt with military methods and devices. And it is in any case not logically justifiable to interpret absence of evidence as evidence of absence.

The earliest surviving text of a classical writer referring to the burning-mirrors is Lucian (born *circa* 120 AD), in his *Hippias* 2, written in the second century AD, where he mentions Archimedes having destroyed the ships of Marcellus by fire 'with his skill'. About the same time the medical writer Galen (*circa* 129–199 AD) gave a more specific account where he actually mentions that it was burning-mirrors which were used.[2] Galen's younger contemporary Cassius Dio (second/third centuries AD) mentions the mirrors, as does the later scholar Johannes Zonaras (a 12th-century Byzantine) in his epitome of Dio's 15th Book.[3] (Dio's original text is lost, and only the summary survives.)

A famous standard reference work for classical scholars is J. Lemprière's *Classical Dictionary*. It has been reprinted in countless editions, and few have seen the original. Much of the information available in 1804 dropped out in subsequent editions, and the first edition is always a useful supplement to more modern sources on almost any subject. In discussing the siege of Syracuse under his entry for Archimedes in 1804, here is what Lemprière says in continuation about the Roman fleet:

> He set them also on fire with his burning glasses. When the town was taken, the Roman general gave strict orders to his soldiers not to hurt Archimedes, and even offered a reward to him who should bring the philosopher alive and safe into his presence. All these precautions were useless; Archimedes was so deeply engaged in solving a problem, that he was even ignorant that the enemy were in possession of the town; and a soldier, without knowing who he was, killed him, because he refused

to follow him, BC 212. Marcellus raised a monument over him, and placed upon it a cylinder and a sphere; but the place remained long unknown, till Cicero, during his quaestorship in Sicily, found it near one of the gates of Syracuse, surrounded with thorns and brambles. . . . The story of his burning glasses had always appeared fabulous to some of the moderns, till the experiments of Buffon demonstrated it beyond contradiction. These celebrated glasses were supposed to be reflectors made of metal, and capable of producing their effect at the distance of a bow shot.[4]

Modern writers no longer refer to the Comte du Buffon and his amazing experiments with burning-mirrors, because he has largely been forgotten. Indeed, few outside France any longer even know Buffon's name, though he was one of the greatest figures in the history of French science during the 18th century, and an astonishing polymath with apparently limitless energy.

It took great efforts to track down the two surviving burning-mirrors of Buffon, and this was largely done by my wife Olivia with assistance from our friend Fiona Eberts, who lives in Paris. For those not familiar with the niceties of French museum culture, the Conservatoire des Arts et Métiers does not immediately spring to mind, much less as the inevitable home of these objects. But they are indeed in their collection. I went to their great warehouse beside the main Paris football stadium – ironically on the same day as a key match in the World Cup in 1998. As I stepped off the RER underground train, I found myself surrounded not by hundreds but by many thousands of excited fans, and my friend Jenny and I were the only people trying to walk against the onrushing tide of humanity, making our way *away from* the coming game instead of rushing towards it. It was an eerie experience, and I felt that we were in a scene of a film where crowds were rushing to celebrate the end of the War.

Of the two Buffon burning-mirror devices possessed by the Conservatoire, the larger of 1741 (Plate 52) was not accessible, as it had been packed away and could not be unpacked for another couple of years. But the smaller of 1740 (Plate 51) was very much in evidence, that is, when one was taken to the shelf against a wall of the warehouse where it stood. The warehouse is very new, clean, and brilliantly organized and lit. Everything is wonderfully displayed even though everything is in storage! I had never seen such a clever setup. Museum warehouses are supposed to be dingy, cramped, with everything either lost or inaccessible, and certainly impossible to scrutinize in the gloom. But this Paris warehouse was the opposite – truly a new concept in storage, both a marvel and a paragon, for all the other museums in the world to emulate.

The 1740 mirror device was fascinating. The 48 little flat mirrors were mounted in such a way that they could be twiddled and teased with the greatest of ease to be pointing at a particular spot. One can imagine Buffon tapping and easing them into the precise positions for the necessary focus to be accomplished. Buffon had lavished money on the device, for the wood was embellished and everything had been prepared with all the care one would have expected of a piece of furniture intended for use in a drawing room. It was presumably this elegant construction with its 48 small mirrors which Buffon meant when he spoke of using a device with '45' mirrors to melt a large tin bottle weighing six pounds. The caption to Plates 51 and 52 give more of the details of both burning-mirrors.

The Comte du Buffon's demonstrations of various burning-mirrors, of constantly improving design, were spectacular in the extreme. No one who was familiar with them at the time was in any doubt that the principle of Archimedes's burning-mirror was viable. In 1747, when Buffon suddenly ignited a piece of wood 150 feet away with his mirrors, he had very nearly replicated the achievements of Archimedes in terms of both distance and efficacy.

But Buffon was by no means the first person to repeat the feat of Archimedes, a point not realized by many of his contemporaries. The irony is that several of the people who have reproduced Archimedes's achievement have been unaware of one another. The only such person alive today is Ioannis Sakas, whom I am privileged to know, and whom I have visited at his home in the suburbs of Athens. I was amazed to learn that Sakas had never heard of Buffon, or for that matter Kircher, Anthemius, Proclus, or any of the other people who had made large burning-mirrors, whether ancient or 'modern'. He had known only of Archimedes, and concerned himself solely with him, believing himself to be the first person to try and reproduce what Archimedes had accomplished.

In Plate 47 may be seen the extraordinary 'Archimedes experiment' of Sakas from the 1970s, a photo which he has very courteously made available for use here. In our own time, therefore, a man who is still very much alive has reproduced the feat of Archimedes in the most spectacular way, setting fire within seconds to a wooden boat in Piraeus Harbour at a distance greater than that achieved by Buffon. But we shall return to Sakas's project a bit later on.

I thought it best to call attention in the beginning to some question marks which had been raised over the truth of the account of Archimedes's burning-mirror, as the sceptical conclusions of many scholars have rather poisoned the discussion of this issue. It has been said many times that because 'the leading historians' did not mention the burning-mirror, that it was likely to be a myth. But these remarks are misleading, as we have already seen, because the deficiency is only in one 'leading historian', Polybius. The other two 'leading historians', Plutarch in his *Life of Marcellus* and Livy in his *History of Rome*, being dependent upon Polybius for their own accounts, also omitted it.

I have called attention to the loss of much of Polybius's text, but the question then arises: granted that much of Polybius's text is lost, presumably it wasn't lost to Plutarch and Livy, who might have quoted from the whole thing. My answer to this is that I suspect that any discussion of Archimedes's burning-mirror did not appear in Book Eight, where the siege of Syracuse is described, but may instead have appeared in the now-fragmentary Book Ten, along with the accounts of the Carthaginian telescopes which have mercifully survived. I believe Polybius compartmentalized his material in this way sometimes. After all, the detailed description of the use of telescopes by the Carthaginians *does not occur within the context of a discussion of the Carthaginian war at Sicily*. In the fragments as they now survive, Polybius is discussing King Philip undertaking to aid the Achaean League against a threatened attack by the Aetolians in alliance with Rome. Quite suddenly, prompted by a comment he has himself made about a fire signal, Polybius changes the subject by saying unexpectedly (Book Ten, Chapter 43):

> The method of signalling by fire, which is of the highest utility in the operations of war, has never before been clearly expounded; and I think I shall be doing a service if I do not pass it over, but give an account of it adequate to its importance.[5]

He then starts talking about the Carthaginian siege of Sicily! This is clear proof, in an optical context no less, that Polybius could interject a detailed technical explanation of military technology into a discussion of quite a different time and place than that relating to the actual use of that technology which he cites by way of its illustration. We cannot safely presume, therefore, that Polybius did not discuss the burning-mirror of Archimedes, because we do not possess by any means the full text of Polybius.

Furthermore, we must remember that the nature of ancient manuscripts was such that Book Eight and Book Ten, both being voluminous in their extent, could not possibly have appeared on the same book roll. (Manuscripts were kept rolled up round pieces of wood and stored in hollow wooden cylinders, which were stacked on shelves.) The ancient historical compilers were limited in the number of materials they could display in front of themselves at any given time. To spread out a single manuscript on a single book roll easily took up the whole table unless you were very agile and clever about it, restricting the amount of manuscript unfurled to only a tiny fraction, and squeezing another equally restricted bit of another roll beside it. But such side-by-side work was essentially impractical and unacceptably cumbersome. Cross-referencing thus was highly inconvenient and necessitated extensive extraction and note-taking by a metal stylus on wax tablets which were later wiped clean. If a historian did not have a very brilliant secretary indeed, things which were not presented side-by-side often did not get extracted from sources jointly.

The needs of Plutarch were to write a *Life of Marcellus*, not to be comprehensive about the activities of Archimedes, whose life he was not writing. Would he therefore have made a search of Book Ten of Polybius for additional technical information about Archimedes's weaponry? Probably not. He would have made do with Book Eight and left it at that. Polybius in Book Eight does not say that he gives a complete description of all the devices of Archimedes. In Chapter Five he says:

> Archimedes had constructed such defences both in the town, and at the places where an attack might be made by sea, that the garrison would have everything at hand which they might require at any moment, and be ready to meet without delay whatever the enemy might attempt against them.[6]

We should take note of the fact that Polybius is referring to a sequence of devices for use at different distances, and he does indeed give wonderful descriptions of the use of varying sizes of catapults, for instance. But he starts his account of the sequence of devices used at distances closer than those which would have applied to a burning-mirror. He does not refer to what happened earlier in the sequence. He therefore omits any description of that stage of the attack to which the burning-mirror would have applied. In the surviving account, he could not have described the use of the burning-mirror, because it would have related to a stage of the attack which he did not describe at all. This is a point which has been conveniently overlooked by certain scholars whose desire to discount the existence of a burning-mirror at all costs blinds them to the obvious.

Now let us look at what Livy wrote to see if the situation may not be quite as it has been painted by some commentators. The detailed description of Archimedes's clever defences against Marcellus in the siege of Syracuse is given in a single brief section of Book 24, in Chapter 34. If you read this chapter carefully, you can see that it is very clear that Livy *has omitted details of many weapons used by Archimedes*. He certainly makes no secret of it. Here are some key phrases in what he says:

> . . . Archimedes [was] a man of unrivalled skill in observing the heavens and the stars, but more deserving of admiration as the inventor and constructor of warlike engines and works, by means of which, with a very slight effort, he turned to ridicule what the enemy effected with great difficulty. The wall which ran along unequal eminences, most of which were high and difficult of access, he furnished with every kind of warlike engine, as seemed suitable to each particular place. Marcellus attacked from the quinqueremes [a form of battle-ship] the wall of Achradina, which, as before stated, was washed by the sea. . . . Against this naval armament, Archimedes placed on different parts of the walls engines of various dimensions.[7]

At this point, Livy mentions means of defence, referring to missiles being larger or smaller according to whether ships were nearer or further away, and describes one invention – a grappling hook which grabbed the ships beside the walls, raised them and dropped them again, swamping them with water. He mentions but does not actually describe 'every kind of warlike engine'. He then turns to the defence on the land side, saying of it 'on this side also the place was furnished with a similar array of engines of every kind, procured at the expense of [King] Hiero, who had given his attention to this object through a course of many years, and constructed by the unrivalled abilities of Archimedes.' And of these 'engines of every kind' he does not describe a single one.

From a close reading of Livy it is abundantly clear, therefore, that Livy refers *obliquely* to a large number of defensive military devices invented by Archimedes without giving a proper description of more than one of them. And his account makes clear that *there were many more* than the one he takes a moment to describe. His account of this subject is very brief, extending to only a single printed page. He had no intention of giving and made no attempt to give anything approaching a complete description of the military defences of Syracuse. The absence of an account of the burning-mirror therefore means precisely *nothing*.

The famous Edward Gibbon, author of *The Decline and Fall of the Roman Empire*, had a crisis of conscience over this matter, which has not always been accurately reported subsequently. For instance, a classicist writing in 1975 claimed:

> . . . Gibbon dismissed the tales of Archimedes and Proclus . . . While admitting that Archimedes could have invented such a device, Gibbon denied its use at Syracuse or anywhere else. Skepticism is still the historian's chief weapon against mendacity and carelessness . . .[8]

Here we see a typical example of someone too earnestly pursuing a sceptical argument, for which he claims a high pedigree and which he describes as his 'chief weapon'. But let us see what Gibbon actually said:

> A tradition has prevailed that the Roman fleet was reduced to ashes in the port of Syracuse by the burning-glasses of Archimedes; and it is asserted that a similar expedient was employed by Proclus to destroy the Gothic vessels in the harbour of Constantinople, and to protect his benefactor Anastasius against the bold enterprise of Vitalian. A machine was fixed on the walls of the city, consisting of an hexagon mirror of polished brass, with many smaller moveable polygons to receive and reflect the rays of the meridian sun; and a consuming flame was darted, to the distance, perhaps, of two hundred feet. The truth of these two extraordinary facts is invalidated by the silence of the most authentic historians; and the use of burning-glasses was never adopted in the attack or defence of places. Yet the admirable experiments of a French

philosopher [he is referring to the Comte du Buffon] have demonstrated the possibility of such a mirror; and, since it is possible, I am more disposed to attribute the art to the greatest mathematician of antiquity [he means Archimedes], than to give the merit of the fiction to the idle fancy of a monk or a sophist. [In other words, he accepts that it was invented by Archimedes rather than imagined by a later historian.] . . . Without any previous knowledge of Tzetzes [a historian who described Archimedes's burning-mirror] or Anthemius [who made burning-mirrors of his own in the sixth century AD], the immortal Buffon imagined and executed a set of burning-glasses, with which he could inflame planks at the distance of 200 feet . . . What miracles would not his genius have performed for the public service, with royal expense, and in the strong sun of Constantinople or Syracuse![9]

In no less than three places in these few sentences, Gibbon confuses glasses with mirrors. His knowledge of optics may be considered less than zero, as he obviously does not appreciate the difference between a lens and a mirror. He insists that no burning-glasses were ever used in the attack or defence of places, and then proceeds to accept that Archimedes *did* invent a burning-mirror. But what does he suppose Archimedes would have done with this burning-mirror? Kept it in the cupboard? Gibbon entirely ignores the important evidence on this subject by Anthemius, choosing instead to refer to Anthemius's pranks played on an annoying neighbour, which included temporarily blinding the man and his friends with strong reflecting mirrors. But we are not required to take seriously the pronouncements by Gibbon on a matter concerning optics of which he has not the slightest physical comprehension. And it is not correct to say that Gibbon dismissed Archimedes's mirror, because his statements on the subject clearly contradict one another. He dismissed it and then a few sentences later he accepted it. I think the only conclusion we can safely draw is that Gibbon was deeply confused and in this matter, unlike so many others, he simply didn't know what he was talking about. And that is certainly the case with some other scholars as well. Throw a classical scholar into the sea of scientific discussion and he will as often as not sink like a stone.

It is best at this point to turn straightaway to the remarkable evidence surviving from the writings of the Byzantine scientific genius Anthemius of Tralles, who died in 534 AD. It was Anthemius who first described the simple method of drawing an ellipse by looping a piece of string around two pins and holding the pencil against the loop.

Every tourist who visits Istanbul has an opportunity to appreciate the genius of Anthemius with great immediacy, for Anthemius was the architect who rebuilt St Sophia Cathedral – now a mosque – for the Emperor Justinian. He was therefore one of the greatest architects in history. But he was far more. As a true polymath, Anthemius was a 'Renaissance Man' long before his time. And as luck would have it, he is important to our story. For among the few fragments of his writings to survive are portions of his important book *On Mechanical Paradoxes*, containing a full description of the construction of a burning-mirror according to the principles of Archimedes, but greatly improved. In fact, we could describe the burning-mirror of Anthemius as a 'second generation weapon'.

However, before describing this, I want to take a moment to notice another of Anthemius's optical inventions – the sustained variable light source. In one of his surviving fragments he gives the problem as follows:

> It is required to cause a ray of the sun to fall in a given position, without moving away, at any hour or season. [He means in the daytime, obviously.][10]

I shall not give the details of Anthemius's geometrical ideas about the use of mirrors in order to achieve this, as they are highly technical and are not really of direct concern. I merely mention this because of its relevance to a problem which the ancient Egyptians must have faced in providing light for the interiors of the tombs and pyramids which they decorated and carved.

Figure 23. Anthemius of Tralles (died 534 AD) was not only a scientific and mathematical genius who constructed successful burning-mirrors to recreate the feats of Archimedes. He was also the chief architect of the spectacular Byzantine cathedral of St Sophia, seen here in a 19th-century engraving. Today this structure in Istanbul has been converted to use as a mosque and is one of the greatest tourist attractions in Turkey. The burning-mirrors and books of Anthemius may be lost, but his building lives on.

For, many people have asked – how did they see? There are no indications of the use of torches. Although when I was in Egypt I overheard a guide who was shepherding another group of people around say to them that there was a special kind of wax burnt in lamps for the illumination of the tombs, which left no smoke, when I asked her about it afterwards I was not entirely satisfied. It may well be that there was something of the kind. But I question whether it would have been sufficient for the painting done in the tombs. The painters and carvers must have made use of systems of mirrors to provide the light.

How interesting, therefore, that Anthemius concerned himself with the essential problem related to such a system. For as the sun continuously changed its position in the sky during the course of the day, the initial collecting mirror would have had to be moved by someone all day long. We must presume that as far as the Egyptians were concerned, they relied on manpower to provide the necessary adjustments for their supply of a continuous source of light. But it may well be that the problem was a famous one and that it was the Egyptian tomb-lighting which was the actual source of the problem which Anthemius considered.

The series of mirrors required by the Egyptians is referred to – or perhaps I should say is speculated upon – by many writers. But some have pointed out that the convoluted passageways in some of the tombs would have required a very large number of reflecting surfaces indeed to relay the distant sunlight to some of the more obscure corners where fine painting and carving was nevertheless accomplished. This is indeed a mysterious matter, and I do not wish to imply that there is anything remotely simple or straightforward about it. However, I do have personal experience of one very amusing and bizarre case of mirrors being used for reflection of images for a greater distance than any of us would normally envisage possible. It was a caution to me, and made me realize that we sometimes think things are not possible because no one would normally even think of attempting them. Perhaps I should briefly give the strange example.

A distant relation of my wife's was probably London's leading eccentric of the 1950s, 1960s and 1970s. Her name was Selina Kay-Shuttleworth, generally called just 'Mrs Shuttleworth'. We called her 'Shuttie'. She was a tragic person, who had been driven mad by grief. Her husband had been killed in the First War and her two sons had both been killed in the Second War. In fact, one of her sons had been a collector of airplanes – real ones, not models! – and the famous Shuttleworth Collection which is visited by hordes of tourists every year was given by Shuttie to the nation. Shuttie had been made demented by this loss of her loved ones. She lived in a large house in Clareville Grove in London, which she renumbered 999, even though Clareville Grove only has about 20 houses. She also called the house The House of the Sons of God, after her dead sons. Although she described herself as a Buddhist, Shuttie had what I can only describe as a Biblical image fetish. She made huge – and really very skilful – pictures of scenes such as Belshazzar's Feast out of smoothed multi-coloured tinfoil sweet wrappings. They were actually quite astonishing creations, and many of them were lit with flashing coloured Christmas lights or neon.

Over the fireplace on the first floor (what in America is called the second floor), Shuttie had the finest Monet painting of the Houses of Parliament in the evening mist which I have ever seen. One day, out of politeness, when we had been admiring her Biblical scenes, I asked her whether that painting were one of hers too. She didn't bat an eye, but with a dismissive wave of her hand, as if she were deprecating an insect which had come into the house, she said: 'Oh no, that's a Monet.'

Shuttie never locked her front door, and if the presence of a Monet upstairs had been suspected by unscrupulous people, this might have had bad consequences. In fact, her front door was often wide open, as we discovered one day when we turned up for tea. We looked around and called to Shuttie but there was no reply. The only sound was the usual bloodcurdling screams of her royal jacobin pigeons which she kept in the courtyard at the back. They are very peculiar birds, with huge ruffs at their neck, who sound as if they are being murdered without respite, even when they are strutting around with puffed ruffs looking like Queen Elizabeth I.

Eventually Shuttie descended from above. She then revealed to us that she had been observing our every move, and that one of her favourite pastimes was to sit at the top of the house – three or four storeys up – and watch the door and the ground floor through her intricate system of mirrors. She then took us on a tour of her mirror system, which involved climbing up past the large framed pedigree showing her imagined direct descent from the Prophet Abraham through her grandfather the Earl of Bradford. (She used to show us his wife's albums, 'Look, here's a small watercolour of the Shah of Persia when he came to stay in the 1880s. And here's a painting of Disraeli, who was such a chum of my grandmother's.') We never got to see Abraham's wife's albums, which we half-expected she must have.

We had never seen or imagined anything like Shuttie's system of mirrors. We were completely astonished how clearly one could see images which had been multiply reflected by perhaps eight mirrors, from an initial image which after all was only in rather subdued light to start with. And the point I wish to make is – who would ever bother to construct such a system of mirrors besides someone like Shuttie who was a bit batty? And never having seen such a thing, who could really imagine that it would work so well? I give this as a cautionary tale to those who think the ancient Egyptians could not have lit their tombs for their painters with intricate systems of mirrors.

Now to return to burning-mirrors rather than reflecting ones. The first thing to bear in mind about a burning-mirror is that it cannot be used to burn anything which is not in the same direction as the sun. So, if you are Archimedes wanting to burn Roman ships in Syracuse Harbour, you can only do it if the ships and the sun are both either west or east of you at the same time. Otherwise you cannot collect the rays in your mirrors.

This was pointed out by Anthemius, who studied Archimedes's feat and constructed his own multiple-mirror in emulation of him. The relevant fragment of Anthemius's text of *On Mechanical Paradoxes* which survives starts by posing this question:

> How shall we cause burning by means of the sun's rays in a given position, which is not less distant than the range of a bowshot?[11]

Anthemius answers the question in full, though we shall cut out the geometrical description:

> According to those who have described the construction of so-called burning mirrors the required experiment would seem to be impossible. [This is interesting evidence of the existence of many lost treatises dealing with such subjects.] For wherever conflagration occurs, the mirrors are always seen to be turned towards the sun. Consequently if the given position is not in the direction of the sun's rays, but inclined to one side or even behind, it is impossible to perform the experiment by means of the said burning mirrors. Furthermore, the required distance to the point of burning necessitates that the size of the burning mirror, according to the explanations of the ancients, shall be unobtainable; according to the aforesaid explanations, the proposed experiment could never be considered reasonable.
>
> But since Archimedes cannot be deprived of the credit of the unanimous tradition [sceptical classicists take note of this clear statement about unanimous testimonies!] which said that he burnt the enemy fleet with the rays of the sun, it is reasonable to suppose that the problem can be solved. We have given as much thought as possible to the matter, and shall explain a device for the purpose, assuming in advance some small preconditions for the experiment . . . [Here the geometrical analysis is omitted.] . . . Thus it is demonstrated that in whatever position or direction with respect to the rays of the sun the point Γ [the Greek letter *gamma*] lies, the reflection will be produced by the mirror towards the same point. And since combustion with burning mirrors occurs in no other way than by the conduction of a number of rays to one and the same point, it is natural that when the greatest heat is gathered, burning will occur.
>
> It is in the same manner that if there exists a fire in any place, the surrounding parts of the air nearby experience a corresponding degree of heat. If, conversely, we consider all the rays to be conducted into the central position, they will engender the power of fire.
>
> Therefore let it be required to conduct to the point which is distant not less than the stated interval [e.g. bowshot], other, different rays, from

smooth, plane mirrors in such a way that the reflected rays being concentrated in one spot produce combustion. The result can be obtained by several men holding mirrors in the required position and aiming them at the point Γ.

To avoid giving trouble by enlisting the help of many persons – we find that not less than 24 reflections are necessary to produce combustion – we devise the following method.[12]

Having come up with this solution which involved 24 men holding mirrors focused on the same spot [similar to the methods adopted in the 1970s by Sakas, as we shall see, although he had never heard of Anthemius], Anthemius then goes on to design an alternative device which does not require any men to stand around holding mirrors at all. It is interesting, by the way, that Anthemius says of the mirrors held by the 24 men *we find that not less than 24 reflections are necessary*', for this demonstrates that he actually carried out a series of attempts with increasing numbers of men until he reached the number of 24. It is important that we realize that Anthemius, architect of one of the greatest buildings of antiquity, was not just an armchair scientist. From his own comments we may see that he went to a great deal of trouble over what must have been a considerable period of time, and incurred what must also have been a great deal of expense (24 mirrors must have cost a lot in those days!), to try to reproduce the feat of Archimedes. Here, then, is what Anthemius says of his alternative invention which does not require the men to hold any mirrors:

Let there be a plane hexagonal reflector ABΓΔEZ and other similar reflectors adjacent and connected to the first along the straight lines AB, BΓ, ΓΔ, ΔE, EZ, each having a slightly smaller diameter and capable of being hinged about those straight lines, the connection being made by strips of leather or by ball and socket joints. If, then, we place the surrounding mirrors in the same plane as the central one, reflection will obviously be in the same direction from each conjoined mirror. Whereas, if the central mirror is left unmoved, and we incline all the surrounding mirrors inwards towards the one at the centre, by a little discovery easily put to use, it is clear that the rays reflected from the surrounding mirrors will be directed to the middle of the original mirror. Then if proceeding in the same way, we arrange other mirrors around those that we have just mentioned, so that they can be inclined towards the central mirror, and then collect the rays in the same spot in the manner described, combustion will occur at the given position.

Combustion will be caused more effectively if fire is produced by means of four or five mirrors, or even as many as seven, if they are distant from each other in proportion to their distance from the point of combustion, in such a manner that the rays cut each other and produce the desired heating more intensely. For when the mirrors are in one place

Plate 1

Plate 2

Plate 3

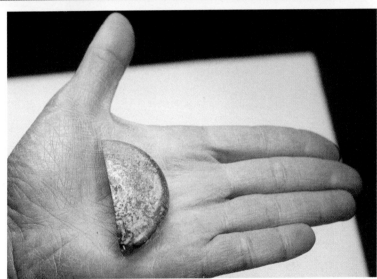

Plate 4

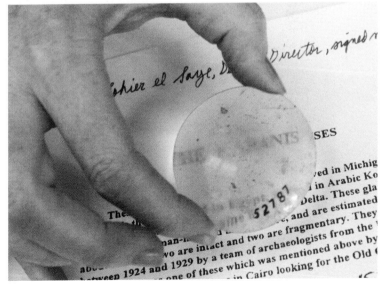

Plate 5

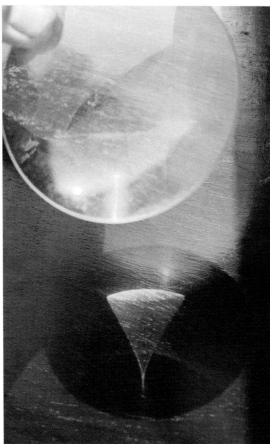

Plate 6

Plate 7

Plate 8

DE LA SPHERE. 3

FIGURE I.

COSMOGRAPHIE
ou
SCIENCE DU MONDE

Région Æthérée

Région Elementaire

TERRE

Plate 9

Plate 10

Plate 11

Plate 12

Plate 13

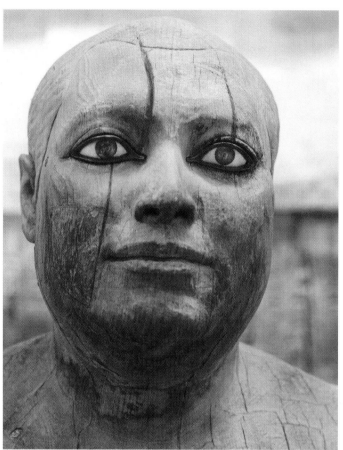

Plate 14

Plate 15

Plate 16

Plate 17

Plate 18

Plate 19

Plate 20

Plate 21

Plate 22

Plate 23

Plate 24

Plate 25

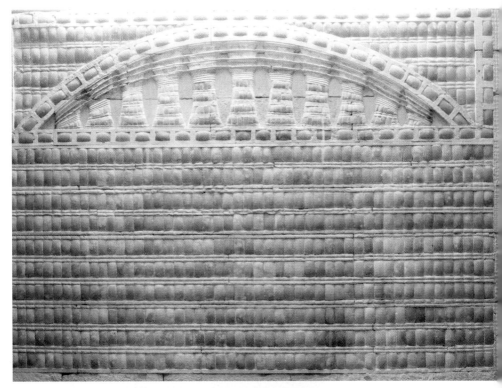

Plate 26

Plate 27

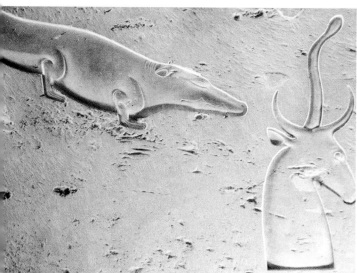

Plate 28

Plate 29

Plate 30

Plate 31

COLOUR PLATE SECTION CAPTIONS

PLATE 1

Really in a nutshell! . . . This Chinese woman with her flowers is actually standing inside half a walnut shell. The figure and the flowers are made by an ancient technique of 'dough sculpture', modelled microscopically from coloured bits of flour dough by Madame Lang Zhi Ying of Beijing, from whom I bought this specimen. She had done another sculpture in which no less than sixteen people were standing inside a nutshell, but it was so expensive I chose this cheaper sample of her work. Another centre of microscopic artwork in China is the city of Suzhou, where one can buy pearls on which whole texts have been written in Chinese characters; I myself bought a pearl with a panda painted on it. These are sold with magnifying lenses to enable you to see the handiwork. Such miniature work is mentioned in Chinese texts over the course of more than 2000 years, which takes it back to the time of the Roman examples mentioned by Cicero, Varro, Aelian, and others, including 'the *Iliad* in a nutshell'. It was this tradition which led to Shakespeare's famous passage in *Hamlet* about a world bounded by a nutshell. The fact that China is the only ancient civilization still in existence today explains why this microscopic art has maintained an unbroken tradition for more than two millennia, while the examples mentioned by the Roman authors seem to belong only to an unreachable and distant past.
(Photo by Kevin Wright)

PLATE 2

This pair of plane-convex glass lenses was discovered embedded in the remains of resin used to preserve the body of a mummy in a stone sarcophagus at Carthage, dating from the fourth century BC. They were found in 1902 by the Rev. Delattre, of the French White Fathers, when Tunisia was still a French colony and the Carthage Museum was known as the Lavigerie Museum. The Carthaginian military telescopes described by the historian Polybius were two centuries later. The identity of the wearer of these spectacles is unknown!
(Photo by William A. Graham)

PLATE 3

The sixteen Carthaginian lenses, two of rock crystal and 14 of glass, which were excavated at the site of Carthage by the French. The two small ones in the centre of the front row are of crystal and are still transparent. The two in the back row, at the right, are the 'Sarcophagus Pair' seen also in Plate 2. All these lenses are plano-convex. They were found together in a box in storage and have apparently never been displayed.
(Photo by William A. Graham)

PLATE 4

The Cuming Lens, which I found amongst tens of thousands of small objects in the storeroom of the Cuming Museum, London. It was excavated in the City of London by C. R. Smith in 1848, apparently during building construction. This lens was not ground but cast in a mould, and the green glass would once have been transparent; it is still translucent. More than half of the lens has broken away and was lost prior to discovery.
(Photo by Robert Temple.)

PLATE 5

The Cairo Lens (object number: Cairo J52787), a Roman glass lens in the Egyptian Museum at Cairo. *Circa* third century AD. This lens was one of four excavated at Karanis, known in

Arabic as Kom Aushim or Kom Ushim in the Fayum region. The other three Karanis lenses are at the Kelsey Museum, University of Michigan, USA.
(Photo by Robert Temple.)

PLATE 6
The shape of an axe-head is easily obtained by focusing the sun's rays through a lens, as seen here. This photo was taken at dusk, so that the more mellow light would allow the pattern to be seen more strikingly and without 'burning a hole in the film'. But when the sunlight is stronger in the daytime the 'double-axe' pattern is easily seen, since by twisting the lens a bit, the pattern of the light is teased out from the bottom point and spreads outwards again to form a second axe-head opposite to the first. I suggest that this phenomenon was one which the ancient Minoans observed with awe, through their many crystal lenses, thinking it to have some profound meaning. It may have led to the sacred 'double-axe' (*labrys*) symbol being adopted for religious use. In addition, it should be recognized that more rounded and blunt stone axe-heads were precious objects since the times of the cavemen, and the two traditions doubtless coalesced to some extent. But the Minoan 'double-axe' was a highly specific motif which was repeated incessantly in Minoan art and design, and was certainly not just a hearkening back to the Stone Age. The fact that a crystal lens industry existed at Minoan Knossos certainly gives good grounds for believing in this theory of the lens origin of the motif.
(Photo by Robert Temple)

PLATE 7
This prehistoric ceremonial hearth was excavated at Lerna, near Argos in the Peloponnese, and dates to *circa* 2500 BC, long before any Greeks existed in Greece. Around the edges of the depression in which the kindling would have been placed, a flame pattern may be seen. The depression itself is made in the shape of a double-axe head, where one end is slightly larger than the other. This is the same pattern of focused light which one can obtain by manipulating a lens in one's hand in sunlight. The double-axe motif later so prominent in Minoan culture on Crete appears to have originated earlier, and this may be the earliest known example of it. The motif appears to have been optical in origin, from the awe created by such patterns associated with 'bringing down fire from heaven' to light the sacred fires with 'pure fire' by means of crystal lenses. It is theoretically possible for a depressed shape such as this to match precisely the pattern of focused light from a lens held above it; however, in this case the hearth is so large that the size of the lens would have had to be enormous, so that in this case the association must be symbolic. Lerna mysteriously persisted in classical Greek legend, since it is supposed to be the site where Hercules went to kill the monster called the Hydra. (This was his 'Second Labour.') The Hydra was 'many-headed', and perhaps this was an echo of the 'double-headed' axe pattern which we see here.
(Argos Museum. Photo by Robert Temple)

PLATE 8
'The Crystal Sun' – a hand-coloured engraving by A. M. Mallet published in the French survey of science, *Description de l'Univers (Description of the Universe)*, in 1683. The earth is shown suspended in space with the rays of the sun streaming down upon it. The sun, suspended in the aetheric regions, appears to be gathering the ambient light of the cosmos and refracting it earth-wards. In fact, this was not actually prepared as an illustration of the ideas of Philolaus but merely resembles his concept because of artist's licence.
(Collection of Robert Temple)

PLATE 9
A piece of rock crystal which I purchased in China, containing a globule of water in its interior which has been there since the formation of the crystal. Such a specimen is called a 'hydro', and is very rare. When the crystal is moved, the water globule slides back and forth in a cavity. The globule is the round shape inside the crystal which can be clearly seen in this closeup

photo. It was specimens such as this which led the ancient Greeks to believe that rock crystal was not an earthly mineral at all, but was ultra-compacted ice which fell from the sky and was too dense to melt (except that occasionally bits in the centre, such as this globule, had evidently 'melted').
(Photo by Robert Temple)

PLATE 10

What is this person doing? – This painted fragment of a fifth/fourth century BC Greek pot was excavated at the Shrine of the Nymph (which was destroyed in 86 BC) on the south slope of the Acropolis in Athens between 1955 and 1960 in connection with the construction of a road. It is roughly contemporary with Plato, whose teacher Socrates was lampooned by Aristophanes in the play *The Clouds*, in a scene where a crystal lens features in the story. This person may even have attended a live performance, in which case an 'opera glass' was clearly available! – Millions of people have filed past this object in the Acropolis Museum at Athens (in an alcove of Room V, Case 6, Object Number NA.55.Aa, 4) without 'seeing' it. *Why do they not 'see' it?* – Is it because we only 'see' what we are told in advance can exist? Is it because something which is 'impossible' takes on a cloak of invisibility so that all the displaying in the world cannot achieve a single perceptual acknowledgement? Presumably we face here the phenomenon of *consensus blindness*.
(Photo by Robert Temple)

PLATE 11

'The Prometheus Lens'. This is the only ancient lens which I actually have in my personal possession. I acquired it from my friend, the late Peter Mitchell, who in turn acquired it from an antique dealer long before I knew him. From the archaic style, the engraving on the flat base may be dated to the sixth century BC in Greece. It may be contemporary with the manufacture of the lens, or it may have been added later. In any case, as it is transparent, it in no way interferes with the optical use of the lens. However, a very crude borehole goes through the length of this plano-convex lens, in striking contrast to the meticulous perfection of the cutting and polishing of the lens itself. The borehole was made so that the lens could be converted into a jewel to be worn on a Greek swivel-ring. Many such rings survive, and they were generally of gold. I have examined several in the British Museum. If the engraving was done when the lens was converted into use for a ring, then the ring was made in about the sixth century BC and the lens must be earlier. These crystal lenses which were recycled for use in swivel-rings may originally have been Mycenaean or even Minoan. Certainly there are a number of Mycenaean lenses on public display in the Athens Museum, although they are not identified as such, and it is possible that they were really manufactured much earlier, in Minoan times, when the crystal lens industry was really in full swing at Knossos in Crete. As for the engraving, it may be seen that the flying winged figure holds a small round object in each hand and is peering through one of them. I believe that since the engraving is *on* a lens, the objects depicted in the figure's hands are themselves lenses. And since all one needs to do when holding a lens in each hand is to hold them up and look through them both at once in order to find that one has 'constructed' a rudimentary telescope, I believe that the engraving is a reference to that phenomenon. Then the question arises: who is the winged figure? Normally one would conclude that it was a 'flying Eros'. However, the optical allusions, and the possibility of using the lens to 'bring fire from Heaven' as a burning-glass, lead me to speculate that the figure is really meant to represent Prometheus, the fire-bringer. (I have explained in the main text that his mythical tube was really a telescope tube.) That is why I call this 'the Prometheus Lens'. Of course, the figure *may* be a flying Eros, and not Prometheus, but it doesn't really matter.
(Photo by Robert Temple)

PLATE 12

The stalk of the huge umbelliferate plant *Heracleum Giganteum*, commonly known as Giant Hogweed. (Be careful, its leaves can give you a skin rash!) It grows readily to a height of fifteen

211

The Crystal Sun

to twenty feet. It may be the closest surviving example we have of something which resembles the stalk of the extinct *narthex*, or Giant Fennel, which grew to about the same height. This sturdy stalk would not make a bad tube for a rudimentary telescope, as it is hollow and strong. The stalk of this plant is only faintly striated, but the Giant Fennel may have had a strongly striated stalk if the Fourth Dynasty Egyptian 'coffee mug' shown in Plate 13 is a model of the extinct plant's stalk. I am not satisfied that the Giant Fennel is necessarily extinct, and I intend to search for it in the small oases west of Siwa by the Libyan border. Its main habitat was once Cyrene, on the coast of modern Libya, and it became 'extinct' two thousand years ago because of its birth control properties. Although the flora of the larger Egyptian oases is surprisingly uniform and limited, anything might survive in a cranny of a small deserted oasis deep in the real desert. Giant Fennel was also reported on a small uninhabited island in the Aegean about a hundred years ago, but that report is probably of a smaller wild fennel which grows only ten feet high. Just to be on the safe side though, I shall make a point of visiting that island on some favourable occasion.
(Photo by Robert Temple)

PLATE 13
'Khufu's Coffee Mug', as my wife and I like to call it. According to Sir Flinders Petrie, who excavated it, this 'durite' ceramic object was made during the reign of the Fourth Dynasty Pharaoh Khufu (Cheops), 2551–2528 BC. It is currently Inv. No. 1935–466 in the London Science Museum, where it has been on loan from the Petrie Museum since 1936 as part of a weights and measures collection. It is 'a cylindrical measure with a loop handle' of 20.8 cubic inches capacity; this is a volume-measure known to us by its Greek name of *one kotula* (Syrian *kotyle*). It is not perfectly round, its diameter varying between 9.08 and 9.16 cm. It is 8.9 cm high and 0.86 cm thick. The importance of this object is that it represents a segment of a thick stalk, which may be the stalk of the extinct Giant Fennel, probably in true size. We do not know whether the Giant Fennel had a ribbed stalk, but this may be evidence that it had. It was the Giant Fennel which is believed to have provided the earliest telescope tubes.
(Photo by Robert Temple)

PLATE 14
The affable face of Ka-aper, who lived four and a half thousand years ago in the Egyptian Fifth Dynasty, and is still with us. He looks sentimental and would have made a good friend. In fact, his 'double' today sells postcards in the same museum, the Egyptian Museum at Cairo. The statue is of wood, excavated from his tomb at Saqqara. The edges of the eyelids are of copper and the eyes are inlaid with alabaster, with perfectly ground and polished plano-convex rock crystal lenses in the centre forming the irises. The pupils are black dots painted behind the lenses, which magnify them and give sparkling life to Ka-aper's face.
(Photo by Robert Temple)

PLATE 15
A side view of Ka-aper's face. This enables us to appreciate the convexity of the crystal lens which forms the iris of his eye, as well as its perfect transparency. The pupil, a black dot painted behind the lens, is magnified and lifelike even from the side. The glow created in the eye by the crystal makes it look as if Ka-aper is about to speak, or is at the very least thinking carefully about what he sees and will at any moment have a comment. It is doubtful whether one could claim that the art of sculpture ever progressed beyond this point, which calls into question the dogma of the 'inevitability of progress'.
(Photo by Robert Temple)

PLATE 16
The face of an unknown man of the Fifth Dynasty, from a statue made of wood. The corneas of the eyes are of beautifully polished convex rock crystal. Experts differ on whether the whites of the eyes are made of bone or limestone, but probably the latter. The eyelids are of metal,

Colour Plate Section

thought to be copper. The perfection of the grinding of crystal lenses of *circa* 2400 BC is well shown in this example.
(The Egyptian Museum, Cairo. Photo by Robert Temple)

PLATE 17

'Scarface', or 'Old Blue Eyes', not to be confused with Frank Sinatra. His real name was King Hor and he reigned during the 13th Dynasty during the collapse of the Middle Kingdom, in the Second Intermediate Period – a brief dynasty (1794–1648 BC) which had approximately fifty competing kings within a century and a half. It was obviously not a stable period of Egyptian history and it ended with the invasion of Egypt by foreigners from the east called the Hyksos, who seized control of the country and imposed alien rule. This magnificent wooden striding statue of King Hor was excavated in his shrine at Dahshur, near the Pyramid of Amenemhat III. Above the king's head are two raised arms, representing his *ka*, or soul, and the statue of the king is meant to be an exact replica of his body. The spooky expression is due to the perfectly ground and polished plano-convex rock crystal lenses which form the irises of the eyes; King Hor appears to be gazing out at eternity. I have not found any Egyptian crystal eyes later than this date, and the art of crystal lens-making in Egypt appears not to have survived the Hyksos invasion in 1648 BC. There is no evidence known to me which indicates that any of the pharaohs of the later New Kingdom knew about or could command the crafts-manship to produce such crystal eyes, and statues such as this were never to be produced in Egypt again.
(The Egyptian Museum at Cairo. Photo by Robert Temple)

PLATE 18

The famous statue of the Third Dynasty Pharaoh Zoser (*circa* 2630–2611 BC), which was found beneath his Step Pyramid at Saqqara. It is now on prominent display near the entrance to the Egyptian Museum, Cairo. The statue once had inlaid eyes in what are now the cavernous empty eye sockets, and as they were stolen by ancient robbers, must have been considered valuable, and not merely of limestone. It is probable that they were of rock crystal, like the many from the Fourth and Fifth Dynasties which followed. Rock crystal was being expertly carved in Predynastic times, and many beautiful pieces from the First and Second Dynasties survive in museums. The Zoser statue may be the earliest evidence of the manufacture of the many Old Kingdom crystal eyes, and as they were perfectly ground convex lenses, their frequent occur-rence proves that the technology for telescopes was readily to hand; indeed any pair of crystal eyes taken from any of the statues if looked through at once would constitute a rudimentary telescope, so that it is impossible to imagine that the uses of such perfect lens-pairs did *not* function in that manner in other contexts than the statues themselves.
(Photo by Robert Temple)

PLATE 19

The dog-headed god Anubis, shown in a wall carving in the Temple of Osiris built by Pharaoh Seti I (19th Dynasty) at Abydos in Upper Egypt. To his right, Seti I bends forward and makes an offering to Anubis of incense, the fumes of which are seen in the usual stylistic depiction arising from the small incense bowl. In his right hand, Anubis holds an *ankh*, symbol of life. In his left hand he carried the *tchām* or *was* staff. The bifurcated bottom of this staff was placed on the ground at the tip of an obelisk or gnomon shadow and precisely defined its edge to within a fraction of an inch for the purposes of measuring the exact length of the year. The curved head of the staff, sometimes shown with canine features presumably in tribute to Anubis, was similarly used 'to give a clear and measurable shadow', according to Egyptologist Martin Isler. The use of these staffs seems to precede dynastic times in Egypt. By the time of Pharaoh Cheops of the 4th Dynasty, a frieze bearing his cartouche which was rescued from a rubble site already portrays them as standardized decorative motifs, indicating that their scientific purpose was becoming subordinated to mere decoration.
(Photo by Robert Temple)

PLATE 20

The 'light-offering' to the god Amun, offered by the Pharaoh Rameses III in his small temple near the entrance to the great Temple of Amun at Karnak. This image shows, at left, the feather of Maāt, followed by the Egyptian numeral III which serves both to identify the king and to evoke the memory of his famous forebear Amunhotep III, who was so closely associated with Karnak. This light-image can be seen for only three minutes, before it vanishes. In November it appears at about 8:30 AM, when I happened to be present.
(Photo by Robert Temple)

PLATE 21

The light-beams shoot through the stone window-grating of the small Temple of Rameses III at Karnak, to form the 'light-offering' to the god Amun seen in Plate 20. (Steel reinforcements to the original roof placed by archaeologists may be seen in the ceiling.) The window-grating is original, dating from the 12th century BC, which was the early Twentieth Dynasty of the New Kingdom. All four openings can be seen to be vertical rectangles. Why, then, does one of them form a feather of Maāt at the moment of the 'light-offering' rather than a normal vertical strip of light like the others? The reason for this is that the curvature of the stone outside the window is such that it moulds the strip of light into the shape of the feather only for a few minutes just as the 'light-offering' hits the incense tray. A quarter of an hour later, the feather has become two golden balls, one atop the other, and then they too vanish. This is genuine 'light-sculpture'.
(Photo by Robert Temple)

PLATE 22

A detail of a ceiling in the Temple of Hathor at Denderah in Upper Egypt. This is part of the famous 'square zodiac' ceiling. Above is the rising sun entering the vagina of the sky-goddess Nut (whose arched body spans the ceiling, and from whose mouth it will emerge at sunset). Its rays stream down in the form of a shower of superimposed mini-obelisks, illuminating the face of the goddess Hathor – who among other things represents the heliacal rising of the star Sirius just before sunrise – with her typical symbolic cow's ears, crowning a column above a temple entrance (presumably representing Denderah itself). This graphic depiction illustrates the tradition preserved by the Roman author Pliny in the first century AD that to the Egyptians the obelisk represented 'a petrified ray of sunlight'. To the right, a celestial crab just below the sky goddess's knee represents the zodiacal sign of Cancer, one of many zodiacal indications on the ceiling. The French astronomer Jean-Baptiste Biot pointed out that the rising of the sun at the summer solstice at the time of the construction of this temple at Denderah was in the sign of Cancer, which is clearly why Cancer is depicted here along with the rising sun. (See R. A. Schwaller de Lubicz, *Sacred Science*, Inner Traditions, USA, 1988, Appendix VII, p. 284.) The condition of the ceiling since its engraving by the French in the mid-nineteenth century has so drastically deteriorated that most of the astronomical designs can no longer be properly discerned. Within a few decades this scene will presumably no longer be visible.
(Photo by Robert Temple)

PLATE 23

The goddess Seshet, goddess of foundations, construction, and surveying, as well as 'lady of the house of books'. She always wears on her head a stalk surmounted by rays, which vary in number between five, seven, and nine. In many depictions over thousands of years she is shown holding a very long notched palm and inserting a reed into one of the notches. Egyptologists do not really know what these scenes are meant to represent. Here we have more detail than usual, in a late carving from Ptolemaic times at Philae, in an obscure corner of the buildings outside the main temple which I did not even notice on my first visit. The goddess grasps in her left hand the mysterious notched palm jointly with a *uas* sceptre. The insertion of the reed into a particular notch looks highly deliberate, and it is hard to avoid the impression that something was being measured. – But what? – Can it have anything to do with shadows and light, as the association with the sceptre would suggest? It is possible that the reason why graduated scales

214

for use with optical proto-theodolites in ancient Egypt have not survived is that they were made of perishable materials, and that notched reeds in fact represented evenly spaced degrees for such surveying measurements. The goddess may thus be depicted making a note of an angular measure by marking the degree in its notch. Whereas *djeds* may have been used for distant vertical foresight measurements, notched reeds may have been much closer to the sighting instrument. Most depictions of Seshet show her holding one or two notched reeds vertically, resting their bases on the ground, and indicating a particular notch; it would not even have been necessary to count from a distance, as the person taking the sighting could merely call out when the reed was inserted into the correct notch, it could then be indicated with a daub of colour, and the notches counted subsequently to establish the degree.
(Photo by Robert Temple)

PLATE 24

An unpublished limestone mould of unknown provenance from Egypt, tentatively dated to the 'Late Period' (i.e., 712 BC – 343 BC). It is on display in the Petrie Museum in London (U.C. 30143). It shows the Benu Bird (the Phoenix, always portrayed as a tufted heron) alighting on a *benben* stone – either a pyramid or a pyramidion. Although this design may be from the Late Period, in typical Egyptian conservative fashion it reproduces accurately a scene which dates from the Second Dynasty (*circa* 2770 BC – 2649 BC), at least two thousand years earlier, as described by Alexandre Moret in his article 'l'Influence du Décor Solaire sur la Pyramide' ('The Influence of Solar Decoration on the Pyramid', in *Mémoires de l'Institut Français* (*Memoirs of the French Institute* [in Egypt]), Vol. LXVI, *Mélanges Maspero* (*Collections relating to [Gaston] Maspero*), Vol. I, pp. 623–36. There he described the same scene as it appears on a Second Dynasty sculpture in the Egyptian Museum in Cairo (p. 624, translation by Olivia Temple): '. . . a monument much more ancient than the Pyramid . . . has preserved (an) allusion to the *Ben* of the Phoenix, because it excellently illustrates . . . passage 1652b [of the Pyramid Texts]. It concerns the archaic statue at Cairo Number 3072, where the Horus names of the Kings of Nebrā, Hetepsekhemui and Netermu (at the end of the Second Dynasty, *circa* 2900 BC) are engraved on the shoulder of a kneeling man. The royal names . . . are preceded by a bird like a tufted heron which is not a falcon but which resembles the Phoenix *benu*; it clutches in its talons the conical end of a baetyl in a vague pyramidal form . . . I have no doubt that this represents the Benu shining like the Ben as in the Pyramid Texts.' [Moret reproduces this inscription and the picture of the Benu bird.] Since this picture was one of the chief symbols of the Temple of the Sun at Heliopolis, a structure now wholly vanished near Cairo, this object may well come from there.
(Photo by Robert Temple)

PLATE 25

A 'visitation by the god Horus.' As I stood observing this obelisk at Karnak, with a carving of the hawk of Horus as its topmost design, a hawk flew up and perched on the tip of the obelisk in the same posture as he is depicted in the carving. The space between the two hawks was originally plated in highly-polished gold, to reflect the rays of the sun.
(Photo by Robert Temple)

PLATE 26

The 'multiple-*djed*' wall panel made of countless blue-green glazed tiles which was found in the underground tunnels beneath the Step Pyramid of King Zoser (Third Dynasty, *circa* 2630–2611 BC) at Saqqara. It was designed, as was the whole pyramid, by the famous architect, scientist, and philosopher, Imhotep. There are eleven *djed*'s along the top, and the slots along the tops which form graduated arcs may have constituted a forward-sighting device for use in surveying.
(The Egyptian Museum, Cairo. Photo by Robert Temple)

PLATE 27

Carvings on a pillar at the Temple of Isis at Philae in Upper Egypt. The central design is a *djed* surmounted evidently by a solar disc, which may indicate the use of the *djed* for measuring positions in the sky of heavenly bodies by means of the equally-spaced sighting-notches (the possible use of the *djed* as a foresight in observation and surveying). Alternatively, the disc could represent a mirror used for sighting at a distance.
(Photo by Robert Temple)

PLATE 28

A celestial crocodile on the wall of the Tomb of Seti II in the Valley of the Kings near Luxor in Egypt. This beast is multiply-defined by 26° angles: a horizontal line intersecting the tip of the crocodile's snout makes a 26° angle with a line which grazes the top of his back, whereas a horizontal line intersecting the tip of his forepaw makes a 26° angle with a line grazing the bottom of his posterior. Furthermore, a horizontal line intersecting the centre of the horned beast's head makes a 26° angle with the tip of the crocodile's snout and hence also is the same line which grazes the top of the crocodile's back. The crocodile is thus not only zooming down at an angle of 26°, but his actual dimensions are defined by the same angles. We thus find that the entire composition is governed by a series of golden triangles. But there is even more: a horizontal line intersecting the centre of the horned beast's eye forms a 26° angle with a line which runs along the edge of the crocodile's own eye, and then goes on to graze the top of the crocodile's back where it meets the other such line; the eyes of the two beasts are thus joined by a golden triangle as well. Their ears are also joined by a further golden triangle: a horizontal line intersecting the tip of the horned beast's ear forms a 26° angle with a line to the centre of the crocodile's ear. The tip of the horned beast's central horn is also joined by a golden triangle with the lowest point of the crocodile's body: a horizontal line intersecting the tip of the horn forms an inverted angle of 26° with a line touching the lowest part of the crocodile's body above its forepaw, thus linking the highest point of the horned beast's bead with the lowest part of the crocodile's body by an inverted golden triangle. The use of the golden triangle as the fundamental principle in the canon of Egyptian art is thus illustrated here in massive redundancy. What is even more extraordinary is that this work of art was sealed in a tomb which was never meant to be entered for eternity, so that there would be no opportunity for anyone to appreciate all the trouble which was taken over the design.
(Photo by Robert Temple)

PLATE 29

Sunrise at Karnak: the light streams through from the Inner Sanctum of the great Temple of Amun towards the west. This is only possible now because of the partial collapse of the walls at the rear. The Temple of Amun was not a sunrise temple but a *sunset* temple for observation of the summer solstice sunset, and the light streaming down the corridor in antiquity went the other way! In ancient times, there was no opening for sunlight at the 'rear' such as we see now. This view is therefore only meant to be suggestive: imagine streaming light like this going the other way, for the enormous distance of 550 yards, and culminating in a solar disc being projected on the back wall of the Inner Sanctum for two or three minutes a year in the presence of the pharaoh, who was thus 'alone with Rā,' as the ancient texts say.
(Photo by Robert Temple)

PLATE 30

Winter solstice at the Giza Plateau in Egypt: on the left is the winter solstice shadow cast upon the south face of the Great Pyramid by the second pyramid (of Khafre/Chephren) at sunset. The shadow has an angle of 26°, which is the same angle as that of the interior Ascending Passage as well as the Descending Passage. It thus indicates on the outside what is concealed on the inside, although at right angles to the interior passages. The vertical line dividing the south face into two, the technical name for which is an *apothegm*, cannot be seen by the naked eye from the ground, but is shown clearly in the aerial photo in Plate 65. Where this solstice shadow

216

Colour Plate Section

meets the apothegm, a golden triangle is formed, just as the Ascending Passage itself forms a golden triangle; the Grand Gallery in the interior is also defined by a golden section measurement (for which see Figure 54). The King's Chamber contains no less than eight golden triangles. The entire Egyptian artistic canon was based upon the golden mean (for an example see Figure 55). It was I who first recognized this winter solstice shadow in 1998 prior to the solstice, and arranged for his friend to photograph it for him on the day. If the Pyramid of Khafre/Chephren had been positioned even a fraction differently, the shadow would not have worked. This suggests that the positioning was precise. But the geometry and mathematics involved in calculating the precise shape and angle of a shadow to be cast upon the Great Pyramid on a certain day at a certain hour as projected by another pyramid more than 500 yards away are so prodigious that we are left marvelling at the audacity of those who planned it, and who if they had made a slight mistake would have had to dismantle the entire second pyramid and try again! The point where the shadow intersects the eastern end of the south face probably indicates an important interior feature, but a precise measurement needs to be made. By counting the courses of masonry in this photo, it seems that it may indicate the level of the King's Chamber. The winter solstice shadow needs careful study, as it probably indicates various concealed interior structures, some of which may still be unknown to us. What corresponds in the interior to the meeting of the shadow with the apothegm, or with a vertical line dropped from that point? What if anything corresponds to the vertical line dropped from the shadow meeting the eastern edge of the south face? What are the other two angles of the whole triangle formed by the shadow? The solstice shadow is not a case of merely showing-off. The fact that the positioning of an entire second pyramid appears to have been decided upon in order for this shadow to be shown means that the shadow must have many secrets to reveal. A determined effort should be made to discover all of these.

The ancient Egyptians believed that the pyramids represented the descending rays of the sun, but at the most important sunset of the year – the shortest day – a 'third ray' (light from the setting sun) caused the 'first and second (frozen) rays' (the two pyramids themselves) to manifest and display a fundamental geometrical principle by interaction. Sacred optics thus underlay this, as well as so many other, aspects of ancient Egyptian civilization.
(Photo by Mohamed Nazmy)

PLATE 31

The ascending passage of the Valley Temple at Giza, near the Sphinx. I discovered that the slope of this passage is the same as that of both the ascending passage and the descending passage inside the Great Pyramid, and also makes the same angle as the winter solstice shadow cast onto the south face of the Great Pyramid. Since this passage makes a golden triangle, like the one which marks the commencement of the Grand Gallery inside the Great Pyramid (see Figure 54), it would be natural to expect a crypt feature beneath the western end of this passage. The floor of the passage is made of a form of alabaster; the walls are of granite blocks which – as can be seen clearly in the photo – fit together perfectly, and the passage was once covered with a roof accessible by a locked passage reached through the small door on the right halfway up the passage.
(Photo by Robert Temple)

the reflected rays cut each other at very acute angles, so that almost the whole space surrounding the axis is heated and bursts into flame. Hence the combustion does not only occur about the single given point. Moreover, it is possible to blind the sight of an enemy by the construction of these same plane mirrors, because when the enemy advances, he does not see the approach of his adversaries, who have plane mirrors fitted to the upper parts, or to the insides, of their shields; so that the sun's rays are reflected to the enemy in the manner described, and they are easily routed.

Therefore combustion at a given distance is possible by means of burning mirrors or reflectors, as well as the other effects described. Indeed, those who recall the constructions of the god-like Archimedes, mention that he effected ignition not by means of a single burning mirror but by several. And I think that there can be no other means of causing burning at so great a distance.[13]

We can probably safely conclude that the brilliant Anthemius was the first person to recreate the techniques of Archimedes with burning-mirrors since the time of Archimedes himself. It is doubtful if anyone else managed the feat during the interval of eight centuries which elapsed between their lifetimes. Archimedes was further back in time for Anthemius than the mediaeval Roger Bacon is for us. This helps us appreciate the extraordinary genius of Anthemius, the loss of most of whose writings is such a tragedy for the history of science.

After Anthemius, burning-mirrors capable of use in war were no longer a mystery at Constantinople. Anthemius was a famous figure. His demonstrations involving many attempts using men holding mirrors, culminating at last when he reached the number of 24, would have been widely known, at least in certain circles. He then published his account, which was widely available for all men of science to read. A wide variety of other treatises, now lost, was of course also available. These would have included the work *On Burning-Mirrors* (*Peri Pyreiōn*) by Diocles, *circa* 200 BC, not long after the time of Archimedes. This work is preserved only in a defective Arabic translation which has been translated into English[14] and two long extracts in Greek by Eutocius, Anthemius's older contemporary (born about 480 AD at Ascalon, Palestine), who wrote three commentaries on works of Archimedes, and who probably was responsible for arousing Anthemius's interest in this subject in the first place.

Nineteen years before the death of Anthemius, in 515 AD, his teacher Proclus is said to have used burning-mirrors to destroy ships of the fleet of Vitalian (or Vitellius) besieging Constantinople Harbour. This is recorded by the 12th-century Byzantine historian, Johannes Zonaras (*Epitome of Histories*, I, 14, p. 55). Zonaras described Proclus 'launching upon the enemy's vessels, from the surface of reflecting mirrors, such a quantity of flame as reduced them to ashes'.[15] From this it seems that Proclus used many men holding mirrors rather than a single device such as that conceived by Anthemius. Since this took place very much in Anthemius's lifetime, and Proclus was his teacher, it is likely that they accomplished this feat together, and it may well have been in connection with this necessity, or its expectation, that Anthemius undertook the experiments which resulted in his discovery that he needed at least 24 men to hold mirrors in order to achieve success. Although some writers have groundlessly accused Johannes Zonaras of making up the story about Proclus, there is no reason whatever to doubt him, since we have the explicit surviving evidence of Anthemius's own text describing the very process which Zonaras said was utilized by Proclus in the same city at the same time.

There is one other record of the use of burning-mirrors as weapons of war against a fleet in antiquity, at the other end of the Mediterranean world, on the Atlantic coast of Spain. And in this instance, the burning-mirrors were actually mounted on ships and used against enemy ships! No notice of this extraordinary event has entered into any of the discussions of ancient burning-mirrors, and I seem to have been the first person concerned with such matters to have come across it. The account is found in the unlikely source of Macrobius, a fourth-/fifth-century AD Latin author. We have already encountered him earlier, and seen his descriptions of optical magnification in his work *The Saturnalia*. It is in that same work (Book I, Chapter 20) where, in the midst of a discussion about the Sun, Macrobius gives this information which appears not to be preserved anywhere else in ancient literature:

Furthermore, the manifold forms of religious observances practised by the Egyptians argue the manifold powers of the god and point to Hercules as the sun 'which is in all and through all'. Another proof of this identification, and that no light proof, is provided by an event which occurred in another land. For when Theron, king of Hither Spain, was driven by a mad desire to capture the temple of Hercules [at Gades, which is today called Cadiz] and fitted out a fleet, the men of Gades sailed out to meet him with their ships of war. Battle was joined, and the issue of the fight was still undecided when the king's ships suddenly took to flight and at the same time burst into flames without warning and were consumed. The very few enemy survivors, who were taken prisoner, said that they had seen lions standing on the prows of the ships of Gades and that of a sudden their own ships had been set on fire by a discharge of rays like those which are represented surrounding the head of the sun.[16]

I have to confess that I am not clear as to the identity of this Theron, King of Hither Spain. He cannot be the same man as Theron, Tyrant of Acragas in Sicily between 488–472 BC. And as he is so obscure, missing from various reference books and not appearing in the indices of various historians, I am unable to give a date for this incident. Gades [Cadiz] itself was a colony of the Phoenicians of Tyre. Since the inhabitants of Gades from this account seem to have possessed small but effective burning-mirrors which they mounted on the bows of their warships, we have here evidence of one of the secret weapons of that people which might help to explain their mastery of the seas for so long. In Appendix Two I mention a lens which had been excavated at Tyre ('the Tyre Lens'), which is the only evidence I know of for optical technology there. But we must remember that the Carthaginians were Phoenicians, and in Chapter Four we saw the clear evidence of their superiority in optical technology – both the survival of many lenses excavated at Carthage, and the textual descriptions of their usage of telescopes. So perhaps we should not be surprised that their kinsmen at Gades had perfected the use of burning-mirrors in sea battles. At a guess, I should say that this incident must have taken place subsequent to the time of Archimedes, for otherwise we would have to postulate an earlier inventor. But it is for someone more learned in the minutiae of the early history of Spain than I to tell us who King Theron was and when he lived.

Not only have modern writers about ancient burning-mirrors not known of this evidence, but Byzantine and later European writers were equally ignorant of it. This is a great pity, since people inclined towards scepticism for its own sake have had great fun in dismissing the accounts of Archimedes and Proclus in one breath, since they actually were discussed together by later historians and can thus be swept away in the same stroke, or so some might imagine. (This is easier to do when they are ignorant of the work of Anthemius, and their purposes are unobstructed by the inconvenient obstacles of evidence.) But if the *wholly separate* account given by Macrobius had ever come to anyone's attention before now, it would have required yet more explaining-away.

After this, no record exists of the use of burning-mirrors in warfare. Some centuries elapsed before the discussion of Archimedes and Proclus is seen again amongst the later Byzantines. The first of which I have been able to find a trace is the philosopher Michael Psellos, who was born in 1018. He studied the works of Archimedes and of Heron of Alexandria [first century AD], and presumably of Anthemius, and carried out actual experiments. Among other things 'he demonstrated the use of a mirror as a burning-glass'.[17] Since the experimental undertakings of Psellos were generally extremely ambitious, it is likely that he reproduced the results of Anthemius and Proclus, but purely as an experiment, and with no actual use in war.

In the succeeding century, the 12th, three scholars recorded information about Archimedes's burning-mirror which they had found in ancient books:

Johannes Zonaras, Johannes Tzetzes, and Eustathius. Zonaras wrote of Archimedes:

> For by tilting a kind of mirror toward the sun he concentrated the sun's beam upon it; and owing to the thickness and smoothness of the mirror he ignited the air from this beam and kindled a great flame, the whole of which he directed upon the ships that lay at anchor in the path of the fire, until he consumed them all.[18]

Tzetzes writes of Archimedes:

> When Marcellus withdrew (his ships) a bow-shot thence [away from the city walls], the old man [Archimedes] constructed a kind of hexagonal mirror, and at an interval proportionate to the size of the mirror, he set similar small mirrors with four edges, moving by links and by a kind of hinge, and made the glass [he means the mirror] the centre of the sun's beams – its noontide beam, whether in summer or in the dead of winter. So after that, when the beams were reflected into this, a terrible kindling of flame arose upon the ships, and he reduced them to ashes a bow-shot off. Thus by his contrivances did the old man vanquish Marcellus.[19]

Tzetzes says that the authorities whom he has consulted for accounts of the burning-mirror of Archimedes include Dio Cassius (second century AD), Diodorus Siculus (a first-century BC historian native to Sicily, the home of Archimedes, and author of a Life of Archimedes which is now lost), Anthemius, Heron of Alexandria (first-century AD mathematician and inventor, author of a book on mirrors and another on sighting-tubes), Philo/Philon of Byzantium (a scientist of the late third century BC, and hence contemporary with Archimedes; this lost text used by Tzetzes being contemporary with Archimedes must have been of the highest importance; we know also that Heron used the works of Philon and knew this source as well), and Pappus of Alexandria (fourth century AD, a scientist and mathematician who wrote about Archimedes and optics among other things).

A third 12th-century Byzantine writer also left an account of the burning-mirror of Archimedes. He was Eustathius, who rose to the high clerical position of Metropolitan of Thessalonica, dying in 1195. His writings were all written prior to 1175, as he devoted the last 20 years of his life to his clerical duties. Eustathius's comments appear in the unlikely context of his *Commentary on the Iliad* (p. 118 in the Basle edition of 1558), where he says: 'Archimedes by a catoptric machine [i.e. a device of mirrors], burnt the Roman fleet at a bow's-shot distance.'[20]

However, long before the Byzantines Zonaras, Tzetzes, and Eustathius, the subject was taken up by the famous Arab writer whom we call Alhazen, but whose Arabic name is Ibn al-Haitham, or, to give his full name, Abū

'Alī ibn al-Hasan ibn al-Haitham. He was born *circa* 965 in Basra, but lived his active life in Egypt and died in Cairo *circa* 1039. His great work of optics is entitled in Arabic *Kitāb al-manāzir* (*Book of Optics*). This was published in Latin translation in 1572 by Federico Risner/Risnero, and the magnificent imaginary scene depicting the sun's rays being reflected by multiple mirrors at Syracuse onto a ship of the Roman fleet by Archimedes, which forms the book's frontispiece, may be seen reproduced as Figure 24. (The artist is not as good at optics as the author, since he shows the sun at an unacceptable angle, but that is artist's licence.) An equally imaginary view of the feat of Archimedes, using a single gigantic refracting lens, and published in 1646, may also be seen in Figure 26.

Manuscript translations of Alhazen's *Optics* into Latin were in circulation for centuries before Risnero finally published the work, and had a pronounced influence upon Roger Bacon in the 13th century. Alhazen's discussion of Archimedes was presumably one of the sources of inspiration which persuaded Bacon (1214–92) to construct his own burning-mirror. Much earlier we have commented on Bacon's construction of a telescope, of how this led him to be accused of heresy and black magic, and so details of his burning-mirrors – doubtless another device of the Devil in the eyes of Bacon's tormentors – are scarce.

We do not know when Archimedes's own work *Catoptrica* (*On Mirrors*) was lost, but it must have been in antiquity, so that by the time of Alhazen, the Byzantines, and Roger Bacon, it could no longer be consulted. It may even have been lost by the time of Anthemius, though the fact that he does not mention it in the brief surviving fragments of his work cannot be considered conclusive, for the very reason that we only have those fragments and we have no idea what he may have said in the extensive sections of his work which do not survive.

Another famous optical scientist contemporary with Roger Bacon was the Pole named Witelo, but generally spelled outside of Poland and Germany as Vitelo or Vitello. He was born between 1220 and 1230 of a mixed Thuringian and Polish family, and he lived in Poland. Not much is known of him personally, apparently not even his first name. His *Optics* was written in Latin in ten books, the ninth of which dealt with burning-mirrors. This work was published in 1572 together with Alhazen, by Risner as already mentioned. Indeed, it takes up the majority of the volume, since the *Optics* of Alhazen is only 288 pages long, but that of Witelo is 474 pages long.[21] It seems that only one book has ever been written about Witelo, by the German scholar Baeumker in 1906.[22] Baeumker stresses that Witelo was inspired by light-theology, and was deeply imbued with Gnostic and Neoplatonic ideas which suggest that light was the origin of space and matter. This was apparently the motivation which drove him to develop expertise in optical science. He developed the geometry of optics to a very high degree, propounding 137 geometrical axioms of optical science.[23]

After the collapse of Byzantine civilization with the conquest of

Figure 24. An imaginary view of the burning mirrors of Archimedes destroying the Roman fleet in the harbour of Syracuse in Sicily. This engraving was published in 1572 as the frontispiece of a huge volume containing the Latin translation of the *Optics* of the tenth-century Arab author called in the West Alhazen and the *Optics* of the 13th-century Polish author Vitello. In the background the optical phenomenon of the rainbow is portrayed. In the foreground, a man standing in the water demonstrates the action of refraction of the light rays in water, which shows his legs slightly splayed, and beside him a man views himself in a trick mirror which shows his head in a different place. The elephants are presumably there never to forget.
(From Alhazen, *Opticae Thesaurus, with Vitellionis Thurinopoloni Opticae libri decem*, edited by Federico Risner, Basle, 1572.)

Constantinople by the Turks, some Byzantine scholars made their way in the 15th century to Florence, where they were welcomed by the Medici. Often these Byzantines, such as Gemistos Plethon, brought trunks full of Greek manuscripts with them to ensure their welcome. The Medici were always happy to pay, and the rediscovery of the Greek tradition transformed Italo-Latin culture; the rebirth or 'renaissance' of the culture of Greece at this time gave its name to that period of European history which we now call after it, the Renaissance.

Amidst these many manuscripts salvaged from the collapse of the Byzantine world were some by or relating to Archimedes, including some which no longer survive. For instance, we do know that the Middle Byzantine scholar Leo the Philosopher (*circa* 790–*circa* 869) possessed a manuscript of a scientific work by Archimedes which seems to have made its way to Florence before being lost. As N. G. Wilson has said of it: 'This manuscript may have survived until the Renaissance, for it is likely to be the very old codex which caused difficulty to the copyists of that period because of its archaic script and numerous abbreviations.'[24] In fact, the oldest manuscripts of Archimedes would originally have been very difficult to deal with indeed, because Archimedes wrote in a dialect of Greek known as Doric, and even in the immediate aftermath of his death, it was found necessary for copyists to render these into the Attic dialect which was used by the wider intellectual circles of ancient Greece.

As a matter of fact, a manuscript preserving the original Sicilian Doric dialect of Archimedes still existed at Constantinople as late as the sixth century AD, more than 800 years after Archimedes' death! It was found by the indefatigably industrious mathematician and scholar Eutocius of Ascalon – best known for his Commentaries on the mathematical work *Conic Sections* by Apollonios of Perga, whose manuscripts Eutocius also worked so hard to preserve, and on Claudius Ptolemy's astronomical work the *Almagest*. Eutocius was a friend of Anthemius, and dedicated his *Commentary on Apollonios* to him.[25] This provides further interesting background to Anthemius's attempt to reproduce the burning-mirror of Archimedes, since there was obviously a group of fellow-scientists at Constantinople then, which was concerned with salvaging what could be found of the works of Archimedes and experimenting with his inventions. This group included Isidore of Miletus, who worked with Anthemius on the construction of St Sophia; Proclus the scientist, who burned the ships in Constantinople Harbour; Eutocius; and Anthemius himself. All were thoroughly brilliant scientists and mathematicians. It seems that this group, united in these aims, has not previously been recognized.

It would be an arduous task to try and trace the discussions of burning-mirrors which may have occurred during the 15th century, as it would mean consulting many obscure manuscripts, and there is probably no point in doing so. But by the year 1550 I have picked up the trail again. That was the year in which the amazing Renaissance genius Girolamo Cardano (1501–76) [also known as Hieronymus Cardanus in Latin and as Jerome Cardan in English] published his famous book *De Subtilitate* (*On Subtlety*), which amongst the myriad of other subjects which fills this mind-numbing encyclopaedia, contains discussions of burning-mirrors inspired by Archimedes. It was at this point that the subject of Archimedes's burning-mirror may be said to have entered into the mainstream of what we could call 'modern' scientific discourse.[26]

In *De Subtilitate*, Book Four, 'De Luce & Lumine' (which means, in the terminology as defined by him: 'Concerning the Source of Light and the Light Rays Which Stream forth from It'), Cardano discusses many optical phenomena, including lenses and mirrors. On p. 105 of the first edition (1550), he enumerates three different ways of causing a fire by using a mirror and cites a proof of Archimedes. On p. 106, he poses the subject: 'On a mirror which burns up distant approaching ships.' He quotes the account preserved by Galen and associates it with the principle of parabolic mirrors which he had just discussed, and for which he prints a diagram.[27] Since Cardano lived and breathed the works of Galen because of his medical activities, it was inevitable that he should come across Galen's account of the burning-mirror of Archimedes; it is doubtful that a single sentence of Galen was unknown to Cardano. Cardano does not cite any other ancient account of the burning-mirror of Archimedes, and presumably did not know of them.

This launched the 'modern' discussions of the burning-mirror of Archimedes. It did not take long for the next mention of it to appear, which actually happened in the following year, 1551. Another brilliant mathematician, Robert Recorde (Record) – the man who invented the sign = to represent 'equals' – discussed the matter in his book *The Path-way to Knowledg, Containing the First Principles of Geometrie*. In praising the usefulness of geometry, he calls attention to its importance in war:

> And as for warres, I might thinke it sufficient that Vegetius hath written, and after him Vasturius in commendation of Geometry, for use of warres, but all their woordes seem to saye nothinge, in comparison to the example of Archimedes worthy woorkes made by geometrie, for the defence of his countrey, . . . he dyd also by arte perspective (which is a parte of geometrie) [he means optical science] devise such glasses within the towne of Syracuse that dyd bourne [burn] their enemies shyppes [ships] a great way from the towne, whyche was a mervaylous politike thynge [marvellous politic thing].[28]

The next person to mention the burning-mirror of Archimedes was another famous Renaissance scientist, Giambattista della Porta, in his best-seller entitled *Magia Naturalis* (*Natural Magic*) – another one of those astonishing encyclopaedias of everything marvellous, and even more sensational than the collections of Cardano, but generally grounded in science. The first edition of this came out in 1558 at Naples when della Porta was in his early 20s; he said he had commenced it at the age of 15, for he was undoubtedly a prodigy.

One sometimes has to draw a line regarding research. I have never seen a first edition of Porta's book, and no copy exists in the British Library, for instance. I believe only three or four copies exist in the world. The first edition was short (in four books), only a fraction of the length of the revised edition (in 20 books) which Porta brought out as a mature adult 31 years later, in 1589. I regret that I cannot say whether the burning-mirror of Archimedes was mentioned by Porta in 1558. But by 1589, he wrote about burning-mirrors at great length, in Chapters 14, 15, and 17 of Book 17. He referred to the use of the burning-mirror not only by Archimedes at Syracuse but by Proclus at Constantinople. And what is most important of all, he recounts the fact that he had himself constructed burning-mirrors so efficient that he believed it was possible in principle to send a focused beam of light to the Moon and project a written message on its surface! (As this would have to take place in the daytime, when the Sun was available for reflection, only inhabitants of the Moon would be expected to read the message.)

It is at this precise point, the year 1589, that one may say that the concept of a weapon which could ignite targets at a distance by means of a burning-mirror escalates into the full-fledged idea of a 'death-ray' as we began to know it in our own time first from science-fiction stories and now from Pentagon research. Historians of the future who write the history of the laser-beam as a weapon should cite this earliest-known instance of the formulation of the concept of a beam capable of reaching the Moon in coherent form, and of acting as a death-ray at what della Porta does not hesitate to call 'an infinite distance', and which 'burns all it meets with in the way'.

It is important to stress that the vivid imagination of this Renaissance scientist took its inspiration directly from the achievements of Archimedes in the third century BC, by a continuous route of tradition a large portion of which I have presented here. No one that I know of has ever noticed the remarkable prediction by della Porta of coherent light beams which now exist in the form of laser beams and can reach the Moon and constitute destructive rays in warfare. The remarks of della Porta are so interesting that I give a section here from the English translation of 1658:

I proceed to burning-glasses, which being opposed against the Sun's beams, will kindle fire upon matter laid under them; in these also are the greatest secrets of Nature known. I shall describe what is found out by Euclid, Ptolemy, and Archimedes; and shall add our own [i.e. his own; the translator is using the polite plural] inventions, that the reader may judge how far new inventions exceed the old. Fire is kindled by reflection, refraction, and by a simple and compound glass. . . . That is called a parabolical section that [which] more forcibly farther off and in shorter time will set matter on fire that is opposite to it: it will melt lead and tin. My friends related to me that [it did this for] gold and silver also, but I have [only] made them red hot. By which invention Archimedes, as appears by the testimony of Galen, and many more, we read that he set the Roman Navy on fire, when Marcellus besieged Syracuse, his country. Plutarch in the Life of Pompilius [he means what we now call the Life of Numa] says the fire that burnt in Diana's Temple [really the Temple of Vesta] was lighted by this glass ['glass' is used here to mean 'mirror'], that is, by instruments that are made of the side of a right triangle whose feet are equal: these made hollow, do from the circumference respect one centre. When therefore they are held against the Sun, . . . it soon sets on fire all fuel that is combustible . . . Cardanus [Girolamo Cardano] teaches how such a glass should be made. . . . And if it be true that Archimedes by a parabolical glass [mirror; Cardano recommended the parabolic shape very strongly] did burn the ships from the wall, the distance [of a bow-shot] could not be above ten paces, as appears by the words of the authors themselves . . . Zonaras the Greek writes in the third tome of his Histories that Anastasius moved sedition against Vitalianus a Thracian, and he got those of Mysia and the Scythians to stand with him; and in the country by [near] Constantinople he plundered the people and besieged the City with a fleet. Marianus the Deputy opposed him; and there being a fight at sea, an engine made by Proclus, a most excellent man, for he then was famous for philosophy and mathematics; for he not only knew all the secrets of the most eminent artificer, Archimedes, but he found out some new inventions for himself; the enemy's navy was vanquished. For Proclus is reported to have made burning-glasses [burning-mirrors] of brass, and to have hanged them on the wall against the enemy's ships; and when the Sun's beams fell upon them, that fire broke forth from them like lightning, and so burnt their ships and men at sea, as Dion [Dio Cassius] reports that Archimedes did formerly to the Romans besieging Syracuse. But I will show you a far more excellent way than the rest, and that no man as ever I knew wrote of, and it exceeds the invention of all the ancients, and of our Age also; and I think the wit of man cannot go beyond it. This glass [mirror] does not burn for ten, twenty, a hundred, or a thousand paces, or to a set distance, but at infinite distance; nor doth it kindle in the cone where the rays meet, but the burning line proceeds from the centre of the glass of any longitude, and it burns all it meets with in the way. Moreover, it burns behind, before, and on all sides![29]

He then goes on to describe how to build this wonder, suggesting that by it one could in principle project a written message upon the surface of the Moon. His descriptions of all sorts of burning-mirrors and burning-glasses are very extensive, but he does not mention any ancient authors or scientists again. It is evident from his statements already quoted that not only he but his 'friends' – whoever they may have been – had constructed burning-mirrors for experimentation purposes. Those of his friends could melt gold and silver, whereas della Porta couldn't match that feat and only made them red hot. It is obvious, therefore, that several people had 'caught the bug' and were not prepared to let Archimedes rest in peace.

It was from the stimulus of this ferment of interest in Archimedes's burning-mirror and possible improvements which could be made to such devices that another extremely remarkable man entered upon the scene. This time we meet Father Athanasius Kircher (1602–80), a Jesuit scholar and scientist, and another 'Renaissance man' even though he lived after the end of the Renaissance. A German by origin, Kircher resided at Rome from

1633 until his death 47 years later, and was closely associated with the powerful Cardinal Barberini. As John Fletcher has said:

> He became the black-robed oracle of Rome, confidante of popes and emperors, correspondent of the leading scholars and minds of Europe and the world. Visitors to the Eternal City seldom left without attempting to see Father Kircher. His bulky works were greedily anticipated, his letters humbly solicited by, among other aspiring scholars, Leibniz.[30]

Anyone who has looked at Kircher's huge books of so many different subjects can only be dazzled at his erudition and wide interests, but even more amazed at the apparently limitless amount of money which must have

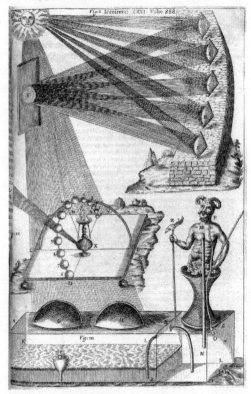

Figure 25. One of the engravings published by Athanasius Kircher in 1646 showing his technique for using multiple mirror reflections to recreate the feat of Archimedes. Here five mirrors are shown jointly reflecting the rays of the sun, from points A, B, C, D, and E, onto the focus at point F, where a hole can be seen burnt through a panel of wood or plate of metal. In fact, Kircher really carried out such experiments by using many separate mirrors simultaneously reflecting solar rays onto a single point. He set fire to wood by these means at a distance of more than 100 feet. In the lower part of the engraving, solar rays descend to heat a steam apparatus with various ingenious devices attached.
(From Athanasius Kircher, *Ars Magna Lucis et Umbrae* (*The Great Art of Light and Shadow*), Rome, 1646; reprinted at Amsterdam, 1671.)

been available to prepare them. The coffers of the Church of Rome must have been tilted heavily for so much lucre to spill out. The magnificent and numerous engravings by the best available artists, the luxurious paper and bindings, make Kircher's books *objets d'art*. Two relevant engravings of burning-mirrors may be seen in Figures 25 and 26; these come from Kircher's book about optics entitled *Ars Magna Lucis et Umbrae* (*The Great Art of Light and Shadow*), a gigantic tome full of spectacular engravings.[31] Kircher even had his own museum full of his contrivances, and funds were available for him to construct just about anything he wanted. This included burning-mirrors.

In *The Great Art of Light and Shadow* Kircher devoted many pages to the subject of Archimedes and his burning-mirror. He published the engrav-

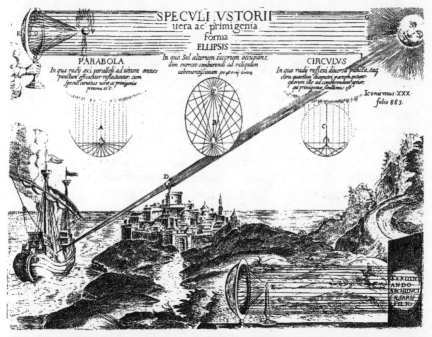

Figure 26. In 1646, Athanasius Kircher published this imagined view of a giant lens (point 'D') on top of a tower at Syracuse in Sicily focusing the rays of the sun by refraction onto the point marked 'S' aboard the flagship of the Roman admiral, Marcellus. The ship can be seen pouring smoke and flames as a result of the focused solar rays. Kircher published this graphic depiction of Archimedes using a lens rather than a mirror despite the fact that his own attempts to recreate the feat of Archimedes used mirrors. However, Kircher also experimented a great deal with burning-lenses. At the top left of the engraving a mysterious hand emerging from a cloud holds a parabolic mirror aloft, which focuses the solar rays and ignites a round object, which is also seen bursting into flames. 'Death-rays' by reflection and refraction are thus both depicted in this dramatic scene. At bottom right, a parabolic mirror reflects the light from a candle (point 'E') onto a surface, revealing a secret message. Different principles of reflection at varied surfaces are shown in A, B, and C.
(From Athanasius Kircher, *Ars Magna Lucis et Umbrae* (*The Great Art of Light and Shadow*), Rome, 1646; reprinted at Amsterdam, 1671.)

ing shown in Figure 26 actually showing the imagined feat as happening by refraction through a giant burning-glass rather than a burning-mirror. Kircher also discussed Proclus's burning-glass at Constantinople. And whereas della Porta cited Zonaras, Kircher went further and quoted a passage in Greek, for which he provided a Latin translation, from Tzetzes. Kircher had obviously read Cardano and della Porta, both of whom he cites, along with Galen, Diodorus Siculus, Livy, and Polybius. He spends a great deal of time discussing della Porta's comments.[32] Kircher was so keen on getting it right that he even visited Syracuse Harbour to inspect the terrain!

Louis Dutens in 1766 gives an interesting summary of Kircher's optical comments:

> Father Kircher, attentively observing the description which Tzetzes gives of the burning-glasses of Archimedes, resolved to prove the possibility of this; and having, by means of a number of plane mirrors, collected the sun's rays into one focus, he so augmented the solar heat, that at last by increasing the number of mirrors, he could produce the most intense degree of it. . . . [Kircher] relates an experiment of his own, whereby he produced a heat intense enough to burn, by means of five mirrors directing the rays of the sun into one focus; he supposes that Proclus by such means might set fire to Vitellius's fleet, and invites the skillful to bring this assay to perfection. . . . Tzetzes's description of the glass Archimedes made use of is indeed very proper to raise such an idea as Kircher entertained.[33]

By the time Dutens wrote this, however, even more spectacular success had been met with by the Comte du Buffon in constructing multiple burning-mirrors, two of which, as I have already described, are preserved at Paris. One of his machines had 168 separate reflecting mirrors, all focused on the same patch. Kircher had used many mirrors, as may be seen in his engravings, and he had set fire to wood at distances greater than 100 feet. But Buffon carried everything to even greater lengths, and his success was so impressive that even the sceptical Edward Gibbon ended up grudgingly changing his mind about Archimedes, as we have already seen.

A modern scholar, Klaus Mielenz, has summarized the situation very well:

> Buffon had initially assumed that a concave mirror would be required, and estimated that such a mirror must have a radius of curvature of about 400 ft and a diameter of at least 8 or 10 ft. A mirror like this could not be made in his or Archimedes's times, but then Buffon realised an important fact. Due to the finite angular diameter of the sun, the spot formed by this concave mirror would be as large as 2 ft in diameter, and almost the same spot size can also be obtained with small plane mirrors.

Whereas infinitesimally small mirrors (like pin-hole cameras) render the same spot size as imaging mirrors, the spot from a real plane mirror is bigger by only about the mirror size itself, that is, only two and a half feet for a 6-inch mirror. Convinced that Archimedes must have realized this, too, Buffon proceeded with the construction of a rectangular array of 168 plane mirrors, each 8 inches by 10 inches in size and individually adjustable so that their spots could all be superimposed on the target. This array was not at all easy to assemble, and the final 168 mirrors had to be selected from a total of 500 to assure that they all produced a well defined, small spot in a target plane 150 ft away. Once assembled, however, the portable array could be set up and aimed at a target within half an hour.

Buffon had expected the effective range of his mirrors to be approximately 150 ft, and confirmed this in a series of tests, using different portions of the array as well as different targets and burning distances. On 23 March 1747, at noon, he ignited a creosoted beech plank from a distance of 66 ft with only 40 mirrors, and one hour later, a creosoted and sulfurized plank at 126 ft with 98 mirrors. On 5 April at 4 p.m. and with partly cloudy skies, he ignited in less than 90 seconds a mixture of sulfurized pine chips and coal 150 ft away using 154 mirrors. In the afternoon of 10 April, in clear weather, a creosoted pine plank at a distance of 150 ft caught fire instantaneously in the heat of only 128 mirrors. On the following day, at a distance of 20 ft, it took 45 mirrors to melt a 6-lb tin flask and 117 mirrors to melt silver chips. Altogether, Buffon performed about a dozen experiments of this kind, all successful. Bad weather did not permit him to continue, but he considered his goal accomplished. Having succeeded in the weak sun of early spring at distances of up to 150 ft, Buffon had no doubt that in the summer his mirrors would have worked at distances of 200 ft, or perhaps even more than 400 ft. Archimedes could have done the same, using metal instead of glass mirrors.[34]

It would be wrong to omit mention of another predecessor of Buffon, Father Gaspar Schott, a Jesuit scientist who was Kircher's disciple. He too constructed burning-mirrors which were very successful, but he is less well known. One quarter of Schott's large book *Magia Universalis* was devoted to optics.[35] The book contained a very extensive account of the burning-mirror or burning-lens of Archimedes, together with the general question of mirrors burning at a distance. The book also contains, as did Kircher's, an engraving of what the author imagined Archimedes's device to have looked like, and just as Kircher's book had a picture of a giant refracting lens, so also Schott's engraving shows a lens mounted on top of a tower rather than a mirror.[36]

We cannot continue to follow the history of the burning-mirror, or consider the vast number of discussions of it in the literature. It is true that subsequent events brought many astonishing discoveries, and I have found many extraordinarily obscure publications full of hair-raising details of feats wrought by burning-glasses and burning-mirrors which reach to quite fantastic levels. Many of the experimenters were Germans, and reports of their activities are found only in forgotten 18th- or 19th-century German periodicals, which I have combed perhaps too assiduously, as in the end I have not used any of that material at all! And a 19th-century English experimenter named Samuel Parker produced a burning-lens so large and so powerful that he could melt just about any metal within seconds. A contemporary engraving of it may be seen in Figure 27. The original device is believed to be stored somewhere in the Forbidden City in Beijing, where I hope one day to find it. One of his smaller burning-lenses is preserved in the Ashmolean Museum at Oxford.

Figure 27. Samuel Parker's burning-glass, from an anonymous contemporary engraving of 1840. According to Parker's friend, the Rev. J. Joyce (*Scientific Dialogues*, London, 1844, pp. 249–50), this burning-glass constructed by 'Mr. Parker of Fleet Street' had a very large lens indeed: 'He formed one of three feet in diameter, and when fixed in its frame it exposed a clear surface of more than two feet eight inches in diameter, and its focus, by means of another lens, was reduced to a diameter of half an inch. The heat produced by this was so great that iron plates were melted in a few seconds: – tiles and slates became red hot in a moment, and were vitrified, or changed into glass: – sulphur, pitch, and other resinous bodies were melted under water: – wood-ashes, and those of other vegetable substances, were turned in a moment into transparent glass ... even gold was rendered fluid in a few seconds; notwithstanding, however, this intense heat at the focus, the finger might without the smallest injury be placed in the cone of rays within an inch of the focus. ... Mr. Parker's curiosity led him to try what the sensation would be at the focus, and he describes it like that produced by the heat of fire or a candle ... a piece of wood may be burned to a coal, when it is contained in a decanter of water. ... If a cavity be made in a piece of charcoal, and the substance to be acted on be put in it, the effect produced by the lens will be much increased. Any metal thus enclosed melts in a moment, the fire sparkling like that of a forge to which the blast of a bellows is applied.' This remarkable apparatus was prior to 1840 collected by the Emperor of China, where it is still presumably amongst all the expensive clocks and mechanical gadgets which litter the display cases and storage rooms of Beijing's Forbidden City.
(*Collection of Robert Temple.*)

The point to keep in mind with all of this is that the whole thing began in the third century BC when Archimedes took the well-known phenomenon of the burning-mirror and enlarged the concept to create the world's first burning-mirror *weapon*. All of the people we have encountered in this story who created powerful burning-mirrors and burning-lenses in order to focus fantastically powerful beams and burn things at a distance were emulating Archimedes. And so were all the others who followed them, whom we must leave unconsidered. This idea of what we can colloquially call the 'death-ray' concept has run and run and run. And now it has found its true form, for the concept has been taken over by those coherent beams produced by 'light amplification by stimulated emission of radiation', the initial letters of which phrase form the acronym *laser*. No sun is needed anymore, but the mirror is still there, for the coherent beams of laser light are emitted only after going back and forth in a tiny chamber between mirrors. Archimedes lives on!

In closing this story, we cannot omit the amazing tale of Ioannis Sakas. Knowing nothing of Anthemius, Proclus, Kircher, Schott, Buffon, or any of the others who had built large burning-mirrors – in fact, knowing only of Archimedes – Dr Sakas decided to have a go himself, as so many had done before. But he thought he was the first! I discovered this when I visited him at his home in a sleepy outer suburb of Athens. He gave me the photo seen in Plate 47, copies of many clippings, and his own writings. It is important to give a short account of his accomplishments, for in many ways they are the most impressive of all those who attempted to imitate Archimedes. And he was, after all, rewarded with a remarkable success which was reported around the world.

Dr Ioannis G. Sakas was born in 1925 at Lastros in Crete, where his father George Sakas was a building engineer. Ioannis was also interested in engineering and gained a PhD in Mechanical and Electrical Engineering. He taught these subjects in the Air Force College of Greece at Athens and from 1954 until June 1973, he was an engineer in the Electric Power Corporation of Greece. From the age of about seven, Ioannis was fascinated by burning-glasses, with which he constantly played as a boy. Then while still a child he was told a piece of local folklore from his region of Crete that the reason why the soil there was so dark was that the ancient Greeks had repeatedly burnt it by walking round the fields holding burning-glasses, and directing the focused rays at the ground. Deeply intrigued by this strange tale, he determined to figure out how they could have done this with burning-glasses much larger than those he played with.

Ioannis also heard as a child the famous story of Archimedes burning the Roman fleet, so he began to study the works and accounts of Archimedes very closely, trying to figure out from this how the fields might have been burnt. Eventually, he realized that the folklore was false. In fact, it was probably a garbled recollection of the use of burning-glasses to start the fires of stubble on top of which the Cretans pile cuttings from the tops of pine trees for better effect; after stubble is burnt, the ground beneath really does look black. By this time, Ioannis was hooked on Archimedes and became obsessed by the desire to recreate the experiment of the burning of the fleet. Several decades later he finally realized his dream. But this was how the whole thing started.

Ioannis is the sort of person who conceives an impossible dream and then doggedly sets about realizing the impossible. His other great interest was the route take by Alexander the Great from Greece to India and back to Babylon in the fourth century BC. But, not being an armchair scholar, Ioannis *twice* walked on foot all the way from Greece to the Indus Valley on the Indian/Pakistani border, and back. But he is so modest that hardly anyone even knows he did it.

In 1966, Ioannis published an article in the Greek periodical *Technikē Chronika* (*Technical Annals*) claiming that Archimedes could have burnt the Roman fleet by using flat copper mirrors the size of a shield.[37] (He was unaware that one description of the feat of Proclus actually described his hanging shields from the walls of Constantinople to burn the fleet of Vitellius, indicating that Proclus's mirrors were also the size of shields.) Even as early as this year, 1966, Ioannis tested his hypothesis with such flat mirrors before publishing his paper, proving experimentally that the feat of Archimedes could have been accomplished by using them.

Ioannis's next relevant publication (in French) was in 1971, in the proceedings of a conference of the Coopération Méditerranéenne pour l'Énergie Solaire (Mediterranean Cooperation for Solar Energy). This dealt with calculations of useful energy which could be obtained from the concentration of solar rays by lenses or mirrors.[38] This article was extremely technical, comprehensible only to scientists and engineers and full of complicated equations.

From 1971, Ioannis began to organize his amazing project to recreate the feat of Archimedes. He had worked out that men holding separate flat mirrors would be the best way to do this. In this, he came to the same conclusion as Anthemius, though he did not know of the writings of Anthemius. He persuaded the Technical Chamber of Greece at Athens to pay for many large rectangular mirrors the size of a person to be made for this experiment. They were all 1.7 metres high and 0.7 metres wide. It proved too expensive to use copper for the mirrors, so he used glass backed by copper foil. He made 200 of them.

Ioannis had decided that Archimedes burnt the Roman fleet by lining up soldiers on the walls of Syracuse with mirrors. As he put it:

It was, however, easy for Archimedes to conceive, test, and use the flat mirrors, which I used in 1966 experimentally, . . . So, I proved experimentally as well that it was possible for Archimedes to set the Roman fleet on fire.

Archimedes would have used large flat shields with polished copper, thus converting them to flat mirrors. These mirrors would have been used by the soldiers on the ramparts upon command. So, according to the distance of the ship to be attacked, the solar energy would have been focused on them by reflection of varying numbers of mirrors. For example, for an average distance of 30 or 40 metres, 50 mirrors would have been enough, whereas for a distance of 100 metres (the maximum distance an arrow can be shot successfully), approximately 200 mirrors would have been enough for setting on fire the rigging of the ships in a short time, especially the black and greasy parts of the rigging or those parts of the ship covered in tar, and for creating a sensation of unbearable heat for the archers and the rest of the men on board.

By such easily constructed flat mirrors, which could be rapidly transported from one place to another and manipulated by each individual soldier, Archimedes could have succeeded in *taking the enemy by surprise*, aiming at the desirable point to attack. Nothing would reveal to the enemy the existence of the mirrors until the very moment of their use, when hundreds or thousands of soldiers would have focused the solar radiation by means of their mirror-shields onto the nearby enemy ships so that the effect would be rapid and certain. The casualties on the ships might not have been as extensive as the *impact on the morale of the crews*.[39]

In order to test his ideas, Ioannis got the support of Professor E. Stamatis, Greek editor of *The Works of Archimedes*. With this scholarly united front, the President of the Technical Chamber of Greece was convinced to put up the money for the experiment and pay for the construction of the mirrors, as already mentioned. Ioannis was able to persuade the Greek Navy to provide a large number of sailors to hold the mirrors. A small wooden boat specially moored at the Piraeus was to be the target. The first rehearsal was carried out on 26 June 1973, at the foot of Mount Hymettus in Athens, using only 50 mirrors, glass-backed with copper and mounted on light iron frames. The target was a wooden model of a ship placed 40 metres away. Although it was a hazy day, within only three seconds of the target being attacked, it began to smoke. The mirrors were manipulated badly during this rehearsal because of a shortage of people; each person (sailors weren't involved yet) was attempting to manipulate five mirrors! As a result, Ioannis estimated that only 60–70 per cent of the mirrors actually coincided with the target. Light was variable because of the weather, but nevertheless the target burst into flame rapidly.

A second rehearsal was planned for 17 July in the same place with 100 mirrors pointed at a wooden target covered in tar 85 metres away, and with 200 mirrors on a wooden target placed 175 metres away. However, a very strong wind made these tests impossible. Fifty-seven volunteers held 57 mirrors pointing at a target 70 metres away made of plywood covered in tar, and the target smoked but did not burn. The volunteers handled their mirrors very badly. Ioannis estimated that for that distance, 70 mirrors were necessary to achieve ignition.

A third rehearsal was held on 22 July at the same location. Each volunteer manipulated five mirrors, for a total of 130 mirrors. The target was wood coated in tar 100 metres away. Two separate points on the target burst into flame. A subsequent attempt was made at 170 metres with two small targets, but only one of them emitted smoke, and Ioannis concluded that 200 mirrors instead of 130 were needed for that distance.

The last rehearsal was held on 3 November in the Bay of Kepal in cooperation with the Greek Navy. Sixty mirrors brought about immediate ignition of a target 55 metres away. (The greater discipline of the sailors probably contributed to this success, as the previous volunteers were not military men.) On this day there was uninterrupted sun and no wind.

The formal experiment was held on 6 November 1973, on a windless day with partial sunshine, at the Bay of Kepal (Skaramagas-Athens Naval Base) in cooperation with the Greek Navy. (See Plate 47.) Seventy mirrors were held by the same number of sailors at an average distance of 55 metres from the target, which was a small wooden moored boat 2.3 metres in length and covered in tar. Within only a few seconds the target gave off smoke. Three minutes later, the entire side of the boat facing the mirrors was in flames. The experiment was a complete and dramatic success.

Worldwide news coverage of this event resulted in articles (most or all of them misspelling Ioannis's surname as Sakkas) in the *New York Times* (Sunday, 11 November, with some inaccuracies), *Time* Magazine (26 November, under 'Science'), *Newsweek* Magazine (26 November under 'Science'), *The New Scientist* of London (22 November, with the name spelled correctly but considerable factual inaccuracies), etc. *Time* and *Newsweek* got the number of sailors and mirrors correct, but the others did not. Ioannis himself wrote up his theory based on the early rehearsals (in Greek) in *Technikē Chronika* (*Technical Annals*) at Athens for September 1973 (pp. 771–9), but the report of the full demonstration appeared (in Greek) in Vol. III (*Tomos I*) of *The Works of Archimedes*, 4 vols, edited by Professor Stamati and published at Athens in 1974 with five poorly reproduced photos (pp. 309–13). Strangely enough, even in this official publication by Ioannis's friend, his surname was still misspelled as Sakkas! That shows how unusual his spelling is, and how difficult it is even for the Greeks to make an exception for it.

There was a sequel. Five years later, the Italians tried to reproduce Ioannis's experiment at Syracuse using smaller mirrors. After his initial rehearsals, Ioannis had sent a report to the Mayor of Syracuse in Sicily (his letter dated 26 July 1973, of which I have a copy), but he never received any reply or acknowledgement. In 1978 he learned indirectly of the Italian attempt to replicate his own experiment, and was disappointed that no Italians ever contacted him, but preferred to work in isolation, basing their efforts on press reports which contained many inaccuracies. No one ever informed him whether the Italians were successful. If I visit Syracuse one day, I will attempt to learn more, and will add the information to later printings of this book. However, anyone who has ever tried to write to an Italian official knows better than to expect ever to receive a reply! I learned that lesson many years ago.

Ioannis Sakas's conclusions from his experiments were that Archimedes certainly could have done what tradition attributed to him. Although long retired, he has not rested on his laurels, however, and he has carried out experiments on another weapon which he believes Archimedes invented and used, a steam-gun mentioned by Petrarch, similar to one later invented by Leonardo da Vinci. He has also done much work on sundials and gnomons, with which he is still busy at the moment. So we move on, full of admiration for this fascinating 'lone-wolf' inventor who succeeded in proving in front of modern cameras that the burning-mirrors of Archimedes were not impossible, but could burn a boat in three minutes at the correct distance. Any number of armchair scholars can quibble, but there is no substitute for physical demonstration.

I want also to refer to two short stories on the subject of 'death-rays' by my friend Arthur C. Clarke. They were both published in the 1960s in his collection entitled *Tales of Ten Worlds*. One is called 'Let There Be Light' and the other is 'A Slight Case of Sunstroke'.[40] Arthur has a great sense of wry humour, and he has always spent much of his time chuckling. Both of these stories are typically amusing. 'A Slight Case of Sunstroke' is a light-hearted fantasy about a South American republic where everyone, not least the Government and Army officials, is obsessed by football. They have a football stadium which can seat 100,000 people. In a game where national honour is at stake and the neighbouring republic have as usual bribed the referee, 50,000 members of the local Army are allowed free seats in the stadium and given very expensively produced programmes with shiny metal backs. When the crooked referee disallows a goal, a bugle sounds and all the soldiers raise their programmes, the backs of which act as mirrors to reflect the sunlight onto the referee. The result, in Arthur's words, was this: 'Where the referee was standing there was a small, smouldering heap, from which a thin column of smoke curled up into the still air.' What would Sakas have accomplished with 50,000 sailors instead of just 70?

And finally, there is Arthur's story 'Let There Be Light'. This tale is told in a pub, about a man named Edgar who retired from business after making a fortune and was only interested after that in amateur astronomy, grinding his own lenses and ignoring his wife in a remote area of the English countryside. The wife had an affair with a younger man named de Vere Courtenay, and Edgar blinded him with a beam of his own reflected headlights in a telescopic mirror – 'a beam 50 times as powerful as any searchlight' – which caused him to drive over a cliff. At the end of the story, the man in the pub says:

'To be killed by a death ray would be a fate much more fitting for a de Vere Courtenay – and in the circumstances I don't see how anyone can deny that it *was* a death ray that Edgar had used. It was a ray, and it killed someone. What more do you want?'

For anyone who thinks this chapter has a title which is over-stated, try that one on for size.

Notes

1. Africa, Thomas W., 'Archimedes through the Looking-Glass', in *The Classical World*, Vol. 68, February 1975, pp. 305–8. See p. 306.
2. *Ibid.*, p. 306. The reference to Lucian is Chapter Two, lines 150 ff. of *Hippias*, edited by N. Nilén, Leipzig, 1906. The reference to Galen is *De Temperamentis*, 3, 2, 657–8 (ed. by C. G. Kuhn, Leipzig, 1821, Vol. I, 657, or otherwise p. 81 of Vol. I of the earlier edition by Basil), p. 93 of the Teubner edition by George Helmreich, Teubner, Stuttgart, 1969; he mentions *tōn pyreiōn* – 'burning-mirrors'. (I do not at all accept the feeble arguments of some scholars who have tried to explain this away by saying the word refers to the use of Greek Fire. Greek Fire was used by Callinicus in defence of Constantinople in 675 AD, but that was approximately a millennium later than the time of Archimedes and more than 500 years after the time of Galen!)
3. *Ibid.*
4. Lemprière, J., *A Classical Dictionary*, London, 1804, unpaginated, entry for Archimedes.
5. Polybius, *The Histories*, translated by Evelyn S. Shuckburgh, Macmillan, London, 2 vols, 1889, Vol. II, p. 41.
6. *Ibid.*, Vol. I, p. 530.
7. 'Livy' (i.e. Titus Livius), *The History of Rome*, translated by D. Spillan and Cyrus Edmonds, George Bell & Sons, London (but published with merger partner's name on the spine, i.e. Bohn's Classical Library), 1875, Vol. II, pp. 938–9.
8. Africa, *op. cit.*, p. 307.
9. Gibbon, Edward, *The History of the Decline and Fall of the Roman Empire*, Chapter 40, second edition by William Smith, John Murray, London, 1887, Vol. 5, pp. 71–2 and note 99.
10. Huxley, G. L., *Anthemius of Tralles: A Study in Later Greek Geometry*, Cambridge, Massachusetts, 1959, p. 6. This booklet of 62 pages is Number 1 of *Greek, Roman, and Byzantine Monographs* edited by John J. Bilitz.
11. *Ibid.*, p. 12.
12. *Ibid.*, pp. 12–13.
13. *Ibid.*, pp. 13–15.
14. Diocles, 'On Burning Mirrors', translated from the Arabic by G. J. Toomer, in *Studies in the History of Mathematics and Physical Science*, Berlin and New York, 1976.
15. Cited by Louis Dutens, *An Inquiry into the Origin of the Discoveries Attributed to the Moderns*, translated from the French anonymously in collaboration with the author (who lived in England), London, 1769, p. 332, language slightly updated.
16. Macrobius, *The Saturnalia*, Book I, Chapter 20, Section 11, translated by Percival Vaughan Davies, Columbia University Press, New York, 1969, p. 139. The original text may be consulted in *Aur. Theodosii Macrobii . . . Opera cum Notis Integris Isacii Pontani, Io. Meursii, Iac. Gronovii quies adiunxit et suas Io. Car. Zeunius*, Lipsiae, 1774, p. 321.

17. Wilson, N.G., *Scholars of Byzantium*, Duckworth, London, 1983, p. 161.
18. Zonaras, Johannes, *Epitome of Histories*, Book 9, Chapter 4, section translated by E. Cary, in *Dio Cassius, Roman History*, Vol. II, Loeb Classical Library, Harvard University Press, 1914, pp. 171–3. Zonaras is here translated because he preserves an epitome of a lost section of Dio's History, Book XV.
19. Tzetzes, Johannes, *Chiliades*, Book 2, 35, 109–23, section translated by E. Cary, as above; see Footnote 14. Tzetzes's comments about Anthemius and Anthemius's knowledge of Archimedes are found at *Chiliades*, Book 12, 457 and 975, and not in this same Book 2.
20. Eustathius, *Commentary on the Iliad*, quoted by Louis Dutens, *op. cit.*, pp. 332–3.
21. Alhazen, *Opticae Thesaurus*, with *Vitellionis Thurinopoloni Opticae libri decem*, edited by Federico Risner/Risnero, Basle, 1572.
22. Baeumker, C., *Witelo, ein Philosoph und Naturforscher des XIII Jahrhunderts*, Münster, 1906.
23. Thorndike, Lynn, *A History of Magic and Experimental Science*, Vol. II, Macmillan, New York, 1923, pp. 454–6, which is an appendix about Witelo to his discussion of Robert Grosseteste, another important figure in the history of optics, and the immediate predecessor in England of Roger Bacon, though for simplicity I omit Grosseteste from my survey. I also omitted Grosseteste for the same reason in the chapter on the telescope, even though he clearly describes their use prior to Bacon. (This should not be taken as an indication of my lack of interest in the remarkable and fascinating Grosseteste!)
24. Wilson, N. G., *op.cit.*, p. 83.
25. *Ibid.*, pp. 45–6.
26. I have a special fondness for Cardano, and have had a close association with him of sorts. I organized a scholarly symposium on 27 November 1976, to mark the fourth centenary of his death. It was held at the Italian Institute in London. It was a very amusing event, because I organized the entire thing single-handed and at my own expense, having never met any of the other people involved until the day of the symposium. I wrote to a variety of scholarly bodies and asked them to co-sponsor the event, letting each of them assume that the initiative had been taken by another of them. The Director of the Italian Institute agreed to act as host and provide the building and the food. I got the Wellcome Institute for the History of Medicine and the British Societies for the History of Science, for the History of Mathematics, and for the History of Alchemy and Chemistry to co-sponsor. I invited the late and very fine scholar Dr Charles Schmitt of the Warburg Institute to attend and give a paper on 'Cardano's Position in the History of Science'. I myself gave an extempore lecture on 'Cardano as Man and Mystic', and there were other papers by experts on Cardano's work in medicine and mathematics. (He is one of the most famous mathematicians who ever lived, from his work on solving cubic equations and recognizing the validity of negative, irrational, and complex solutions to algebraic equations.) I had to laugh at the extraordinary and ubiquitous complacency of everyone, for no one asked who I was. I had absolutely no official qualifications of any kind for this task, but no one ever questioned me. I think they were all too afraid they might be asked for some money towards the expenses.

    All the great and the good turned up on the day, the Director of the Italian Institute and I stood side by side and shook their hands as they arrived, the symposium lasted for six hours, and afterwards everyone went away feeling very happy and asking casually when the proceedings would be published. Even after it was all over, no one knew I had thought of the thing alone and had essentially hoodwinked them all into participating. Of course, the proceedings couldn't be published because there was no one to collect, edit, and publish them. Various people including Schmitt kept writing to me about the book of the symposium, but it was impossible to explain that I was a lone figure with no capacity for organizing such a thing. To this day, none of the participants has apparently ever shown any curiosity as to how the symposium occurred. This was one of my little practical jokes. But of course it had a serious purpose: no one was recognizing Cardano's anniversary, so I took matters into my own hands.

27. Cardanus, Hieronymus (Cardano, Girolamo), *De Subtilitate* (*On Subtlety*), Nuremberg, 1550, pp. 105–6.
28. Recorde (Record), Robert, *The Path-way to Knowledg, Containing the First Principles of Geometrie*, London, 1551. A photographic reprint of this book was also issued in 1974 by Walter J. Johnson Inc., of Norwood, New Jersey, USA. The entire book is unpaginated, and these remarks occur near the end of the Preface.
29. Porta, John Baptista (Giambattista, i.e. Giovanni Battista, della Porta), *Natural Magick*, translated anonymously into English, London, 1658, pp. 371–5; I have modernized the spelling.
30. Fletcher, John E., 'Astronomy in the Life and Correspondence of Athanasius Kircher', in *Isis*, Smithsonian Institution, Washington, DC, USA, Vol. 61, 1, No. 206, Spring 1970, pp. 52–67. The quotation is from p. 52.
31. Kircher, Athanasius, *Ars Magna Lucis et Umbrae* (*The Great Art of Light and Shadow*), Rome, 1646; reprinted at Amsterdam, 1671.
32. *Ibid.*, 1671 edition, pp. 757–65.
33. Dutens, Louis, *op. cit.*, pp. 323–6. (1766 was the original date of publication in French, although the place of publication was London.)
34. Mielenz, Klaus D., 'Eureka!', a letter published in *Applied Optics*, Vol. 13, No. 2, February 1974, p. A14. I am indebted to Professor Allan A. Mills for this reference.
35. Schott, Gaspar, *Magia Universalis Naturae et Artis . . . Opus Quadripartitum. Pars I, Continent Optica . . .*, Frankfurt, 1657. A German translation later appeared: *Magia Optica, das ist, Geheime doch Naturmässige Besicht- und Augen-Lehr Unterschidliche Bücher Abgetheilet* (Optical Magic, that is, Secrets of Viewing-Lore and Vision Theory according to Natural Principles, Divided into Ten Distinct Books), Bamberg, 1671.
36. *Ibid.* (German edition, 1671), pp. 382–6. The engraving is Figure XXI opposite p. 382.
37. Sakas, Ioannis, in *Technikē Chronika* (*Technical Annals*), Vol. 3, July-August-September, 1966.
38. Sakas, Ioannis, 'Calcul de l'Énergie Utile d'un Système de Concentration du Rayonnement Solaire et Prévision de Son Fonctionnement Répété Pendant Plusieurs Années' ('Computation of Useful Energy from a System of Concentrating Solar Radiation and Estimate of Its Function over a Period of Several Years'), in proceedings of *Rencontre Générale d'Athènes* (General Meeting at Athens), 4–9 October 1971, of *Coopération Méditerranéenne pour l'Énergie Solaire* (Mediterranean Cooperation for Solar Energy).
39. Sakas, Ioannis, 'Archimedes Burned up the Roman Fleet by Means of Flat Mirrors', a pamphlet privately circulated at the Piraeus in Athens on the occasion of Sakas's successful experiment, Summer 1973. Please note that I have improved Dr Sakas's English grammar and phraseology, as English is only his third language.
40. Clarke, Arthur C., *Tales of Ten Worlds*, Dell Publishing, New York, 1965: 'Let There Be Light' is pp. 98–105, and 'A Slight Case of Sunstroke' is pp. 151–60.

SECTION THREE

THE ANCIENT LORE

Chapter Six

Phantom Visions

In the fourth century BC, the philosopher Democritus appears to have suffered from visual hallucinations. They must have upset him, since in order to try and understand what was happening to him, he was driven to carry out the first recorded experiments in sensory deprivation. I discovered this from a stray remark preserved from an otherwise lost Life of Democritus written by one of the followers of Socrates:

> He would train himself, says Antisthenes, by a variety of means to test his sense-impressions by going at times into solitude and frequenting tombs.[1]

This observation survives from Antisthenes's lost work *On the Successions of the Philosophers*, as preserved by a writer thought to have lived in the first half of the third century AD, Diogenes Laertius. I found another strangely garbled passage derived – but certainly secondhand – from this same account in yet another author, Aulus Gellius, who lived two or three generations earlier, in the second century AD. He says:

> It is written in the records of Grecian story that the philosopher Democritus, a man worthy of reverence beyond all others and of the highest authority, of his own accord deprived himself of eyesight, because he believed that the thoughts and meditations of his mind in examining nature's laws would be more vivid and exact, if he should free them from the allurements of sight and the distractions offered by the eyes. This act of his, and the manner too in which he easily blinded himself by a most ingenious device, the poet Laberius has described in a farce called *The Ropemaker*, in very elegant and finished verses . . . 'Democritus, Abdera's scientist/ Set up a shield to face Hyperion's [the Sun's] rise/ That sight he might destroy by blaze of brass/ Thus by the sun's rays he destroyed his eyes . . .'[2]

Here the temporary sensory deprivation of sight by going into darkened tombs has been garbled and confused with another experiment of Democritus using mirrors to reflect the rising sun, and the conclusion wrongly drawn by Aulus Gellius that Democritus went permanently blind. But then, with the author of a stage farce as a partial source, it is no wonder that the information became confused. It may well be that Democritus also experimented by staring at blazing mirrors, to study sun-blindness, but there is no other record of his having lost his sight permanently. It is interesting that Democritus was a figure of fun on stage in the lost play *The Ropemaker*, just as Socrates was a figure of fun in the play *The Clouds* by Aristophanes, which does survive.

Antisthenes also recorded that Democritus travelled all over the known world, exhausting his family fortune in the process, visiting priests and apparently seeking initiation into their mysteries. He is said to have learnt geometry from the Egyptian priests, and also to have studied under the Babylonian priests, the Persian magi, the Pythagorean sages, and even the Hindu Brahmans and the Ethiopians. It is possible, therefore, that meditation and even yoga were a regular part of his exercises.

Although all the works of Democritus are lost (except for extensive fragments), before they were, a catalogue was made of them in the Alexandrian Library, and we have that list. The following intriguing titles are to be found on the list:

Description of Rays of Light; Causes concerned with Fire and Things in Fire; Of the Different Shapes of Atoms.

Plato hated the very mention of Democritus's name, and he wanted to burn all the treatises of Democritus which he was able to collect. We are told this by the historian Aristoxenus, who was a pupil of Aristotle. But some friends of Plato, doubtless including Aristotle himself, prevented Plato from doing this, pointing out that there would be no advantage in it, since the works were in many other hands as well. This shows how emotionally unbalanced Plato could be on some occasions. As the ancient historian of philosophy Diogenes Laertius records:

And there is clear evidence for this in the fact that Plato, who mentions almost all the early philosophers, never once alludes to Democritus, not even where it would be necessary to controvert him, obviously because he knew that he would have to match himself against the prince of philosophers, for whom, to be sure, Timon has this word of praise: 'Such is the wise Democritus, the guardian of discourse, keen-witted disputant, among the best I ever read.'[3]

One of the most serious causes of intellectual and personal friction between Plato and his student Aristotle was with regard to Democritus, who had been a contemporary of Socrates (died 399 BC) and hence of the generation just preceding Plato's. Despite Plato's passionate hatred of Democritus and his works, Aristotle himself often refers favourably to Democritus.

Aristotle had a predilection for science, not shared by his Master, and in his own work *On Generation and Corruption*, he goes out of his way to praise Democritus:

> A similar criticism applies to all our predecessors with the single exception of Democritus. Not one of them penetrated below the surface or made a thorough examination of a single one of the problems. Democritus, however, does seem not only to have thought carefully about all the problems, but also to be distinguished from the outset by his method. For, as we are saying, none of the other philosophers made any definite statement about growth, except such as any amateur might have made.[4]

This is a very savage criticism by Aristotle of the non-scientific atttitudes of all his predecessors except for Democritus. And it should be obvious, since he was Plato's star pupil, that Aristotle's strongest criticism of all is implied against Plato, and suggests that he too was 'an amateur'. But this is not all. Aristotle then goes on to attack 'the Platonists' actually by name – they were a group which included all his own former colleagues, from whom he had broken away – as well as the deceased Plato himself. He compares them all unfavourably to Democritus who by contrast 'would appear to have been convinced by arguments appropriate to the subject, i.e. drawn from the science of nature'.[5]

In other words, Plato and his school ignored Nature, were not true scientists, were merely amateurs, and their discussions of natural questions were puerile and ridiculous – that was Aristotle's opinion! And since he was Plato's student for 20 years, he ought to know. Aristotle clearly believed that only Democritus before him had appreciated the principles or spirit of a scientific method. It was this method which Aristotle was the first to evolve and establish properly in the world of philosophy (at least its foundation, since the full scientific method as we think of it today was built upon it from the Renaissance onwards), and which was eventually to give birth to modern Western civilization, science, and technology.

Having considered this background, we can all the more appreciate why the views of Democritus on optical matters are appropriate for us to consider. We are very lucky to have the snippet of information from Antisthenes about Democritus's experiments into the nature and effects of sensory deprivation. He had the true scientific spirit, in that he actually went and sat in dark tombs for long periods in order to experiment on himself.

Among the lost works of Democritus was one entitled *Peri Eidōlōn* (*On Eidōla*'). The Greek word *eidōlon* is the origin of our modern word 'idol', from the sense of its meaning of 'image'. In fact, if we look in an English dictionary, we will find that there is a little-used meaning of 'idol' as 'a form or appearance visible but without substance, as an image in a mirror'.

245

This obscure meaning of our own modern word is actually closer to the original ancient meaning. For, to the Greeks, *eidōla* were not merely 'images' but 'phantoms, apparitions, any insubstantial forms, phantoms of the mind'.

Now we can begin to see the connection between this optical term for 'images' in Greek and the visual hallucinations which Democritus presumably experienced in his darkened tombs. His work *On 'Eidōla'* was partially concerned with foreknowledge, with which he associated the 'phantoms of the mind' gained through sensory deprivation. As Arthur Pease, the scholar who edited Cicero's *On Divination*, remarks:

> Democritus . . . seems to have accepted most forms of the mantic [prophesying] art, explaining them by the theory of *eidōla* (including) dreams and prophecy . . .[6]

It seems that Democritus, in addition to visual hallucinations, also had direct personal prophetic experiences, for Diogenes Laertius says:

> . . . his reputation rose owing to his having foretold certain future events; and after that the public deemed him worthy of the honour paid to a god.[7]

So Democritus must have made some truly extraordinary predictions. Since he wrote about foreknowledge in connection with 'mental phantoms', we may assume that his own personal experience of foreknowledge took this form, and that he may have had vivid visual hallucinations, which tended to be accurate visions of future events. It has been pointed out by classical scholars that Democritus's individual contributions to philosophy tended to be particularly in the area of 'the theory of perception [which] is distinguished as [his own].'[8] And evidently the area of perception which interested him the most was vision.

It may well have been because of his personal experience of 'phantoms of vision' that Democritus is reported as having adopted a philosophical attitude where 'he did not regard being as more real than non-being'.[9]

That is a rather extreme position to take, reminiscent of the Indian Brahmans with whom he is said to have resided for some time. But what is important for us is that Democritus believed that visions were *real things* which floated around in the air.

There have been many puzzled comments about Democritus's curious visual theories. It is generally thought that his theories of the nature of visual perception are strange and eccentric – which perhaps they are. It was his conviction that physical objects sloughed off transparent membranes into the air which travelled through the atmosphere and impinged upon the eye, thus transmitting images to us and explaining the process of vision.

I suspect that Democritus was forced into his odd theory in order to explain his personal visual hallucinations. Cicero explicitly cites

Democritus (whose works still existed in Cicero's day) as saying that men's minds during sleep 'are affected with external and non-inherent visions'.[10] It is important to realize that Democritus believed that the visions which came in sleep – and evidently the visions which come when one is alone in a dark tomb – are strictly external. This was apparently the only way Democritus could make sense of his own visions. He was not prepared to believe that they could have been generated internally, as psychological phenomena. It is thus through an externalization of his own psychological experience that he formulated his theories of vision. No one before seems to have suspected that Democritus was driven into a corner by his own psychic experiences, which could explain why certain aspects of his philosophy were thought peculiar even by his contemporaries and by Aristotle. They did not quite see that Democritus was trying to embrace within his scheme of nature certain anomalous paranormal experiences. But today, in retrospect, when we are so familiar with such experiences and have a highly developed science of sensory deprivation studies, and when we know that visual hallucinations routinely occur in such conditions, we can clearly see what it is that Democritus was struggling with.

One classical scholar who is an expert on Democritus has written:

> His psychology was an extension of his theory of sense-perception. . . . The soul is a body within the body . . . Cicero complained that Democritus gave various opinions on the nature of divinity: sometimes he said that the gods were the visions we see, often deceptive and injurious, sometimes the nature that produces these . . . the reason for the belief in gods is that there are certain visions, some beneficent, some harmful, which visit men, especially in dreams; these visions are real, and not easily destroyed . . . gods are visions present in air . . . There is no divine creator; all is due to natural causes . . . as all perceptions have some foundation in reality, and men undoubtedly see dreams and visions of the gods, the gods must have a corporeal existence . . . He believed that dreams in general were emanations from bodies, especially living bodies; and that therefore they are subject to material laws: for instance, they are less trustworthy in autumn, owing to the disturbance of the air at that time. Some visions are willfully emitted by persons wishing to injure another. He is said to have believed in divination, and to have prayed to meet only with propitious visions.[11]

It is interesting that Democritus had apparently been challenged in his theory that dreams are all real, by someone who asked: what about when we dream of the gods? So he agreed that the gods must be real, since if they were not, how could we receive images of them in dreams? Here we find an incredible process of reverse-philosophizing! Democritus doesn't start by believing in gods, he starts with a theory of vision, and since that theory then requires all visions to be emitted by real things, visions of the gods must come from real gods, hence the gods must be real! Rarely in the history of either philosophy or theology can a theory of the gods have been arrived at by such a circuitous route. It goes to show us just how dominated Democritus was by his vision theory. It clearly took precedence over everything for him.

The passage of Cicero which was referred to a moment ago says:

> Then in what a maze of errors is Democritus involved, who at one moment ranks as gods his roving *imagines* [a not particularly accurate Latin translation by Cicero of the Greek word '*eidōla*'], at another the substance that emits and radiates these *imagines*, and at another again the scientific intelligence of man![12]

We see here clearly that Democritus *must* have had personal visions. For despite being of a distinctly sceptical turn of mind, as witness some of his other theories not discussed here, he was compelled to find some explanation for these personal visions. And his visions must occasionally have been frightening and unpleasant, since he stressed this side of the phenomenon and 'prayed to meet only with propitious visions'. It is Plutarch who actually preserves this last fragment of Democritus in his essay *On the Cessation of Oracles*. The 1889 Bohn translation of this essay conveys the sense particularly well:

> Democritus, when he prays that 'he may meet with auspicious *eidōla* (apparitions)', shows plainly that he knows of others that have morose and mischievous dispositions and inclinations.[13]

Plutarch discusses the same subject again in another of his works, entitled in English *Table-Talk*. This work consists of a large collection of interesting subjects for discussion at intellectual dinner parties, together with imaginary dialogues of dinner guests (based on real people whom Plutarch knew, and sometimes real discussions) expressing their views. One such subject in Book Five of *Table-Talk* is 'Of Those Who Are Said to Cast an Evil Eye'. It begins as follows:

> Once at dinner a discussion arose about people who are said to cast a spell and to have an evil eye. While everybody else pronounced the matter completely silly and scoffed at it, Mestrius Florus, our host, declared that actual facts lend astonishing support to the common belief. Yet the reports of such facts are commonly rejected because of the want of an explanation; but this is not right, in view of the thousands of other cases of indisputable fact in which the logical explanation escapes us.[14]

A fascinating discussion then ensues, near the end of which Florus's son-in-law is recorded as saying:

248

What, do we completely despise and leave out of account the simulacra or shapes [in the original Greek text, the word used is of course *eidōla*] of Democritus, . . . ? Democritus says that these *simulacra* are emanations emitted not altogether unconsciously or unintentionally by the malevolent, and are charged with their wickedness and envy. According to him, these *simulacra* with their burden of evil, adhering to their victims and in fact permanently lodged in them, confound and injure both their bodies and their minds. So, I believe, runs his text and his intention, expressed in language both lofty and inspired.

Plutarch then replies to the young scholar:

. . . the only things that I (deny) to the emanations (are) life and free will. Don't think that I want to make your flesh creep and throw you into a panic late at night like this by bringing on sentient, purposeful shapes and apparitions. Let's talk about such things in the morning, if you like.

And earlier Plutarch had also stated:

Self-bewitchment is most frequently brought about by the streams of particles reflected from sheets of water or other mirror-like surfaces; these reflections rise like vapour and return to the beholder, so that he [who has the 'evil eye'] is himself injured by the same means by which he has been injuring others. And perhaps when this happens in the case of children, the blame is often fastened upon those who gaze at them.[15]

In his landmark book *The Greeks and the Irrational*, E. R. Dodds makes a number of pertinent remarks of interest to our subject:

In most of their descriptions of dreams, the Homeric poets treat what is seen as if it were 'objective fact'. The dream usually takes the form of a visit paid to a sleeping man or woman by a single dream-figure . . . This dream figure can be a god, or a ghost, or a pre-existing dream-messenger, or an 'image' (eidōlon) created specially for the occasion; but whichever it is, it exists objectively in space, and is independent of the dreamer.[16]

I have done a complete survey of Homer's *Odyssey*, to see how many times *eidōla* are mentioned there, and what they mean. It is interesting to consider these strange scenes. Perhaps I should just explain first that in Greek *eidōlon* is the singular and *eidōla* is the plural, to avoid confusion.

The mention of *eidōla* in *The Odyssey* begins in Book IV, which is the book in which Odysseus's son Telemachus goes to Sparta to visit his father's old friend King Menelaus, whose wife Helen started all the trouble of the Trojan War. At IV. 796, we find a passage where the goddess Athena makes an *eidōlon* and sends it to Odysseus's wife Penelope in a dream, to speak to her. Robert Fitzgerald translates this as follows:

> Now it occurred to the grey-eyed goddess Athena to make a figure of dream in a woman's form – Iphthime, great Ikarios's other daughter, whom Eumelos of Pherai took as a bride. The goddess sent this dream to Odysseus's house to quiet Penelope and end her grieving. So, passing by the strap-slit through the door, the image came a-gliding down the room to stand at her bedside and murmur to her . . . Then pensive Penelope made this reply, slumbering sweetly in the gates of dream . . . Now the dim phantom spoke to her once more . . . Then said Penelope the wise . . . The dim phantom said only this in answer: 'Of him I may not tell thee in this discourse, alive or dead. And empty words are evil.' The wavering form withdrew along the doorbolt into a draught of wind, and out of sleep Penelope awoke, in better heart for that clear dream in the twilight of the night.[17]

In the Loeb Library translation by Murray, Athena becomes 'flashing-eyed' instead of 'grey-eyed' (*glaukōpis*) but Murray invariably uses the word 'phantom' for the *eidōlon*. And he also says 'dim phantom' for the phrase *eidōlon amauron*.[18] The latter adjective means 'dim, shadowy, faint, hardly seen, living in darkness, obscure, having no light,' etc. It should be noted that Fitzgerald varied the translation of *eidōlon*, sometimes calling it a 'phantom', sometimes a 'figure of dream', and sometimes an 'image'.

We shall see what the other occurrences of such phantoms are like in *The Odyssey*. But it is already clear that the concept of a paranormal *visitation* was traditional in Greek culture, and that the thing which did the visiting was called an *eidōlon* from the times of the earliest Greek literature.

Anyone who has had a particularly striking dream-visitation will recognize the description from *The Odyssey*. It does no good to strike a coy attitude when dealing with these experiences, and so I hasten to say that I have had a few of these dream-visitations myself. During 1997 I had two. I was visited on separate occasions by the spirits of two dead people, my mother and my cousin Stella Norman, both of whom had things of special importance to impart to me. These visitations, which are certainly very rare, are of a character which is entirely different from normal dreams. I was in no doubt whatsoever at the time of the visitations that these were real contacts, and in my sleep I held dialogue with both of them in precisely the manner described in *The Odyssey*.

My mother appeared in a grey linen shroud, with no colour of any kind, and offered me a large jar of honey as a gift, saying simply: 'Please forgive me.' (I should point out that she had done some awful things on certain occasions, so that an apology was certainly called for.) She was in some doubt as to whether I would respond in a friendly manner, but I told her I forgave her and set a certain task upon her as my condition, which she responded to by a message in a dream to my wife Olivia a few days later, which was the information which I required and thereby completed her task and set her free. (I was on the Swedish island of Gotland at the time and Olivia was in England.) My mother announced to me that she had completed her purging (it took four years and two months of earth-time) and was about to 'move on to somewhere else', from where it would be impossible for her to communicate with me again, and she wanted to say goodbye, and had received special permission to do so and to depart with my blessing if she could possibly obtain it, which I am pleased to say she did. I was able to detect that her extremely serious psychological problems had all literally been purged away, and she was entirely free of the serious psychopathic condition which had plagued her, and all harmful or disturbed emotions were gone in their entirety. Her condition was nothing short of astonishing and miraculous, so it does seem as if death solves some problems! She had been 'processed' in some way which was absolutely effective, and the choice of the word 'purged' seems the best and most accurate, which must be why she used it.

With my cousin Stella, the dialogue was much more lengthy and complicated, and involved many personal matters. She was not in a shroud and had chosen to delay moving on, nor was she about to depart for 'somewhere else'. In both of these cases the spirits had to be assisted by professional spiritual helpers in 'getting through', and there was enormous noise and interference to be overcome, like the worst telephone connection imaginable, with occasional bursts of clarity lapsing into noise again, so that I lost half of what Stella was saying to me.

These experiences are extremely vivid and of an order altogether different from 'dreams'. That is why I call them 'visitations'. In my personal opinion, I am entirely convinced that I was genuinely 'visited' by my mother and my cousin Stella. A sceptical reader is free to scoff at my opinion, but I cannot stress strongly enough how utterly convincing the experiences were, not least in the phraseology and utterances of the spirits, which had a certain peculiar pungency and conviction about them, and were noteworthy for their succinctness and aptness to the occasion. Anything further from the vagueness, meandering quality, or fantasy of an actual 'dream' cannot be imagined.

This leads me to be convinced that the ancient Greeks must have had these experiences. They are clearly recorded in Homer and they must equally clearly have been experienced by Democritus. And they helped to shape his theory of vision, thus impinging upon the history of optics!

Let us now quickly survey the other *eidōla* which occur in *The Odyssey*. They come in a great flurry in Book XI, where they appear in no less than

four passages. This fact is one more indication that Book XI was not
written by the same author as the rest of *The Odyssey*, as countless scholars have indeed suggested. This book is the section of *The Odyssey* known
as the *Nekyia*, which is a word meaning 'a magical rite for the invoking of
the spirits of the dead'. This is the book where Odysseus descends to the
Underworld, or Hades, and it seems certain that it was *inserted* into what
we now call *The Odyssey*. Originally, in my opinion, there was a long poem
by Homer called *The Homecoming of Odysseus*, which was complete in
itself, and which still constitutes about 80 per cent of *The Odyssey* as we
know it today. But into this stirring if somewhat mundane epic poem, which
did not contain anything particularly weird or bizarre, were inserted the
sections about the Descent into Hell (Book XI), the encounter with the
Cyclops (something of which we will have more to say later), the encounter
with Scylla and Charybdis, and most of the wondrous, mystical and weird
material. Part of what was inserted also seems to have been the record of an
ancient voyage of exploration in the northern seas, in the vicinity of Britain
and Scandinavia; this was attributed to Odysseus as a way of inflating the
epic and helping to fill in his 20 years of absence from home.

Since the Homeric bards were a caste of travelling storytellers, some of
them must have inflated the original epic with this colourful material in the
generations shortly after Homer's death, though certainly no later than the
eighth century BC or thereabouts. The section about the Descent into Hell
which contains most of the *eidōla* is therefore probably by a different
author than Homer, but I doubt if it is any younger than *circa* 750 BC. As it
happens, that is the date of the foundation of the earliest Greek city in Italy,
Cuma, and the probable date of the construction of the Oracle of the Dead
nearby, for which I believe the *Nekyia* was a propaganda piece of literature.
I have discussed the associations between the tale of the Descent into Hell
and the place where one actually physically descended into the replica of
Hell, which was carved out of the solid rock and extended a fifth of a mile
into the Earth, in an earlier book.[19]

In the *Nekyia* section of *The Odyssey*, at XI, 213, we find that Odysseus
confronts the apparition of his own dead mother. Odysseus has visited
Hades to consult various spirits, and he says at first to the spirit of Teiresias
with whom he is speaking:

'Teiresias, my life runs on then as the gods have spun it. But come, now,
tell me this; make this thing clear: I see my mother's ghost [the word he
uses here is *psychē*] among the dead sitting in silence near the blood [the
blood of a lamb and a ewe whose throats he had slit, which poured out
in sacrifice to attract the ghosts, who like to drink blood]. Not once has
she glanced this way toward her son, nor spoken. Tell me, my lord, may
she in some way come to know my presence?'

To this he answered: 'I shall make it clear in a few words and simply.

Any dead man whom you allow to enter where the blood is will speak to you, and speak the truth; but those deprived will grow remote again and fade.'

When he had prophesied, Teiresias' shade [*psychē*] retired lordly to the halls of Death; but I stood fast until my mother stirred, moving to sip the black blood; then she knew me and called out sorrowfully to me: 'Child, how could you cross alive into this gloom at the world's end? – No sight for living eyes; great currents run between, desolate waters, the Ocean first, where no man goes a journey without ship's timber under him. Say, now, is it from Troy, still wandering, after years, that you come here with ship and company? Have you not gone at all to Ithaka? Have you not seen your lady in your hall?'

Some dialogue then ensues, and Odysseus's mother reveals that she died by pining away for him. Odysseus is very upset and says:

I bit my lip, rising perplexed, with longing to embrace her, and tried three times, putting my arms around her, but she went sifting through my hands, impalpable as shadows [*skiē*, which is a Homeric form of the word not used in the *Iliad* but occurring twice in the *Odyssey*] are, and wavering like a dream [*oneiros*]. Now this embittered all the pain I bore, and I cried in the darkness:

'O my mother, will you not stay, be still, here in my arms, may we not, in this place of Death, as well, hold one another, touch with love, and taste salt tears' relief, the twinge of welling tears? Or is this all hallucination [*eidōlon*], sent against me by the iron queen, Persephone [a goddess of the Underworld], to make me groan again?'[20]

In this harrowing description of Odysseus meeting the ghost of his mother, Murray translates *eidōlon* as 'phantom' rather than as 'hallucination' as Fitzgerald has just done.[21]

It is interesting to note that in this passage, an actual ghost is called by the word *psychē*, and the word *eidōlon* is used to describe an illusory *visual phenomenon* as distinct from a real ghost – in other words, not a real ghost but *an image of a ghost*. In nearly all cases, the word *eidōlon* has an optical or visual implication. We see this again in the *Odyssey* at XI, 476, where Odysseus is asked in Hades:

'How did you find your way down to the dark where these dimwitted dead are camped forever, the after-images of used-up men?'[22]

That was Fitzgerald's inspired translation of the passage. Needless to say, the Greek word which he translates as 'after-images' is *eidōla*. And at XI, 602, when Odysseus sees the *image* though not the actual soul of Herakles

(Hercules), this purely visual phenomenon is once again called an *eidōlon*. Both Fitzgerald and Murray translate the actual word as 'phantom' here, but it is instructive to read what they both actually translate for the whole passage, since the author of this section of the *Odyssey*, whether he was Homer or someone else, was at pains to distinguish between the sight of a real spirit and the sight of a visual hallucination of a spirit:

> Next I saw manifest the power [*biēn* – 'force'] of Herakles – a phantom [*eidōlon*], this, for he himself has gone feasting amid the gods, reclining soft with Hebe [his wife in the afterlife] of the ravishing pale ankles, daughter of Zeus and Hera, shod in gold. But, in my vision, all the dead around him cried like affrighted birds; like Night itself he loomed with naked bow and nocked arrow and glances terrible as continual archery. . . . The eyes of the vast figure rested on me . . . [Herakles speaks briefly, and then:] . . . And Herakles, down the vistas of the dead, faded from sight . . .[23]

Murray's translation is:

> And after him I marked the mighty Heracles – his phantom [*eidōlon*]; for he himself among the immortal gods takes his joy in the feast, and has to wife Hebe, of the fair ankles, daughter of great Zeus and of Hera, of the golden sandals. About him rose a clamour from the dead, as of birds flying everywhere in terror; and he like dark night, with his bow bare and with arrow on the string, glared about him terribly, like one in act to shoot . . . He in turn knew me when his eyes beheld me, and weeping spoke to me winged words . . . So saying, he went his way again into the house of Hades . . .[24]

I remember well when I was 14 or 15 at school I was fortunate enough to have a teacher who decided to give an experimental course in 'Mythology', which was of great excitement to me. The thing that most disturbed me in my teenage study of mythology was this very anomaly, and I grilled my teacher about it. For I could not accept the account that Hercules went to Olympus after his death to join the gods, but that his phantom went to Hades. I asked Father Chapman, my teacher, how this logical contradiction could possibly be explained, and he shrugged his shoulders in his usual good-humoured way and said he didn't have any idea. (He was always very honest!) I repeated, how can there be *two souls*, one the real fellow himself who goes to enjoy himself on Mount Olympus, and one an image of the fellow who goes and dwells in Hades with the shades of the dead? Once again, Father Chapman merely shrugged and grinned. I have worried about the two souls of Hercules about half a dozen times a year since I was 15.

Autenrieth's *An Homeric Dictionary* (1916) translates *eidōlon* with great accuracy as 'illusive image', and under *psychē* clarifies its meaning further by saying that the word *psychē* can have the meaning 'in derived sense, *eidōlon*, the *soul of the departed* in the lower world, disembodied, and so without *phrenes* [consciousness], yet retaining the outward appearance which it had in life . . .'[25]

Always the *eidōlon* is an *outward appearance, an image* (of a supernatural kind) in Homeric usage. Knowing what we do about the theories of Democritus, it is obvious that this traditional concept was directly adopted by him, and that it existed for centuries before his time. But where did the idea come from? Did it originate with the archaic Greeks, or does it have some earlier source? In answering this question, we are led back to ancient Egypt, and a strange combination of metaphysics and optics in Egyptian religious thought.

Here I turn to a little-known work of 1898 which I value highly, although its author is known to only a handful of people. I refer to George St Clair, and his extraordinarily intelligent book *Creation Records Discovered in Egypt (Studies in the Book of the Dead).*[26] St Clair followed this with a two-volume work entitled *Myths of Greece Explained and Dated* (1901).[27] Of the first I have a signed presentation copy, and of the second I have a copy containing several letters from the author elucidating his points and making large numbers of typographical and numerical corrections, so that I therefore have what I believe to be the only existing record of St Clair's amendments to his work.

St Clair was able to decode many of the astronomical and cosmographical beliefs which underlie the strange religious symbology of the Egyptians, some of which also passed into Greek mythology where they have not always been recognized for what they really are. St Clair is not correct in all his efforts, and sometimes admits as much, but his elucidations from *The Book of the Dead* are often crucial, and he makes sense of many things which no other author known to me has ever managed to do. I shall be returning to St Clair's work much later in this book, when I deal with ancient Egypt at greater length. Here I wish to cite him only insofar as he has light to shed on the subject of the visual aspects of what the Greeks called *eidōla*. In his book about Egypt, St Clair is discussing the curious Egyptian concepts of multiple souls, and says the following:

[An ancient Egyptian] passage occurs in which the elements of a person, disparted at death, are enumerated, not as body and soul merely, but as five in number at the least . . . Thus it appears that besides the body, which is the material person, and the mummy, which is the same when the life has left it, there are in this psychology the soul and the spirit, each attended by a shade. The spirit is called *ka*. Wiedemann says that the *ka* of a man was his individuality as embodied in his name – the *picture* [my italics] of him which was or might have been called up in the minds of those who knew him, at the mention of his name. But there are representations of the *ka* which suit well with the idea that it stands for what we should call the man's ghost or double. In bas-reliefs which represent the birth of [the Pharaoh] Amenophis III, his *ka* is born at the same time as the king, and both are presented to [the god] Amen-Ra, as two boys exactly alike, and blessed by him. A man lived no longer than his *ka* remained with him, and it never left him until the moment of his death. The *ka* could live without the body, but the body could not live without the *ka*. . . . Is it not likely that the form of the *ka*, as the double of the man, was suggested by the image or likeness reflected in a mirror, or in another person's eye? The *ka* of a man would then correspond, in a way, to the reflected image of the sun called the Eye of Ra.

The Pyramid texts show that even in the times of the Vth and VIth dynasties, Thoth, Set, Horus, and other gods, were recognised as having *kas*. The statues of the gods represented and embodied divine *kas*.

We find occasional mention of the *Ka* of the East and the *Ka* of the West (Wilkinson, *Manners and Customs* [*of the Ancient Egyptians*], 2nd ed. III, pp. 200, 201): and Wiedemann says they are to be considered as being the *kas* of the deities of the east and of the west, and not as the *kas* of the abstract conceptions of the east and west. That, indeed, seems probable; and may they not be the reflected disk of the sun, over the altar, in the temple?

A *ka* image of the sun, in the temple, is spoken of in the time of Amenophis.

But while, in the case of man, there appears to have been only one soul and one spirit [in fact there were more human 'souls' than two, as we have seen] the Sun is stated to have seven *ba* (souls) and fourteen *ka* (eidola or phantasms), two such images being attached to each soul. The statement must have appeared to be inexplicable, but it is not likely to have been made without meaning, and when we are on the track of truth, things begin to fall into their right places. . . . [He then goes into his explanation for the seven *ba*, which we skip here.] . . . These, perhaps, are the seven *ba* or souls of the sun; and each *ba* . . . has reproduced its own image or phantasm in the temple of morning and the temple of evening [i.e. at sunrise and sunset, hence double the number], making fourteen *ka* or ghosts, or reflections of rising and setting suns. . . . The reproduction of the Eye of the Sun, in the properly oriented temple, showed the year completed and enabled the calendar to be kept right.[28]

St Clair elsewhere states: '[A god or goddess could be called] the Eye of the Sun, . . . because the sun, from [a solstice or equinoctial point] sent his rays straight along the telescopic entrance-passageway to the inner sanctuary [of an Egyptian temple], there to form an image of himself.'[29]

St Clair quotes the famous astronomer Sir Norman Lockyer, then editor of the journal *Nature*:

. . . Lockyer has not hesitated to say that the Two Eyes of Ra, which look in different directions, are the two extreme points of the sun's amplitude north and south (at summer and winter solstice).

'Now see,' says Lockyer, 'how these were observed, and how naturally they suggest an Eye. The temple sanctuary was dark, and the beam of light came through the pylons and traversed the long passage and lighted up the shrine of the god, on those days of the greatest amplitude of the sun – on those particular days, because the temple was oriented to catch the first or last rays of the sun on the day of the summer solstice. The beam of sunlight would flash into the sanctuary and light up the shrine for about a couple of minutes, and then pass away. The flash would be a crescendo and diminuendo, but the whole thing would not last above two minutes, or thereabouts, and might be considerably reduced by arrangements of curtains.'

All this helps our conception: but what Lockyer fails to point out is that such a beam of light, so received, through apertures which might be square or irregular in shape, would nevertheless, by the laws of sight, throw a sun-image, circular like an eye. The great length of the avenue [inside the temple] would lend perfection to the effect; for the law with regard to light passing through apertures is this – that an image of the aperture itself will be produced when the screen is rather close, but an image of the source of light when the screen is at a considerable distance. Thus the sunlight through a window gives an image of the aperture of the window on the wall or floor of the apartment, but would give an image of the sun if the wall were a mile away.[30]

So it may well be that Democritus, when he was deep within his tombs, may sometimes have been experimenting with just such phenomena, especially as there was the garbled mention (given earlier) of his using a mirror to reflect the sun within a tomb.

There were actually more 'souls' in ancient Egyptian conceptions than St Clair mentions, and these are enumerated at greater length by Wallis Budge in his Introduction to his translation of the Egyptian *Book of the Dead*. There, Budge used the word *eidōlon* in connection with the *ka*, just as we have already seen St Clair do:

The *ka* . . . a word which by general consent is translated 'double' . . . can in most cases be rendered by one of the meanings of *eidōlon*. [He was writing at a time when most of his educated British readers could be expected to know this word because they had read the *Odyssey* in Greek at school.] The *ka* was an abstract individuality or personality which possessed the form and attributes of the man to whom it belonged, and, though its normal dwelling place was in the tomb with the body, it could wander about at will; it was independent of the man and could go and dwell in any statue of him. It was supposed to eat and drink, and the greatest care was usually taken to lay abundant supplies of offerings in the tombs lest the *kas* of those who were buried in them should be reduced to the necessity of leaving their tombs and of wandering about and eating offal and drinking filthy water.[31]

There may well have been perceptual experiences of deceased 'shades' behind all of this as well. When my dog Kim died, I saw her three days later sitting on top of her grave in the garden looking perplexed. I could tell that she wanted to get up and wander about, but she felt that she had better guard her body because she might well need to use it again. She was gazing intently at an empty chair in which she obviously saw someone she knew sitting and meeting her gaze, for she continually almost went towards the chair as if torn between the instinct to guard her body and the desire to go to the familiar person. She took no notice of me. The appearance was of her being in a different reality, at a different time, at a different speed, although her movements were at normal speed. She was silvery in appearance and two years old again. I can well understand that such apparitions, having been perceived countless times throughout history, have always given the impression of a visual image which does not relate to or 'connect with' the viewer, and thus seems a mere picture, because such 'images' do not have their true existence in our reality but are in their own. To perceive them is always a rare occurrence, and Kim's failure to perceive me was like the initial failure of Odysseus's mother to perceive him. After all, why should the dead see us any more often than we can see them?

But having said all this about perception and spirits, the central point is that the Greek concept of the *eidōlon* appears to have derived directly from the Egyptian concept of the *ka*. And St Clair is probably correct in believing the *ka* to be linked with solar image-manifestations at the solstices and equinoxes in the inner sanctums of a variety of appropriately-oriented temples. This concept, which was therefore from the earliest times linked with optical phenomena, was always essentially optical in nature in the *Odyssey* and was then linked explicity with optics by the philosopher and proto-scientist Democritus.

Democritus's concept then spread down the corridors of time and continued to exercise influence for centuries afterwards. Democritus lived in the fifth century BC (born between 460 and 457 BC). His theories about *eidōla* were taken over by Epicurus (341–270 BC), and through him by Lucretius (94–55 BC), who in his famous book about Nature, *De Rerum Natura*, in Book IV speaks of them at very great length. Amongst many other aspects of them, Lucretius writes as follows:

> . . . there exist what we call images [*simulacra*] of things; which, like films drawn from the outermost surface of things, flit about hither and thither through the air; it is these same that, encountering us in wakeful

hours, terrify our minds, as also in sleep, when we often seem to behold wonderful shapes and images of the dead, which have aroused us in horror while we lay languid in sleep; lest by chance we should think that spirits escape from Acheron or ghosts flit about amongst the living . . . I say, therefore, that semblances and thin shapes of things are thrown off from their outer surface, which are to be called as it were their films or bark, because the image bears a look and shape like the body of that from which it is shed to go on its way. . . . as often when cicadas drop their thin coats in summer, and when calves at birth throw off the caul from their outermost surface . . . a thin image must also be thrown off from such things, from the outermost surface of things. . . . There are thus fixed outlines of shapes and of finest texture which flit about everywhere, but singly and separately cannot be seen. . . . whatever similitudes we see in mirrors, in water, in any bright surface, since they are possessed of the same outward appearance as those things, must consist of images thrown off from those things. There are therefore thin shapes and like semblances of things, which singly no one can perceive, yet being flung back by incessant and unremitting repulsion give back a vision from the surface of mirrors. Nor does there seem to be any other way in which they could be preserved so that figures so like each other should be given back. . . . There is always something streaming from the outermost surface of things for them to shoot off. And this when it meets some things passes through, particularly through glass. . . . An image may also be transmitted from mirror to mirror, so that five or six images have often been produced. For whatever lies hidden behind in the inner parts of a house, however tortuous and secluded be the ways in between, may yet be all brought out through these involved passages by means of a number of mirrors and seen to be in the house. So truly does the image shine from mirror to mirror . . . [and] whatever is submerged under water seems to be all broken back and wrenched and turned flat upwards and thus bent back . . . And when the winds carry scattered cloudlets across the sky in the night time, then the shining stars seem to glide against the clouds and to pass above them in a very different direction from their true one . . .[32]

Lucretius thus manages to include descriptions of both *reflection* and *refraction* (and I have not quoted by any means the whole of his remarks) in his account, much of which is obviously derived, probably through Epicurus, from Democritus's lost works *Description of Rays of Light* and *On Eidōla*, since few believe that the material is to any significant extent original with Lucretius himself, who was a compiler and a poet.

In the first/second centuries AD, Plutarch continued the discussion. And it is interesting that Plutarch discussed the *eidōla* of both Democritus and the *Odyssey*, so that he too drew the connection which I have made in this chapter. I have quoted earlier his remarks in his essay 'On the Cessation of

Oracles', and also in his book *Table-Talk*.

Plutarch's longest discussion of *eidōla* is to be found in his treatise 'On the Face in the Moon', which is one of Plutarch's most bizarre and recondite essays. In this passage, he tackles the subject on the basis of the account of the *eidōlon* of Hercules in the *Odyssey*:

> . . . when the mind has been separated from soul; the separation comes by love of the image which is in the sun [this would appear to be a reference to the bright white light seen in near-death experiences]; through it there shines upon them that desirable, beautiful, divine, and blessed presence for which all nature yearns, yet in different ways. . . . That nature which is the soul remains on the moon, retaining traces and dreams of the former life, and of it you may take it that it has been rightly said – 'Winged as a dream the soul takes flight away.' – Not at the first, and not when it is quit of the body does this happen to it, but afterwards when it becomes deserted and solitary, set free from mind. Of all that Homer has told us I think that there is nothing more divine than where he speaks of those in Hades – 'Next was I aware of mighty Hercules, His ghost [*eidōlon*] – [for he] himself among the immortals dwells.'[33] (The translation of Prickard.)

Continuing the passage in the translation of King, we read:

> For each individual of us is not anger, nor fear, nor desire, just as he is neither pieces of flesh nor humours; but that wherewith we think and understand is the soul, impressed by the mind, and in its turn impressing the body, and impinging upon it from all parts it models the form; so that, though it may continue a long time separated from both the mind and the body, yet as it retains the likeness and imprint, it is properly denominated the 'Image' or spectre (*eidōlon*). Of these images [*eidōla*] the moon is the element: for they are resolved into her substance, like as bodies into earth; for being let go from the mind, and no longer subject to the passions, they wither away.[34]

And in the translation of Goodwin we see these aspects again emphasized:

> And the soul being moulded and formed by the understanding [mind], and itself moulding and forming the body, by embracing it on every side, receives from it an impression and form; so that although it be separated from the understanding [mind] and the body, it nevertheless retains still its figure and semblance for a long time, that it may with good right be called its image [*eidōlon*].[35]

From all of this we may see clearly that the many components of the human being survived in Plutarch's philosophy, and that these undoubtedly had their origins in the ancient Egyptian conceptions, where the *ka* was the source of the *eidōlon*. And the fact that Plutarch points to the passage about the *eidōlon* of Hercules as being the 'most divine' passage in the whole of the *Odyssey* shows how central all of this was to the 'theosophical' ideas of one of the leading Greek intellectuals of the second century AD. And we should remember that Plutarch was also the High Priest of Delphi as well as a philosopher and historian. By this time, the image of the Sun and the concept of the *ka* were nearly 3,000 years old, but still going strong! Indeed, in his Life of Brutus, the phantom who appears in Brutus's dream before the Battle of Philippi to predict his death by saying they shall meet again there (well known to all familiar with Shakespeare's *Julius Caesar*, since he took this from Plutarch) was an *eidōlon*.

Cicero (first century BC) discussed *eidōla* at some length in a letter to Brutus's co-conspirator Cassius (Letters to His Friends, XV, 16), but we need not give the details here. Cicero discussed the *eidōla* (he used the Greek word itself, despite writing in Latin) also to his best friend Atticus: 'In finding fault with the narrowness of my windows, let me tell you . . . If our sight resulted from the impact of *eidōla*, the *eidōla* would be horribly squeezed in the narrow space: but, as it is, the emission of rays goes on merrily.'[36] By saying this, Cicero is teasing his friend Atticus, who had become a follower of Epicurus and thus believed in the theory of *eidōla* to explain vision, which Cicero himself did not accept. Cicero's letters to his boyhood friend are full of such banter.

The *eidōla* of Democritus were also mentioned by Clement of Alexandria, an early Church Father who was born about 150 AD. Clement was a Greek intellectual of immense erudition who 'got hooked on Jesus' and wrote thundering, learned treatises to his contemporaries urging them to become Christians. In his famous *Exhortation to the Greeks*, in which he summarizes the ideas of Greek paganism, mythology, and philosophy, and tries to show the superiority of Christianity to them, he preserves much otherwise lost information (as he does in his other writings as well). In Chapter Five, he seeks to dismiss the philosopher Heraclides of Pontus, who had been a member of Plato's Academy by saying:

> What of Heraclides of Pontus? Is there a single place where he too [he has just mentioned Epicurus] is not drawn away to the *eidōla* of Democritus?[37]

This passage was overlooked by H. B. Gottschalk in his book about Heraclides (whose works are lost) and the usefulness of this information in attempting to reconstruct the philosophical ideas of Heraclides was a point which was thus missed.[38]

We have now discussed *eidōla* sufficiently to see how pervasive the notion had become in classical times. It could form the basis of a joke by Cicero and an excuse for an early Christian to discredit pagan philosophy. And under the Roman Empire, it could form part of the theosophy of a High Priest of Delphi. Such notions also worked their way into that form of later Platonic philosophy known as Neoplatonism, and from there (as we shall see in a later stage of this book) into the more esoteric schools of Christianity, constituting an underlying assumption in what were to become the mediaeval 'theologies of light' and the modern theories of 'light mysticism' which are still going strong today.

What began as an image of the Sun projected onto the wall of the inner sanctum of an ancient Egyptian temple led to the creation of a whole theory of an additional human soul which was believed by entire civilizations for more than 3,000 years. And the idea still survives today, 2,000 years later still, in many of the philosophies and theologies in which the origins of this concept have long been totally forgotten.

We shall see, as we continue, that the histories of such optical ideas are every bit as important as the history of optical science and technology, and that ancient optics at the conceptual level in fact permeates much of our current world in other ways as well, and also explains countless mysteries of Western cultural history which otherwise have no solution.

Notes

1. Diogenes Laertius, *Lives and Opinions of Eminent Philosophers*, Book IX, 38–9; translated by R. D. Hicks, Loeb Classical Library, Harvard University Press, USA, Vol. II, 1965, p. 449.
2. Aulus Gellius, X, xvii, translated by John C. Rolfe, Loeb Library Series, Harvard University Press, USA, Vol. II, 1968, pp. 259–61.
3. *Ibid.*, Book IX, 40; translation pp. 449–51.
4. Aristotle, *On Generation and Corruption*, Book I, 2, 315a–b; translated by H.H. Joachim, in Sir David Ross, ed., *The Works of Aristotle* (in English), Oxford, Vol. II, 1970, 315a–b.
5. *Ibid.*, 316a.
6. Pease, Arthur Stanley, *M. Tulli Ciceronis de Divinatione*, text edited with extraordinarily elaborate notes and Introduction by Pease. University of Illinois Studies in Language and Literature, Vol. VI, No. 2, May 1920, Urbana, Illinois, p. 58n.
7. Diogenes Laertius, *op.cit.*, Book IX, 39; translation, p. 449.
8. Kirk, G. S., and Raven, J. E., *The Presocratic Philosophers*, Cambridge University Press, 1969, p. 402.
9. Gomperz, Theodor, *The Greek Thinkers: A History of Ancient Philosophy*, John Murray, London, 1964, Vol. I, p. 345.
10. Cicero, Marcus Tullius, *De Divinatione (On Divination)*, Book II, 58, 120. Translation based upon that by C. D. Yonge, Bohn's Classical Library, London, 1878, p. 250, which I find better than the translation of this passage later published by the Loeb Classical Library. I have substituted the expression 'non-inherent' for the rather vague and unfamiliar word 'adventitious', which in Latin is *adventicia*. W. A. Falconer, in the Loeb Classical Library translation, 1964, p. 507, renders *externa et adventicia visione* as 'phantoms from without', which is a genial compromise, but distracts us from the more precise meaning which is of importance to us.
11. Freeman, Kathleen, *Companion to the Pre-Socratic Philosophers*, Blackwell, Oxford, 1966, pp. 314–15.
12. Cicero, Marcus Tullius, *On the Nature of the Gods (De Natura Deorum)*, Book I, 12, 29;

translated by H. Rackham, Loeb Classical Library, Harvard University Press, USA, 1967, p. 33.

13. Plutarch, *On the Cessation of Oracles*, XVII, 419a; translation by C. W. King, in *Plutarch's Morals: Theosophical Essays*, Bohn's Library, London, 1889, p. 33.

14. Plutarch, *Table-Talk*, Book V, Question 7, translated by Paul A. Clement and Herbert A. Hoffleit, Loeb Classical Library, Harvard University Press, Vol. VIII of *Moralia*, 1986, p. 417.

15. *Ibid.*, pp. 431–3.

16. Dodds, E. R., *The Greeks and the Irrational*, University of California Press, 1951, p. 104.

17. Homer, *The Odyssey*, translated by Robert Fitzgerald, Heinemann, London, 1962, pp. 70–1.

18. Homer, *The Odyssey*, translated by A. T. Murray, Loeb Classical Library, Harvard University Press, USA, Vol. I, 1919, pp. 165–9.

19. Temple, Robert K. G., *Conversations with Eternity*, Rider, London, 1984, Chapters One to Three.

20. Homer, trans. Fitzgerald, *op. cit.*, pp. 169–71.

21. Homer, trans. Murray, *op. cit.*, Vol. I, p. 401.

22. Homer, trans. Fitzgerald, *op. cit.*, p. 180.

23. *Ibid.*, pp. 184–5.

24. Homer, trans. Murray, *op. cit.*, pp. 429–31.

25. Autenrieth, Georg, trans. from German by Robert Keep, *An Homeric Dictionary*, Macmillan, London, 1916, pp. 97a and 334a–b.

26. St Clair, George, *Creation Records Discovered in Egypt (Studies in the Book of the Dead)*, David Nutt, London, 1898.

27. St Clair, George, *Myths of Greece Explained and Dated*, Williams and Norgate, London, 1901, 2 vols.

28. St Clair, *Creation Records*, *op. cit.*, pp. 97–9.

29. *Ibid.*, p. 120.

30. *Ibid.*, p. 93.

31. Wallis Budge, Sir E. A., *The Book of the Dead*, Routledge & Kegan Paul, London, 2nd edition, revised and enlarged, 1899, pp. lix–lx.

32. Lucretius, *De Rerum Natura*, trans. by W. H. D. Rouse, Loeb Classical Library, Harvard University Press, USA, 3rd edition revised, 1937 (reprinted 1959), pp. 251–79.

33. Plutarch, 'On the Face Which Appears on the Orb of the Moon', trans. by A. O. Prickard, Winchester, England, 1911, Section 30, pp. 46–7.

34. Plutarch, 'On the Apparent Face in the Moon's Orb', trans. by C. W. King, in *Plutarch's Morals. Theosophical Essays*, George Bell, London, 1889, Section 30, pp. 255–7.

35. Plutarch, 'Of the Face Appearing in the Orb of the Moon', trans. by William W. Goodwin, in *Plutarch's Morals*, Little, Brown and Company, Boston, Vol. V, 1874, p. 290.

36. Cicero, Marcus Tullius, Letter to Titus Pomponius Atticus, II, 3, dated December, 60 BC, in Vol. I of *Letters to Atticus*, trans. by E. O. Winstedt (I have slightly altered the translation), Loeb Classical Library, Harvard University Press, USA, 1962, p. 115.

37. Clement of Alexandria, *Exhortation to the Greeks*, in *Clement of Alexandria* volume of the Loeb Library Series, trans. by G. W. Butterworth, Harvard University Press, USA, 1982, p. 151. I have slightly changed the translation.

38. Gottschalk, H.B., *Heraclides of Pontus*, Oxford University Press, 1980. He does mention *eidōla* just in passing on p. 53 and acknowledges on p. 142 that Heraclides drew some atomist ideas from Democritus, which are described in Chapter Three of Gottschalk's book. But of the three ideas which Gottschalk (p. 142) believes Heraclides drew from Democritus, he does not know of or include anything relating to the *eidōla* which the testimony of Clement indicates were central to Heraclides's thought.

Chapter Seven

The Crystal Sun

... the Sun shines as crystal, which receives its splendour from the Fire
of the World and so reflecteth its light upon us; so that the body of Fire,
which is celestial, hath a resemblance in the Sun, and reflecting from its
own light, from itself upon the Sun as upon a glass, and this we call the
Sun ...[1]

It was as I was nearing the end of my literary research that I came across
this fragment of a lost book by an ancient Pythagorean named Philolaos. I
thought I already had some notion of Philolaos's ideas. I had known for
nearly 30 years that he believed the earth went round the sun, for instance.
Many times I had read accounts of Pythagorean astronomy. But why had I
not noticed this before? Philolaos obviously thought that the sun was a
huge sphere of either crystal or glass, and that sunlight did not emanate
from the sun itself, but was a celestial fire which was either *reflected*, as by
a mirror, or *refracted*, as through a crystal lens, *by the sun*. The sun was
essentially a gigantic crystal ball much larger than the earth, as far as many
of the ancient Pythagoreans were concerned; and Philolaos (fifth century
BC) is the earliest recorded Pythagorean writer.

I could not understand why this did not form a major feature – or even a
minor feature – in all the histories of science I had read. And how could I
possibly never have come across it before, considering how much I had
read about ancient astronomy?

I might never have discovered the crystal sun if it were not for the fact
that I had come across one or two curious footnotes to a treatise of Plutarch
in 17th- and 18th-century books abbreviated *De Placit. Philos*. I had never
heard of *De Placit. Philos*. What on earth could it be? Loose ends like that
niggle away at me and I always have to pursue them, as the tiniest thread
often leads to the biggest surprise.

I was bothered by the fact that I thought I knew the treatises of Plutarch
fairly well. Plutarch is best known for his *Lives*, but the other half of his
surviving works is generally grouped together under the heading of
Plutarch's *Moralia (Morals)*. Perhaps the reason why that general title has
been given to the treatises is that several of them actually do concern moral
questions, such as the quaint treatise 'On How to Praise Oneself

Inoffensively'. I tend to call the genuinely moral ones the 'Ethical Treatises', and they do not interest me nearly as much as the many weird treatises with titles like 'On the Face Appearing in the Orb of the Moon', 'On Isis and Osiris', 'On Fate', 'On Superstition', 'On the E at Delphi', 'On the Sign of Socrates', and 'Why Oracles Are No Longer Delivered in Verse'. Plutarch was High Priest of the Oracle of Delphi in the first and second centuries AD. He had travelled in Egypt and knew much astounding mystical lore. Indeed, his account of Isis and Osiris is the only surviving coherent account of them from antiquity, since the Egyptian information about those central Egyptian deities is so fragmentary and incomplete. Egyptologists tend to be more familiar with the *Moralia* of Plutarch than many classicists, as they cannot pursue their discipline without referring to Plutarch's 'On Isis and Osiris' as a standard text of reference whenever they discuss ancient Egyptian religion and mythology.

I had been reading Plutarch's treatises over and over since the 1960s. But I did not know of any called *De Placit. Philos.* Had the footnotes somehow made a mistake? I thought not. So I took the time to comb through all the treatises of the *Moralia* in the modern Loeb Library edition (15 volumes bound in 16 volumes) once again, though I had already done this several times. Once more, I confirmed that none of the titles in the 15 volumes remotely resembled the mysterious title *De Placit. Philos.* However, this time I looked at the preliminary section entitled 'The Traditional Order of the Books of the *Moralia* as they appear since the edition of Stephanus (1572), and their division into volumes in this edition', which helpfully appears near the beginning of Vol. XIII, Part 1, of the Loeb edition, and there I finally found it, the only one of the long list with a star in front of it: *De Placitis Philosophorum, libri V (Peri tōn areskontōn tois philosophois, biblia ε)*. The star referred to a footnote which stated: 'This work, by Aëtius, not Plutarch, is omitted in the current edition.' I had found the elusive treatise only to lose it.

Classical scholars have some weird habits, none perhaps weirder than their insistence upon referring to Greek writings by Latin names. Everything which Plutarch wrote was in Greek, and yet classical scholars inevitably use Latin titles for all of his treatises. This habit presumably goes back to the time when Latin was the European language of learning, during the late Renaissance, and when Greek writings began to be circulated in Latin translations because hardly anyone knew Greek. Greek writings thus came to be viewed as rare things one collected, like plants, and just as botanists have settled on Latin names for all their specimens, so the Greek writings are treated as if they too had roots, seedpods, and burrs. For instance, normal people might call Plutarch's treatise about Isis and Osiris by its English title, simply 'On Isis and Osiris'. But a classical scholar will rarely do this. He will generally speak of 'De Iside et Osiride', or perhaps he will merely use a Latin nickname and call it for short simply 'De Iside . . .' This kind of thing goes on all the time. One could take the uncharitable view that it is intended to keep the ordinary person out of the conversation.

Hence the mysterious missing treatise was referred to as *De Placitis Philosophorum*, and never by its Greek name, despite the fact that its author never called it that, and the Latin titles are all unnecessary translations *into Latin* by later scholars for purposes of professional chat.

It was clear, then, that the Loeb Library was going to let me down, and I would have to track down *De Placitis Philosophorum* by other means, as it had been purged from the canon. The title in itself was a strange one, meaning more or less *On that which Was Pleasing to the Philosophers*. What was meant by that? Did it describe their favourite armchairs and their cushions, the decor of their bedrooms or their best quill pens? Rarely can a serious ancient Greek treatise have had a more misleading title, as I was to discover.

I suddenly remembered that I had an old 18th-century translation of Plutarch's *Moralia*, in several volumes, published in 1704, sitting on a high shelf. I had bought it in a disintegrating and largely disbound state and rarely consulted it. I tend to collect many different translations of the same texts, as well as different editions of the texts themselves, and sometimes, I have to confess, I forget that I have some of them. I rooted round in the old 1704 edition, when they were less fussy about false attributions of texts, trying to find the mysterious missing treatise, and there it was, in Vol. III, on pp. 121–95, under the quaint title (by no means immediately identifiable!): 'Plutarch's giving an Account of those Sentiments concerning Nature with which Philosophers were Delighted'. When I read through it, I was very surprised, because it was obviously a most valuable collection of the opinions of early scientists and philosophers, of the type which is called a 'doxography', from the Greek word *doxa*, meaning 'opinion' or 'notion'. These used to be compiled by Aristotle and his disciple, Theophrastus. And on the first page the work even spoke of the division of philosophy by the Aristotelian school. It seemed to me that this was not the sort of treatise one should omit from modern translation in the Loeb Library simply because it had drifted into Plutarch's works and was actually written by another chap called Aëtios (Aëtius being another of those Latin affectations).

I began to leaf through this fascinating treatise, which I had never seen before, and came across a chapter entitled 'Of the Essence of the Sun' (Book II, Chapter 20; pp. 153–4). It gives the opinions on this subject of many ancient philosophers and scientists, and the theory of the Sun as a crystal ball is identified as that of 'Philolaus the Pythagorean'. I knew his name well, but I had no idea he had ever believed that the sun was a crystal ball! Once again, something didn't seem right.

I turned to the *Ancilla to the Pre-Socratic Philosophers* by Kathleen Freeman, to look under *Philolaos* and see if I had missed something on the many occasions when I had read his surviving fragments there. Could I be having memory problems?

This book by Kathleen Freeman is meant to be the English translation of the complete surviving fragments of those Greek philosophers who lived before Socrates (who died 399 BC) – they are called 'Pre-Socratics' by classical scholars. So I turned to pp. 73–7, to read through the Fragments of Philolaos once more.[2] There was no fragment there about any crystal sun. I was reassured that my memory was not playing tricks on me. But I was extremely puzzled. On her title page, Kathleen Freeman says that her *Ancilla* (a Latin word quaintly meaning 'maidservant', but here referring to a book which is ancillary to another, namely her book of commentary, referred to in a moment) is a *complete* translation of the Pre-Socratic Fragments as gathered together in several volumes by the German scholar Hermann Diels (his fifth edition). But then I realized I had misunderstood. It is a translation only of the actual fragments-as-quotes, not of fragments-as-paraphrases. For this reason, it is very dangerous to rely solely upon Kathleen Freeman's *Ancilla*. One must not be lazy, one must consult Diels himself. So I got him off the shelf and looked under *Philolaos* – and there in Greek was the fragment by Philolaos about the crystal sun as big as life, but not a *quoted fragment*, and hence not translated by Freeman.[3] Just as Freeman does not translate vast amounts of text into English because it is in the form of paraphrases by later authors, so Diels does not translate it into German either. (Freeman does not give all the source data that Diels gives either, even for what she does translate.)

So there it was – under the untranslated 'Lehre' ('Doctrine') section in Diels. Everything that Aëtios has to say, being a paraphrase, does not make it into the category of Fragments, and hence is translated into neither English nor German. This means that the whole of *De Placit. Philos.* was left untranslated by both Diels and Freeman, though published in Greek by Diels in bits and pieces scattered throughout his volumes.

I turned then to Kathleen Freeman's other book, *Companion to the Pre-Socratic Philosophers*, which is nearly 500 pages long and contains both discussion of the Pre-Socratics and summaries of the material which is not officially described as Fragments. There I found a reference to the crystal sun:

> The sun is transparent like a lens, receiving the rays from the (outer) universe, and transmitting their light and heat to us, so that there are two 'suns', the fiery element of the heavens (that is, the periphery or outer Aether) and the fiery lens; or perhaps one should speak of rays disseminated by this lens as the 'sun' we see, making yet a third, an 'image of an image'.[4]

Kathleen Freeman had admirably grasped the optical aspect of the theory of Philolaos, correctly realizing that he was not referring to the sun as a mirror which reflected, but as a crystal which *refracted* light towards earth. Nor was she afraid to use the word 'lens' to describe this, by which she showed more courage than most.

I pursued the matter further, and looked in Sir Thomas Heath's book *Greek Astronomy*. There under 'Pythagoreans' and under 'The Sun', he gives the passage, but misunderstands the actual meaning, and interprets what is going on as a reflection by a mirror, which Kathleen Freeman was inspired enough to correct. Heath gives the material as follows:

Aëtius, II, 22, 5. The Pythagoreans held the sun to be spherical.
Ib., II, 20, 12. Philolaus [the Latin form of Philolaos] the Pythagorean holds that the sun is transparent like glass, and that it receives the reflection of the fire in the universe, and transmits to us both light and warmth, so that there are, in some sort, two suns: the fiery (substance) in the heaven, and the fiery (emanation) from it which is mirrored, as it were, not to speak of a third also, namely, the beams that are scattered in our direction from the mirror by way of reflection (or refraction); for we give this third also the name of sun, which is thus, as it were, an image of an image.[5]

It is evident here that Heath has become confused about the optical phenomenon which is meant to be taking place. Speaking of it as reflection by a mirror, he then qualifies the statement by saying in parentheses 'or refraction' but, of course, mirrors don't refract.

I then turned to Heath's much longer book about Greek astronomy, *Aristarchus of Samos*, which fortunately I had just been given for Christmas! There is a section titled 'The Pythagoreans', and sure enough, Heath gave some additional material about the crystal sun there. First, he gives exactly the quote I have just cited, but he then follows it with a paragraph from another author, Achilles Tatius (*circa* third century AD), giving further details, and adds his comments:

'Philolaus says that the sun receives its fiery and radiant nature from above, from the aethereal fire, and transmits the beams to us through certain pores, so that according to him the sun is triple, one sun being the aethereal fire, the second that which is transmitted from it to the glassy thing under it which is called sun, and the third that which is transmitted from the sun in this sense to us.'

Thus, according to Philolaus, the sun was not a body with light of its own, but it was of a substance comparable to glass, and it concentrated rays of fire from elsewhere, and transmitted them to us. . . . But there are difficulties in the descriptions above given of the sources of the beams of fire. The natural supposition would be that they would come from the central fire [in other Pythagorean texts, the Earth was said to orbit around a mysterious 'Central Fire', which is not actually mentioned in these Philolaos fragments]; in that case the sun would act like a mirror simply; and the phenomena would be accounted for because the beams of the fire would always reach the sun except when obstructed by the moon, earth, or counter-earth [another mysterious Pythagorean body said to circle the 'Central Fire'], and, as the earth and counter-earth move in a different plane from the sun and moon, eclipses would occur at the proper times. But the first of the above passages [the one from Aëtios] says that the beams come from the fire in the *universe*, and that one of the suns is the fiery substance in the *heaven*, while the second passage [from Achilles Tatius] says that the beams come from *above*, from the fire of the aether. . . . Boeckh [a famous classical scholar] . . . admitted, with [Thomas Henri] Martin, that the beams come from the *outer* fire, the fire of Olympus . . . Accordingly the beams coming from outside would be *refracted by the sun*, which would act as a sort of lens. Tannery takes a similar view . . .[6]

We thus see that Heath clarified his thinking and realized that the crystal sun had to be a refracting lens, not a reflecting mirror. And Kathleen Freeman must have taken heart from this sufficiently to use the word 'lens' in her own discussion.

I found another translation of the crystal-sun passage in a very rare book which I happened to have, which was never properly published but only circulated in a bound mimeographed form. (Mimeograph copies were popular in the first half of the 20th century before photocopying or computers existed. They were essentially stencils put on a rotating drum and smeared with ink, from which copies were cranked out – an early form of 'desktop publishing'. But they were usually a mess!) I am referring to translations of Pythagorean writings done by the enthusiast Kenneth Sylvan Guthrie in 1919. Dr Guthrie was as short of money as he was full of energy. Early in the 20th century he translated huge quantities of Platonic and Pythagorean writings from the Greek, many of them translated for the first time into English. But few of Guthrie's translations were ever actually published. Poor Guthrie discovered that at that time he was butting his head against a stone wall; no one would publish his efforts because the materials he was translating were not fashionable. He was, quite simply, a victim of appalling prejudice, and his magnificent work was largely wasted by the stupidity of the academic establishment of his time. Deeply frustrated by these troubles, Guthrie set up the Platonist Press, Box 42, Alpine, New Jersey, USA, and later of Teocalli, North Yonkers, New York, USA. And he proceeded to type out his translations and use the primitive mimeograph process to duplicate small numbers of them, which he attempted to sell privately. He put his postal address on the front of these bound mimeographed volumes, hoping that enlightened souls would write to him and buy copies. He was a real Don Quixote, whose life was largely one of poverty and frustration – a true test to a man who viewed himself as a living, breathing Platonist whose principles were those of the noblest Greek philosophers.

I had been fortunate enough to acquire one of Guthrie's most intriguing mimeograph volumes – his *Pythagoras Source Book and Library*. In it, he translated for the first time into English all the surviving ancient biographies of Pythagoras (by Iamblichus, Porphyry, Diogenes Laertius, and Photius). Although not mentioned in the table of contents in the front of the volume, so that one could easily be unaware that they were there, Guthrie could not resist adding at the back a second half to the book, with extensive translations of Pythagorean fragments, and related material of a fascinating kind; the volume is thus a double-volume, with the second half having a fresh pagination, and being entitled *Pythagorean Library: A Complete Collection of the Surviving Works of Pythagoreans*, bearing the date 1920. This section includes the Fragments of Philolaos in a much more extensive form than Kathleen Freeman ever managed, since the translations include the vast quantities of untranslated material which neither Freeman nor Diels ever rendered into a modern language.

In this second half of the pathetic, tatty volume, on p. 17 is yet another version of the crystal sun fragment, taken this time from the fifth-century-AD anthologist Stobaeus, and translated as follows:

14. (Stob. Ecl. 1:25:3: p. 530). The Pythagorean Philolaus says that the sun is a vitrescent body which receives the light reflected by the fire of the Cosmos, and sends it back to us, after having filtered them, light and heat; so that you might say that there are two suns, the body of the fire which is in the heaven, and the igneous light which emanates therefrom, and reflects itself in a kind of mirror. Perhaps we might consider as a third light that which, from the mirror in which it reflects, falls back on us in dispersed rays.[7]

We see here that a confusion has once more arisen between reflection and refraction, but we have already discussed that.

As I began to nose around in other sources, rechecking things which were easily overlooked before because the clue was not there, I noticed what Plutarch (first century AD) was supposed to have reported about the theories of the early philosopher Empedocles (fifth century BC), whose original works are lost except for fragments. However, this information is in turn preserved in a fragment which turns out not to be by Plutarch after all. The work is called *Miscellanies*, although the Loeb translator F. H. Sandbach prefers to translate the title literally as *A Patchwork* (the word the Greeks used as we use *Miscellanies* today). Much of the content of this compendium is drawn from a lost work by Theophrastus (fourth century BC), the successor of Aristotle, listing the opinions on physics of various philosophers. And under Empedocles this time, rather than Philolaos (who is not mentioned), we read:

Empedocles of Acragas . . . says . . . The sun is not in reality fire, but a reflection of fire [*antanaklasis* – 'reflection of light'] like that which comes about from water.[8]

We here see the same tradition of the refracting or reflecting sun, but this time attributed to another early philosopher, Empedocles.

As I looked back over some books about ancient Greek science, such as Sambursky's *The Physical World of the Greeks*, I found some tentative mention of the notions related to the crystal sun without their being fully comprehended or explicated. For instance, Sambursky quotes from some remarks made by Aristotle (died 322 BC) in his book *On the Heavens* (often called in Latin *De Caelo*), Book II, 293a–b, and makes some indirect comments which from what we know now we can interpret properly. Part of the passage from Aristotle says:

> It remains to speak of the earth, of its position, of the question whether it is at rest or in motion, and of its shape. As to its *position* there is some difference of opinion. Most people – all, in fact, who regard the whole heaven as finite – say it lies at the centre. But the Italian philosophers known as the Pythagoreans [of whom Philolaos was one] take the contrary view. At the centre, they say, is fire, and the earth is one of the stars, creating night and day by its circular motion about the centre . . . The Pythagoreans . . . hold that the most important part of the world, which is the centre, should be most strictly guarded, and name it, or rather the fire which occupies that place, the 'Guard-house of Zeus' . . . All who deny that the earth lies at the centre think that it revolves about the centre . . . Some even consider it possible that there are several bodies so moving, which are invisible to us owing to the interposition of the earth.[9]

This is the classic source of the evidence that many people (in fact, 'all who deny that the earth lies at the centre') in antiquity believed the earth went round the sun, 2,000 years before Copernicus. Because Aristotle disagreed with these people, he gives them the usual courtesy of being mentioned, but does not bother to record all the details of their theories. And hence it is that his mention of a 'central fire' is a bit fuzzy. He very carefully does not say that these people believed that the sun was at the centre, but takes care to be accurate and say that a 'central fire' was at the centre. Scholars writing about ancient astronomy have been confused by Aristotle's habitual terseness of expression here. After all, in citing the many variant theories held in his time, which he always did conscientiously, Aristotle had no intention of addressing his remarks to people living 2,500 years later when all the other texts had been lost, so that we would be hanging on his every word. He was merely making abbreviated comments referring to books which in his day were readily available, and where the full details could be found. In other words, Aristotle was writing for people alive then, not people alive now. Hence it is inevitable that his comments are often difficult to interpret, when we have been deprived of the full texts to which he casually refers in passing.

Many historians of science, reading this famous passage in Aristotle, have not known quite how to interpret it. On the one hand, Aristotle is careful to say that what is at the centre is a 'central fire', not just the sun. That is because he was punctilious in his accuracy and finicky about detail. But he didn't go on to explain what had happened to the sun in these theories, and how one was supposed to explain that the sun was obviously also at the centre in some unspecified way. For we have later references to these theories where it is made plain that the sun was also somehow at the centre.

I believe that the explanation for this muddle is the crystal sun concept. Aristotle would have known about it, but did not bother to go into it because it was too great a distraction from his main argument. I would suggest that he speaks of the fire at the centre rather than the sun at the centre because the Pythagorean theory stressed that the sun was a refracting and not originating source of sunlight. Aristotle, not wishing to be inaccurate while also not wishing to bother to go into detail, meticulously did not say that the sun was at the centre because he knew that strictly speaking the theory he was referring to considered the actual body of the sun to be a medium rather than a source, and he wished to do justice to this distinction in passing.

We return now to Sambursky. He considers the Aristotle passage and draws the conclusions which have become usual among historians of science, that the 'central fire' is supposed never to be seen from earth because the earth, in its revolution around it, always turns its uninhabited side to it. But this is nonsense, as I shall explain in a moment. Sambursky says:

> The origin of this theory of the central fire is uncertain. Perhaps the discovery that the moon has no light of its own, but receives light from the sun, led to the further conjecture that the sun too merely reflected the light of a central source, i.e. the central fire. This fire is hidden from our sight because the terrestrial globe in its revolution around it always presents its other uninhabited side to it.[10]

It is good to see that Sambursky is admitting that the Pythagorean theory held that the sun 'merely reflected light', while not originating it. (We would correct that to say refracted rather than reflected.) But his attempt to make sense of the idea by postulating a central fire towards which one side of the earth is always turned cannot be accepted because he forgets that there would therefore be no day and night. It is clear if you think about it that the sun and the central fire must *both* be in the centre in some sense, albeit clearly distinguished. Sambursky has abolished night and day, and we cannot allow a historian of science to go so far.

When I used to read passages like this years before describing the 'central fire', I merely became confused because it just didn't make any sense. And many scholars who have encountered the ideas have been inclined to lessen the credit to which the Pythagoreans are due for saying that the earth revolved around something else by saying: 'Well, it wasn't the sun, so they didn't have things right, and were just silly.' But as soon as one gets the concept of the crystal sun clear, things become comprehensible. And then we can see that they did indeed hold a correct theory about the earth going round the sun, but it was qualified by a peculiar theory of the sun being a gigantic crystal ball whose light came from outside itself, and seems to have been imagined as gathered in as ambient light from the surrounding cosmos.

Just to dispel confusion, I shall be a bit more specific about how we know this from the text. The 'three suns' described by Philolaos are really two, the 'third' being merely the light which travels to us by refraction. The 'first sun' is the ambient light, and the 'second sun' is the actual object of crystal which gathers it in and refracts it to us. 'Three suns' should thus really more properly be expressed as 'three stages of sunlight': (1) ambient light exists round the centre of the cosmos; (2) the crystal sun gathers it in and refracts it towards us; and (3) that refracted light then travels from the crystal body to the earth and our eyes. We see therefore that Philolaus is only speaking of one *body*, but three *light phenomena associated with it*. We only see the third stage, which is the light which actually reaches us.

What is particularly interesting about this is the concept that the crystal sun gathers in the ambient light of the cosmos, like a light-condensing lens, concentrates it and emits it towards us. This may sound peculiar – but is it really? Can it be that such phenomena really happen, and indeed happen with surviving ancient lenses?

In connection with this strange notion, perhaps I should mention an unexpected incident which occurred to me in the British Museum of Natural History, which may help us to understand the Pythagorean thinking. Back in 1980 I had tracked down two collections of ancient British lenses which had been missing for some time. They are all of polished rock crystal, convex, and excellent magnifiers. I found one of the collections in the Natural History Museum, classified as mineral specimens! They had once belonged to Sir Hans Sloane, the founder of the British Museum. (I describe them fully in Appendices Five and Eleven.) But in 1998 I decided to go back and measure and study them again.

When I first studied the lenses of the Sloane Collection, I did so in a room which was brightly lit by sunlight. However, upon my return visit so many years later, things had been moved around and I had to study the lenses in a room which was very dark, assisted by a lamp. I made an unexpected discovery because of these changed circumstances. One of the best of the lenses, which I was attempting to study properly despite the lack of proper lighting, turned out to have an extraordinary property. As I was trying to measure its magnification, I noticed that what was being magnified was simultaneously being illuminated. And then I realized that the ambient light of the dark room was being gathered in by the lens and focused upon the words which one saw considerably magnified through it. A full description of this lens is given in Appendix Eleven. A photo of it is seen in Plate 53. And thus it was, due to the inconvenience of a darkened room, that I came to realize what I would normally never have known – that some convex ancient lenses not only enlarged words or objects beneath them, but also illuminated them! They were thus light-condensers. Because it is not customary to study ancient objects in the dark, I had never been in a situation before where it was possible to notice this. But ancient people, of course, spent much of their lives in semi-darkened rooms, where a candle or a lamp was as much as they could expect at night, and in the daytime only small windows or feeble light might be available. So what they were gaining by the use of their lenses was not only the ability to see things enlarged but to see things lit!

Having had this experience – an experience doubtless familiar to an ancient man but certainly unfamiliar to us with our modern brightly lit rooms – I came to realize that another quality of the crystal balls and crystal lenses which must have awed our ancestors was their ability on occasion to gather ambient light and focus it. It was really very impressive indeed to be sitting in circumstances as dark as mine were and to have the equivalent of a torch/flashlight beam shone upon what I was looking at. This cannot have failed to impress the ancients. And I believe it explains how the Pythagoreans came to think of a gigantic crystal ball in the sky being able to gather up the ambient light of the cosmos and refract it to earth.

That's just my thought on the subject, but I think a valid one. Please look at Plate 53, the photograph I took of this phenomenon, and see what *you* think.

My friend Buddy Rogers in 1999 gave my wife a translucent moonstone egg about the size of a bantam egg. When held up to the light it has the extraordinary quality of appearing to have a golden yolk in the centre of the milky whiteness of the stone – which resembles egg albumin – and it is thus 'more like an egg than an egg' because both the interior and exterior properties may be seen at once, and you don't have to break it to reveal a yolk. It is possible that moonstones ground as globes or eggs contributed to the concept of the crystal sun in antiquity, as they provide such splendid and eerie examples of refraction of ambient light by a translucent object resembling a crystal ball.

The so-called Hermetic books, a collection of philosophico-mystical writings drawn partially from ancient Egyptian sources and rewritten by Neoplatonists around the second century AD in Greek, contain a treatise known as 'Definitions of Asclepius to King Ammon', which includes apparent allusions to the crystal sun concept. This treatise is adamant that the sun is at the centre of the cosmos, not the earth:

'For the sun is situated in the center of the cosmos, wearing it like a crown. . . . Around the sun are the eight spheres that depend from it: the sphere of the fixed stars, the six of the planets, and the one that surrounds the earth.'[11]

The sun and the light which it emits are distinguished from one another, and the light is said to come from 'near to' the sun, although only the sun knows 'from whence it flows':

'But if there also exists some intellectual essence, it is the sun's mass, whose receptacle may be sunlight. Only the sun knows . . . of what this essence is composed or whence it flows since by location and nature it is near to the sun. . . . a vision of the sun is . . . the visual ray itself . . .'[12]

Although many scholars raise doubts about the Hermetic writings preserving Egyptian traditions, there is certainly strong language in this treatise about the superiority of the Egyptians to the Greeks:

'Therefore . . . keep the discourse uninterpreted, lest the mysteries of such greatness come to the Greeks . . . For the Greeks have empty speeches . . . We, by contrast, use not speeches but sounds that are full of action. . . . My teacher, Hermes . . . used to say that those reading my books would find their organisation very simple and clear when, on the contrary, it is unclear and keeps the meaning of its words concealed . . . The very quality of the speech and the [sound] of Egyptian words have in themselves the energy of the objects they speak of.'[13]

This Hermetic reference is rather vague in its actual description of the sun, but emphatic about the heliocentric theory. And it does say that the light of the sun comes from 'near' the sun, not from inside the sun. The only way that would seem to be possible would be in the manner described for the crystal sun, which gathers in the ambient light.

Returning to the crystal sun of the Pythagoreans, we see another historian of science, D. R. Dicks, struggling to make sense of the same confused tradition, but in a way both more humorous and more penetrating than Sambursky was able to manage:

Aëtius says that Philolaus regarded the sun as glassy (*hyaloeidēs*) [note that the same word also means 'of rock crystal', but Dicks uses the later meaning], 'receiving the reflection of the fire in the cosmos, and filtering both light and warmth through to us, so that in a certain sense there are twin suns, the fiery one in the heavens (*en tō ouranō*) and the fiery one by reflection from it' (*DK* 44 A19). Unfortunately, it is not clear which fire is meant here, for Philolaus seems to have envisaged two sources of fire, the outermost surrounding fiery sphere (this originally Heraclitan idea was, according to the doxographers, common to several later Pre-Socratics) and the central fire (*DK* 44 A16); anyway, it is difficult to see how a reflected sun really helps matters.[14]

Once again, one wishes the notion of *refraction* had been grasped, rather than *reflection*, in which case the matter would have been clearer. For once one sees that it was a refracting sun rather than a reflecting sun, it really does help matters after all.

In Plate 8 may be seen an interesting hand-tinted engraving of 1683 which gives something of an impression of a sun gathering light from a surrounding 'aetheric region', but the earth is in the centre.

Another scholar who has touched on the matter is J. A. Philip, in his book *Pythagoras and Early Pythagoreanism*. Philip does not mention the name of Aëtios but merely speaks of 'the doxography' as if it were an author. He compares its account to that given by Aristotle:

> The doxography, though it cannot be said to contradict Aristotle's report, differs in character, as may be seen from one principal extract (*Vors* 44: 16 = *Dox. Gr.* 336–337):
> 'Philolaus maintained that there was fire in the middle of the universe round about its centre. He calls this Hearth of the World, House of Zeus, Mother of the gods, Altar, Meeting-place, Goal of Nature (*physis*). And again he maintains that the periphery is another fire at the highest point of the universe. The middle is by nature first in rank. Around it move in choral dance ten divine bodies; the sphere of the fixed stars, the five planets, after them the sun and beneath it the moon; beneath the moon the earth and beneath that the counter-earth; after all these the fire that fills the role of hearth in the area of the centre. He calls Olympus the uppermost part of the periphery where are present the elements in their purity. The part under the revolution of Olympus, where are the five planets, sun, and moon he calls *Cosmos*. The sublunary, circumterrestrial part, where are the things subject to birth and change, he calls the heavens. Wisdom appertains to the order of the heavenly bodies, virtue to the lack of order of things that come to be; the former being perfect, the latter imperfect.'[15]

Before commenting further, I want to point out one detail of this passage which can easily not be noticed:

> Philolaus maintained that there was fire in the middle of the universe *round about its centre*. [The italics are mine.]

In the passage from the doxographer which Philip has just quoted, we can readily see that the information is greatly garbled by the doxographer (Aëtios, 'Pseudo-Plutarch', or whoever he was). I would like to point out that the above sentence specifies that the central fire is ambient, and surrounds the centre. This fits in with the crystal sun concept, and gives the added detail which we needed. For the sun as a crystal then gathers in this ambient light and refracts it to earth. As for the sun then being included in the list of planets and occupying yet another place, I believe this is a garbling by the doxographer, since it directly contradicts the other information. Philip was aware of the difficulties of the sun being misplaced here, but like Sambursky gets in a hopeless muddle about how we deal with day and night. He says:

> If the earth and its accompanying counter-earth [a body which Aristotle says the Pythagoreans invented to bring the number of cosmic bodies up to the perfect number of ten, but which could just as well be a garbled and misunderstood survival of some knowledge of the antipodes] move in orbit around the central fire, thus causing day and night, and one face of the earth is always turned away from the central fire, then the sun must stand still to cause day and night of constant length and it is difficult to see how the seasons can be produced.[16]

Here again we see a scholar not realizing that the earth cannot keep one face to the central fire when it revolves around it because then there would be no night and day. Philip, although he cannot grasp this problem, nevertheless feels uncomfortable. So he thinks maybe if the sun stands still it will somehow result in 'day and night of constant length'. This is equally incomprehensible, and I cannot imagine what Philip was thinking. He rightly expresses unease about the seasons.

This is all getting a bit murky. We have seen two scholars now staggering around in a dark room like drunks. But partly this is the fault of the garbled material. And it seems to me that the only thread which enables us to find our way through the labyrinth is that of the concept of the crystal sun – but unfortunately for Philip, he does not mention it or quote the relevant passage, or indeed show any awareness of it.

As I made my way through these standard works which had been in my library for so many years, I began to realize why I myself had not been able to make head or tail of any of this. For I had read most of these passages before, and more than once. But it is obvious to us now that the experts in this matter are no guides at all.

What Philolaos and his friends seemed to have believed was that there was a gigantic crystal ball at the centre of the Universe, which gathered ambient light into it and refracted that light outwards as what we call 'sunlight'. Far from being on fire, the crystal sun was inert, acting simply as a medium.

Perhaps Aristotle was thinking of these concepts when he spent so much time discussing light, colour, and transparency in his treatise *On the Soul*. At Book II, 7, 14, he says:

> . . . light . . . is the presence of fire or something resembling fire in what is transparent.[17]

277

While not wishing to misrepresent my favourite philosopher, Aristotle, whose comments on these subjects were much longer than this, we can nevertheless take this clear statement to represent the attitudes of the Pythagoreans towards their crystal sun. They believed that there was a 'central fire' which was ambient around the centre of the Universe, and that its light was condensed within the gigantic crystal ball larger than the earth which was actually at the centre, and that from this huge crystal the ambient light was refracted as sunlight to the bodies revolving around it, including the earth and the moon which reflected sunlight and had no light of its own.

One of the names of the 'central fire' was Altar. And that no doubt referred to the use of crystal burning-lenses and burning-spheres to light the sacred fire on earthly altars, with that light coming as it did from the Great Altar in the Sky. Another of the names, 'Meeting Place', may refer to the focusing of light rays (*visum colligere*). Olympus was that highest point

Figure 28. Another possible meaning of the Pythagorean name 'Meeting Place' may be a reference to the meeting of the sun and moon in eclipses, as seen here in an early-16th-century woodcut. The sun looks sadly at a dour-faced moon who is going straight ahead, with a glassy-eyed stare, to eclipse his glorious friend.

from the centre – the surrounding periphery of the Universe, where regions of fire were once more encountered. But we must not imagine that this was just a confining sphere, for Aristotle was specific earlier when he said that the people who believed the earth went round the centre believed in an infinite universe. So that the implication is that the Pythagoreans believed that 'Olympus' went on forever, and there 'all the elements reached their perfection' side by side with the gods and the divine heroes. It is ironical therefore that the divine sunlight of the crystal sun came from the lowest point, generally reserved in cosmologies for Hell. And that leaves us with a good question: Where was Hades meant to be, if the furthest down you could go was into the crystal sun? The inevitable conclusion is that it was simply under the soil of the earth, and therefore a local rather than a cosmic phenomenon.

But this kind of thinking can lead further. For once Hades is relegated to being under the soil of a single body in space, the door is left open to have a *further* Hades under the soil of another body in space. And then before you know it, you have *many* inhabited worlds. And this is precisely the sort of thinking which we find expressed by Heraclides of Pontus, a prominent member of the Academy of Plato who was profoundly Pythagorean in his sympathies. Heath sums up these idea of Heraclides as follows:

The universe is infinite; each star is also a universe or world, suspended in the infinite aether and comprising an earth, an atmosphere, and an aether.[18]

Heraclides also believed that those many worlds were inhabited. And so we see how one thing leads to another. You start with a crystal sun and before you know it, you have many inhabited worlds and an infinite universe. Perhaps we should call the crystal sun 'Pandora's Crystal'.

Notes

1. [Aëtios, or sometimes 'Pseudo-Plutarch'] 'Plutarch's Giving an Account of Those Sentiments concerning Nature with which Philosophers Were Delighted; contained in five books', translated by John Dowel, in Vol. III of *Plutarch's Morals: Translated from the Greek by Several Hands*, 4th edition, London, 1704, p. 153.
2. Freeman, Kathleen, *Ancilla to the Pre-Socratic Philosophers: A Complete Translation of the Fragments in Diels, Fragmente der Vorsokratiker*, Basil Blackwell, Oxford, 1966, pp. 73–7.
3. Diels, Hermann, *Die Fragmente der Vorsokratiker: Griechisch und Deutsch (The Fragments of the Pre-Socratics, in Greek and German)*, 6th edition edited by Walther Kranz, Berlin, 1951, Vol. I, p. 404. (The text is identified as coming from Aëtios II, 20, 12.)
4. Freeman, Kathleen, *Companion to the Pre-Socratic Philosophers*, 2nd edition, Basil Blackwell, Oxford, 1966, p. 226.
5. Heath, Sir Thomas L., *Greek Astronomy*, Dover, New York, 1991 (reproduction of edition of 1932), p. 35.
6. Heath, Sir Thomas L., *Aristarchus of Samos: The Ancient Copernicus, A History of Greek Astronomy to Aristarchus together with Aristarchus' Treatise on the Sizes and Distances of the Sun and Moon*, Oxford, 1997 (reprint of 1913 edition), pp. 115–17.
7. Guthrie, Kenneth Sylvan, *Pythagoras Source Book and Library*, Part Two, *Pythagorean Library* (which has its own pagination separate from Part One), Platonist Press, Alpine, New Jersey, and Yonkers, New York, privately printed, 1919–20, section of Philolaus Fragments, p. 17.
8. Pseudo-Plutarch, *Miscellanies* (or *A Patchwork*), 10, edited and translated by F. H. Sandbach, in *Plutarch's Moralia*, Volume XV, *Fragments*, Loeb Classical Library, Harvard University Press, USA, p. 337.
9. Aristotle, *On the Heavens (De Caelo)*, Book 2, translated by Sir David Ross, in Vol. II of *The Works of Aristotle*, Oxford Press, 1970, 293a–b.
10. Sambursky, S., *The Physical World of the Greeks*, translated from the Hebrew by Merton Dagut, Routledge & Kegan Paul, London, 1963, pp. 65–6.
11. Copenhaver, Brian P., translator and introduction by, *The Greek Corpus Hermeticum and the Latin Asclepius in a New English Translation, with Notes and Introduction*, California University Press, USA, 1992, Treatise XVI, Sections 6 and 17, pp. 59 and 61.

12. *Ibid.*, Section 6, p. 59.
13. *Ibid.*, Section 1, p. 58.
14. Dicks, R.D., *Early Greek Astronomy to Aristotle*, Cornell University Press, Ithaca, New York, USA, 1970, p. 68. Unfortunately, in the following two pages, Dicks goes on to state that any notion that Philolaos could have known of the precession of the equinoxes, of which there seems to be some evidence, 'is quite out of the question'. However, I believe there is no doubt whatever that the precession was familiar to the Egyptians at a very early date indeed, and the Greeks could easily have learned of it from them.
15. Philip, J. A., *Pythagoras and Early Pythagoreanism*, University of Toronto Press, 1966, pp. 113–14.
16. *Ibid.*, p. 115.
17. Aristotle, *On the Soul* (*De Anima*), translated by J. A. Smith, Oxford Press, 1931, 418b.
18. Heath, *Aristarchus, op. cit.*, p. 254.

Chapter Eight

Thunderstones

It may seem strange to start this chapter by discussing an extraordinary fact about Chartres Cathedral, but let's do it anyway. People all over the world seem to be familiar with the strange design on the back of the American one-dollar bill, which features a radiating eye placed at the pinnacle of a truncated pyramid. As is well known, it is a Masonic symbol, since most of the American founding fathers were Freemasons, and they applied their principles to the foundation of a new concept of democratic government designed to protect rights and freedoms by a system of ingenious constitutional checks and balances. The occasional Masonic symbol couldn't help but creep in here and there in the iconography of the new republic, and the one on the back of the one-dollar bill was apparently put there by direction of an American Vice President under Roosevelt (Henry Wallace) who was a prominent Freemason.

In the next and final chapter of this book, 'The Eye of Horus', we will consider eyes on the tops of pyramids. So let us leave that aside until then. What I want to reveal is something very odd indeed – something which will shake all Freemasons when they read it, and doubtless intrigue them. We all know the tradition that the Freemasons are supposed to have evolved from mediaeval guilds of stone masons who constructed the European cathedrals

Figure 29. The back of the American one-dollar bill has this strange design, of a radiating eye as the pyramidion on top of a pyramid. It is a Masonic symbol, and was placed there at the direction of Henry Wallace, Vice President under Franklin D. Roosevelt.
(*Design courtesy of the United States Government; obtainable for one dollar from any bank.*)

281

such as Chartres. And although there is far more to Masonic origins than that, there is no doubt that there is some truth in that tradition too. In fact, it is one of the few suggestions about Masonic origins which no one seems to dispute.

But one thing which may seem to be missing in the mediaeval cathedrals is any possible equivalent to the eye on the top of the pyramid. The tips of the Egyptian pyramids were flat and had tiny mini-pyramids resting on them called 'pyramidions', many of which survive. But no one has ever heard of any special 'tip' to a mediaeval cathedral. *Not until now!*

While writing the previous chapter I was reading by way of relaxation a fascinating book of which I was fortunate to own an original copy, Dr Martin Lister's *A Journey to Paris in the Year 1698*. Martin Lister (1638–1712) was one of England's leading scientists of the time, and the memoir he wrote of his six months in Paris is no ordinary travel book. In it he describes in detail his visits to the chief men of learning in Paris at the turn of the 17th century, what they said, which books they had in their libraries, and which specimens of natural history they had in their cabinets. He also records much interesting information about paintings, and describes several privately owned Rembrandts which he admired, for instance. One of the men he knew in Paris was not French at all but an Englishman, although there is no notice of him in the *Dictionary of National Biography*. Here is the part of the passage which interests us:

> Mr Butterfield is a right hearty honest Englishman, who has resided in France 35 years, is a very excellent artist in making all sorts of mathematical instruments, and works for the king and all the Princes of the Blood, and his work is sought after by all the nations of Europe and Asia.
>
> He more than once shewed me (which is his great diversion) a mighty collection of loadstones [lodestones], to the value of several hundred pounds sterling. . . . He shewed us a loadstone sawed off that piece of the iron bar, which held the stones together at the very top of the steeple of Chartres. This was a thick crust of rust, part of which was turned into a strong loadstone, and had all the properties of a stone dug out of the mine. Mons. de la Hire has printed a memoir of it; also Mons. de Vallemont a treatise. The very outward rust had no magnetic virtue, but the inward had a strong one, as to take up a third part more than its weight unshod. This iron had the very grain of a solid magnet, and the brittleness of a stone.[1]

So we see that the Cathedral of Chartres had a large magnetic lodestone at the top of its steeple. This is such a strange thing that I think we should investigate other mediaeval cathedrals to see if the tips of their steeples preserve any original metalwork which is magnetic. Unfortunately, it is likely that any such metal would have perished by now, since the piece from Chartres was already succumbing to rust three centuries ago. (Chartres actually has two steeples, and the account must refer to the shorter one dating from 1140–60, rather than the taller one which only dates from 1507–13; my thanks to Roderick Brown for this information.)

Can it be that the stone mason guilds which built the mediaeval cathedrals placed secret magnetic equivalents to pyramidions at the tips of the European cathedrals, unknown to anyone until the 1690s, and presumably forgotten from then till now?

The ancient Egyptians knew about lodestones. They used the expression *res mehit ba*, which means 'north-south iron', as their name for a lodestone. And Plutarch [first century AD] specifically records in his treatise *On Isis and Osiris* (Chapter 62):

> But Typhon . . . is called *Seth* . . . being meant to declare a certain forcible and impeding check, opposition, and turning upside down. Besides, they call a loadstone 'Bone of Osiris', but iron 'Bone of Typhon' (as Manetho [third-century BC Egyptian High Priest who wrote in Greek, only fragments remaining] relates), for just as the iron is often, like something alive, attracted to and following after the loadstone, but often turns away and is repelled from it in the opposite direction, in like manner the salutary good and rational motion of the world often attracts by persuasion, draws to itself, and renders more gentle that harsh and Typhonian force; and again, when it has been driven back into itself, it upsets the latter, and plunges it once more into helplessness.[2]

Magnetic phenomena and lodestones were thus familiar to the Egyptians and were discussed in a lost portion of the writings of Manetho. Whether lodestones were ever significantly used by the ancient Egyptians in association with architecture I have no idea. But we shall see in a moment that iron was critical to Egyptian religion, and that much of it was magnetic.

Of course, I do not mean to suggest that the masons who built Chartres Cathedral had any knowledge whatever of ancient Egyptian attitudes towards lodestones. But I do believe that the concept of the pyramidion and its relation to occult forces of some kind (as witness the radiating eye on the one-dollar bill) was a tradition which has demonstrably survived into modern Freemasonry – for whether we can explain this or not, the fact in itself cannot be denied – and if this is still known today to the Masons, it was certainly known in the 14th century to the masons. And hence the lodestone on top of Chartres Cathedral may have been an esoteric object intended to be the mediaeval European equivalent of an ancient Egyptian pyramidion, a kind of symbolic *homage* to a secret tradition.

And with that, we leave the Middle Ages and go back to our more usual surroundings of ancient Egypt. Anyone who studies lodestones, as we see that the Egyptians did, does not have to be a genius to see that the lodestone points to something similar to north and south. When they called the lodestone 'the north-south iron', the ancient Egyptians clearly saw this as the lodestone's main feature of interest. Since no ancient culture was more careful in its geographical north-south alignments of monuments (the pyramids at Giza are perfectly so aligned), the ancient Egyptians must have noticed that the magnetic north and south poles were not the same as the geographical north and south poles. This is a fact which many archaeologists are vague about, and many plans of ancient monuments are maddeningly unhelpful because they contain an arrow pointing north without specifying which of the two norths is meant!

Not only must the Egyptians have been aware of the discrepancy between the two norths and the two souths at, say, Memphis, but because Egypt is such an immensely long country where the magnetic variation

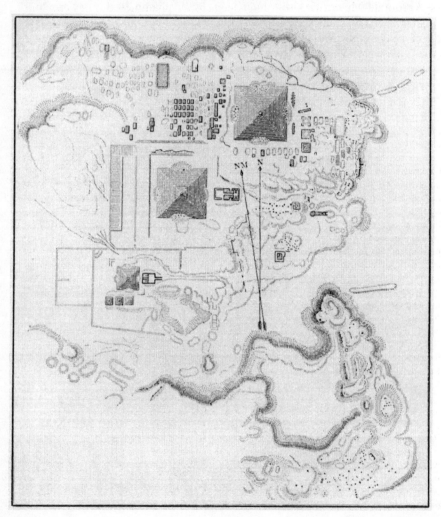

changes, they must have been aware that the discrepancy was different at, say, Thebes. What they made of this we do not know, but it is doubtless referred to in some veiled way in their texts.[3]

But this is not our concern at the moment. I mention it because it gives a deeper dimension – an unexplored one so far – to the issues we now encounter. For we have now come to the 'Bone of Typhon', i.e. the 'bone of Seth' – *iron* in ancient Egypt. And since cast iron and wrought iron made from earthly iron ore did not yet exist in the ancient Egyptian civilization, this leaves us with iron obtained *from meteorites*. Meteoritic iron is often magnetized in space, and thus occurs as lodestones. It should be pointed out that it is easier to see meteorites land in the clear skies of Egypt than elsewhere, and easier still to find them after they have landed in the desert, since they are sitting in clear view on the sand, dark against a pale background. Meteoritic iron has been found hammered into precious objects in tombs since the earliest dynasties in Egypt. Scientists are able to check the composition of the iron and such tests have confirmed that these iron objects are indeed meteoritic.

We are fortunate to have at least one ancient Egyptian text which gives a very specific account of the importance of meteorites in connection with

---

Figure 30. 'The two norths' may be clearly seen indicated on this plan of the Giza Plateau, reproduced from Sir Norman Lockyer's *The Dawn of Astronomy* (London, 1894, p. 81). He in turn reproduced it from the reports of the earlier archaeologist Lepsius, who led a Prussian Commission to Egypt in 1844. Unlike so many exasperating archaeologists' plans, this one clearly differentiates between the geographical 'true' north N and the varying magnetic north NM. As may be seen, the pyramids are precisely oriented to the true geographical north, south, east and west. However, if one consults a magnetic compass this does not appear to be the case, because the magnetic north is not truly north but off to one side. The 'crossed arrows', a convention used by modern surveyors to show the two norths, may possibly refer to the same phenomenon as the 'crossed arrows' so prominent in ancient Egyptian symbology, a precise explanation for which is lacking. This is at least possible since we know that the ancient Egyptians were certainly aware of the difference between 'true' north and magnetic north; one was determined from solar shadows and the other was determined from 'the bones of Osiris', i.e. meteoritic lodestones, and the two alternative sets of bearings may have been interpreted as relating to two alternative religious complexes. For instance, the cult of the god Ptah, the god of Memphis which was near Giza, was a polar and 'true north' cult; everything at Giza was rigorously oriented to the 'true' directions. But in the Pyramid Texts of the later Fifth and Sixth Dynasties, Ptah is barely mentioned, and is indeed rather pointedly excluded, and meteoritic iron, the magnetized form of which responds to the magnetic north, takes on prominence as a feature of the rival Horus Cult.

The rivalry of these cults may have been one between the two ways of determining north, and there may have been priestly disputes about which was the more important: north which could be demonstrated to be a genuine cosmic alignment, or north which was indicated by the invisible powers of a heavenly substance (lodestone) held in the hand. The fact that these were incommensurable was as shocking as the fact that there are irrational numbers, or indeed (as we learn in Chapter Nine) that the musical fifth and the musical octave are mathematically incommensurable, as the Egyptians also realized. Probably the 'two norths' were assigned respectively to the two musical phenomena: the 'true' north was assigned to the octave and the magnetic north to the fifth. But for these matters, see the later extended discussion.

some of the chief deities. The text is Coffin Text Spell 148, a full analysis of which was only published in 1983 by Robert H. O'Connell.[4] It was O'Connell who first deciphered how the Egyptians referred to meteorites, and he was most ingenious in this! He pointed out that they combined two non-vocalized hieroglyphs which Egyptologists call 'determinatives' (because they determine by symbolism what the word means rather than spell it out, and they generally come just after the spelled word to avoid ambiguities of words which are spelled the same) – the one for a star and the one for 'crocodile'. Hence, you might say, 'crocodile star' instead of 'shooting star'.

O'Connell wrote that this joining of the two symbols 'combines the ideas of an attacking crocodile's sudden rushing with that of the streaking of a falling star across the heavens'. He even found another text carved on a stone stela at the site of Gebel Barka in the reign of Pharaoh Tuthmosis III (18th Dynasty; he reigned *circa* 1479–1424 BC) which had the phrase 'rushing as a crocodile (rushes), like a (falling) star between the two bows (of heaven) when it crosses the sky'. He cleverly concluded:

> This might suggest that the crocodile was a stereotype for sudden movement in Egyptian literature and would commend combining the ideographic determinative of sudden movement with the designation for a star when the Egyptians intended to designate a falling star, as opposed to a fixed star.[5]

Having figured all of this out, O'Connell was able to give an accurate translation of the text for the first time. As we can see, it deals with the birth of the god Horus, his conception inside his mother Isis, by the seed of his father Osiris. And we should remember that Osiris was identified by the Eygptians with lodestones, as we have already seen. Here is how the text in its new translation begins (the brackets are those of the translator and represent implied words):

> '[After] the blast of a meteorite such that [even] gods fear
> Isis awoke pregnant by the seed of her brother Osiris!
> Thus the woman raised herself abruptly,
> her heart pleased with the seed of her brother Osiris,
> as she said:
>   'O gods!
> I, Isis, sister of Osiris, who wept concerning the loss of the
> patriarchy of Osiris,
> Judge of the slaughtering of the two lands,
> Whose seed is now within my womb –
> I have conceived the form of a god within the ovary as my son,
> the foremost of the Ennead, who will rule this land, who will be
> the heir to Geb,

who will argue on behalf of his father, [and] who will slay Seth
the enemy of his father Osiris.'[6]

[Geb is the earth god and the Ennead is the Group of Nine Gods.]

Here we see an unambiguous reference to the conception of the god Horus
by Isis and the entering of Osiris's seed into her coinciding with the blast
of a meteorite. Even for a country where many things were very weird, this
really is weirder than usual!

But it gets even weirder. The entity whose conception has taken place in
association with the meteorite is specifically described as a falcon, and in
the text Isis further says: 'Protection has been granted the Falcon within
this womb of mine by Atum-Rā, lord of the gods.' (I have changed the
transliteration of Rā to a form more recognizable to readers. He was the sun
god.) The falcon's chief attributes are that he can soar higher and further
and see from higher up than any other creature. Later in the text, after he is
born, Horus boasts: 'My flight has reached the horizon, I having surpassed
the gods of the sky . . . I am Horus, born of Isis, whose protection was
within the ovary. . . . I am Horus, far distant from people and from the gods.
I am Horus, son of Isis.'

We can see from this that the text stresses, in association with the god
whose birth was related to a cosmic body landing on the earth, that he is the
type of being who is himself not of this earth, but far above it. The
meteorite is thus associated with the bringing to earth of a form of life
which is non-earthly, far higher and more remote than the realm of the
normal gods. Horus is purely celestial, and as he says: 'nor can what you
say against me reach me'.

There is another ancient Greek reference concerning the Egyptian
knowledge of meteorites which has never attracted any notice before. It is
from the unlikely source of Ammianus Marcellinus's *Roman History*.
Ammianus lived in the fourth century AD and one can find the most
wonderful titbits in his history – I highly recommend him for those who
like to come across oddities in the midst of their narratives. In Chapter 22
of Book XXII, in the midst of a fascinating discussion of Egypt, Ammianus
suddenly says:

Here it was that Anaxagoras [Greek philosopher of the fifth century BC]
derived the knowledge which enabled him to predict that stones would
fall from heaven . . .[7]

I was surprised at coming across this, to say the least. There is more to this
reference than meets the eye. Only fragments of his single book survive,
but Anaxagoras's views on astronomy were considered scandalous in
Athens in his day, and he was indicted for religious impiety, which carried
the death penalty. Unlike Socrates, who was similarly indicted later on at

Athens, Anaxagoras fled the city and saved his life. But his indictment was associated particularly with the fall of a meteorite at Aegospotami in 468–7 BC, which he had apparently predicted, and which he described as 'a stony star'. It was considered impious by various conservative Athenians that Anaxagoras had spoken like this of heavenly bodies, and had actually stated that the sun was a blazing stone 'bigger than the Peloponnese'. The scholar Kathleen Freeman believes that the reason why Anaxagoras said this 'was doubtless his belief that meteoric stones fell from a whirling mass of stones in the sky, and that of these the sun was the largest . . .'[8]

Anaxagoras also believed that the moon was a huge stone, which gets its light from the sun, and that it was very like the earth, being essentially level-surfaced, but with mountains, plains, ravines, rivers, houses, and even living creatures. It would appear, therefore, that he had been looking at the moon through a rudimentary telescope in the same way that Democritus seems to have done, as described earlier. He believed that a mythological creature, the Nemean Lion, fell to earth from the moon.[9] Killing and flaying the Nemean Lion was the first Labour of Hercules, and this lion was said in mythology to be the offspring of Typhon – the Greek name of the Egyptian god Seth – and also to have been dropped by the moon goddess onto Mount Tretus near Nemea in Greece, beside a two-mouthed cave subsequently known as the Lion's Cave, about two miles from the city of Nemea.[10] I can't say I know the significance of Mount Tretus – assuming there is any – but the point of interest is that Anaxagoras believed a mythical creature who was the offspring of Seth fell from the sky, and we have already seen that Seth was equated with meteoritic iron. Therefore we can glean some hint of a coherent Egyptian tradition behind Anaxagoras's lore of meteorites, and if it were not for the fact that we possess only very limited fragments of Anaxagoras's work, the picture would probably be a great deal clearer to us. But Anaxagoras went even further, – he stated all animal life on earth was created originally by the fall of 'seed' from heaven to earth.[11]

This is the earliest recorded reference I know of to the 'panspermia' theory, so popular at the end of the 19th century, that life on earth was seeded from outer space! In 1979 this theory was revived in a new and far more sophisticated form by the astronomers Sir Fred Hoyle and Chandra Wickramasinghe. They suggested that comets which pass close to our sun evaporate ('volatilize') some of their materials which eventually fall to earth as microscopic particles, and that these include viruses. They believe that life may originally have appeared on earth as a result of its transmission across interstellar space by cometary bodies, some of which are known to go from star system to star system.

The story of Anaxagoras takes on a new importance in the light of Ammianus's comments and what we are in the process of learning about Egyptian ideas concerning meteorites. And from what little we can learn of Anaxagoras's ideas, if as Ammianus insists they really originated in Egypt, then by extension we have some further notion of what it is the Egyptians believed. The interplay of Egyptian direct evidence and Greek indirect evidence can often give a joint impression which either source alone cannot give. And when it is possible to cross-check Greek information and substantiate it, the reliability of what people like Plutarch or Ammianus tell us takes on increased importance. We have already seen that Plutarch identified iron with Seth. This can be substantiated and confirmed by extremely ancient native Egyptian texts, so that we can see that Plutarch is definitely accurate in what he says, preserving information correctly which was at least 2,400 years old by his time. Wallis Budge cites a text from the time of Pharaoh Pepi II (Sixth Dynasty, *circa* 2278–2184 BC) which speaks of 'the iron which came from Set [Seth], and was in the form of the forearm of Set; it transferred to the deceased the power of the Eye of Horus.'[12] We cannot ask for a more direct confirmation of this important point recorded by Plutarch about the association of Seth with iron.

Ten years after O'Connell made his interesting textual discoveries about the birth of Horus being associated with the descent of a meteorite, a key study was published by Ann Macy Roth which provides even more astonishing information about meteoritic iron in ancient Egypt. This time the context is a strange ritual conducted by the Egyptians in association with mummies and statues, known as 'The Opening of the Mouth Ceremony'.

Once again, it was Plutarch who was the first non-Egyptian to provide a clue which could help to unravel one of the bizarre Egyptian traditions. In *On Isis and Osiris*, Chapter 16, he describes how Isis suckled her child Horus:

Isis is said to have suckled the child by putting, instead of her nipple, her finger into his mouth . . .[13]

For anyone familiar with the countless depictions in Egyptian art of Isis suckling Horus at her breast – a motif which was carried over into Christianity as 'the Madonna and Child' – this statement by Plutarch doesn't appear to make any sense. See Figure 31 for three illustrations of Isis suckling Horus. Not only do we know that Isis gave Horus her nipple in these carvings and paintings, but we even have an astronomical explanation for the scene propounded by the ingenious Sir Norman Lockyer. In *The Dawn of Astronomy*, he suggests that one aspect of the symbolism of Isis is to represent a star which is rising, and one aspect of the symbolism of Horus is to represent the sun rising; the suckling scene thus represents the star which rises just before the sun (which astronomers call *rising heliacally*) nursing the young sun which is just being born at the horizon.[14] The suckling scene probably does have that essential meaning as an iconographical motif.

So why does Plutarch say Isis suckled Horus with her finger? This is where we come back to the strange ceremony of 'The Opening of the

Figure 31. 'The Madonna and child', in its original form as Isis suckling Horus.
(From Sir Norman Lockyer, *The Dawn of Astronomy*, London, 1894, p. 292.)

Mouth', which is described at such tedious length in the highly bizarre ancient text, *The Book of the Opening of the Mouth*, which Wallis Budge translated and published in two volumes in 1909.[15] At first sight, this 'Opening of the Mouth Ceremony' seems one of the craziest things ever done in ancient times, and borders on being rather disgusting, not to say wholly incomprehensible. But never doubt that the Egyptians always knew

Figure 32. Isis suckling Horus, a 19th-century engraving of a bronze statue in the Louvre dating from the period of the Ptolemies (*circa* second/first centuries BC). The goddess Isis has risen above the horizon as a star – Isis-as-star was identified with the star Sirius, although she represented other functions in other contexts – and now the infant sun appears, and she nurses him over the horizon to become manifest in his sunrise-birth. The scene thus is an iconographical representation of the heliacal ('with-the-sun') rising of Sirius, which occurred once a year and was the commencement of the Egyptian calendar.

Figure 33. On the left is the deceased Pharaoh Tutankhamun-as-Osiris, wrapped in mummy bandages. The new pharaoh wearing the blue headdress, in the role of Horus, approaches him with the adze made of meteoric iron to perform the sacred 'Opening of the Mouth' ceremony, to ensure Tutankhamun of eternal life. This painting is on the north wall of Tutankhamun's burial chamber in the Valley of the Kings.

exactly what they were doing and why. There is sense beneath the nonsense even here.

It is Ann Macy Roth in 1993 who seems to have been the first person to come up with the clue which finally makes sense of 'Opening the Mouth'. And, as it happens, it is directly connected with Plutarch's strange comment about Isis suckling Horus with her finger. For, what do we see in her ground-breaking article of 1993 as Figure 5? We see a reproduction of an adult's little finger inserted into a newborn baby's mouth – *taken from a modern medical reference book*.[16] It turns out that Isis inserting her finger into Horus's mouth has some basis after all!

Perhaps the problem was that most Egyptologists have been men and not midwives, hence they were unaware of one of the fundamental facts concerning newborn infants. For this, I think, they can be forgiven.

I shall substitute for Ms Roth's unpronounceable *ntrwj* (from which I have omitted a special underlining of the *t*) the far cosier and friendlier spelling of *neterti*, which was used by Wallis Budge. It is true that in his *Hieroglyphic Dictionary* (407b) he put a question mark after this transliteration, and it may well be that *ntrwj* is the modern corrected reading. But that is not our problem. Wallis Budge didn't have all the answers in 1911, but at least it was possible to read the Egyptian words in his books! Here, then, is what Ann Macy Roth says about the finger in the mouth of the babe, in her description of the iron blades used in the ceremony of The Opening

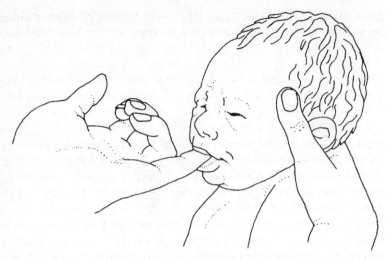

Figure 34. An illustration from a modern medical reference book reproduced by Ann Macy Roth, showing the probable origin of Isis inserting her finger into the infant Horus's mouth.

of the Mouth performed on the mummy of King Unas of the Fifth Dynasty (*circa* 2375–2345 BC):

> The accompanying spell, 'Osiris Unas, I have split open for you your mouth', clearly indicates the function of the *neterti*-blades. Why should a newly reborn king [that is, a dead king whose mummy is submitted to this symbolic resurrection ceremony] need to have his mouth opened? At birth, a baby's mouth is obstructed by mucus that must be cleared before the baby can breathe. In modern births, the mouth is cleared using a bulb syringe, but the physician's little finger is also put into the mouth to test for any abnormalities of the palate. The small size, softness and sensitivity which make the little finger appropriate for this task would make it equally suitable for cleaning the mouth. Today, the clearing is normally done immediately before the umbilical cord is cut. . . . The most likely prototypes for the *neterti*-blades are the two little fingers of the midwife. The model *neterti*-blades are shaped like fingers, with the single curved corner representing the soft part of the finger behind the nail. If they represented the little fingers of the left and right hands of the midwife, both their consistent duality and the fact that they are mirror-images of one another would be explained. . . . Originally [in Predynastic times], the gesture was probably performed by the little fingers of the priest, mimicking the little fingers that would have been used at an actual birth. . . . In one Sixth-Dynasty tomb scene (fig. 6) the cult functionary extends his two little fingers towards the deceased, in a gesture very like the one that I have hypothesized as the original 'opening of the mouth' act. . . . A similar gesture, in which one little

finger is offered . . . [is seen in fig. 7] . . . The gesture of offering either a single little finger or both is shown in some of the New Kingdom mouth-opening scenes (fig. 8).[17]

She then explains that the metal blades used as substitutes for the little fingers are made from meteorites:

A significant peculiarity of the *neterti*-blades is their composition. They are said in all the textual sources to be of . . . a material thought to be meteoritic. Meteoritic iron has been found in Egypt in burials as early as the Predynastic period. It was thought to have a magical significance, since the same word is used to mean 'marvel, miracle'. That this material came from 'falling stars' was apparently well understood by the Egyptians . . . [as witness] the fact that the *neterti*-blades . . . are sometimes called . . . 'stars'. The context in which this name is used, in inventory documents rather than religious inscriptions, suggests that it was the vernacular name of the implements, and that the mouth-opening instruments were thus popularly thought of as fallen stars.

   Except for the initial human little fingers, all the tools used in the 'opening of the mouth' ritual are associated with iron, meteoritic material, or stars. Iron-bladed chisels found in the tomb of Tutankhamun resemble closely chisels shown in representations of 'opening of the mouth' tools. The adze itself theoretically had a blade of meteoritic iron and was originally and most frequently called the *dua-ur*, a name that is written with a star and is clearly related to the *duat*, the place where the stars are. The constellation we see as a 'Great Bear' or a 'Big Dipper' was called *Meskhti* by the Egyptians [also 'the abode of the soul of Set', or Seth, according to Wallis Budge] and was compared to both the adze (fig. 9) and the *khepesh* [Khephesh was another name for the same constellation], the foreleg of an ox (fig. 10). Both the foreleg and the adze were added to the offering ritual at the same time, in the Pyramid Texts of Mernere [a Pharaoh of the Sixth Dynasty, *circa* 2283–2278 BC], and their association there was probably due to their common association with this constellation. This stellar element was presumably connected principally to the realm of the dead, which in some conceptions of the afterlife was clearly located in the region of the circumpolar stars. . . . Meteoritic material may have been comparatively common in ancient Egypt. Farouk el-Baz has suggested that a 4-kilometre-wide crater south-west of Dakhla Oasis is meteoritic in origin. Such a crater, among the largest known, would yield thousands of kilograms of meteoritic iron . . .[18]

Ms Roth has been extremely clever to work all of this out. Her reconstruction of this complex of symbolism makes the inexplicable suddenly become explicable. We owe her a great debt of gratitude. The lore of 'thunderstones' which we shall shortly be considering seems to take its origins from two sources. First, the earliest traditions of stones which fall from heaven and their occasional representation in the form of ceremonial axe blades seem to date from Palaeolithic times, and the religious notions of our Stone Age ancestors which have largely been lost in the mists of time. But the second source, and the earliest we can trace in a high civilization, is the meteoritic iron cult of the Egyptians. But there was more to the Egyptians' ideas than just meteorites falling at random in the desert. As we would expect with a people so thorough as they, the Egyptians had a bit more of a system worked out than just that. In one version of their cosmology, they believed as follows:

> . . . in (the Pyramid Texts) it is always assumed that the flat slab of iron which formed the sky, and therefore the floor of the abode of the gods, was rectangular, and that each corner of it rested upon a pillar . . . That this is a very ancient view concerning the sky is proved by the hieroglyphic . . . which is used in texts to determine words for rain, stone, and the like; . . . (it shows) a picture of the sky falling . . .[19]

Clearly, if there is a vast iron plate up in the sky somewhere, bits could fall off of it, and these would be the meteorites. They could also have the mysterious property of magnetism.

These strange ideas are not really so strange at all. The Egyptians came across meteoritic iron, knew it came from heaven, and knew that this metal was not available to them on earth. They quite naturally assumed that iron was a heavenly substance. But they associated it with night – possibly because it was black – and with the night sky. More particularly, they associated it with the circumpolar region of the stars which never set – the 'deathless stars' – and which was the region of the god Set or Seth (Typhon to the Greeks). Iron was his 'bone'. And occasionally one was tossed to earth. This rare celestial material was then hammered into adzes in the shape of the constellation known to us as the Great Bear or Big Dipper – the ultimate circumpolar constellation – and pressed against the mouths of mummies and statues in a ritual meant to 'open their mouths' so that they could, like infants, be born and live again in the world of the dead. It all makes sense if you are an ancient Egyptian.

The reverence with which the Egyptians treated meteoritic iron brings to mind that prominent religion of the present day, Islam. When the Moslems bow down and pray towards Mecca it is not the city of Mecca towards which they orient themselves, but the sacred shrine of the Kaaba which happens to be in Mecca, And when Moslems make their sacred journeys to Mecca, they go there in order to do something which is called 'the circumambulation of the Kaaba'. This means that they walk round the Shrine of the Kaaba seven times.

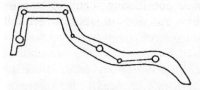 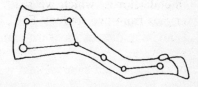

Figure 35. On the left, we see that the adze made of meteoritic iron which was used to 'open the mouth' of each recently deceased pharaoh was the strange shape that it was because it represented the circumpolar star constellation *Ursa Major*, the Great Bear or Big Dipper. The reason for this was that meteoritic iron was believed to fall from the floor of heaven, the centre of which was the celestial pole. On the right, we see the same constellation conceived as a foreleg of an ox. Such forelegs are seen on many of the offering tables in Egyptian tomb scenes and papyri; their symbolism has not generally been appreciated by Egyptologists. The relation of the constellation to the adze is the discovery of Egyptologist Ann Macy Roth, who points out that in the Pyramid Texts in the Pyramid of Unas, the two are actually called by the same name, so that there is no room for doubt on the matter. The association with the foreleg has been known for a long time, as a picture of a foreleg was actually used as a hieroglyphic determinative sign in texts which mention the constellation; in Babylonian tradition, the constellation was known as 'the Thigh' rather than 'the Foreleg'.
(Reproduced from Ann Macy Roth, 'Fingers, Stars, and "The Opening of the Mouth"': The Nature and Function of the NTRWJ-Blades', in *The Journal of Egyptian Archaeology*, London, Vol. 79, 1993, p. 70.)

But what is the Kaaba? It is a small building containing the most sacred object to all Moslems – the Kaaba Stone. And what do you suppose the Kaaba Stone is? *It is a meteorite.*

And with that, we leave meteoritic iron behind and enter more familiar territory. For now we come to the other heavenly substance which many cultures believed fell from the sky – rock crystal. And this, of course, brings us back to our crystal lenses. The lore of heavenly crystal was not restricted to a crystal sun. Just as the Egyptians occasionally spoke of an iron plate in the sky from which bits could drop, so perhaps the crystal sun might lose a few bits as well.

For we have now come to the subject of 'thunderstones'. Thunderstone lore is spread all across Europe, Asia, Africa, and the Americas and has its origins, as I said a moment ago, in the Stone Age. Any traditions so widely spread must have had origins that far back in order to be found round the whole world in the way that they are. It is unfortunate that thunderstone lore has been left largely to folklore scholars and has been essentially ignored by archaeologists. And as for historians of science, they have never heard of it. So its importance has been missed. However quaint it may be for people who like folklore, the importance of thunderstone lore for the history of science is in its relation to optics, as we shall see. This lore is the key to several Greek myths, for instance, which can only be correctly interpreted by reference to their optical allusions.

Perhaps the best way to begin describing the Greek and Roman traditions of rock crystal is to quote from a scientific work by Seneca, the *Natural Questions* (III, 25, 12), written in the first century AD. In the context of a discussion of the nature of water, Seneca says this:

> Anyone would suppose that water which turns into *crystallus* or ice is the heaviest. But the opposite is true. For this happens to the thinnest water, which the cold easily freezes because of its very thinness. Incidentally, where a stone of this type comes from is obvious from the very term among the Greeks: for they call 'crystal' both this transparent stone [rock crystal] and the ice from which it is believed to be formed. Rainwater has very little in it of earthly element, but when it has frozen it becomes more and more condensed by the persistence of prolonged cold until all the air is excluded and it is entirely compressed upon itself, and what had been moisture has become stone.[20]

The Greeks and Romans did not recognize rock crystal as a mineral at all, but believed it to be unnaturally compacted ice which had fallen to earth, and which through its compactness had, as Seneca says, all the air excluded from it, so that it could no longer melt.

Such views are facilitated by the fact that rock crystal occasionally occurs with trapped liquid bubbles inside, making it resemble ice all the more. I myself have many such pieces which I purchased in China, which

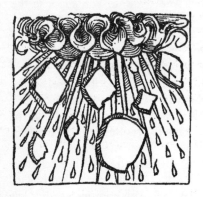

Figure 36. Above; an early-16th-century woodcut showing chunks of ice falling from the sky as thunderstones, which the Greeks believed to be the origin of rock crystal. *Right*: in a late-15th-century woodcut, two witches putting a snake and a cock into a pot conjure a thunderstorm with hailstones, indicating another aspect of the magical affiliations of celestial ice.

are very delightful. When you turn them this way and that, trapped portions of water inside slide back and forth inside small cavities. Imagine that you are an ancient person without proper geological knowledge – what would you think? You would think that these were intensely compacted bits of ice unsusceptible to melting, but which nevertheless had small melted portions in their interiors. For that is *what they look like*, and the ancients were often intensely literal. See Plate 9 for a photo of a crystal bubble.

In Greek the word *krystallos* means both 'rock crystal' and 'ice'. The same is true of the Latin word *crystallus*, which is simply a Latinization of the same word. Here is a passage from Pliny (first century AD) in which he describes the nature of rock crystal in his *Natural History* (37, 9); he has just described a substance created by heat:

A cause contrary to the one mentioned [i.e. cold instead of heat] is responsible for creating rock-crystal, for this is hardened by excessively intense freezing. At any rate, it is found only in places where the winter snows freeze most thoroughly; and that it is a kind of ice is certain: the Greeks have named it accordingly [i.e. *krystallos*]. Rock-crystal also comes to us from the East, for that of India is preferred to any other. It is found also in Asia Minor, where a very poor variety occurs around Alabanda and Orthosia and in the neighbouring districts, and likewise in Cyprus; in Europe excellent rock-crystal occurs in the ranges of the Alps. Juba [Juba II, King of Mauretania in North Africa, a prolific writer (in Greek) of the first century BC, all of whose books are lost] assures us that it is to be found also on an island called Necron, or Island of the Dead, in the Red Sea facing Arabia [possibly Socotra?], as well as on the neighbouring one which produces peridot: here, according to him, a piece measuring a cubit in length was dug up by Ptolemy's [Pharaoh Ptolemy I, when he was still a general of Alexander the Great; fourth century BC] officer Pythagoras. . . . The inevitable conclusion is that rock-crystal is formed of moisture from the sky falling as pure snow. For this reason, it cannot stand heat and is rejected except as a receptacle for cold drinks.[21]

One strange fashion amongst Roman ladies of elegance arose because of the conviction that crystal was highly compacted ice. They used to spend ludicrous sums of money trying to obtain globes of rock-crystal which they could ostentatiously hold in front of their friends, for their cooling effect on the hands, during hot summer afternoons. There wasn't enough rock-crystal of sufficient size to go around, and the less fortunate women of fashion who were disappointed in their desires for a crystal hand-globe had to make do with globes of amber instead. This weird tradition was described evocatively by Carl Böttinger in 1806, in his rather peculiar book (in German) entitled *Sabina: or, Morning Scenes in the Parlour of a Rich Roman Lady*.[22] I have translated this for Appendix Six.

To return to the Pliny passage, we find more things of interest about rock crystal:

> Why it is formed with hexagonal faces cannot be readily explained; and any explanation is complicated by the fact that, on the one hand, its terminal points are not symmetrical and that, on the other, its faces are so perfectly smooth that no craftsmanship could achieve the same effect. The largest mass of rock-crystal ever seen by us is that which was dedicated in the Capitol by Livia, the wife of [Caesar] Augustus; this weighs about 150 pounds. Xenocrates [fourth-century BC disciple of Plato] . . . records that he saw a vessel [of crystal] that could hold six gallons, and some authors mention one from India with a capacity of four pints. What I myself can unequivocally affirm is that among the rocks of the Alps it generally forms in such inaccessible places that it has to be removed by men suspended from ropes. . . . Pieces of rock-crystal are impaired by numerous defects . . . cloudy spots, occlusions of moisture that are sometimes hidden within it, and also what are known as 'salt-specks'. These can be concealed by the engraver. Pieces, however, that have no defects are preferably left unengraved: these are known to the Greeks as 'acenteta', or 'lacking a core', and their colour is of clear water, not of foam. Finally, the weight of a piece is a part of its value. I find that among doctors there is considered to be no more effective method of cauterizing parts that need such treatment than by means of a crystal ball so placed as to intercept the sun's rays. Rock-crystal provides yet another instance of a crazy addiction, for not many years ago a respectable married woman, who was by no means rich, paid 150,000 sesterces [a very large sum indeed] for a single dipper. Nero, on receiving a message that all was lost, broke two crystal cups in a final outburst of rage by dashing them to the ground. This was the vengeance of one who wished to punish his whole generation, to make it impossible for any other man to drink from these cups. Once it has been broken, rock-crystal cannot be mended by any method whatsoever. Glass-ware has now come to resemble rock-crystal in a remarkable manner . . .[23]

We should note that Pliny makes several remarks in the above passage about crystal's apparent connection with water. He refers to the water which is sometimes trapped within crystal, and describes different qualities as being, on the one hand like foam, and on the other like clear water.

There is a remarkable variant theory about rock crystal which was held by the Greeks. Although this too suggests that crystal is formed from water, the method of its formation is not by cold but by heat! This tradition is recorded by the historian Diodorus Siculus (first century BC), in his *Library of History* Book II – the same book which contains the description of the temple believed to be Stonehenge, which we encountered in Chapter Four.

In a section of the book where he is describing the exotic animals and gems of very hot countries, owing to the sun's strength there, he says:

> In these countries are generated not only animals which differ from one another in form [i.e. exotic creatures] because of the helpful influence and strength of the sun, but also outcroppings of every kind of precious stone which are unusual in colour and resplendent in brilliancy. For the rock-crystals [*krystallous lithous*], so we are informed, are composed of pure water which has been hardened, not by the action of the cold, but by the influence of a divine fire [*hypo theiou pyros dynameōs*], and for this reason they are never subject to corruption and take on many hues when they are breathed upon. For instance *smaragdoi* [green stones] and *bēryllia*, as they are called, which are found in the shafts of copper mines, receive their colour by having been dipped and bound together in a bath of sulphur . . .[24]

This is extraordinarily interesting information, and crystal-lore is here mixed up with alchemical lore, especially as the author continues with even more details of alchemical techniques. But before we look at them, let us fix our attention on the hint which Diodorus here gives us as to what the *smaragdus* (emerald) used by Nero may really have been. For what Diodorus is actually telling us is that *smaragdi* were a form of rock crystal which received their (green) colour artificially. In other words, crystal which was *tinted* green by some process which involved a bath of sulphur. *Smaragdi* of course included true emeralds, but it is clear from this that the term also referred to green-tinted crystal, and Nero's 'emerald', which has aroused so much speculation (as we discovered much earlier in this book), may thus have been a lens which was artifically coloured green to soothe the eyes, in the manner described so clearly by Pliny in a passage quoted previously.

The translator of Diodorus was unaware that in the passage which I have quoted, Diodorus used a highly technical ancient Greek alchemical term – *baptomenōn*. This word means much more than just 'dipped', in reference to the crystal being put into the sulphur bath and turned green. The Greek word *bapsis* refers to the second alchemical state known in Latin in the Middle Ages as *baptisma*. As Joseph Needham pointed out in one of his volumes on alchemy in the *Science and Civilisation in China* series:

> The late Middle Ages here preserved one of the most ancient terms in the art, *baphē*, *baphikē* (*bapsē*, *bapsikē*)) and *bapsis* . . . being the dipping of the cloth in the 'baptism' of dyeing, that technique out of which arose so many incalculable consequences.[25] [He then gives various references to old Greek alchemical texts.]

One of the 'incalculable consequences' was the concept of baptism in mystical Christianity. It is possible that John the Baptist was a far more esoteric character than the conventional view of him would imply. The origins of baptism as a sacrament may not really be in purification rites by bathing – which after all was a daily rather than a single occurrence for millennia amongst the priests of Egypt – but may be a mystical transformative concept deriving from the physical practices of ancient alchemy. The very early Church Father Saint Irenaeus, Bishop of Lyons (second century AD), preserves an explicit reference which makes this clear. Irenaeus wrote a passionate work in five books called *Against Heresies* (*Adversus Haereses*) in which he attacked the mystics known as the Gnostics, some of whom were pagan and some Christian (and it is not always easy to draw the line at that period between them). In fact, Irenaeus is often considered the first systematic Christian theologian – an orthodox one, of course, or he would not be a 'Saint'. Considering the great interest there is amongst the public even now in the subject of 'The Beast 666' mentioned in the Biblical Book of Revelation, it is probably worth pointing out that Irenaeus's identification of this man may be the earliest recorded. Irenaeus was in no doubt that The Beast 666 was the Emperor Nero, for *Neron Caesar* written in Hebrew letters gives the value 666 (Hebrew letters, like the Greek, doubled as numerals).

In his work *Against Heresies*, after attacking the notorious Simon Magus, who was a contemporary and rival of Jesus, Irenaeus turns his attention to Simon's immediate successor, who was named Menander. Of him he writes:

> This man's successor [i.e. Simon's] was Menander, a Samaritan by birth: who also himself came to perfection in magic. He affirms . . . that the world was made by Angels . . . Moreover that by the magic which he taught he gives knowledge for the overcoming the very Angels who made the world. For that his disciples receive resurrection by the baptism which is in him, and can no more die, but continue undecaying and immortal. . . . And the God of the Jews [Yahweh, or Jehovah] he said was one of the Angels [i.e. a wicked and wrathful power]. And . . . [Jesus] Christ came to destroy the God of the Jews, and to save them [that is, the Jews, from their false doctrine] . . .[26]

The idea of baptism as a bath which could arrest decay and bring about immortality seems to have its origins ultimately in the bath of natron used for the Egyptian mummies, which enabled them to 'continue undecaying and immortal'. But because with the development of alchemical techniques in Egypt, the Greek term *bapsis* was explicitly associated with real chemical processes and was a technical 'trade term', we can be in little doubt after seeing this testimony by Irenaeus that the Gnostics of the first century AD saw baptism as a mystical concept analogous to the alchemical process. Let us see now what the process accomplished, and how it is related to rock crystal – a substance which we should remember unites water and divine light, and was therefore a good symbol of a sacrament of baptism.

Diodorus has already associated rock crystal with divine fire, since he has identified this divine fire as the actual means by which water is transformed into crystal (*hypo theiou pyros dynameōs*). But he now goes on to say that when crystal is 'baptized' (that is, submitted to the alchemical process of *bapsis*), it can be transformed into a *smaragdos*, or artificial emerald. He then continues by describing the manufacture of 'false gold' (*pseudochrysous*) by mortal fire (*anthrōpōn gegonotos pyros*), and says that it is 'made by man dipping the rock crystals into it [the fire]' – i.e. by submitting rock crystal to the alchemical process of *bapsis* by 'fire', one may also manufacture false gold. Here Diodorus is alluding to complicated *bapsis* procedures which resulted in ancient times in the manufacture of so many different versions of false gold and silver, as well as crystal tinted so satisfactorily that it imitated the most valuable precious stones. In discussing these subjects, Needham quotes this interesting passage from Themistius of Byzantium in the fourth century AD, to show how common these stones and metals had become by then:

> If someone brings to the market-place artificial gold or imitated purple, or false gems, are you not angry? Do you accept them? Don't you have the market superintendent arrest the merchant for punishment by stripes as a charlatan and trickster? Is it not for the same reason that you search out many means of assaying gold, and testing for true purple dye and precious stones; and that you have assayers in attendance at the market whom you can consult when you buy, so that you may get expert advice in the purchase of these valuable things?[27]

We must not detain ourselves any longer in the fascinating byways of ancient alchemy. I only made this diversion in order to put into context the comments of Diodorus, which are of profounder importance than may appear at first sight. Whatever his source of information may have been, it was one deriving from a tradition of practical alchemy, and it represents a profounder level of physical science than the sources accessible to Pliny and Seneca. The iridescent finishes which the alchemists routinely applied to metals (for instance, one process gave real gold an attractive reddish sheen, another purple) were associated with the hues taken on in the sunlight by rock crystal when breathed upon. The practising alchemists – real working scientists rather than armchair ones like Pliny and Seneca – did not fall for the folklore of rock crystal being highly compacted ice. Instead, they postulated a rival and more sophisticated theory – that it was indeed derived from water, and may well have fallen from heaven, but its hardening was 'by the influence of a divine fire'. (One might almost call such a substance meteoritic crystal!) And this, of course, fits with heavenly origins from the region of divine fire, with esoteric concepts of a crystal sun, and with the uses of crystal to ignite fires and focus solar rays.

So we see that the rock crystal that fell from heaven was every bit as awe-inspiring to the Greeks as the meteoritic iron had been to the Egyptians. And we must keep in mind that there is a very simple reason for the change of material. Meteorites could not so readily be seen and retrieved in Greece, whereas the sands of Egypt made this so much easier. Nor did Egypt have the storms, ice, and snow of Greece which could conceivably have led to any theory of crystal as compacted heavenly ice falling from the sky. Rather, the theory of crystal as hardened by divine fire may have its origins in Egypt.

Now let us see what the actual lore of the thunderstones was all about. To do this, we must realize that a variety of names were given in Greek to stones falling from the sky. And we shall see that there was never any clear borderline between meteorites and crystals, and certain terms like *baetyl* could actually refer to both. We should start with the actual word which literally means 'thunderstone'. In Greek this is *keraunios* (from *keraunos*, 'a thunderbolt'). Strictly speaking, a 'thunderbolt-stone', or stone cast down by a thunderbolt – in other words, what we call a 'thunderstone' – should really be a meteorite. But let us see what Pliny says they are, speaking of the *ceraunia*, which is the Latin form of the name:

> Among the bright colourless stones there is also the one called 'ceraunia' ('thunder-stone') which catches the glitter of the stars and although in itself it is like rock-crystal, has a brilliant blue sheen [or 'bloom']. It is found in Carmania. Zenothemis [an author, now obscure, whose works are lost] admits that it is colourless . . . Sotacus [another forgotten author whose works are lost] distinguishes also two other varieties of the stone, a black and a red, resembling axe-heads. According to him, those among them that are black and round are supernatural objects; and he states that thanks to them cities and fleets are attacked and overcome, their name being 'baetuli', while the elongated stones are 'cerauniae'. These writers distinguish yet another kind of 'ceraunia' which is quite rare. According to them, the Magi [the Persian Zoroastrian priests] hunt for it zealously because it is found only in a place that has been struck by a thunderbolt.[28]

In a footnote at this point, Professor Eichholz adds: 'Presumably meteorites.' And he is certainly correct. Here in this passage of Pliny we see a wonderful garbling of traditions and the total confusion of crystal and meteorites – with the latter actually described as being black and supernatural. The mention of the Magi is intriguing, because the chief ritual of the Zoroastrian religion is the sacred fire ceremony, as is still the case with the Parsis of Bombay today. But in ancient times it may well be that the sacred flame was lit by crystal lenses. However, the search for what lay at the site of a thunderbolt is in itself an interesting subject.

Of course, as the result of a meteor striking the earth and forming a meteorite, one finds a lump of meteoritic iron. And the meteorite may even be rather large. We have all seen the giant ones displayed in the natural history museums, even if only as school children. Just to show how you never know when one sizeable enough to take notice of will turn up, here is an interesting item I clipped from the London *Times* of 12 April 1997:

PARKING SPACE
   Paris: A meteorite hit a parked car and set it on fire in the French Alpine town of Chambéry, France-Inter radio said. A 3lb block of basalt magma was recovered from the roof. (*Reuter*)

There are two different kinds of 'heavenly stones', therefore. In Egypt, where thunder and lightning are rare because of the climate, it is meteors which are seen rather than thunderbolts, and meteorites which are retrieved from the place where a heavenly object has struck the ground. But in Greece and Italy, where thunder and lightning are extremely common, it is thunderbolts which are commonly seen, and which repeatedly strike the earth. And whatever is retrieved from the site – whether a real or imagined product of the thunderbolt – is a 'thunderstone'.

In fact, there really *is* something which you can find if you inspect the site where a thunderbolt has struck the ground. It is what is called a *fulgurite*. This is from the Latin *fulgur*, 'lightning', or 'a lightning-flash that descends and strikes, a thunder-bolt', as Lewis and Short say in their Latin Dictionary. What, then is a fulgurite exactly? And does it have any connection with the ancient 'thunderstones'?

The best fulgurites are formed when a thunderbolt strikes sand, and so it is a great pity that there are so few – if any – thunderbolts in Egypt. Just think of all that sand! But never mind, fulgurites in Greece and Italy will do. Or even America. Why don't we just turn our attention to an article in the *New Scientist* from 1993, sent to me by courtesy of the writer John Brunner (whom I greatly thank), to learn a little bit more about fulgurites and their surprising connection with a strange atom!

First I have to explain what 'buckminsterfullerene' is. Don't even try to pronounce it. (Or if you must, try to envisage it as Buckminster-Fuller-ene.) And so now, before I can explain what *it* is, I have to explain who *he* was. He was more commonly known as Bucky Fuller, and I was very fortunate to know him and even to spend time on his private island off the coast of Maine long ago. He has been dead now for many years, but in the 1960s and 1970s he was one of the most famous people in the world. Everybody had heard of Bucky. He was a genuine certifiable Twentieth-Century American Genius, and was best known as the inventor of geodesic domes.

Previously he had invented many other things and yet was always in dire poverty. His uncle, who was a high-powered banker or businessman, got tired of Bucky always being totally broke, so he took him in hand and organized his latest invention – which happened to be geodesic domes – got the patents straightened out for him and made various arrangements to exploit them, and as a result Bucky finally became a millionaire and was freed from poverty. One of the quainter aspects of going to stay with Bucky was that he had a gigantic Great Dane named Sailor, who always insisted on sitting in my lap. Since then my lap has never been the same.

Another interesting thing was that Bucky, the Genius of the Future, lived happily all summer on an island which had no electricity. All light was by oil lamps. The best part of it was the clam-bakes and lobster-bakes on the beach by moonlight and a roaring fire, and watching Bucky sail in the glittering sea by moonlight which was like myriads of diamonds tossing about upon the briney deep, his sail a feather that slid across them on the wind. He liked to race other members of his family around the island in this way at night in their own boats. He generally won.

Bucky was a master geometer, and in recent decades, when chemists discovered a massive carbon molecule called 'carbon 60', written symbolically as C_{60}, they named this molecule after Bucky because it embodied geometrical principles which he had discussed before it was found. And since scientists these days, in order to keep themselves from going mad, indulge in a great deal of humorous banter and use increasing amounts of amusing slang in their technical discussions, they now speak of bits of buckminsterfullerene as 'Buckyballs'. That's because, whether they knew him personally or not, everybody feels how deeply endearing and eccentric Bucky was and wants to call him Bucky out of affection. And when when you are able to attach some hydrogen to two Buckyballs, you construct what is called a 'fullerene hydrocarbon'.

So now that you have the background, I can quote the article:

The Weird and Wonderful World of Buckyballs

Buckyballs are full of surprises. Recently, one group of researchers found the football-shaped molecule in the mineral fulgurite, which is formed when lightning strikes. . . . Peter Buseck and his colleagues of Arizona State University in Tempe . . . have discovered both C_{60} and C_{70} in a sample of fulgurite collected several years ago on Sheep Mountain in Colorado (*Science*, vol. 259, p. 1599).

The carbon content of the fulgurite is very low. Buseck suggests that the C_{60} and C_{70} came from pine needles that were carbonized when a bolt of lightning struck the mountainside. The temperature reached nearly 2000° C, sufficient to fuse the rock into a hard black glassy lump.[29]

When fulgurite is found in sand, the glassiness is all the more pronounced, in that the silicon of the sand has melted in lightning-shaped forked 'fingers'. (There is a spectacular bronze replica of a fulgurite on display in the Athens Archaeological Museum. Unfortunately, I was unable to take a photo of it due to the display conditions, reflections, etc. It is in Room 36, Case 8, Item 266. It is described as 'part of a thunderbolt' and dated to 'probably the end of the sixth or beginning of the fifth century BC'. It was excavated at the oracular centre of Dodona in north-western Greece. This is the kind of fulgurite which forms when a thunderbolt strikes sand.) But even on a mountainside, something resembling black glass is formed from the very rock, so the melting of silicon is not required. It is readily apparent that fulgurite is something which in being black, apparently falling from the sky (its creation by heat from the ground itself was not appreciated; the ancients thought it had *fallen*), but also being glassy makes it something of a half-way house between a meteorite and a crystal 'thunderstone'. The glassiness would have encouraged associations of crystal and glass with heavenly stones, as this would have appeared to be a characteristic of heavenly detritus.

Another ancient Greek name for a 'thunderstone' was *brontia*, from *brontē*, 'thunder'. (Admirers of Charlotte, Emily, and Anne please note.) Words like *brontia* are not really in Liddell and Scott's Greek Lexikon, but one has to look beyond such conventional sources. For instance, the word

Figure 37. When sacred sites such as this Temple of Hercules were situated on eminences, they attracted lightning and thunderbolt strikes, and fulgurites and 'thunderstones' could be collected in the vicinity.
(From Antonius van Dale, *De Oraculis*, Amsterdam, 1700.)

may be found listed in Henricus Stephanus, *Thesaurus Graecae Linguae* (Graz, 1954). And it also points out that *Brontēs* was the name of one of the Cyclopes. Since the single eye of the Cyclops represented a crystal globe, it is not surprising that one of them was called 'Thunder', as his eye was equivalent to a thunderstone, as we shall see. Pliny reports the following (*brontea* being the Latin for *brontia*):

> 'Brontea', or 'thunder-stone', which is like the shell of a tortoise, is supposed to fall from thunderclaps and to extinguish fires where lightning has struck, or so we are led to believe.[30]

A stone which is shaped like the shell of a tortoise has the shape of a plano-convex lens. Henricus Stephanus tells us there was another name for such stones, and stresses that they referred specifically to *convex gems*: *chelōnia lithos* or *chelōnitis lithos*, meaning literally 'tortoise stone', from the word *chelōnē*, 'tortoise'. These two words are actually listed in Liddell and Scott. These stones were associated with eye symbolism and also with extraordinary magical properties, as recounted by Pliny:

> The 'chelonia', 'tortoise-stone', is the eye of the Indian tortoise and, according to the false allegations of the Magi [Persian priests], is the most miraculous of all stones. For they claim that the stone, if it is placed on the tongue after the mouth has been rinsed with honey, confers powers of prophecy . . .[31]

Yet another ancient Latin name for 'thunderstone' was *ombria*, from the Greek *ombros*, 'a storm of rain, a thunder-storm (sent by Zeus)'. This name had a curious later history, as *ombriae* became confused with fossil sea urchins in the 16th and 17th centuries in Europe, due to the shape of the latter being plano-convex. Here is what Pliny tells us of the *ombriae*:

> The 'ombria' ('rain stone'), otherwise known as 'notia' ('south-wind stone'), is said to fall, like the 'ceraunia' and the 'brontea', in company with heavy rain and thunderbolts, and to have the same properties as these stones. But in addition, so we are told, it prevents offerings from being burnt away if it is placed on an altar.[32]

This is a very good joke! And Pliny obviously didn't get it. Since all of these thunderstones were associated with the use of rock crystal to start sacred fires on altars, the source which Pliny consulted for this last bit of information was pulling everybody's leg. The *ombria*, another one of the plano-convex crystals used as a burning-lens, can only focus the rays of the sun onto the altar if it is held *above* the altar – that's obvious. So if you *place it on the altar*, it cannot kindle any fires, can it? Even ancient mineralogists had to have their little jokes, didn't they?

The *ombria*, the *brontea*, the *ceraunia*, and the *chelonia* were often discussed together as thunderstones. A typical example is in the *Musaeum Metallicum* of Ulyssis Aldrovandi of 1648,[33] who also refers to Georgius Agricola, *On the Nature of Fossils*, Book 5, to Agricola's *De Re Metallica*, Chapter 43, to Pliny's *Natural History*, and to George Marbodus.

Thunderstones go back further than the Greeks, of course, and were part of the lore of the Near East as well. For the collectors of curious titles, I have the following to offer: 'Thunder-Stones in Ugaritic'. This article published in 1959 commences with this urgent problem:

> Since the publication of Ugaritic Text V AB.C. scholars had and still have difficulty with the translation of *abn brq*.[34]

However, later in the article we come to things which concern us. The author gives various possibilities of translation which have been advanced by learned scholars, and then says:

> No one, however, as far as my knowledge goes, connects *abn brq* with a common belief in many countries, both ancient and modern, of the thunder-stone (German: 'Blitzsteine' or 'Donnerkeil'). The only problem is that traces of a thunder-stone idea are very sparse in the Semitic world. The only possible reference to it is . . . an Akkadian prayer . . . A very probable translation [of which] is 'rain and thunder-stones, fire'. . . . [there was a] conception that in lightning a stone is sent down. These stones are regarded as precious and filled with 'mana' to ward off evil spirits, to protect a person against lightning, or to make the earth fertile. This conception is present all over the world, in various countries with minor differences.

An entire book has been written about thunderstones. – *The Thunderweapon in Religion and Folklore: A Study in Comparative Archaeology* by Christopher Blinkenberg. It was originally published in 1911, but was very conveniently reprinted in 1987. I believe the market for the reprint was largely folklorists.[35] It is surprising how much information is omitted or missed by Blinkenberg; everything that I have said above in this chapter, for instance. His main interest is in Scandinavian folklore, with only derisory attention paid to ancient times. Blinkenberg is interested, for example, in how thunderstones are meant to protect children against trolls! But he has a section on the confusion of fossilized sea-urchins with thunderstones, but explains it by saying that people 'believed they had a diamond inside'. These plano-convex fossils were still believed to fall down with thunderbolts, but the fact that they were opaque was explained away by insisting that the equivalent of a crystal was concealed within them.[36] I have a beautiful little fossilized sea-urchin, but I feel no temptation to smash it and look for a diamond!

Thunder-stone lore is vast, but ancient traditions become so debased by the time they become modern folklore that it can be off-putting. So at this point, we should concentrate on the specific identifications of crystal lenses with thunderstones. The country where this became essential to our story is Britain. During the 17th and 18th centuries, an assortment of keen antiquarians began digging up the ancient tumuli and burial mounds of England, and in the course of their amateur excavations they recovered a substantial number of both crystal lenses and crystal balls. The crystal balls are all well known to British archaeologists, but the crystal lenses got shunted to one side, miscatalogued as mineral specimens, and wholly forgotten. Indeed, they were actually 'lost' until I rediscovered them after the most arduous searching.

Some of the crystal lenses which were found by the British amateurs were quaintly known as 'mineral pearls'. The British have always been good at coming up with picturesque names for things: pieces of rock crystal found near Bristol in the old days were called 'Bristol diamonds', or sometimes simply 'Bristol stones'. I have found a mention of them in a book of legal theory by John Cooke, who three years later was to become the prosecutor of King Charles I at his trial for treason, dating from 1646. In discussing a spurious legal argument masquerading as a sound one, Cooke says:

> I am sorry the reverend Author should put a Bristol-stone amongst so many diamond Reasons as are in that case, what manner of reasoning is this?[37]

John Aubrey, author of the famous *Brief Lives* of the 17th century, wrote in his book *Miscellanies,* in his chapter about 'Visions in a Berill, or Crystall':

> The Magicians, now, use a Crystal-Sphere, or Mineral-Pearl for this purpose [scrying, or foretelling the future by crystal-gazing], which is inspected by a Boy . . . James Harrington Author of *Oceana* told me that the Earl of Denbigh then Ambassador at Venice did tell him, that one did shew him there several times in a Glass, things past, and to come.[38]

Aubrey went on in the same chapter to describe a crystal which was 'a perfect sphere', used for the same purpose. He gave an illustration of it, and also gave one of the 'Mineral-Pearl', which he showed as a biconvex crystal lens.

Martin Lister, the same man whose account of the lodestone at the top of Chartres Cathedral we considered at the very beginning of this chapter, wrote an account of ancient British crystal lenses in the *Philosophical Transactions* for June 1693, in which he included an engraving of five of them. He speaks of them as 'mineral pearls', but uses other names as well which are familiar to us, as we may gather from the title of his article, which is 'An Account of Certain Transparent Pebles, Mostly of the Shape of the Ombriae or Brontiae'.[39] So, we see that in 1693 Pliny's nomenclature was still going strong.[40]

In this work, Lister referred to a 'Dr Plot'. This set me on a real search. Who was this Plot fellow, and what did he have to do with *ombriae*? I never leave a Bristol-stone unturned, and so it was inevitable that I would track down someone named Plot who lived before 1693, and could conceivably be the man. He turned out to be Dr Robert Plot. And here he thickens. For he was a very grand fellow indeed – the author of a mammoth and impressive *Natural History of Stafford-Shire*, published in 1686, every word of which must have been read with rapt attention by Martin Lister, all the more so in that Lister himself is quoted, as on p. 178. And sure enough, Plot had a chapter called 'Of Formed Stones'. This is the exciting part:

Next the formed stones relating to the heavenly bodies . . . I descend next, to such as are thought at least, to come from the inferior heaven, to be generated in the Air amongst the Clouds, and discharged thence in thunder showers, whence they are termed by Authors *Brontiae* and *Ombriae:* whereof I met with one in this County, in the hands of Thomas Broughton Esq: . . . it being a regular solid Hemisphere (which may be apprehended well enough without a Cut) as transparent as Chrystall; and much harder, most likely, of any sort, to be of the pebble-kind. As I think I must also reckon a more oblong sort of transparent *Ombriae*, of a triangular form, near two inches long, and an inch broad; the bottom and sides not flat, but protruberant, and carryed up round at the ends, till meeting with the top ridge; the angles not sharp like the Prismaticall glass, nor representing any of those vivid colours though held to the Eye in the due posture; but more obtuse, as engraven Table 11, Figure 5, which was found near Fetherston in this County, and given me by the ingenious and most obliging Gent. Mr John Huntbach of the same Village. [This stone, of which he publishes an engraving, is a typical ridged cabochon crystal lens, of which I have seen so many. It is incredible to think that Dr Plot actually thought that such a manufactured item could conceivably be natural!] These transparent pebbles are sometimes also found in a globular forme [i.e. crystal balls], whereof the most exquisitly transparent, without any blemish, was shewn me by the virtuous young Lady Madam Ann Bowes of Elford in this County, in whose Closet I take it (amongst many others) to be a principal rarity.

I saw another of these express't Fig. 5 [in other words, another ridged cabochon crystal] found near Lichfield, in the hands of Mr Zach. Babington of Whittington, and there are many of them in the Ashmolean Musaeum at Oxford, and in that of the Royal Society at Gresham College London. They are not found in digging, either amongst Gravel, or in Quarries [i.e. are not mined], as most other form'd stones, but upon the surface of the earth, as the ingenious Mr Beaumont also says they are in Somersetshire and Gloucestershire, . . . produced, as he thinks, in clear Evenings from a coagulation of dew . . . Howbeit, they still come from the inferior heaven . . .[41]

Dr Plot was Keeper of the Ashmolean Museum at Oxford as well as Professor of Chemistry at Oxford University. One would think that as he had seen several ridged cabochons in his own and one other museum, he would have drawn the conclusion that these were man-made objects. But the miscataloguing of the ancient British lenses as naturally occurring crystals which fell from heaven was obviously well under way by the 1600s, and the ones which I have found are still in mineralogical collections today, unknown to all archaeologists. So imprisoning was the concept of the 'thunderstone'! After all, a crystal which fell from heaven *couldn't* be man-made, and so it must be natural (or, as the Magi would say, supernatural).

It was only with the great chemist Robert Boyle that we finally escaped the notion that rock crystal was a product of the heavens! He had insisted upon this in 1672, but Dr Plot, being a very distinguished Professor of Chemistry and naturally an *expert*, scorned Boyle's outrageous theory and persisted in the tried-and-true theory which had been around for thousands of years. *Of course* rock crystal came from the clouds! Everyone knows *that*!

But Robert Boyle didn't know that. In his book *An Essay about the Origine & Virtues of Gems* of 1672, he first stated this general hypothesis:

. . . I propose the Conjecture or Hypothesis . . . the substance of which may be compriz'd in these Two particulars: First, That many of these Gems, and Medical Stones, either were once fluid Bodies, as the Transparent ones; or in part made up of such substances as were once fluid . . .[42]

He later mentions a piece of crystal containing water, of which I have many specimens myself, as I have mentioned:

. . . a very ingenious and qualify'd Lady, who had accompany'd her Husband in an Embassy to a great Monarch, assur'd me, that she brought thence among several Rich Presents and other Rarities (some whereof she shew'd me) a piece of Christal, in the midd'st of which there was a drop of Water, which by its motion might be very easily observ'd, especially when the Chrystal was made to change its posture.[43] [The variation in spelling of crystal above is Boyle's own.]

Boyle then struck a great blow for the triumph of science, and did that rarest of all things – he *used his brains and eyes*:

I found (the) weight (of Rock-Cristal) to be to that of Water of equal bulk as two and almost two-thirds to one: Which, by the way, shews us, how groundlessly many Learned Men, as well Ancient as Modern, make Crystal to be but Ice extraordinarily harden'd by a long and vehement Cold; whereas Ice is bulk for bulk lighter than Water (and therefore swims upon it) and (to add that Objection against the vulgar error) Madagascar and other Countreys in the Torrid Zone abound with Crystal.[44]

Even so, Boyle was not wholly home and free. He concluded that rock crystal was a solidified 'pretrescent juice, or liquor', and he connected this with a theory of fossils whereby '. . . Petrifick agents may insinuate themselves into the pores of various Bodies, and turn them into Stone . . .'[45]

Dr Plot clearly turned his back on all this, still believing crystal to fall from the sky! He presumably did not like the reflection 'how many Learned Men, as well Ancient as Modern' were idiots, so he determined to be more an idiot than ever in order to cock a snook.

Can you believe that as late as this people were still struggling to free themselves from the *theory of the thunderstone*?

Just to make transparent stones that much more mysterious – as if falling from heaven, starting fires, and magnifying images were not enough – we must not forget that stones resembling these can emerge from both animal and human bodies! The ubiquitous Martin Lister tells us this disturbing news:

> But to return to Monsieur Budelot's Stores [i.e. collections – in Paris in 1698]. . . . I enjoyed this Gentleman's Company very often . . . He shewed me also a Stone taken lately out of the Body of a Horse at Paris, which was his Death [i.e. which had caused him to die]; and dying strangely, they Dissected him, that is, certain ignorant People; in the lower part of the Body, (probably the Bladder) was found this Stone: It weighs, as I guess, two Pound; it is as round as a Cannon Ball; it is laminated like an Onion; for the first Couche was broken up in some Places, of a dark hair colour, and transparent . . . Such like Transparent Stones I had a Patient voided often in Yorkshire. I saw another Transparent one, which was cut out of the Buttock of an Alderman at Doncaster; he was twice cut in the same place, at some years distance. Another I had in some measure transparent, voided by a Patient, which was of the very colour of a Coffee-Berry when burnt . . .[46]

At another point in the same book, Lister speaks of a vast amethyst which he had seen which was 'most perfectly figured both point and sides, after the manner of a Bristol Diamond, or common Rock Crystal . . .'[47]

What can we suppose that ancient people thought about the sudden voiding of transparent kidney stones? Was it a heavenly sign?

311

Even stranger still, perhaps, is the phenomenon known as *piezoelectricity*. If you take two pieces of quartz (i.e. rock crystal) and strike them sharply together in the dark like flints, a magnificent luminous electric spark may be seen. I won't bother giving the physical explanation for this, as it is the phenomenon which is important and not the cause. So we see that the heavenly substance which fell from the sky in a thunderbolt amidst the lightning could give off a bit of lightning of its own when colliding with one of its brethren. And this must have given a further air of mystery to *the combination of two crystal lenses* which already, as we have seen, is sufficient to give anyone a rudimentary telescope with an inverted image. In theory, if you got tired of looking at the moon through your telescope during the night, you could remove your lenses and amuse yourself by creating artificial lightning with them. A good occupation for insomniacs, perhaps.

No wonder the figure on my sixth-century BC Greek crystal lens is flying through the air holding what looks like two crystal globes. When he gets tired of scrutinizing the earth far below him, using them in juxtaposition optically, he can bash them together and get jolly sparks. Everybody who could fly in those days clearly had even more fun than we do with in-flight movies.

Now we come to crystal lentils. Well, the fact is that the French came to them from the very beginning, and quite naturally, for in the French language *lentille* is the word for 'lens'. And it was adopted for this use in the first place because of the lentil-like shape of a lens. But we are introduced to lenses by way of lentils in a different manner in English, if we read the work of John Woodward published in 1729 dealing with a natural history of fossils. He methodically proceeds by considering lentil-shaped stones, and makes these observations first:

> Strabo [first centuries BC/AD] *Geography* Book 17, p. 808d, takes Notice, that in Egypt, near the Pyramids, there were Heaps of the Chippings and Hewings of Stone . . . And in these were found Stones of the Shape and Bigness of Lentils . . . The fancyful Tradition of the Inhabitants [the Egyptians of Strabo's day] concerning these was, that they were the Remains, of what were wont to be eat by those that work'd in Building the Pyramids, in tract of Time turn'd into Stone. He observes also that there were plenty of these Lenticular Stones on an Hill, where he dwelt, in Pontus . . .[48]

So Strabo's neighbours ate lentils too! Well, this is indeed, as Woodward says, a fanciful tradition. Just imagine – fossilized lentils on the Giza Plateau! What next? And will more of them be found in a secret chamber?

But then Woodward, working along methodically, increases the size of his lenticular forms and rises to the grandeur of our crystal lenses. And the three objects which he next describes were, after interminable struggles and enquiries, located by me in the John Woodward Collection (together with his oil portrait [see Plate 54] and cabinets) at the Sedgwick Museum of Geology at Cambridge, to which they had been sent in 1907 from the Fitzwilliam Museum at Cambridge (which had not kept a record of this). In fact, my report on these three objects may be found as Appendix Five. One of them is a ridged cabochon lens, such as Dr Plot had already encountered and 'engraven'. Another is one of the lenses engraved by Martin Lister.[49]

It is notable that Woodward corrected Lister's mistaken view that the crystal lenses were natural, and with the advice of professional lapidaries established that they were man-made artifacts, and suggests that they predated the Roman Invasion of Britain. Such insights were to prevail with subsequent scholars, especially as it became more apparent where these crystals were coming from. For the fact is that many of them were being excavated by zealous local antiquaries who were relentlessly plundering the burial mounds of the ancient Britons in search of treasure.

The optical nature of these objects began to be appreciated also, which is no surprising thing, considering that as soon as you have one in your hand you have to be blind not to notice that it is a magnifier. The scientist Joseph Priestley mentioned the ancient British crystal lenses in his book *The History and Present State of Discoveries Relating to Vision, Light, and Colours*, in 1772:

> The antient engravers of gems are supposed to have made use of a glass globe filled with water to magnify their figures, and thereby to work to more advantage. The authority for this is a book published by [Laurent] Natter, upon that subject. [We considered this in an earlier chapter.]
>
> That the power of transparent bodies of a spherical form, &c. in magnifying or burning, was not wholly unknown to the antients, is farther probable from certain gems preserved in the cabinets of the curious, which are supposed to have belonged to the Druids. They are made of rock crystal of various forms, amongst which are found some that are spherical, and others lenticular [i.e. lens-shaped]; and though they are not so well wrought as to perform their office as well they might have done, if they had been more judiciously executed, yet they are so well wrought, that one can hardly suppose it possible, that their effect, in *magnifying* at least, could have escaped the notice of those who had often occasion to handle them; if indeed, in the spherical or lenticular form, they were not purposely intended for the use of magnifying or burning. One of these, of the spherical kind, of about an inch and an half in diameter, is preserved amongst the fossils given to the university of Cambridge by Dr [John] Woodward, in whose catalogue it is to be found.[50]

Now we were getting somewhere! Priestley also mentions the passage in Seneca [first century AD] which we considered earlier, about the magnifying power of a glass globe full of water for enlarging letters when you read, and he also cites a passage by Alexander of Aphrodisias [third century AD] about apples appearing larger when immersed in water.[51]

Reports began to be published about new crystals which were being excavated from burial mounds, which took the crystals out of the realm of the fabulous and placed them firmly in a realistic context. It was quickly being forgotten now that the 'thunderstones' were supposed to have fallen from the sky, and Boyle's theory that crystal was not made of compacted ice but was a natural mineral appeared to have won out. Still, the proto-archaeologists managed to combine mystery with fact as best they could. The Rev. James Douglas reported some crystal finds in his *Nennia Britannica: or, A Sepulchral History of Great Britain*, in 1793. In that work, the report of an excavated crystal ball is mixed with confusion as to its status: Douglas says 'The crystal appears to be in its native state unpolished by art . . .' which we know cannot be true. It precipitates a gigantic footnote in small print running for five full folio pages. In this we learn of Roman crystal balls, the crystal ball found in the tomb of King Childeric II of France (shown in Figure 38, below), several found in a Farnesan urn, of Pliny, of the Magi, of Moses and the Jews, of Delrio's disquisition on magic, of Urim and Thummim in the Bible, of the astrologers Dr Dee and John Lilly, of crystal-gazing, of the four Archangels, and culminating in this observation:

> If my crystall-ball be productive of these wonderful virtues [too many to repeat here!], surely my laborious researches among the sepulchres of the antients are sufficiently rewarded by this valuable discovery; but as I am afraid of tampering with the devil, and perfectly satisfied with my good friends of earthly condition, so I refer the more inquisitive genius to a conference with Michael, Gabriel, Raphael, and Uriel, and the rest of them; and for which purpose he is highly welcome to make use of my crystal and the curious invocation which I have here cited.[52]

Whether this invitation to one and all to come on over to the Reverend Douglas's house for a consultation with the Archangels was ever taken up, we do not know.[53]

The earliest published description I can find in French of the discovery of a royal crystal ball (symbol of divine kingship, as representing the crystal sun) in the urn containing the ashes of the French King Childeric II is found in the Rev. Bernard de Montfaucon's massive book *l'Antiquité Expliquée et Représentée en Figures* (*Antiquity Explained and Portrayed in Figures*), second revised edition, 1722. In one chapter, de Montfaucon describes twenty small balls or globes of rock crystal recovered from an ancient urn, and refers to the separate royal find:

> . . . in the tomb of King Childeric, father of Clovis, which was discov-

ered at Tournai, with a great number of gold pieces, an axe, and several other things which can be seen today [1722] in the Library of the King [at Paris].[54]

The assiduous 17th-century scholar Sir Thomas Browne in his strange book *Hydriotaphia: Urne-Burial, or a Discourse of the Sepulchrall Urnes Lately Found in Norfolk*, speaks of the following:

And notably illustrated from the Contents of that Roman Urne preserved by Cardinal Farnese, wherein besides great number of Gemmes with heads of Gods and Goddesses, were found . . . a Crystal Ball, three glasses, two Spoons, and six Nuts of Crystall.[55]

Globus Crÿstallinus.

Figure 38. The royal crystal ball found in the tomb of the early French King Childeric II, engraved for John Chifletius, *Anastasis Childerici Francorum regis, sive Thesaurus Sepulchralis*, Antwerp, 1655, p. 243. See also Rev. Bernard de Montfaucon, *Antiquity Explained and Portrayed in Figures*, Vol. 5, Part 1 (second edition, 1722). The symbolic crystal ball, which in its origins represents the crystal sun, was the emblem of divine kingship, and was often placed at the tips of royal sceptres in mediaeval Europe. The original English Crown Jewels lost during the Civil War in the 17th century would have contained such a sceptre, but the modern ones now displayed in the Tower of London (i.e. post-Restoration in 1660, which I consider as modern) were made after such symbolism had faded from consciousness and had ceased to be represented. Therefore, do not make the mistake I did of a special trip to the Tower to see the crystal-tipped sceptre, as it disappeared 350 years ago.

It may have struck some readers as peculiar that iron and rock crystal were somehow viewed as connected, not only because both fell from heaven, but by implication for other reasons which are not wholly clear to us. Berthold Laufer, the great Sinologist, provides us with a valuable clue to help explain this, and it is one which could easily have escaped us if it were not for his inexhaustible scholarship. One of his more fascinating monographs is entitled *The Diamond: A Study in Chinese and Hellenistic Folk-Lore*, published in 1915. (The word 'Hellenistic' refers to the period in the aftermath of King Alexander the Great, commencing 322 BC.) I am a great admirer of Laufer's work and collect his rare publications, as they are incomparable and deal with so many extraordinary subjects. People like Laufer no longer exist. Joseph Needham, who of course drew heavily upon Laufer in his own work on the history of Chinese science, was the last in the great tradition of Orientalists who also had profound familiarity with ancient Western culture as well. But Laufer was a worthy predecessor in this regard. We live now in an age where scholarship has become fragmented and over-specialized, and nobody knows anything which isn't an inch from his or her nose anymore. Scholars live in their little boxes, and that is that.

Here, then, is what Laufer said in his study of *The Diamond*:

> Dioscorides of the first century AD distinguishes four kinds of diamonds, the third of which is called 'ferruginous' because it resembles iron, but iron is heavier; it is found in Yemen. According to him, the adamantine fragments are stuck into iron handles, being thus ready to perforate stones, rubies, and pearls. The concept of a mysterious association of the diamond with iron survived till our middle ages. Konrad von Megenberg, in his Book of Nature, written in 1349–50, observes that, according to the treatises on stones, the virtue of the diamond is much greater if its foundation be made of iron, in case it is to be set in a ring . . .[56]

Before considering more of this, however, we must make the immediate point that the diamond and rock crystal were not specifically differentiated by mineralogists as separate substances until just over 200 years ago. Laufer himself tells us:

> The opinion that diamond, according to its composition, was a glass-like stone of the nature of rock-crystal, prevailed in Europe till the end of the eighteenth century, when it was refuted by Bergmann in 1777 . . .[57]

To the ancients, therefore, diamond seemed to be but a variation of rock crystal. And furthermore, there was a form of black diamond [today called 'industrial diamond', used for drills] which so strongly resembled iron that there appeared to exist a kind of hybrid form of 'rock crystal iron', as we might as well choose to call it. The two heavenly stones therefore could be interpreted as a transparent thunder-stone and a black meteor-stone – twins but opposites of one another – which fused their natures on rare occasions to form that substance known to the ancient Greeks as *adamas* (from which we get our modern word 'adamantine'). This word was used at different times in Greek history to refer to iron, to steel, and to diamond. But its essential meaning – a great puzzle to classical scholars – is *the hardest known substance*, whether mineral or metal is not quite clear. It had mythological associations with the heavenly regions, and the chains of Prometheus were supposed to have been made of it (hence yet another esoteric optical reference in that myth, considering the associations of *adamas* with diamond and crystal).

Pliny (first century AD) has some curious remarks about *adamas*:

> The most highly valued of human possessions, let alone gemstones, is the 'adamas', which for long was known only to kings, and to very few of them. . . . Our recent authorities thought that it was found only in the mines of Ethiopia between the temple of Mercury [Hermes = Thoth] and the island of Meroe [in the Northern Sudan] . . . There is the Indian, which . . . has a certain affinity with rock-crystal, which it resembles in respect of its transparency and its smooth faces meeting at six corners. . . . It can be as large even as a hazel nut. Similar to the Indian, only smaller, is the Arabian, . . . All these stones can be tested upon an anvil, and they are so recalcitrant to blows that an iron hammer head may split in two and even the anvil itself can be unseated. Indeed, the hardness of 'adamas' is indescribable, and so too that property whereby it conquers fire and never becomes heated. Hence it derives its name, because, according to the meaning of the term in Greek it is the 'unconquerable force.' [*Adamos* literally means 'unvanquished'.] . . . there is (also) the 'siderites' or 'iron stone', which shines like iron and exceeds the rest in weight, but has different properties. For it can not only be broken by hammering but also can be pierced by another 'adamas'. This can happen also to the Cyprian kind . . . When an 'adamas' is successfully broken it disintegrates into splinters so small as to be scarcely visible. [Doubtless lenses were needed to see them and use them.] These are much sought after by engravers of gems and are inserted by them into iron tools because they make hollows in the hardest materials without difficulty.[58]

We thus have textual proof that the use of diamond cutters and diamond drills was a commonplace by the first century AD, and without question long before that, for there is no indication by Pliny that this is anything new. We must entertain the possibility that diamonds for cutting and drilling were known to the Egyptians in very early times, especially as such a ready supply was available from the regions just beyond Upper Egypt, as Pliny also informs us. Egyptologists, as I have said before, are generally weak on science and technology. From time to time questions have been raised by outsiders – and have met with silence by way of reply – as to how the ancient Egyptians could have shaped the coffer inside the so-called King's Chamber of the Great Pyramid. I recall seeing one modern engineer in a television documentary standing beside the coffer and saying that it was made of diorite, the hardest form of granite, and it could not have been shaped without modern diamond drills. What he did not realize – but then no one else does either – is that there *may well have been ancient diamond drills*. And, as we shall see in the next chapter, there were other advanced instruments in ancient Egypt.

Another answer to the mystery of the coffer has been given by my friend Professor Joseph Davidovits. He is an inorganic chemist who believes that the ancient Egyptians may have 'cast' rather than carved the coffer. They would have done this by creating a liquid slurry of diorite made from chips mixed with Nile mud (which has a peculiar composition not found in mud elsewhere in the world) and the natural Egyptian salt, natron, and 'casting' the coffin within the chamber after its construction. The result would be 'agglomerated stone', which would harden quickly and appear always to have been solid. It is impossible from merely looking at or feeling such an object to tell whether it is carved diorite or agglomerated diorite. The special techniques employed, which Davidovits has success-fully recreated in a variety of forms and patented internationally, create what is called an 'inorganic polymer'.

Davidovits, who started his scientific career as a polymer chemist working on polyurethane, was the first modern discoverer of 'inorganic polymers' – which took about 20 years to be accepted by the scientific community because nobody thought such substances could exist. Since Joseph has recently finished a book about his ideas, I recommend to curious readers that they read it when it appears, as in my opinion he is one of the most brilliant and creative scientists alive today. I shall be referring to his work at much greater length in a future book of my own.

Apart from his views on ancient stone technology, Davidovits has many contributions to make towards a better contemporary world. For instance, he has created the only known light-weight replacement for plastic on the insides of aircraft which is totally heat- and fire-resistant (a geopolymeric resin which is used to coat carbon fibres and form a fire-proof fabric; this material – which gives off no gas – can be used for fire-barriers in trains and in ships, and 5 cm-thick cladding using this substance can render tunnels fire-resistant and prevent the concrete exploding as it did in the Mont Blanc Tunnel), and has been passed by the Federal Aviation Administration of the American Government; it is also an inorganic polymer which has the potential to save thousands of lives in aircraft cabin fires. It is strange to think that its ancestry possibly extends back to the King's Chamber of the Great Pyramid!

As for diamond drills, archaeological evidence of ancient Egyptian diamond tips and drills would be hard to find, as the items would be extremely small and would not necessarily be recognized even if they were found, since one would need to be a mineralogist to spot them. And after all, the world's museums are full of crystal and glass lenses, all perfectly visible to the naked eye and also rather obvious, but they have never been recognized. Why, then, should diamond drill tips be recognized?

Laufer finds textual evidence of the existence of industrial diamonds as early as 1000 BC in China. The name for the substance in Chinese was *kun-wu* [+ *shi* = 'stone']. The characters are 昆吾石. Laufer comments:

> F. Porter Smith was the first [modern scholar] to speak of a *kun-wu* stone [instead of trying to translate it as 'steel'], intimating that 'extraordinary stories are told of a stone called *kun-wu*, large enough to be made into a knife, very brilliant, and able to cut gems with ease'. He also grouped this stone correctly with the diamond, but he did not cope with the problem involved.
>
> The *Shi chou ki* ('Records of the Ten Insular Realms'), a fantastic description of foreign lands, attributed to the Taoist adept Tung-fang So, who was born in 168 BC, has the following story: 'On the Floating Island (Liu chou) which is situated in the Western Ocean is gathered a quantity of stones called *kun-wu*. When fused, this stone turns into iron, from which are made cutting-instruments brilliant and reflecting light like crystal, capable of cutting through objects of hard stone (jade) as though they were merely clayish earth.'
>
> Li Shi-chen, in his *Pen ts'ao kang mu* [Chapter 10], quotes the same story in his notice of the diamond, and winds up with the explanation that the *kun-wu* stone is the largest of diamonds. The text of the *Shi chou ki*, as quoted by him, offers an important variant. According to his reading, *kun-wu* stones occur in the Floating Sand (Liu-sha) of the Western Ocean. The latter term, as already shown, in the Chinese records relative to the Hellenistic Orient, refers to the Mediterranean . . . Accordingly, we have here a distinct tradition relegating the *kun-wu* stone to the Anterior Orient; and Li Shi-chen's identification with the diamond appears plausible to a high degree . . . the *Hüan chung ki* by Kuo of the fifth century . . . reports as follows: 'The country of Ta Ts'in [the Roman Empire] produces diamonds (*kin-kang*) termed also "jade-cutting swords or knives". The largest reach a length of over a foot, the smallest are of the size of a rice or millet grain. Hard stone can be cut by means of it all round, and on examination it turns out that it is the largest of diamonds. This is what the Buddhist priests substitute for the tooth of Buddha. [The tooth of the Buddha is an important sacred relic in Buddhism.] Chou Mi [of the Sung Dynasty, 960–1278 AD] . . . states, 'The workers in jade polish jade by the persevering application of river gravel, and carve it by means of a diamond-point. Its shape is like that

of the ordure [dung] of rodents; it is of very black colour, and is at once like stone and like iron.' Chou Mi apparently speaks of the impure, black form of the diamond, which is still used by us for industrial purposes, the tipping of drills and similar boring-instruments. These texts render it sufficiently clear that the *kun-wu* stone of the *Shi chou ki*, which is found in the Hellenistic Orient, is the diamond, and the cutting-instrument made from it is a diamond-point. The alleged transmutation of the stone into iron is further elucidated by the much-discussed passage of Pliny [which we have already given] . . .[59]

The fact that the Buddhist monks used diamonds to represent the Buddha's Tooth as sacred relics in their temples reminds us of the use of the meteoritic stone which is the sacred relic of Islam, the Kaaba at Mecca.

It is obvious now that the associations of iron and crystal were multifarious and profound in ancient times, and we have only begun to unravel these traditions. There is one ancient Greek word for 'thunderstone' which we have not yet considered, and that is *baitylos* (it has a diminutive form also, *baitylion*). In Latin it is *baetulus*. In the revised 1996 edition of Liddell and Scott's Greek Lexikon, the editors say in the supplement: 'Compare Semitic *bethel*'. This seems to be a half-assertion that the words may be cognate, or in other words that they presumably have the same origin in both Hebrew and Greek, which is not normal, since the languages are unrelated. This curious half-statement led me to check the ancient Egyptian to see if the words could all come from that source. I was not disappointed.

There seems little doubt that *baitylos* (the *-os* merely being a Greek noun ending) takes its origin from Egyptian *baa*, 'metallic substance', which was specifically used for meteoritic iron. In its form *baa-em-seh-t-neter*, the word *baa* described the instruments used for the Opening of the Mouth Ceremony, which as we have already seen, are now known to have been made of meteoritic iron. And in the form *baa en pet*, the Egyptians spoke of 'iron of the sky', which is of course meteoritic iron. Another meaning of *baa* is 'the material of which heaven was supposed to be made', referring to the rectangular iron plate thought to constitute the floor of heaven. The double-vowel *aa* consists of two separate sounds which have effectively become a dipthong, just as in the case of *ai* in *baitylos*. Linguistic principles are therefore followed in proposing this derivation. In fact, there could hardly be a more specific case for it, since Liddell and Scott give the meaning of *baitylos* as 'meteoric stone' and add 'held sacred because it fell from heaven'. We can be quite certain, therefore, that the Greek *baitylos* is the Egyptian *baa*. (As for the Hebrew *bethel*, I have too little knowledge to say. That would be for Semitic scholars.)

Sometimes scholars speak of the *baitylos* in English, when they simply call them baetyls. I have seen the meteoritic stone of the Kaaba in Mecca called a baetyl, which indeed it is. When we began to discuss thunderstones earlier, and I introduced the *ceraunus* as mentioned by Pliny, baetyls were mentioned in passing, and it would do just to review what was said of them once again:

> ... those [thunderstones] that are black and round are supernatural objects; and [Sotacus] states that thanks to them cities and fleets are attacked and overcome, their name being 'baetuli', while the elongated stones are 'cerauniae'. These writers distinguish yet another kind of 'cerania' which is quite rare. According to them, the Magi hunt for it zealously because it is found only in a place that has been struck by a thunderbolt.[60,61]

The baetyl is discussed by the great scholar A. B. Cook, whose massive five-volume work *Zeus* is one of the monuments of 20th-century scholarship. In Vol. III, he has a section called '*Baityloi, Baitylia* and Zeus *Betylos*'. Here is some of what he has to say, in which we learn even stranger things than we have so far encountered, including the fact that the god Kronos (Saturn) had a brother called Baitylos, according to the Phoenicians:

> Few terms in the nomenclature of Greek religion have been more loosely used than the word *baitylos*. It is so persistently misapplied to sacred stones in general that in 1903 Professor G. F. Moore of Harvard felt constrained to protest against its indiscriminate employment and quite rightly insisted that *baityloi* or *baitylia* formed a distinct class of holy stones endowed with the power of self-motion. Yet more than thirty years later Sir Arthur Evans still strews broadcast his allusions to 'baetylic' pillars and 'baetylic' altars.
>
> Sotakos [Sotacus], a well-informed lapidarist of the early Hellenistic age [whom we have seen cited by Pliny], argues that certain *cerauniae*, black and round, were sacred. Towns and fleets could be captured by their means. And they were called *baetuli*.
>
> Sanchouniathon of Berytos [modern Beirut] in his Phoenician history had more to say. Ouranus [Uranus] married his sister Ge [Gaia, the Earth] and had by her four sons – Elos called Kronos, Baitylos, Dagon that is Siton, and Atlas. Later we learn that Ouranos invented *baitylia* or living stones.
>
> The qualities of magic potency mentioned by Sotakos and animation recorded by Sanchouniathon [an extremely ancient Phoenician writer, said to have lived prior to the Trojan War, fragments of whose writings are preserved] both come out in Photios' extracts from Damaskios' *Life of Isidorus*. The Isidorus in question was the neo-Platonic philosopher, who was in Athens at the time of Proklos' death (485 AD) and shortly afterwards for a while succeeded Marinos as chief of the Athenian school. The scornful and at times indignant Photios [a ninth-century AD Byzantine scholar and Patriarch of Constantinople who left summaries

of many lost works] gives the following *résumé* of Damaskios' narrative.

He says that at Heliopolis in Syria Asklepiades [a Neo-Platonist expert in Egyptian theology] made the ascent of Mount Libanos [Mount Lebanon] and saw many of the so-called *baitylia* or *baityloi*, concerning which he reports countless marvels ... He declares too that he himself and Isidoros subsequently witnessed these things with their own eyes ... I saw, he says, the *baitylos* moving through the air. It was sometimes concealed in its garments, sometimes again carried in the hands of its ministrant. The ministrant of the *baitylos* was named Eusebios. This man stated that there had once come upon him a sudden and unexpected desire to roam at midnight away from the town of Emesa as far as he could get towards the hill on which stands the ancient and magnificent temple of Athena [who at Emesa was associated with 'Zeus Keraunos', or 'Zeus of the Thunderstone'!]. So he went as quickly as possible to the foot of the hill, and there sat down to rest after his journey. Suddenly he saw a globe of fire leap down from above, and a great lion standing beside the globe. [This is reminiscent of the Nemean Lion which the Greeks believed had fallen to earth from the moon, which we mentioned earlier.] The lion indeed vanished immediately, but he himself ran up to the globe as the fire died down and found it to be the *baitylos*. He took it up and asked it to which of the gods it might belong. It replied that it belonged to *Gennaios*, the 'Noble One'. (Now the men of Heliopolis worship this *Gennaios* and have set up a lion-shaped image of him in the temple of Zeus.) He took it home with him the same night ... Having told us this trash and much more to the same effect, our author, who is veritably worthy of his own *baitylia*, adds a description of the stone and its appearance. It was, he says, an exact globe, whitish in colour, three hand-breadths across.[62]

I need hardly point out that a whitish globe cannot possibly be a meteorite. We see here clearly, then, the confusion reigning in antiquity between black meteorites and transparent crystals. No wonder Photios was fed up as he reported this.

The most famous role which the baetyl played in mythology was as the substitute for the baby Zeus, when his father Cronus (Kronos), known to the Romans as Saturn, wished to swallow him as he had done his five older children. Clearly this rather gruesome myth has allegorical meanings. Cronus's wife Rhea had already had to hand over Poseidon, Demeter, Hera, Hestia and Hades to their father so that he could swallow them immediately after their birth. But having lost five children in that way, Rhea suddenly found her courage and decided she wasn't going to let her husband swallow their sixth child, the baby Zeus. So she spirited Zeus away to Crete where he was hidden in a cave so that his infantile crying could not be heard by his father. And she wrapped a stone in a skin, handing it to Cronus as if it were the baby wrapped in swaddling clothes, and he promptly swallowed that, believing it to be his son. After Zeus grew up, he forced his father to

Figure 39. Rhea presenting a stone wrapped in swaddling clothes to her husband Cronus, for him to swallow as he had swallowed their five previous children. In the top scene, Cronus (left) believes the wrapped stone to be his baby son, Zeus. But Rhea has tricked him, and in the second scene, she has turned away and hides a smirk because Cronus has swallowed the stone thinking it was his son, while she has secretly hidden Zeus in a cave to save him. In the first scene, Rhea is accompanied by two handmaids or 'ladies-in-waiting'. In the second, Rhea's friend Nike smiles knowingly at the deception.

(From a red-figured Greek *krater* excavated in Sicily and now in the Louvre, dating from *circa* 460–450 BC. Reproduced from Arthur Bernard Cook, *Zeus*, Vol. III, Part 1, Cambridge, 1940, Fig. 775, p. 930.)

regurgitate his five brothers and sisters – who had still not yet been digested, so that the intestines of Cronus must have been pretty inert! – and then threw Cronus from his heavenly throne and took his place as king of the gods. This led to the war between Zeus and his friends and the old Titans, which was touch and go for quite some time. Zeus finally won, aided by his thunderbolts. Cronus was banished to an island where he was put into a deep sleep from which, it is said, he will one day awaken.

Now, the important thing about this story is that the stone which Rhea gave to Cronus to swallow in place of Zeus was a *baitylos*. This fact is recorded by several writers including Herodian (second-century AD grammarian). As Cook says, in his long account of 'The Stone of Kronos':

> The stone swallowed by Kronos is described by late writers as bearing more than one significant name. It was *diskos*, perhaps with a solar connotation. [One might point out that this is a possible reference to a lens.] It was *baitylos* because of its wrappings [to be explained in a moment]. . . . These two elements, the folk-tale motif of the child-devourer and the ritual usage of a *baitylos*, were perhaps first fused in ancient Crete. . . . Further, in view of the relations between 'Minoan' Crete and Pytho [Delphi], it is not surprising to find that what purported to be the actual stone swallowed by Kronos was still to be seen at Delphi in the second century of our era. . . . [this] stone oiled and clad in wool was certrainly a *baitylos* and possibly, as Sir James Frazer and others have conjectured, an aerolite [meteorite] . . . [it was] an oval stone.[63]

For Zeus-as-sun to avoid being swallowed by the darkness of Cronus's stomach could refer to the avoiding of an eclipse, but that is unlikely. Perhaps we have a myth related to the crystal sun – the surrounding skin being the ambient light of the cosmos, which surrounds the crystal sun in the darkness of the cosmos. Ultimately the light triumphs over the darkness.

The reference to the stone being clad also refers to its having been wrapped in an animal skin, which in Greek is called *baitē*. This is more than just a sacred pun. First, animal skins were fundamental to the most ancient Egyptian religious rites, as Ernest Thomas was able to explain at length as long ago as 1923, in his two articles in the journal *Ancient Egypt* entitled 'The Magic Skin'.[64] These articles explain the *Tekenu*, a figure of a man wrapped in a skin, which was drawn on a sledge at Egyptian funerals. Sacred animal skins make a whole subject in themselves, and there can be little doubt that the skin wrapped around the *baitylos* carries associations with such age-old traditions.

But the other meaning which I suspect for the *baitē* of the *baitylos*, or the skin of the baetyl, is the concept of a 'skin' being sloughed off visually by the crystal, of the sort which we have encountered in the visual theories of Democritus. I believe that the notion of images being a succession of incredibly thin 'skins' which are shed into the air may be extremely ancient, and that Democritus, who after all studied for some time in Egypt, resurrected the idea. For baetyls were, according to the various traditions, several things at once: iron meteorites, crystal globes, and crystal 'discs', or lenses. They fell from heaven and were associated with the sun, whose rays (when of crystal) they focused. One of the sisters of Zeus who spent a considerable time within her father's digestive tract was Hestia (Latin: Vesta), and it was her altar which Plutarch said had its perpetual flame renewed by the focused rays of the sun.

The ancients never managed to separate iron meteorites from crystal lenses and crystal balls entirely. And we have seen that the existence of black 'iron-like' diamonds provided them with a convenient point of linkage between the two.[65] Also, the two were an effective pair of heavenly 'opposites' – literally night-stones and day-stones which fell from the sky, revealing the two sides of the divine but being equally sacred and awe-inspiring. For both were actual *pieces of the sky*.

Notes

1. Lister, Martin, *A Journey to Paris in the Year 1698*, second edition, London, 1699, pp. 80–4.
2. Plutarch, *On Isis and Osiris*, Chapter 62, in *Plutarch's Morals. Theosophical Essays*, translated by C. W. King, George Bell (although the book says Bohn's Library on the spine, as Bohn bought out Bell), London, 1889, pp. 53–4.
3. Cast iron was invented in China in the fourth century BC, but did not reach the West until the late eighth century AD in Scandinavia (very restricted), and was not widely available in Europe until 1380 AD, as I have described in my book on the history of Chinese science. But I have just suggested in Chapter Four that cast iron might be the mysterious 'Chinese metal' which was specially imported for use in connection with the Pharos Lighthouse by Pharaoh Ptolemy III Euergetes (died 221 BC). If so, however, the process of its production was certainly not revealed by the Chinese, and this would have been an expensive 'one-off' for one of the world's most expensive projects by a pharaoh for whom absolutely no expense was to be spared. (And in any case, this is pure speculation on my part.)
4. O'Connell, Robert H., 'The Emergence of Horus: An Analysis of Coffin Text Spell 148', in *The Journal of Egyptian Archaeology*, Egyptian Exploration Society, London, Vol. 69, 1983, pp. 66–87.
5. *Ibid.*, p. 71.
6. *Ibid.*, pp. 72–3.
7. Ammianus Marcellinus, *The Roman History*, Book II, Chapter 22, translated by C. D. Yonge, Bohn's Classical library, London, 1862, p. 315.
8. Freeman, Kathleen, *The Pre-Socratic Philosophers*, 2nd edition, Basil Blackwell, Oxford, 1966, p. 270.
9. *Ibid.*, p. 268.
10. Graves, Robert, *The Greek Myths*, Vol. I, George Braziller, New York, 1959, 123.b–c., pp. 103–4.
11. Freeman, *op. cit.*, pp. 268–9.
12. Wallis Budge, E. A., *Osiris and the Egyptian Resurrection*, 2 vols, London and New York, 1911, Vol. I, p. 102, and footnotes 1 and 2.
13. Plutarch, *op. cit.*, p. 13.

14. Lockyer, Sir Norman, *The Dawn of Astronomy*, London, 1894, pp. 292–4, with three illustrations of Isis suckling Horus on p. 292.
15. Budge, E. A. Wallis, *The Book of the Opening of the Mouth. The Egyptian Texts with English Translations*, Books on Egypt and Chaldaea Series, London, 2 vols, 1909.
16. Roth, Ann Macy, 'Fingers, Stars, and the "Opening of the Mouth": the Nature and Function of the *NTRWJ*-Blades', in *The Journal of Egyptian Archaeology*, Egypt Exploration Society, Vol. 79, 1993, pp. 57–79; Figure 5 is on p. 64.
17. *Ibid.*, pp. 63–9. Her Figures 6, 7, and 8 clearly show the use of little fingers in this way, and Figure 7 shows Pharaoh Seti I himself doing this.
18. *Ibid.*, pp. 69–72. Her figures 9 and 10 show the constellation of *Ursa Major*, the Great Bear, in the shape of a typical adze of meteoritic iron from the Ceremony of the Opening of the Mouth and also as the foreleg of an ox, or a 'thigh' as it is more commonly called. I have changed the transliterations of her Egyptian words so that people can read them! I have a great hatred for the linguistic symbols used by Egyptologists today, which have no genuine justification and which serve merely to exclude the public from the material and their discussions, making Egyptology a 'closed clique', which is not the true purpose of scholarship.
19. Wallis Budge, E. A., *The Gods of the Egyptians, or Studies in Egyptian Mythology*, 2 vols, London, 1904, Vol. I, pp. 156–7.
20. Seneca, Lucius Annaeus, *Naturales Questiones (Natural Questions)*, Book III, 25, 12, translated by T. H. Corcoran, 2 vols, Loeb Classical Library, Harvard University Press, USA, Vol. I, 1971, p. 265.
21. Pliny the Elder, *Natural History*, Book 37, Chapter 9, translated by D. E. Eichholz, Loeb Classical Library, Harvard University Press, USA, Vol. 10, 1971, pp. 181–3.
22. Böttinger, Carl August, *Sabina: oder Morgenszenen im Putzzimmer Einer Reichen Römerin (Sabina: or, Morning Scenes in the Parlour of a Rich Roman Lady)*, 2 vols, Leipzig, 1806. The relevant sections are in Vol. II, Eighth Scene, pp. 185–7, and Notes pp. 208–10. One of Böttinger's references to Pliny is in error. He does not mention magnifying or burning.
23. Pliny, *op. cit.*, Book 37, Chapter 10, pp. 183–5.
24. Diodorus Siculus (Diodorus of Sicily), *The Library of History*, Book II, 51–2, translated by C. H. Oldfather, Loeb Classical Library, Harvard University Press, USA, Vol. II, pp. 54–6.
25. Needham, Joseph, and Lu, Gwei-djen, *Science and Civilisation in China*, Vol. V, Part 2, Cambridge University Press, 1974, p. 23, note b.
26. Irenaeus, *Against Heresies*, Book I, Chapters 23–4, translated by the Rev. John Keble, part of series *A Library of Fathers of the Holy Catholic Church Anterior to the Division of the East and the West*, Oxford and London, 1872, pp. 70–1.
27. Needham and Lu, *op. cit.*, p. 19. The passage is taken from Themistius's Oration Number 21; the English version is by Needham and Lu, from a French translation by Hammer-Jensen.
28. Pliny, *op. cit.*, Book 37, Chapter 51, pp. 273–5.
29. Emsley, John, 'The Weird and Wonderful World of Buckyballs', *New Scientist*, London, 8 July 1993.
30. Pliny, *op. cit.*, Book 37, Chapter 55, p. 287.
31. *Ibid.*, Book 37, Chapter 56, p. 291.
32. *Ibid.*, Book 37, Chapter 66, pp. 309–11.
33. Aldrovandi, Ulyssis, *Musaeum Metallicum*, 1648, Liber IV, Chapter XII, pp. 613–17.
34. Fensham, F. Charles, 'Thunder-Stones in Ugaritic', in *Journal of Near Eastern Studies*, Vol. XVIII, 1959, p. 273.
35. Blinkenberg, Christopher, *The Thunderweapon in Religion and Folklore: A Study in Comparative Archaeology*, Cambridge University Press, 1911, reprint by Aristide D. Caratzas, 481 Main Street, New Rochelle, New York 10802, USA, 1987.
36. *Ibid.*, pp. 76–83.

37. Cooke, John, *The Vindication of the Professors and Profession of the Law*, London, 1646, pp. 67–8. I have to confess I have read the whole book and found it fascinating.

38. Aubrey, John, *Miscellanies*, Chapter 15, in *Three Prose Works*, ed. John Buchanan-Brown, Centaur Press, Fontwell, Sussex, England, 1972, pp. 98–9. The reference in an earlier version is Aubrey, John, *Miscellanies upon Various Subjects*, 5th edition, London, 1890, pp. 154–7.

39. Lister, Martin, 'An Account of Certain Transparent Pebles, Mostly of the Shape of the Ombriae or Brontiae: Wherefore I Have Called Them Brontiae Laeves, Pellucidae, Resplendentes, Adamantum Aemulae', in *Philosophical Transactions*, London, Number 201, June 1693, pp. 773–80.

40. Lister mistakenly believed that the ancient lenses were natural objects, and naturally polished. He was certain that no one could have ground and polished them so well. This, actually, is a tribute to the excellence of their manufacture! He says of them:

> The Figures [i.e. the five engraved figures] are taken from certain very clear and transparent Stones found in England, of a constant shape . . . figured like a Drop of Water, which these Stones have of themselves naturally, and without any Artifice; some of them being exactly Spherical, others like a Half Globe, others like a half Oval, with an edge raised on the top [here he refers to the ridged cabochons, which are especially common in Sweden] . . . As for their Figure, it comes nearest that of the *Ombriae*; and many of them are very *Ombriae* in shape. . . . As these Stones are of a very different Nature and texture from all other *Ombriae* I ever yet saw, and having no *Vestigia* [traces] of any *Spinae* [spiny protrusions, which cover the fossilized sea urchins] in any part of them, I may reasonably enough conclude them to be Stones of their own kind: And they are in shape like some of the *Ombriae*, yet for the Reasons above-said, they will not come, I think, within the suspicion of having been Animal Substances.

He goes on at considerable length about fossilized sea urchins, having with the greatest difficulty made himself differentiate these crystals from the fossils, and declared them to be pure mineral rather than fossilized animal substances like the sea urchins. It is ironical that Lister had to struggle so hard to reach this conclusion. After all, *ombriae* started life as rock crystals, and it was only through a confusion of their round plano-convex shape with the identical shape (minus tiny spines, of course) of the fossilized sea urchins that the fossils came to be called *ombriae*. What Lister was really doing, without realizing it, was untangling an earlier confusion and restoring true *ombriae* to themselves again. From crystals the name was misapplied to fossils, and with Lister the name was rescued again for a separate class of crystals – the original objects for which the name had been intended! As I write this, I have a fossilized sea urchin in my hand. It is much more than half a sphere, merely a sphere with a modest portion of its bottom 'sliced off', as it were, and one wonders how anyone would have the nerve to pinch the name *ombria* from a self-respecting crystal lens and misapply it to this object. Sorry, I shouldn't say object; how cruel of me. I mean creature. We musn't hold it against a poor unfortunate fellow creature that he has had the misfortune to become petrified and can't defend himself.

41. Plot, Robert, *The Natural History of Stafford-Shire*, Oxford, 1686, pp. 176–9 and Table XI, Figure 5 for a picture of the ridged cabochon crystal lens from above.

42. Boyle, Robert, *An Essay about the Origine & Virtues of Gems: Wherein are Propos'd and Historically Illustrated some Conjectures of the Matter of Precious Stones, and the Subjects wherein their chiefest Virtues reside*, London, 1672, p. 5.

43. *Ibid.*, p. 43.

44. *Ibid.*, p. 81.

45. *Ibid.*, p. 125.

46. Lister, *Paris, op. cit.*, pp. 49–52. He mentions the transparent stone taken from the Alderman of Doncaster again on p. 234, and calls it 'Crystal like'.

47. *Ibid.*, p. 77.

48. Woodward, John, *An Attempt towards a Natural History of the Fossils of England*, 1729, Part I, p. 31.
49. Here are some of Woodward's remarks:

> C.12. [now labelled A.7.11.] A Flint [this is a misleading term, and he does not really mean what we call flint] perfectly pellucid [i.e. perfectly transparent], of a lenticular Form [like a lentil, because biconvex], the longest Diameter about an Inch and a Quarter [actually 3.58 cm]. The Surface is very smooth and polite. [It is always a great pleasure to learn that a lens can have good manners.] This was given me for English; but I have forgot where t'was found: and the Person that gave it me is now dead. There are said to be some of these Stones found somewhere about Bristol. Dr Lister has described and graved some of them. *Philos. Trans.* N. 201.
>
> C.12.a. [now A.7.12.] A Crystal, or pellucid Flint, wrought into an orbicular form [i.e. a sphere], found somewhere in England. This is of that sort that is call'd mineral Pearl: and probably the same mentioned by Suetonius, in *Caesare* Section 47. [Life of Julius Caesar, Chapter 47, which is discussed below.] . . .
>
> C.13. [now A.7.13.] Another Crystalline Flint, of an oblong Form [a footnote here refers to the engraving and description of Dr Plot by way of comparison], the Basis near flat, the upper Part terminating in a Ridge. [This is a ridged cabochon gem.] The Base, and Sides are not plain, but somewhere swelling and convex. 'Tis regular and polite [another well-behaved crystal!], as if wrought by Art. . . .
>
> I have since shewn this to some Lapidaries; who agree that this Body is cut and polished. 'Tis part of a Crystalline Nodule. There's one of this Figure set forth by Dr Lister, *Phil. Trans.* N. 201, who thinks those naturally Polished, but erroneously: 'tis very probable all these Bodies were us'd for Ornaments among the ancient Britains. Mr [John] Aubrey was wont to assert they were us'd in Magick by the Druids: and I believe intimates some such thing in his Natural history of Wiltshire . . . he mentions a Crystal Sphere, or Mineral Pearl, us'd by Magicians: and to be inspected by themselves or by a Boy. Mr [John] Webster in his Book of Witchcraft also treats of these Bodies . . . This was found near Barkhamstead: and made use of, as Mr Steel informs me, by the late Dr Woodhouse, there, as a Magical Speculum, he pretending that a Spectrum [spirit] was wont to discover it self to him in it. Mr Steel fancies the Glass, as 'twas call'd of Dr [John] Dee, and Mr [Edward] Kelly [Dee's friend], mention'd by Dr Meric Casaubon, was of this sort. For my own part I can imagine these to be nothing other than Baubles, used formerly as Ornaments by the Britains, while Savage, and before the access of the Romans. Mr Morton found one of this sort in Kettering-Field, Northamptonshire. [Woodward, *op. cit.*, pp. 31–2.]

The reference to Suetonius [first century AD] is to his *Lives of the Caesars*, section on Julius Caesar, Chapter 47:

> They likewise report that he [Julius Caesar] invaded Britain in hopes of finding pearls (*margaritarum*), the size of which he would compare together, and ascertain the weight by poising them in his hand; and that he would purchase, at any cost, gems, carved works, statues, and pictures, executed by the eminent masters of antiquity; and that he would give for young and handy slaves a price so extravagant, that he forbad its being entered in the diary of his expenses. [Suetonius, *The Lives of the Twelve Caesars (De Vita Caesarum)*, translated by Alexander Thomson, revised and corrected by T. Forester, George Bell, London, 1893, p. 31. The book says Bohn's Libraries on the spine because Bohn bought Bell.]

I fear that as Julius Caesar was one of the most lascivious of men, and being bisexual, interested in anything that moved on two legs, the unfortunate slaves were intended as sexual playthings. Woodward thinks that the pearls referred to may have included 'mineral pearls'

– i.e. crystals. It is difficult to imagine just what other 'gems' produced by eminent masters Caesar could hope to acquire in a place like Britain in the first century BC, other than the beautifully polished rock crystal lenses which the British produced.

The reference to the book on witchcraft is interesting. Woodward refers to John Webster's rather unsettling tome *The Displaying of Supposed Witchcraft, Wherein Is Affirmed That There Are Many Sorts of Deceivers and Impostors and Divers Persons under a Passive Delusion of Melancholy and Fancy, But That There is a Corporeal League Made betwixt the Devil and the Witch, Or That He Sucks on the Witches Body, Has Carnal Copulation, or That Witches Are Turned into Cats, Dogs, Raise Tempests, or the Like, Is Utterly Denied and Disproved*, pubished in 1677. I regret that I had to cut the title short, as it goes on to include sidereal spirits, charms, and philtres, etc. Rather an exhausting title page!

Webster touches on our subject as follows:

> There is another kind of supposed Apparitions, that are believed to be done in Beryls, and clear Crystals, and therefore called by [the alchemist and author] Paracelsus *Ars Beryllistica*, and which he also calls Nigromancy [necromancy], because it is practised in the dark by the inspection of a Boy or a Maid that are Virgins, . . . The only story that seems to carry any credit with it, touching the truth of Apparitions in Crystals, is that which is related of that great and learned Physician Joachimus Camerarius in his Preface before Plutarchs Book . . . [Webster, John, *The Displaying of Supposed Witchcraft, etc.*, Chapter 16, London, 1677, p. 310.]

He then goes on with a fascinating story, but not relevant to lenses.

50. Priestley, Joseph, *The History and Present State of Discoveries Relating to Vision, Light, and Colours*, London, 1772, p. 8.
51. *Ibid.*, pp. 7–8.
52. Douglas, the Rev. James, *Nennia Britannica: or, A Sepulchral History of Great Britain: from the Earliest Period to Its General Conversion to Christianity*, London, 1793, pp. 14–19. The crystal ball is illustrated in this book. See also pp. 103, 130, and 131 for more mention of crystal balls.
53. I should just mention that the Reverend Douglas's personal 'author's extra-illustrated' copy of *Nennia Britannica*, together with all the original watercolour illustrations and many more which were never engraved, is deposited in the British Library under shelfmark G.6863, and that several additional original illustrations of ancient British crystal balls are found only in this special copy of the book. I have omitted a summary of all the excavation details, the descriptions of the barrows and tumuli, etc., which is something we leave for the archaeologists, if they ever get so far.
    The crystal ball symbolized the crystal sun, as ruler of the cosmos. Orbs are good at magnifying and burning, but only close up, as their curvature is too great to be useful at any distance. But suspended globes next to an object are absolutely brilliant magnifiers.
54. de Montfaucon, Rev. Bernard, *l'Antiquité Expliquée et Représentée en Figures (Antiquity Explained and Portrayed in Figures)*, Vol. Five, Part One, second edition revised and corrected, Paris, 1722, pp. 75–6. (The British Library shelfmark for this is L.50.35, to save people the difficulty of locating it!)
55. Browne, Sir Thomas, *The Works of*, edited by Charles Sayle, Edinburgh, 1927, Vol. III, p. 110.
56. Laufer, Berthold, *The Diamond: A Study in Chinese and Hellenistic Folk-Lore*, Field Museum of Natural History, Chicago, USA, Publication 184, Anthropological Series, Vol. XV, No.1, 1915, p. 32.
57. *Ibid.*, p. 31, Note 3.
58. Pliny, *op. cit.*. Book 37, Chapter 15, pp. 207–11.
59. Laufer, *op. cit.*, pp. 28–31.
60. Pliny, *op. cit.*, Book 37, Chapter 51, p. 275.

61. The 17th-century writer Samuel Bochart said that baetyls were round and were actually caused by round thunderbolts! (Bochart, Samuel, *Geographica Sacra*, Frankfurt, 1674, 786c.) He gives a description of a baetyl as a *lapis sphaericus* (spherical stone). (Bochart, *op. cit.*) This serves to remind us that however much the baetyl was thought to be an iron meteorite, it was still bundled with the other thunderstones and thought of in terms of crystals, the spherical shape being of course the artificial shape given to a crystal ball.
62. Cook, Arthur Bernard, *Zeus: A Study in Ancient Religion*, Vol. III: *Zeus of the Dark Sky (Earthquakes, Clouds, Wind, Dew, Rain, Meteorites)*, Cambridge University Press, 1940, pp. 887–8.
63. *Ibid.*, pp. 927–38.
64. Thomas, Ernest S., 'The Magic Skin', in two parts, in *Ancient Egypt*, British School of Archaeology in Egypt, London and New York, 1923, Part I, pp. 3–8, and Part II, pp. 46–56.
65. What can the ancient Egyptian name have been for dark 'iron-like' diamonds? The verb *tem/temi/temtem* means 'to engrave'. Perhaps the related word *temu* which Wallis Budge said meant 'some hard, compact substance' and its alternative *temi* which he said meant 'a kind of close hard stone', and also *temch* 'a kind of precious stone', could all refer to the industrial diamond, or otherwise they may be some other stone used by engravers.

SECTION FOUR

ORIGINS

Chapter Nine

The Eye of Horus

The most fantastic of all the world's ancient optical traditions was unquestionably that of Pharaonic Egypt. We shall see in a moment how the axis of the great temple at Karnak was effectively a stone telescope tube 600 yards long. Also we shall see one of the many 'light tricks' at Karnak – that of the 'offering of light' placed onto the tray held by the Pharaoh Rameses III, and which was actually captured on film in Plates 20 and 21, despite the fact that it only lasts for three minutes and then vanishes. I have briefly mentioned the 'Eye of Horus' in its form of a water-filled crystal sphere for creating fire from the rays of the Sun. But all of this is but the smallest beginning to this vast subject.

In Plates 14, 15, 16 and 17 may be seen some of the magnificent rock-crystal eyes for statues produced during the Old Kingdom in Egypt. These eyes were plentiful during the Fourth and Fifth Dynasties, in the middle of the third millennium BC. I believe they existed also in the Third Dynasty and were removed by robbers from the statue of King Zoser (Plate 18), *circa* 2600 BC. These eyes, and those of the Middle Kingdom wooden 'ka'-effigy of King Hor, found in his fortunately intact tomb, are not only eerie to look at. The point is that they are perfectly ground and polished convex crystal lenses. As used in the statues, they magnify the painted or inserted pupils behind them and create an impression of life which is unrivalled by any other technique. The existence of many of these crystal eyes, of such perfect workmanship, demonstrates in conclusive fashion that the technology for advanced optics existed at that time – and I do not believe it is possible for us to deny that it was used for other purposes besides eyes of statues.

We shall be seeing that only with optical surveying instruments was it possible to construct many of the Old Kingdom Egyptian buildings. In fact, *it was physically impossible* to construct the Giza pyramids without the use of theodolites or something similar to them. Their precision *could not have been achieved in any other way*. But we know that the lenses needed for optical surveying instruments did indeed exist, and I will also show the evidence for other aspects of ancient Egyptian surveying. This does not involve any far-fetched theorizing; we are dealing with inescapable facts of construction and surveying requirements for which there must be an answer. And unless one accepts optical surveying, there is nothing left but some form of magic!

There is an aspect of ancient Egyptian science which I think we should consider to start with, as it relates in an unsuspected way to telescopes. The first person to work this out was the Victorian astronomer Sir Norman Lockyer. He and Professor Nissen of Germany were the first moderns to realize that ancient temples were astronomically oriented. These discoveries, investigated in the field at great length, were reported in the historic book by Lockyer *The Dawn of Astronomy*, published in 1894, and of which I am fortunate to own an original copy.[1] I reproduce his plan of the Temple of Amen-Rā at Karnak in Figure 40, below. From the vast riches of Lockyer's book, I take these remarks from Chapter Ten, 'The Solar Temple of Amen-Rā at Karnak', which will surprise anyone not already familiar with such things:

This temple of Amen-Rā is beyond all question the most majestic ruin in the world. There is a sort of stone avenue in the centre, giving a view towards the north-west, and this axis is something like five hundred yards in length. The whole object of the builder of the great temple of Karnak – one of the most soul-stirring temples which have ever been conceived or built by man – was to preserve that axis absolutely open; and all the wonderful halls of columns and the like, as seen on one side or other of the axis, are merely details; the point being that the axis should be absolutely open, straight, and true. The axis was directed towards the hills on the west side of the Nile, in which are the tombs of the kings. From the external pylon the South-eastern outlook through the ruins shows the whole length of the temple, and we see at the very extremity of the central line a gateway nearly six hundred yards away. This belonged to a temple pointing towards the south-east. There were really two temples in the same line back to back, the chief one facing the sunset at the summer solstice, the other probably the sunrise at the winter solstice. The distance which separates the outside entrances of both these temples is greater than from Pall Mall to Piccadilly; the great temple covers about twice the area covered by St Peter's at Rome, so that the whole structure was of a vastness unapproached in the modern ecclesiastical world. . . . Some of the structural details are of a very curious nature, while the general arrangement of the temple itself is no less extraordinary. First, with regard to the temple axis. It seems to be a general rule that from the entrance-pylon the temple stretches through various halls of different sizes and details, until at last, at the extreme end, what is called the Sanctuary, Naos, Adytum, or Holy of Holies, is reached. The end of the temple at which the pylons are situated is open, the other is closed. . . . From one end of the temple to the other we find the axis marked out by narrow apertures in the various pylons, and many walls with doors crossing the axis.

In the temple of Amen-Rā there are 17 or 18 of these apertures, limiting the light which falls into the Holy of Holies or the Sanctuary. This construction gives one a very definite impression that every part of the temple was built to observe a special object, viz., to limit the light which fell on its front into a narrow beam, and to carry it to the other extremity of the temple – into the sanctuary, so that once a year when the sun set at the solstice the light passed without interruption along the whole length of the temple [i.e., straight down the central axis], finally illuminating the Sanctuary in most resplendent fashion and striking the Sanctuary wall. The wall of the Sanctuary opposite to the entrance of the temple [i.e., the east end] was always blocked. There is no case in which the beam of light can pass absolutely through the temple.

The point was to provide an axis open at one end and absolutely closed at the other, . . . It is easy to recognize that these arrangements bear out the idea of an astronomical use of the temple.

First of all we know that the temple was directed to the place of the sun's setting; and if the Egyptians wished to lead the narrow shaft of light which was bound to enter the temple, since it was directed to the sunset, they would have contrived the very system of gradually narrowing doors which we have found to be one of the special features of the temple. . . . This idea is strengthened by considering the construction of the astronomical telescope. Although the Egyptians knew nothing about telescopes [How Lockyer would have been interested to learn otherwise!], it would seem that they had the same problem before them which we solve by a special arrangement in the modern telescope – they wanted to keep the light pure, and to lead it into their sanctuary as we lead it to the eyepiece. To keep the light that passes into the eyepiece of a modern telescope pure, we have between the object-glass and the eyepiece a series of what are called diaphragms; that is, a series of rings right along the tube, the inner diameters of the rings being greatest closest to the object-glass, and smallest closest to the eyepiece; these diaphragms must so be made that all the light from the object-glass shall fall upon the eyepiece, without loss or reflection by the tube.

These apertures in the pylons and separating walls of Egyptian temples exactly represent the diaphragms in the modern telescope.

What then was the real use of these pylons and these diaphragms? It was to keep all stray light out of the carefully roofed and darkened Sanctuary; but why was the Sanctuary to be kept in darkness?

The first point that I wish to make is that these temples – whatever view may be entertained with regard to their worship or the ceremonial in them – were undoubtedly constructed among other reasons for the purpose of obtaining an exact observation of the precise time of the solstice. The priests having this power at their disposal, would not be likely to neglect it, for they ruled by knowledge. The temples were, then, astronomical observatories, and the first observatories that we know of in the world.

If we consider them as horizontal telescopes used for the purpose I have suggested, we at once understand the long axis, and the series of gradually narrowing diaphragms, for the longer the beam of light used the greater is the accuracy that can be obtained. . . . it is quite clear that the darker the sanctuary the more obvious will be the patch of light on the end wall, and the more easily can its position be located. It was important to do this on the two or three days near the solstice, in order to get an idea of the exact time at which the solstice took place. We find that a narrow beam of sunlight coming through a narrow entrance some 500 yards away from the door of the Holy of Holies would, provided the temple were properly oriented to the solstice, and provided the solstice occurred at the absolute moment of sunrise or sunset according to which temple was being utilised, practically flash into the sanctuary and remain there for about a couple of minutes, and then pass away. The flash would be a crescendo and diminuendo, but the whole thing would not last above two minutes or thereabouts, and might be considerably reduced by an arrangement of curtains. . . . We may conclude that there was some purpose of utility to be served, and the solar temples could have been used undoubtedly, among other things, for determining the exact length of the solar year. . . . The magnificent burst of the light at sunset into the sanctuary would show that a new true solar year was beginning. . . . If the Egyptians wished to use the temple for ceremonial purposes, the magnificent beam of light thrown into the temple at the sunset hour

---

Figure 40 (opposite). A plan of the great temple complex of the god Amun-Rā (i.e., Amon-Rā or Amen-Re) at Karnak near Luxor (ancient Thebes) in Egypt. The Roman numeral II marks the location of the original 'Holy of Holies' or inner sanctum, into which the sunlight at the summer solstice sunset would pour after travelling down the long 'horizontal telescope' or 'horizontal sighting-tube' of the central axis past points VI, g, h, IV, III, 7, and 9 on this plan. At such moments either the Pharaoh or the High Priest would be 'alone with Rā', as the ancient texts record. The central corridor is so long – nearly five hundred yards! – that the image of the sun god would have appeared as a perfect shining disc. It was this disc, called in its literal form the Aten ('disc'), projected on the back of the inner sanctum wall on the evening of the summer solstice (and at other temples on equinoxes and winter solstice, at both sunrise and sunset), which became the central object for worship of the heretical Pharaoh Akhenaten, father of Tutankhamun. Karnak itself was not a 'sunrise' temple but a 'sunset' temple, so those tourists who visit the location early to witness the sunrise are viewing the wrong astronomical phenomenon. (Lockyer believed Karnak once also had a smaller temple for observing the winter solstice sunrise.) To the upper right is the Sacred Lake, which still exists; that is where the priests used to bathe themselves regularly in order to purify their bodies prior to religious observances. The building at the lower right marked 1 is the temple built by Rameses III where we observed the 'light offering' seen in Plate 20; it was a morning phenomenon, giving an opportunity for other esoteric religious observances at a different time of the day. Doubtless when the structures were complete, there were many such light-phenomena such that the course of the sun throughout the day was harnessed to successive light-events marking a series of observances like a kind of solar 'stations of the cross' plan of worship. Since no one has previously looked for such things, those which are still possible because of surviving windows and ceilings should be sought and studied systematically.
(From *The Dawn of Astronomy* by Sir Norman Lockyer, London, 1894, p. 101.)

would give them opportunities and even suggestions for doing so; for instance, they might place an image of the god in the sanctuary and allow the light to flash upon it. We should have a *manifestation of Rā* with a vengeance during the brief time the white flood of sunlight fell on it; be it remembered that in the dry and clear air of Egypt the sun casts a shadow five seconds after the first little point of it has been seen above the horizon. So that at sunrise and sunset in Egypt the light is very strong, and not tempered as with us. . . . [The Pharaoh] Thothmes III., in

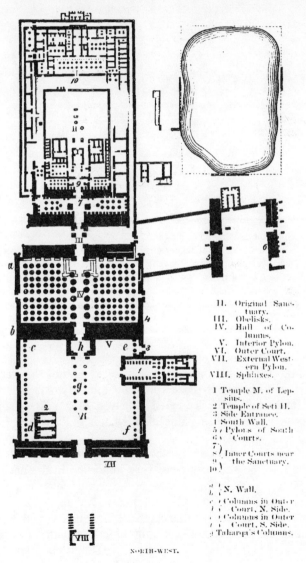

II. Original Sanctuary.
III. Obelisks.
IV. Hall of Columns.
V. Interior Pylon.
VI. Outer Court.
VII. External Western Pylon.
VIII. Sphinxes.

1 Temple M. of Lepsius.
2 Temple of Seti II.
3 Side Entrance.
4 South Wall.
5 } Pylons of South
6 } Courts.
7)
8 } Inner Courts near
9 } the Sanctuary.
10)

a } N. Wall.
b }
c } Columns in Outer
e } Court, N. Side.
c } Columns in Outer
f } Court, S. Side.
g Taharqa's Columns.

NORTH-WEST.

PLAN OF THE TEMPLE OF AMEN-RA AND SOME OF ITS SURROUNDINGS, INCLUDING THE SACRED LAKE.

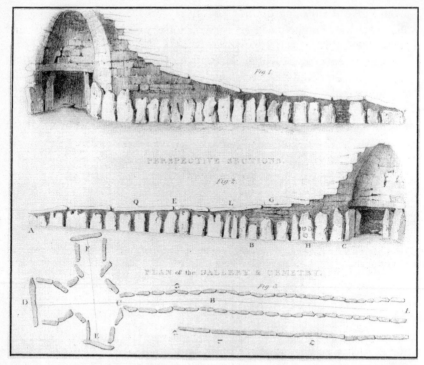

Figure 41. A 19th-century engraving of Newgrange in Ireland, showing the long underground passage which is oriented towards the winter solstice sunrise. Every 21 December, at 8:58 a.m. precisely, the solar rays shine into the Newgrange passage. A special slit near the entrance allows a ray to strike the end recess, which is the Irish equivalent of the inner sanctum. The details of this solstice light-event, together with many illustrations, may be found in Martin Brennan, *The Stars and the Stones: Ancient Art and Astronomy in Ireland*, Thames and Hudson, London, 1983, pp. 72–86.

(From Godfrey Higgins, *The Celtic Druids*, London, 1827. Collection of Robert Temple.)

his account of his embellishments at Karnak, says of the statues of the gods and of their secret place (possibly the Adytum) that they were 'more glorious than what is created in heaven, more secret than the place of the abyss, and more [invisible] than what is in the ocean.'[2]

All of this should prove a sobering account to anyone who is not aware that beams of light at the solstices were very important in the ancient world. Many people now realize that sunrise at the winter solstice threw a beam down the corridor at the centre of Newgrange in Ireland, for instance. I have watched a solstice sunrise from the centre of Stonehenge, and the sun really does roll along the heel stone like a lump of golden butter, just as they say in books. These things are becoming increasingly familiar today, but Lockyer was the first to mention them. And his description of the axis of the Karnak temple as being like a giant stone telescope had never been

338

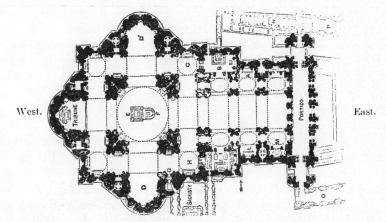

West.   East.

PLAN OF ST. PETER'S AT ROME, SHOWING THE DOOR FACING THE SUNRISE.

Figure 42. St Peter's Cathedral, Rome, has its central aisle oriented (if so desired) due east, so that on the mornings of the spring and autumn equinoxes, the rising sun could flood the altar with its light, travelling along a long corridor which is not unlike that of an ancient Egyptian temple, though much less narrow.
(From *The Dawn of Astronomy* by Sir Norman Lockyer, London, 1894, p. 96.)

bettered. As for the precise length of the solar year, we shall see later in this chapter that the ancient Egyptians did indeed know its value – and instruments such as the temple at Karnak undoubtedly enabled these precise measurements to be made.

Can we believe that a people capable of the mammoth construction of a stone optical device 500 yards long at Karnak were incapable of constructing small hand-held telescopes in fennel tubes for optical surveying, especially when there is such abundant evidence that numerous perfect crystal magnifying lenses existed in Egypt by at least the Fourth Dynasty, and in use by the middle of the fourth millennium BC?

Just as this book was going to press, an article by John L. Heilbron appeared in the magazine *The Sciences*, published by the New York Academy of Sciences, which relates to our subject in a surprising way. The article, entitled 'The Sun in the Church',[3] is an extract from the same author's subsequent recent book on the subject,[4] which reproduces an extraordinary photograph showing a solar disc projected onto a cathedral meridian line, which is highly relevant for us, as it is a Renaissance European example of the kind of thing that took place in ancient Karnak. I reproduce in Figure 44 the design of a coin of 1702 which Heilbron gives in his article and his book showing the streak of sunlight entering a cathedral in Rome and striking a meridian line. Everyone interested in these subjects should consult Heilbron's book for more details.

What Heilbron reveals is that meridian lines (oriented precisely north-south) were embedded into the floors of mediaeval cathedrals in Europe during the Renaissance and afterwards, small holes made in the cathedral roofs to allow shafts of sunlight to stream through onto them, and images of the sun's disc were observed as they moved back and forth over the course of the year. The purpose of this was to establish by measuring the distances moved by the solar disc-image the precise date of Easter and rectify the calendar, which are similar to the preoccupations of the ancient Egyptians, of course. However, another phenomenon was observed as well: the size of the disc was seen to vary when the sun was nearer or farther from the earth, and by a close study of the way in which this occurred, it became clear that the earth moved in an elliptical orbit rather than a circular one. This had the ironical result of supporting the 'heretical' views of Kepler. But for more details, the reader should turn to Heilbron. What is remarkable is that huge dark cathedrals, like huge dark temples, had the same uses as Karnak had, *but 3,000 years later!* As usual, the public are always the last to know.

There are still astonishing light-effects to be observed at Karnak, even in the surviving ruins. My wife Olivia and I have observed several, and she in fact discovered one remarkable one herself inside the Processional Shrine of Rameses III, a small building which still stands largely intact on the right as you go in the front (West) entrance. We arrived at Karnak before sunrise, to view the beautiful light effects at that time, although of course the temple

Figure 43. St Peter's at Rome not only has its central aisle corridor oriented due east towards the rising sun on the equinox, but just to remind us of the profundity of the Egyptian influence, an obelisk transported from Egypt has been erected in the line of sight with the equinoctial rising sun as seen from the altar. '*Those who have ears to hear, let them hear.*'

Figure 44. The design of a coin minted in 1702 by Pope Clement XI, showing a beam of sunlight streaming through a hole in the church of Santa Maria degli Angeli in Rome. The image of the sun's disc falls upon the meridian line laid along the church floor. During the course of the year, this disc image moves back and forth; the maximum and minimum are at the two solstices. Thus, the year can be measured.

was a *sunset* temple rather than a *sunrise* temple. It just so happened that at 8:30 a.m. on that day, which was at the end of the third week of November, we happened by serendipitous good fortune to enter the Shrine of Rameses III, having seen most of the rest of the ruins. The chamber we were in was roofed, and we were peering at the wall carvings in the gloom when Olivia noticed a most amazing thing. A beam of light was streaming in from a small high window with stone bars and striking the wall opposite. Several of these ancient stone gratings which served as windows survive at Karnak. The architectural term for them is *claustra*, which is Latin. See Figure 45 for an illustration of them in the main temple.

Olivia noticed that the light shone directly onto an empty incense tray being held up by the Pharaoh as an offering to the god Amun. The window effectively projected a block of light onto the tray, so that the Pharaoh was shown to be standing and making an offering of pure light to the god. The block of light was divided into four vertical strips by the window bars. The positioning was absolutely precise; one moment the tray was empty, and the next moment it bore a light-offering. This light-phenomenon only lasted for about three minutes, and then by the movement of the earth on its axis, it vanished away entirely, and the shapes of light changed as they left the tray.

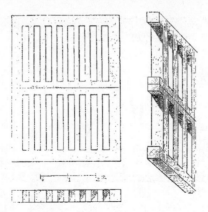

Figure 45. Drawings of some of the sandstone *claustra* (stone window-gratings) surviving in the hypostyle hall of the great Temple of Amun at Karnak. They were placed very high up, not at eye level. They resemble the smaller one which produced the 'light-offering' by Rameses III.

I had my camera with me, although with only ASA 200 film in it, so I pressed myself as tightly against the wall opposite the light-offering as I possibly could to try and get the right sort of time exposure photo which would show the Pharaoh while also showing the light-offering. The result may be seen as Plate 20. The next year, on a return visit, I was able to get the photo, in Plate 21, of the light rays shining through the grating, showing that the bars and rays give no hint of the feather-pattern which I must now describe.

The light-offering in itself is symbolic in rather a complex and intriguing way. At the left, the first vertical strip is not like the others, but only half as high and rounded at the top. It depicts the Feather of Truth (Maāt), which was commonly shown in Egyptian iconography weighed in the balance scale against the heart of the deceased, in the many scenes in papyri of *The Book of the Dead* where the Judgement takes place before the gods, to see whether the heart of the deceased is weighed down by sin, or is light and pure enough for the soul to enjoy eternal life. The next three strips are straight high vertical stripes – a depiction in fact of the Egyptian numeral *three*. Since the Pharaoh on the wall is Rameses III, these stripes would seem to be intended to identify him.

Apparently, therefore, the light-pattern cast by the contemporary stone window grate was meant to show Pharaoh Rameses III offering the Feather of Truth made of light to the God Amun, followed by the numeral identifying which Pharaoh he is. However, I believe there was more to it than that. To Rameses III, the most distinguished of his predecessor-Pharaohs relating to Karnak would have been his ancestor, Pharaoh Amenhetep III of the previous dynasty, whose likeness and works at Karnak are still to be

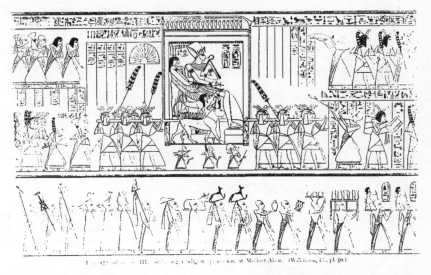

Figure 46. The Pharaoh Rameses III is carried in his throne-palanquin in a great religious procession at Thebes, shown here in a painting from Medinet-Habu, near Luxor. It was he who built the small temple which contains the 'light-offering'. At the top right of this picture a priest may be seen turning backwards with a curious dotted line emanating from his hand. Generally in Egyptian art when these dotted lines appear, they depict water being poured or flying through the air. But it may be that an allusion is here intended to the 'light-offering' as a fleeting image. The 'feather of Maāt' portrayed in the 'light-offering' is also seen carried here by many members of the procession.

seen on every hand. (Apart from anything else, it was he who installed several *hundred* stone statues of the goddess Sekhmet at Karnak.) I believe that the light-offering of Rameses III has a double meaning, and that at another level it was an act of homage to Amenhetep III. First, the numeral *three* applies to both pharaohs, so that the vertical stripes of light can be taken either way. But what is it that Rameses III is actually portrayed as doing? He is shown making an Amun-Offering. And although the name of Amenhetep would generally have the conventional meaning of 'Resting in Amun' or 'Depending upon Amun', or 'Amun is satisfied', everyone would have known that the original and fundamental meaning of the word *hetep* was 'offering' (to a god or to the deceased), so that the archaic and literal meaning of the name Amenhetep was really 'Amun-Offering'. In his depiction on the wall, Rameses III was shown enacting an 'Amun-Offering' and thus invoking the name of his predecessor by sacred gesture, so that in strictly iconographical terms what was portrayed was 'Amun-Offering III', or in other words, Amenhetep III. The literal meaning was 'Offering to Amun by Rameses III', but the symbolic meaning was 'Amenhetep III'. Such double meanings delighted the ancient Egyptian priests, and were certainly intentional. The Light-Offering is thus a *light-pun*.

Figure 47. The Pharaoh Amenhetep ('Amenophis' in Greek) III himself presenting an offering to the god Amun, as portrayed on a contemporary carving from Thebes. In this case, the offering is the scent of the blue water lily, which the Pharaoh symbolically holds to the god's nose. An offering of a scent is almost as evanescent as a light-offering!

The feather of Maāt which features in the 'light-offering' is a major feature also of the carved wall itself. The god Amun, to whom Rameses is making the offering, is shown with tiny images of the goddess Maāt and Hathor sitting on his shoulder. And beside his shoulder there is a dog with a man's head surmounted by a crown of two Maāt feathers. The feather of Maāt made of light which comes to rest on the incense tray of offering exists only for a few minutes and, after it leaves the tray, it distorts and becomes unrecognizable, eventually becoming two golden balls, one atop the other, and then vanishing. The bars and slits of the stone window-grating are not curved or distorted at all, and the sculpting of the light is accomplished by the stonework outside the window, which is rounded in just such a way as to enable these phenomena to occur.

This is important photographic evidence of the kind of thing that was going on the whole time in these Egyptian temples when they were intact. The

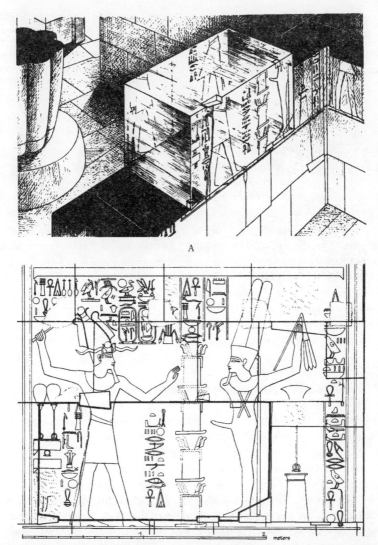

A

Figure 48. 'Transparency' in the Temple of Luxor. At the top we see a drawing by Lucie Lamy showing a stone block in the wall separating Room XII from Room V in the temple as if it were made of glass, so that you can see the carvings on both sides of the block. Below we see the scene on the north wall of Room V of a number of empty stacked boxes of cloths standing in front of the god Amun with his two high plumes on his head and his prominently erect phallus which indicates his divine fecundity. Standing before the god is the pharaoh making the offering of cloths. The hieroglyph for the cloths is carved opposite on the side of the block which is in Room XII. If we imagine the block as being transparent, then the boxes of cloths become filled with the hieroglyphs for cloths as if the images were projected through the solid stone. This concept treats matter as illusory and light as primary. It was Schwaller de Lubicz who noticed this extraordinary phenomenon during his many years of study of the temple. See his book *The Temple of Man*, translated by Deborah and Robert Lawlor, Inner Traditions, Rochester, Vermont, USA, 1998, 2 vols, Vol. I, p. 463, and Vol. II, pp. 996–1002; the drawings are Plate 98 preceding p. 996.

345

manipulation of beams of light for special purposes was practically routine, and was as much a part of the design of the temples as the corridors and columns and carvings. Indeed, even the stone itself was viewed as being in some way 'transparent', for Schwaller de Lubicz discovered that some of the wall carvings in the Temple of Luxor complemented each other from opposite sides of the same stone wall, such as for instance an empty box of cloths on one side of a wall being 'filled' with cloths carved in the precise spot on the opposite side of the wall! He calls this phenomenon 'transparency', and he was evidently the first to discover it. It is described at length in his remarkable book about the Luxor Temple, *The Temple of Man*.[5]

There are numerous other light-projection phenomena which we have discovered in Egyptian temples. We found one in the Temple of Horus at Edfu, which the guide Ahmed told us about, as we were not able to witness it. It occurs in the enclosed ascending stairway. Once a year, on what he called December 1st but which I suspect he meant as December 21st – the winter solstice – since his English was imperfect, the sun streams in the window on the stairway and strikes the face of Horus which is carved on the wall of a landing opposite the window, which is higher. It does not do this at sunrise but at about noon, so that it is apparently a meridian solstice phenomenon. The light only rests on Horus's face for five minutes and then vanishes, and this happens only once a year. For the rest of the year, Horus's face is in darkness.

A similar window may have light-phenomena associated with it, owing to some carved indications. I refer to a landing window in the enclosed stairway of the Roman birth house which is off to the right as you approach the Temple of Hathor at Denderah. Streaming down the sloping window ledge are depictions of stylized rays made of streams of mini-obelisks like those seen in the Temple of Hathor itself and reproduced in Plate 22. (More such rays as those of Plate 22 are seen in the side chapel of Hathor in the main temple.) My attempts to photograph these carved rays were unsuccessful, owing to the deep gloom and the ineffectiveness of flash, which washed out the carvings. But these carved rays are really very stunning, and suggest a light-projection on some undetermined day which I hope shall one day be noted.

At Karnak we witnessed yet more light-projection phenomena inside the small Temple of Ptah, in the Chapel of Sekhmet. At about 9 (am) in late November, a ray streams in through a slit in the back wall and strikes an eye carved on the wall. Only the eye is illuminated and nothing else. My attempts to photograph this were also unsuccessful, not least because I was totally unprepared and had to change film. The illumination of the eye lasts only for a few minutes. At the back of the statue of Sekhmet a thin slit in the stone which appears from the rear of the building to have been purposeful allows during much of the morning a tiny ribbon of light to bisect the back of the statue, giving Sekhmet from behind the eerie appearance of having an electric spinal cord. This is all the more extraordinary because of a strange dream my wife Olivia had of this statue after our first visit to it (we only discovered the electric spine on a subsequent visit). Olivia dreamt that she was standing in front of the statue and that she herself was being subjected to powerful currents of electricity coursing up and down her own body through its influence. When we discovered on another trip that Sekhmet herself was 'electric' from behind, it came as quite a shock to realize that she looks as if electricity is coursing up and down *her* body, but you can only see this if you squeeze round her back. This ribbon of light is so thin, and it looks electric-blue in the darkness. Sekhmet's statue is made of black basalt and she is the last Egyptian goddess left standing in her own original chapel, which goes back to the Middle Kingdom about 3800 years ago. She is thus a very old lady indeed.

When you enter the building (which is normally kept locked) and close the door behind you, the stream of light through the ceiling hole falls down upon Sekhmet's head and face, and she looks at you so intently and the feeling of her presence is so uncanny that you feel you are in the presence of someone from another world. If the guard likes you, he will go up onto the roof and use a reflector to bring powerful light down through the hole and dazzle you with spectacular lighting effects on the statue, so that the repose in which the mysterious figure had quietly glowered at you changes to vivid animation, as if Sekhmet were fired by powerful electric discharges such as Nikola Tesla used to play with. The effect is as startling as if fireworks had gone off, as I suspect that such focused light tricks were often used in ancient times.

The oldest illumination phenomenon in an Egyptian structure which archaeologists have been able to discover occurs at Saqqara. It was found during the excavations of the causeway of the small pyramid of Unas, the last king of the Fifth Dynasty (2356–2323 BC). The Egyptian engineer and archaeologist, Dr Mohamed Raslan, figured out how the structure worked and published a drawing diagram of it in 1973.[6]

Raslan, in a section entitled 'Illumination', describes the masterful technique by which the admission of sunlight into the covered causeway through this light slit was designed in such a way that the direct light would never strike the paintings and make their colours fade:

'The architect therefore saw to it in his design that light should only come in through a narrow opening in the axis of the Causeway roof . . . the opening was designed in such a manner as to cut out any possibility of the rays of the sun shining directly into the causeway (whatever its angle at any part of the year) from falling on any other part of the causeway but the floor. . . . He wanted to avoid any direct sunlight on the carvings and paintings on the walls lest the light affect the colours and rob them, in time, of their brilliance and sheen. . . . He wanted to display the carvings on the walls in a diffused indirect light reflected from the shining flooring of the Causeway. This kind of lighting would show up the carvings in their most delicate and best display.'[7]

We thus have definite archaeological evidence that sophisticated manipulation of sunlight by Egyptian architects inside structures was practised at least 4300 years ago, and we may be sure that the various examples I have given of New Kingdom and Ptolemaic structures where these phenomena still occur because the buildings are standing were in a continuous tradition which derives from the Old Kingdom, and which was probably used in most or all sacred structures. Later in this chapter, we shall find another example in the even older Valley Temple at Giza, for which see Plate 60.

Now, however, we need to consider some other matters, an understanding of which is also crucial for us. In order to understand fully the optical lore of ancient Egypt and its strange importance, it is necessary to be informed about what I believe may have been the greatest secret of the ancient Egyptians. *This secret is a number*, and having it is like having the combination to a safe containing all the gold you could ever want. Without this number, you are lost and can get nowhere. No matter how clever or even inspired you are, you cannot solve the riddles of ancient Egyptian astronomical mythology. You have to have this combination to the safe.

Strangely enough, I stumbled across the combination to this safe independently in 1971. But it was only in 1998 that I realized the existence of the safe to which I had the combination. Perhaps I'd better explain.

Between 1970 and 1972, I went through a phase of intense interest in mathematics and astronomy. I spent countless hours making computations, inspired by reading about Johannes Kepler and Tycho Brahe, the 17th-century astronomers. Kepler discovered the only three known Laws of Planetary Motion, and I thought his unorthodox methods could produce more interesting results, so I tried to imitate them.

Coincidentally, 1971 was the year my friend Brenda Francklyn died, aged 93. The story of Brenda Francklyn (full name Mary Brenda Hotham-Francklyn) is such a saga that if only enough details survived, it would make a book in itself. How can I even begin to describe her? And yet it is only because of her that I was able to discover 'the greatest secret of ancient Egypt'. So I believe I should try to tell something of her story, so that she can be appreciated properly, by way of a prelude.

Brenda's father was Colonel Francklyn of the Indian Army Staff Corps, and Brenda was born in India. She was descended from the famous Admiral Sir Henry Hotham (1777–1833), some of whose effects she still possessed, and as I believe this was through her mother, it may have been Brenda herself who added the Hotham to her surname from time to time. She was immensely proud of this descent and often talked of it. Hotham had quite a place in history, for it was he who prevented Napoleon fleeing to America, and thereby altered the entire history of the Western World.

Brenda's father Colonel Francklyn was not wealthy, and so after his retirement from the Army he found work as the personal secretary to his friend and his wife's distant relation, the last Duke of Buckingham and Chandos, who lived at Stowe in Buckinghamshire (now a famous British boys' school). Brenda grew up at Stowe and her best friend was the Duke's granddaughter, who was a bit younger than herself. The Duke should have had a son, but Brenda told me that the last Duchess was a headstrong woman addicted to hunting, who insisted on riding sidesaddle in the hunt at full pelt when she was eight months pregnant. She took a fence at a gallop but fell, and had a very unpleasant miscarriage. The baby was a boy, and of course it did not survive. The Duchess was unable to have children again after this. As a result of the Duchess's wilfulness, the double-dukedom became extinct upon the Duke's death for want of a male heir, and eventually the family went bankrupt and Stowe was sold at auction, becoming a school in 1922. The story of the last Duchess, being considered somewhat scandalous, has never before been committed to writing, and is a part of the family annals which has been suppressed.

I also knew the last Duke's granddaughter, whom I met through Brenda. She was called May Close-Smith, a very sweet woman who was somewhat younger than Brenda and hero-worshipped her. It was Mrs Close-Smith who told me many things about Brenda which Brenda herself was too modest to reveal. May was moderately rich, retaining a butler in traditional style, and she used to send a car and chauffeur down to Tunbridge Wells to fetch Brenda and drive her up to Buckinghamshire, where she lived at Boycott Manor just next to Stowe, as she could not be without Brenda's visits for long. As for Brenda, she was always penniless and had never been anything else for very long.

When Brenda was 21, way back in 1899, she fell out with the strict regime of her parents, who would not allow her to become an artist and wanted her to become a social butterfly (which she despised), and she left home in defiance, with little more than the clothes she was wearing and a box of watercolours and some paper. I believe she had one shilling to her name, which she had been given by May, who stole it from her mother's purse which was sitting on the dressing-table. May used to love to recount the tale and praise the fantastic bravery Brenda showed on that and all occasions. Brenda never went home again. She walked towards London, where she intended to settle and begin an independent and liberated life. This took many days, and she soon got through her shilling on bread and cheese purchased from a village shop. It was not high summer, and on one particular evening her habit of sleeping behind a hedge in a field became most uncomfortable, as a hard frost descended. The temperature plunged well below freezing, and she was in danger of dying of hypothermia, as she had no coat or blanket, only a light jacket.

Brenda herself told me of this incident, and of the profound effect it had on the rest of her life. As she sat in the wet grass of a cow pasture, and the dew turned to ice around her, she decided to commune with the higher powers and let them save her, as she could not save herself. Although she had never done such a thing before, she went into a very deep trance, out of the desperation which I suppose comes when faced with imminent death. Much later she realized that the trance was what she called a 'yogic trance'. For she put her future into the hands of the Higher Powers, and as she meditated she felt a strange glow rise up within her from the base of her spine and extend all the way to the crown of her head. She started to become warm, and she generated an enormous amount of heat through the release of some form of normally dormant bodily energy which she later called by the yogic name of 'the kundalini power'. Later, she noticed that she had melted the ice in her vicinity. She remained like that all night, so blazing hot that she seemed to be in the tropics. In the morning she rose and went on her way, transformed forever by this experience. For the kundalini power had saved her. It was from this early and spontaneous encounter with the powers of yoga that Brenda began her lifelong study of Indian yoga, and eventually wrote her book *Harmonic Yoga in World Religions*, the unpublished (and alas incomplete) manuscript of which I still have today, and frequently wonder what to do with. It contains many remarkable insights, and foreshadows a number of the discoveries of Schwaller de Lubicz about the detailed anatomical knowledge of the ancient Egyptians.

From that day, Brenda could be described as a mystic. She went on to London where she scraped a meagre living and found some lodgings, and entered art school in South Kensington on a scholarship. May secretly sent her more money pinched from her mother's purse when she could, to keep her from starvation. Brenda became associated with Emily Pankhurst and I have an old leaflet billing her as a major speaker at a suffragettes' rally with the Pankhursts. She also set up as a miniature portrait painter, and began to get commissions and achieve a modest income to enable her to travel, so that she took herself off to Paris where she studied at the Julian Academy. There she won the Gold Medal. She was instantly catapulted to the top of society as its 'pet' miniature painter, and soon she maintained simultaneous studios in Paris, Monte Carlo, and London. Her hero was the famous 17th-century miniaturist Samuel Cooper, and her work was nearly on his level! I am fortunate to have one of her miniatures, which were always painted on ivory and can only be described as truly exquisite and inspired. By the 1920s she was exhibiting in New Bond Street and was considered the best miniaturist in Britain.[8]

Brenda's esoteric philosophical interests were what really made her interesting. At one time, early in the 20th century, she had espoused something called 'The New Thought'. But no one remembers what that was. She flirted with Theosophy, but I think was uncomfortable about it. She became a leading Mason, despite being female. That was apparently quite difficult in those days in Britain – as I believe it still is. She used to cause havoc in lodge meetings by making speeches about the need to stop drinking beer and get back to the profound truths of Masonry – something few knew anything much about. I believe she was a member of a special research lodge in London, but I have forgotten the details. Some famous figures knew and supported her at one time in her attempts to revivify the Masonic Movement single-handed. She earned quite a lot of respect as well as a great deal of criticism by those who want a quiet life. And she continually practised yoga, becoming something of a Master at it. (Her attempts to promote yoga within Masonry were not appreciated.)

Apart from being a brilliant painter, Brenda had benefited from a long and expert tutelage in music whilst living at Stowe, which I believe was practically from infancy. She was deeply learned in musical theory in a manner which non-professionals simply aren't today. And she was also perfectly fluent in French. So she took an interest in a deeply obscure 18th-century French work on Pythagorean music by the Abbé Roussier, entitled *Mémoire de la Musique des Anciens* (Paris, 1770), which she translated as *Thesis on The Music of the Ancients* – the typed manuscript of which (completed in its final revision in 1964, with her notes) came to 439 quarto pages. A copy of this manuscript is to be found in the British Library, and I also have a photocopy. And thus it was that she became thoroughly grounded in one of the greatest musical preoccupations of the Pythagoreans, known as The Comma of Pythagoras, which is a *number*.

It is here that we leave Brenda, and turn to the combination to the safe. For the number of the Comma is 1.0136, expressed in modern decimal terms, and this important universal constant, which Brenda taught to me, turns out to be 'the greatest secret of ancient Egypt'.

But as I said earlier, it was not until 1998 that I realized that I had been sitting on the combination to the safe for 27 years! Of course, I had done a lot of work on this strange number, but I had not appreciated just how much the ancient Egyptians really did know about it, and why it formed the basis for so much of their mythology, and was even related to the optical phenomena with which we are concerned.

But now we return to 1971, the year Brenda died, a year when I was obsessed by logarithms and planetary orbits, and other such matters, and sat for hours with my nose in a notebook doing calculations. There were no electronic calculators in those days, so I had to do everything either on paper or in my head. I used to astonish friends by dividing 12 digits by 12 digits entirely in my head. (I have a kind of mental blackboard where I see and can manipulate numbers, which used to show up white on a black background, although nowadays they are black on white.) But that took a phenomenal amount of energy, and it was absolutely exhausting. I suppose chess grandmasters do something like this when they play blind chess. But I can't do that, so I don't know for sure.

I began to become fixated with the duration of the earth's year and its closeness to the number of degrees in a circle, which I hope everyone knows is 360°. The origin of the system of degrees in the circle is unknown, except that we know the ancient Babylonians used it, and we have inherited it from them. It seems to be of great antiquity, its origins entirely lost in the mists of time. It is part of what is called 'sexagesimal mathematics', based on the number 60, and we use the same system to measure time – hence 60 minutes in an hour and 60 seconds in a minute.

There was something about this which haunted me and bothered me, as if I already knew there was an importance to it. It niggled away at me. So it didn't take me long to investigate. I divided the duration of the earth's year, which is 365.242392 days, by 360. My feeling was that an 'ideal' year would be 360 days, and I wondered what the relationship between the two numbers could be. I was very surprised when I saw that the result was 1.014562, for I instantly recognized that it was the same as the Comma of Pythagoras to the third decimal place (1.0136 rounded off is 1.014). In fact, I even later discovered that the tiny discrepancy of 9.6 ten-thousandths was in itself possibly highly significant. The square of 1.0136 is 1.0273849, which is 9.6 ten-thousandths in the other direction, and is a number which also occurs in various physical phenomena.

The number 9.6 is very important in physics. Its precise value is really 9.604. It was discovered by the physicist Sir Arthur Eddington, who denoted it by the Greek letter sigma and called it the 'Uncertainty Constant' when expressed in the form 9.604×10^{-14}, which is at the dimensions of nuclear particles. In his last great book, *Fundamental Theory*, published posthumously in 1953, Eddington said this number was absolutely fundamental to the Universe. Because there are no such things as the 'points' which we pretend to use in geometry (they are abstractions, not realities), when we try and use geometry in the form of coordinates ('a coordinate frame') to measure reality, there is a tiny discrepancy. Eddington found that the Uncertainty Constant could be used to measure this. He actually explained that his entire book was based upon this number:

> Starting with an abstract geometrical coordinate frame, we step over from pure geometry into physics by introducing a physical coordinate frame whose origin has (a) probability distribution . . . relative to the geometrical [point of] origin. We shall find that the standard deviation *sigma* of this distribution *puts the scale into* the physical frame and everything constructed in the physical frame, whether it be a nucleus, an atom, a crystal or the whole extent of physical space. The main problem in this book is to investigate the way in which the extensions of these various structures are related to *sigma*, and to evaluate the numerical ratios for some of the simpler structures.[9]

After reading this, we can hardly be in any doubt about the significance of the number in question. In my own investigations, I have repeatedly come across the number 9.6 in association with the Comma of Pythagoras as the numerical expression of the 'wobble' of the discrepancy between the ideal and the real. But because the contexts where I have encountered it have nothing to do with the contexts explored by Eddington, and are not expressed as the same power of ten, I cannot call the number as he does the Uncertainty Constant. Instead, I take the raw number and call it the Universal Uncertainty *Coefficient*. (A coefficient is a raw number which can occur at any power of ten, and can slide up and down the scale of size from, say 9,604,000 to 0.00009604. The raw number remains the same and it is merely the scale that changes.)

The Universal Uncertainty Coefficient has relations with other key natural constants. But in order to understand how these things work, you have to break the natural constants down into their two separate components. The really important part of a key natural constant is its decimal value. The integer standing before that can be looked upon as a dimensional indicator and not part of the intrinsic value. Thus, the number *pi* is 3.1416, but the important part is .1416, which I call the *particle of pi*. The 3 merely indicates that it operates at the level of three-dimensionality. The numbers *e* and *phi* are 2.7182818 and 1.618 respectively, but the 2 and the 1 can be taken to refer to two-dimensionality and uni-dimensionality. If you take the decimal particles of these constants, stripping away the integers which stand before them as indicators, you can find the relations between these natural constants. The technique of stripping away the integers was inspired by the brilliant insight of John Napier (died 1618), who adopted this technique for the creation of logarithms. He called the integer standing at the front the *characteristic* and the decimal he called the *mantissa*. In doing this he was able to break free of the restrictive conventional concept of number and make spectacular progress. Sometimes I call the decimal a *particle* and sometimes, in emulation of Napier, a *mantissa*.

One of my discoveries using this technique was that if you multiply the mantissa of *pi* by the Universal Uncertainty Coefficient operating at a low power of ten as .09604, you get the Particle of Pythagoras. (0.1416 x 0.09604 = 0.0136.) One could say on this basis that the Particle of Pythagoras is a function of the mantissa of *pi*.

There are many such relationships. There is also a way to express the area of a circle in terms of the mantissa of *pi* multiplied by the square of the Universal Uncertainty Coefficient, which enables you to see that the circumference of a circle equals the diameter of that circle's cycloid plus a function of the circle's area.

Another way to define the Universal Uncertainty Coefficient is to say that it is equal to the number of degrees of freedom of the electron (136) divided by the mantissa of *pi* x 10^2.

The importance of this and the many occurrences of the Coefficient in my studies of planetary orbits shows that a natural constant which Eddington claimed to be fundamental at the nuclear level is seen to be operative also at the macroscopic level, and indeed apparently at all levels and scales.

Having discovered that the Particle of Pythagoras is a function of the mantissa of *pi* makes its occurrence in relation to a celestial orbit more sensible. For if we view the earth as a limb of the sun rather than as a hurtling body, its portion of the solar system can be conceived of as undergoing a rotation once a year; this is different from thinking in terms of a separate hurtling body (the earth) performing a revolution once a year. And since a rotation in mathematics is expressed as 2π, to express the tiny discrepancy between two nearly identical rotations (an ideal and a real) by a number which is a function of the mantissa of *pi* makes the entire subject more satisfying and coherent. As far as circular motion is concerned, therefore, the Comma of Pythagoras and *pi* are seen to be two different numerical aspects of the same phenomenon. And this in turn means that inherent to all circular motion, upon basic underlying mathematical principles – built into it, as it were, as a fundamental building block of reality – is the factor that gives the tiny numerical discrepancy to all circular motion in the Universe. And this in turn may be viewed as a product of the uncertainty of the point of origin of any system, and of the nonexistence of those fictitious 'points' which we use in geometry but which only exist in the real world in a different form – where they actually have size and are not infinitely small as we imagine in our fantasies. This, then, is the real difference between the ideal and the real.

But before we can understand fully, we have to know just what the Comma of Pythagoras is in music, so that we can try to appreciate its importance in any other context. And then we shall begin to see that there is something really important here.

People who play a musical instrument or sing, and especially people who play the piano, will not find what I am about to say at all difficult. But people who have no experience of a keyboard may find it somewhat confusing because it is unfamiliar. If you play eight consecutive white keys on a piano, you end up with the same note where you started, except that it is an 'octave' higher. (In fact, a note an octave higher than another note has precisely double the frequency.) So if you were to play 'C', for instance, anywhere on the piano, and then play through all the succeeding (white key) notes until you get to the higher 'C', it would have double the frequency of the initial 'C' and would be the eighth note. If you take your thumb and your little finger and play the two 'C's together, it is called 'playing an octave'.

The octave is the fundamental fact of music. There is no limit to octaves in principle: you can go on and on doubling the frequency of a note until it becomes inaudible and you run out of physical means to produce them. But in actuality, the physical vibration of matter which produces musical notes (generally vibrating strings or air in pipes, the basis of what we call musical instruments) never produces a single note on its own. Higher notes are always automatically generated by a process called 'resonance', and they are known as 'overtones'. A good grand piano produces 42 measurable overtones when you strike a single key! Some of these are higher octaves of the original note. The human ear can only actually detect a few of these overtones consciously, but even at the subliminal level, they go to add much richness of texture to music. The electronic music so common today is pure-toned and generates no overtones, so that it is uninspiring and lacks all resonance, and is thus impoverished of texture. That is why it does not move us as much as does the sound of real instruments being played.

LES SEPT JOURS DE LA   SEMAINE

M. le premier président Bon

Figure 49. This old French engraving is generally regarded as showing the gods and goddesses of the seven days of the week. But it could more properly be regarded as showing the seven notes of the octave, and the boat in which they sit represents their consummation by the eighth note, which is the first repeated, and which makes them a unity.
(From Bernard de Montfaucon, *l'Antiquité Expliquée et Représentée en Figures*, Paris, 1722. Collection of Robert Temple.)

But octaves are essentially boring, and you cannot produce music from them alone, because they are repetitive. One longs for variety. And so there are various combinations of notes used to produce chords, which when sounded together are either harmonious or unharmonious as the case may be. (A chord is simply two or more notes played together.) And it has been found through all the ages that the most harmonious of all combinations of notes (what are called concords – that is, chords which are harmonious) are two notes *five* white keys apart on the piano. Together they are called *a fifth*. If you take your thumb and middle finger and play 'C' and the 'G' immediately above it together on the piano, you are playing a fifth. It is as simple as that.

So for harmony, the best chords are always fifths. And very early in civilization's history, people investigated what it was about notes five notes apart which made them so harmonious when played together. We have much information about the ancient Greek Pythagoreans, and they used to experiment by pressing stretched strings (like guitar strings) on a long board. They discovered that there were certain mathematical relationships – some of them amazingly simple – between sounds when the different lengths of the strings were pressed as on a fret and struck. They measured these lengths and found that for the playing of fifths with any two notes which made a fifth, the string length of one note and that of the other always had the mathematical ratio of two to three. And because an octave is a doubling of frequency, they also discovered that a note and its higher octave of itself always had string lengths with the mathematical ratio of two to one (i.e. doubled!). Such discoveries, which were made also at the beginning of Egyptian civilization, if not even before, showed the early investigators that there was a mathematical basis to music. Music is not just random sound, it has underlying order dictated by precise numbers. To the discoverer of such a thing, this might be astonishing. And to know all about it, an early man might well believe he was discovering some of the secrets of the gods. (A modern man rarely concerns himself with the awe and wonder of such simple principles, as today we are all jaded and lacking in the capacity for reverence of natural phenomena.)

Now we come to the pay-off: the early investigators did not take long to realize that there was a very upsetting problem to all of this apparently cosy scheme. For it was found that fifths and octaves do not 'fit' into each other mathematically or in terms of actual sound either. They are like oil and water, and refuse to mix. Having discovered the divine secrets of the ratios of two to three and of two to one, imagine the consternation which was felt when it was realized that these two ratios might as well be at opposite ends of the universe, for they were like a squabbling couple who could not inhabit the same house.

The problem arises when you try and reach the same note by climbing two different sets of stairs: if you climb the octaves and if you climb the fifths, you do not get to the same note by those two separate routes until you have gone through twelve fifths. (Technically, this is called 'the spiral of fifths'.) And when the octaves and fifths do finally mesh after such a long climb, they are a slightly imperfect 'fit'. The sound made at the end of seven octaves and the sound made at the end of twelve fifths differ by a tiny amount precisely equal to 1.0136. Because this was known to have been measured by Pythagoras (sixth century BC), it is called after him 'the Comma of Pythagoras'. But he was not its first discoverer. You might think the decimal is so tiny it would make no difference, but you would be wrong. The human ear is so sensitive that it can detect the difference. You can also measure it mathematically without much trouble: the ratio of two to one doubled seven times over gives a frequency 128 times higher than when you started (i.e. a note seven octaves higher than the original note has a frequency 128 times greater, which can in principle be measured by string lengths as well). But if you proceed on the basis of the ratio of two to three, which is 1.5, and go up by twelve fifths, 1.5 to the twelfth power gives the number 129.75. This is not equal to 128, and if you divide 129.75 by 128, you get the decimal 1.0136.

This may seem obscure and unimportant, but it is not. It may also appear impossible at first glance that ancient people should have discovered it, but that too is an illusion: it was certainly known to Pythagoras, and I have shown in the revised (1998) edition of my book *The Sirius Mystery* that an ancient Greek text actually concealed the value of this number to nine decimal places in a kind of code; the text concerned was the Pythagorean treatise *Katatomē Kanonos* (Division of the Canon), and to find this magic number you have to carry out two separate arithmetical processes suggested by an obscure statement which would only be noticed by experts who already knew the answer in advance.[10;11]

This extremely technical and abstruse Pythagorean treatise seems to have been put together in some form in the fifth century BC or at the turn of the fourth century BC, and then reworked several centuries later.[12] But much of the content seems to date from an earlier time. Although the value of the Comma of Pythagoras to an astonishing nine decimal places is preserved in this mysterious text, it is done so in a manner which is purposely designed to conceal the information from the uninitiated, which must be why no one before ever noticed it, including the editor and translator. What the text actually says is that the number 531,441 is greater than twice 262,144. The only explanatory statement accompanying this strange information is: 'Six sesquioctave intervals are greater than one duple interval.' One could be forgiven for scratching one's head and moving on. But I realized what was being referred to here, and multiplied 262,144 by two to get 524,288. Dividing 531,441 by that number gives the result 1.013643265. And in case anyone wonders whether that really is accurate to nine decimal places or is just an approximation, I can point out that the identical number to nine decimal places occurs in a modern book published in 1995 entitled *Math and Music*.[13]

The precision of the ancient computation is truly amazing, and the care taken to *state but conceal* the information indicates that it was considered both precious and secret; the author wanted to preserve the number for posterity while at the same time preventing the profane from noticing it, so he made it necessary for the reader to do two computations in order to arrive at it. So successful was the ancient author in veiling his purpose that André Barbera, the immensely learned modern editor and translator of this text, who seems to know just about everything else there is to know about the subject, never once mentions the Comma of Pythagoras or gives any indication of being aware of the true significance of the passage which he himself translated (nor does he appear to have carried out the multiplication and division, or if he did, he did not recognize the number which resulted, since he does not mention it).[14]

The ancient Pythagoreans were well aware of the momentous consequences of their knowledge, and the modern scholar Flora Levin has grasped the importance of this probably better than any of her contemporaries. Dr Levin has spent much of her life studying the harmonic writings of Nicomachus of Gerasa (second century AD). As long ago as 1975 she published *The Harmonics of Nicomachus and the Pythagorean Tradition*,[15] a book full of profound insights. Nineteen years later she finally brought out her translation of *The Manual of Harmonics* of Nicomachus together with an extended commentary.[16] In this book she makes a great point of showing how Nicomachus tries to avoid the awful truth about the incommensurability of the octave and the fifth by coyly diverting the discussion from time to time. Although she never actually mentions the Comma of Pythagoras as such, she concludes:

> In the final analysis, it was to this that the Pythagoreans' harmonic analysis of the universe led: the discovery of incommensurables [i.e. incommensurate numbers]. And no matter how they might juxtapose the numbers, no matter to what lengths they might extend their mathematical circumlocutions, one fact remained, a fact that has ever since proved resistant to mathematical rationalization: there is no fraction m/n that will divide the whole-tone into two equal parts.[17]

Elsewhere she points out that 'the Pythagoreans could prove that melodic space is irrational – that whole-tones are indivisible mathematically, that semi-tones and all the other micro-intervals which were employed by ancient Greek musicians, such as quarter-tones and thirds of tones, are only auditory chimeras.'[18]

The earliest writer to put Pythagorean ideas into writing was Philolaos (fifth century BC), and he was drawn upon by the many subsequent writers on harmony including Nicomachus. Unfortunately, Philolaos's writings are all lost, and we only have fragments. But from what we can learn of what he said, it seems clear that he had a more profound grasp of his subject than most of his successors, who did not always seem to understand the niceties of his ideas. (Nicomachus for instance was a popularizer, not an original thinker.) The lack of Philolaos's original writings is a great handicap to us, but one crucial idea of his which is mentioned by Flora Levin is this:

> For Pythagoras and his disciples, the word *harmonia* meant 'octave' in the sense of an 'attunement' which manifests within its limits both the proper 'fitting together' of the concordant [musical] intervals, fourth and fifth, and the difference between them, the whole tone. Moreover, as Pythagoras proved, whatever can be said of one octave holds true for all octaves.[19]

Although an explicit elaboration of this idea by Philolaos is lost with the disappearance of his manuscripts, we are able to discern enough to realize that the Pythagoreans had faced the challenge of the Comma of Pythagoras by pronouncing that *harmonia* was the answer to everything. *Harmonia*, which has given us our word 'harmony', comes from the Greek verb *harmosdō*, 'to fit together, to join, to bind fast'. What the Pythagoreans were fitting together and binding fast were the incommensurate numbers, as represented by the octave and the fifth which 'don't fit'. *Harmonia* was the grand unity which they envisaged to reconcile these unreconcilables. Their explorations of the extent of the unreconcilability obviously led to them either calculating or inheriting from the Egyptians the value of the Comma to nine decimal places, which shows a fair degree of desperation. Their approach was obviously to try and see the full extent of the problem and face it with courage. But so abstruse was all of this that later writers, many of whom were second-raters, did not fully grasp the grand vision, and the true nature of the Pythagorean concept of *harmonia* as a 'grand unified theory of the Universe' has been obscured for more than two millennia. (The loss of the writings on Pythagoreanism by Aristotle and his school and also of the mathematical writings of Plato's immediate successors contributed greatly to our ignorance.) In fact, it was not until 1584 in China that a practical attempt at forging a fully-fledged system of *harmonia* was to occur again, and it has now been universally adopted round the world.

The Comma of Pythagoras is so fundamental a problem in music that the Ming Prince Zhu Cai-Yü at the end of the 16th century in China invented a special system to cope with it. Today, this system is known to us as 'equal temperament'. It adopted by Bach, having spread rapidly to the West through Dutch traders. Bach wrote his famous *Well-Tempered Clavier* as a work of propaganda on its behalf – and he was passionately opposed by his contemporary, the composer Giuseppe Tartini, who hated equal temperament. The *Well-Tempered Clavier* was an astonishing effort on Bach's part; he composed a prelude and a fugue in every key in succession, to be played on an equally-tempered keyboard instrument. This group of compositions includes some of his most striking and beautiful work, and its classic performance on the piano by the late Glenn Gould is generally considered its finest and highest expression, though in saying that I do not wish to diminish the harpsichord performances by many fine players such as Wanda Landowska.

Equal temperament has now been universally adopted in the West, though its Chinese origins are generally unknown. I told the whole story in my book *The Genius of China* (original title: *China: Land of Discovery and Invention*; 1986).[20] This was a book I wrote in loose collaboration with Joseph Needham, the world's greatest sinologist. When I asked Joseph what he thought of my book *The Genius of China*, he said the part that impressed him most was my account of equal temperament, a subject he said he had never really understood before, and he professed himself amazed at what was really involved in it.

Equal temperament solves the problem of the fact that octaves and fifths don't 'fit' by cheating in a systematic manner: it shaves a tiny bit off each note and creates something called 'semitones', which are essentially artificial. The result is that every note which is played on a modern piano (the strings of which are tuned according to equal temperament, with a little shaved off each note) is slightly flat. What enraged people like Tartini was that the ear can detect this, and it meant that 'pure' tones were not being used any more in music, that all music was henceforth and uniformly slightly flat. Previously, the tuning of a piano dealt with the problem by bunching up the discrepancies at the top and the bottom of the keyboard, which are rarely used, so that brilliant 'pure' tones could be played in the middle. That has all gone now.

By creating flat tones in this new system, we are enabled to modulate from key to key without stopping and retuning the instruments every time. It was only equal temperament which made possible the powerful symphonies and concerti of the great 19th-century composers, who constantly shift key for emotional effect. Before equal temperament, the orchestra would have had to stop, retune, and then continue with the new section!

But the ancient Egyptians and the Greek Pythagoreans were not concerned with composing Brahms or Rachmaninov symphonies, they were interested in what they regarded as *secrets of the universe*. And the Comma of Pythagoras was certainly one. For it is built into the deep structure of the cosmos, and applies anywhere in the Universe under any conceivable conditions, at any time and in any place. It is a true universal constant, for its roots are in the fundamentals of mathematics and in the vibrations of matter, on whatever planet and in whatever galaxy one can imagine. And just in its musical origins alone, it has every appearance to an ancient priest/philosopher of one of the divine numbers of the gods. But imagine how important it must have seemed to the ancient Egyptians when they realized that *it was also the crucial number for the calendar!*

The Egyptians were obsessed by the calendar. They were 'obsessive-compulsives' who simply had to observe their religious feast days at the right time or the world might come to an end. No anorexic or bulimic is more obsessive, no fanatical washer is more compulsive, than an ancient Egyptian priest was about his calendar. It was a life and death matter.

When I discovered that the length of the earth's year in days differed from the number of degrees in a circle by the Comma of Pythagoras, I studied the other planets and found that there were rounded-off 'ideal' years for all of them which differed from their real years either by the Comma of Pythagoras or by its square, generally within 9.6 ten thousands, as with the earth. I began to speculate about there being some universal significance to this, and that this natural constant might actually occur in every conceivable celestial orbit, just as it occurs in every conceivable material vibration. I even postulated some laws of motion, including one which stated that the absolute duration of the year and the absolute duration of the day of every body in space had a fixed ratio (i.e. every body's rotation and revolution have a fixed ratio), so that if one changed the other had to change commensurately (and since the earth's day changes, I predicted that it would be found that the earth's year changed by a commensurate tiny fraction as well, though no one has ever looked for this). But these speculations are complicated, and it would not be appropriate to include them here. But sufficient to say that all the planets for which I could obtain sufficient data could be demonstrated to have 'ideal' and 'real' years which differed by the Particle of Pythagoras, after calculating the numbers of their own days in their years. (Mercury and Venus, the inner planets, gave the same results also in terms of 'earth days', indicating that there is perhaps a hierarchal cascade of orbital motion as you move outwards away from the sun. I have already explained in my book *The Sirius Mystery* how the diameters of the earth, of Venus, and of Mercury, are linked by a common numerical co-efficient, 2.94.)

It seems that the Comma of Pythagoras may very well be the number which specifies the percentage of mass converted into energy in the explosion of the hydrogen bomb. The four protons of hydrogen which are converted into a helium nucleus when a hydrogen bomb explodes exceed the helium nucleus by an amount of mass just about equal to the Particle of Pythgoras. However, I have failed to discover the precise number, despite enquiries, presumably because it is a military secret.

On the other hand, the United Kingdom Atomic Energy Authority informed me in 1978 that 'this is not a figure known to us', and perhaps they are right – maybe no one ever thinks about it. Another apparent occurrence of the Comma of Pythagoras is in the ratio between 238 and 235 – the two types of uranium (i.e. Uranium 235 and Uranium 238). The ratio is 1.0128, which is within 0.0008 of the Comma of Pythagoras.

As regards the element helium, it is notable that Helium^4 liquefies at 4.2216°K and Helium^3 liquefies at about 3.2°K. The mean between these two is 3.7, and that value is precisely .0136th of the boiling temperature of water. The Particle of Pythagoras thus mediates these respective boiling temperatures. One might be inclined to view this as a coincidence were it not for the precision of four decimals. Also, phase transitions such as boiling points are key milestones in Nature, and are likely to manifest universal constants. And if we compare yet another substance with water, we find that liquid mercury has a density 13.6 times that of water, which is the Particle of Pythagoras multiplied by one million.

Another possible occurrence of the Particle of Pythagoras is in connection with the formation of all the chemical elements of the Universe from the simplest, hydrogen – a process which occurs in stars. As the astronomer Martin Rees has recently made clear in his fascinating popular book *Just Six Numbers: The Deep Forces that Shape the Universe* (Weidenfeld & Nicolson, London, 1999), there is a tiny number governing this whole process which is 0.007. He says: '. . . what is so remarkable is that no carbon-based biosphere could exist if this number had been 0.006 or 0.008 rather than 0.007.'(p. 51) It is commendable that Rees has highlighted this amazing fact. The ancient Egyptian term 'the tiny gap' would seem applicable in this instance as well, wouldn't it? We wouldn't even exist if the tiny number had varied even slightly. But what is this number exactly? It is the percentage of the mass of hydrogen gas (hydrogen being the simplest and first element) which is converted into energy when the second element, helium, is produced inside stars by the fusion of the hydrogen. And the production of helium in turn leads to the production of all other chemical elements. If the hydrogen couldn't fuse into helium nothing else would be formed, and the universe would just be a sea of boring hydrogen. But since the process of helium formation takes place in two stages rather than one (first the hydrogen becomes deuterium, then helium), the number 0.007 needs to be taken twice in order to articulate the natural constant in its 'operational' form. If we just speak of 0.007, we are describing half a process rather than a whole process. And 0.007 doubled is 0.014, which is the rounded-off expression of the Particle of Pythagoras (0.0136), which in turn is related to the physicists' dearly-beloved 'fine structure constant', which is also related to the hydrogen/helium process.

As I do not wish to get involved in complicated physics here, you will be relieved to know that I won't go into further detail. I just wish to point out that if it weren't for the Particle of Pythagoras I wouldn't be writing this book and you wouldn't be reading it, there would be no planet Earth, no trees to make the paper on which the book was printed, no eyes in your head because you would have no head, and no you and no me at all. But this also indicates that the Particle of Pythagoras is so fundamental that it precedes all forms of matter but hydrogen, and is thus rooted in the very fundamentals of atomic physics. Our ability to measure it, and even the value we attribute to it, are at a less fundamental level than our personal experiences – in other words, 'the tiny gap' created us, we did not create 'the tiny gap'.

If one looks for the Comma of Pythagoras in pure geometry, it occurs in an unexpected way. The face angles of the dodecahedron (one of the five regular solid shapes – called polyhedra – which has 12 faces) are 108°. That angle times the Comma of Pythagoras gives the angle 109° 28' 7.7", which is within less than $8^{1}/_{2}$ seconds of the angle 109° 28' 16" (cosine – $^{1}/_{3}$) found at the centre of the tetrahedron. Such are the phenomena with which I was once preoccupied, before I decided I was being overrun by numbers and had to stop all of this![21]

The Particle of Pythagoras seems also to have another fundamental aspect.

It appears that it may be required to act as a correction factor to the general relativity equations of Albert Einstein. It was Dr Philip Goode who first came up with a calculation connected with the Theory of Relativity which was slightly different from one made by Einstein. And in the 1980s, the physicist Dr Henry Hill took this up as a matter requiring urgent investigation. The problem relates to the precession of the planet Mercury. The orbit of Mercury rotates (like a spinning top that slightly wobbles) at 5,600 seconds per century. That may not sound like much, but it's really frightfully important.

Newton's gravitational theory accounted for 5,557 seconds of these 5,600 seconds, leaving only 43 seconds unaccounted for. Einstein's theory was supposed to have accounted for these, but because Einstein assumed the sun to be a perfect sphere, which it is not, Einstein was in error and his correction could only account for 42.3 seconds, according to Hill and Goode. Using a special solar telescope, Henry Hill had discovered that the sun was slightly squashed at its poles, is oblate and therefore not a perfect sphere. As a result, the whole of Einstein's theory is threatened by this discrepancy left in the precession of Mercury. Now I wouldn't want Einstein's theory to be threatened, would you? So clearly it is our duty to try and help dear old Albert, who got his sun wrong.

Here is where the Particle of Pythagoras comes in. If we take the 43 seconds which Einstein assumed on the basis of a spherical sun, and divide it by the 42.4 seconds which Hill and Goode insist is all the slightly squashed sun can justify, we get the number 1.016, which is within two hundredths of a decimal of the Comma of Pythagoras. It may even be that these two hundredths of a decimal would vanish if I had more precise figures, but 43 and 42.3 are the best I have available. On the other hand, 1.016 is equal to the square of the Comma of Pythagoras rounded off to the fourth decimal, so perhaps that should be the quantity we are dealing with.

The discrepancy between the two figures of 43 seconds and 42.3 seconds appears thus to be proportionally equal to the Particle of Pythagoras (or its square), which suggests a correction factor to reconcile the two figures and thus save Einstein's theory. I suggest that this correction figure has a cosmological status, due to the universal nature of this natural constant.[22]

What does all of this mean? One thing it means is that the proportion of oblateness (flattening) of spheroidal bodies in space, such as the sun, is not accidental but reflects concealed constraints and is a function of the Comma of Pythagoras. We are led to infer, for instance, that the sun could only be as oblate as it is, no more, no less. It seems to me only to be expected that this natural constant should be seen to be operative in the measure of discrepancy of the gravitational effects of an ideal sphere and that of the real spheroid which actually occurs in reality, just as it distinguishes an 'ideal year' from a 'real year'. The Comma of Pythagoras is nothing less than a general universal measure of the discrepancy between the ideal and the real. It is part of the fabric of the Universe, as fundamental as the Heisenberg Uncertainty Principle – indeed, I should say more so.

The uncanny, almost unbelievable, point for us is that the ancient Egyptians had discovered the Comma of Pythagoras in relation to the earth's year too! (And so we may wonder how many other applications they understood and further scientific truths which in the modern world we are only just beginning to understand.) I just didn't know that in 1971. I only discovered this in 1998 when I made myself sit down and read the book which I have previously mentioned, *Creation Records Discovered in Egypt* (1898) by George St Clair.[23] The book had been sitting around demanding to be read for about 15 years, but one can't do everything at once, and I delayed.

George St Clair must have been a remarkable man, because he correctly intuited the significance and meaning of many aspects of Egyptian mythology in a way in which no one else really has. He saw clearly the calendrical mania which afflicted the Egyptians, and their passion to know every last detail about the different years (lunar, solar, and others). St Clair also realized that the Egyptians were obsessed by the problem of the precession of the equinoxes, a very long-range phenomenon resulting from the fact that the earth wobbles slightly like a top on its axis, and over the course of every 25,868 years, the earth's poles make a small circle in space, which results in the identity of the Pole Star changing and then going back again to where it was. The Egyptians were a sufficiently long-lived civilization to have noticed the shift of their precious stars. It is this precession of the equinoxes which causes the change in the zodiacal sign associated with an age. For instance, all who are keen about astrology know that we are currently leaving 'the Age of Pisces' and entering 'the Age of Aquarius'.

The point is that amongst all these astronomical and calendrical phenomena which concerned them so passionately, the Egyptians discovered the same thing I discovered in 1971 – that an 'ideal' year of 360 days was exceeded by the true year of 365 days, 5 hours, 49 minutes, by the number 1.014, which they had already presumably discovered in musical theory. And by coming across this number twice, they became convinced that the Comma of Pythagoras (which seems to have been known to the Egyptians as '*the tiny gap*') was the most important secret number of the gods. The god Thoth was known as 'the Eighth', who 'completed the Seven', and he thus represented the Octave. (This is the mythological background to the widespread Greek tradition that Pythagoras added an eighth string to the lyre and 'completed the Octave'.) The musical fifth was represented by five gods including Isis and Osiris, known as 'the Five' – and they represented the five extra days which were added onto 360 to make 365; the fraction of a day added to them to give the true year was called Horus. The phallus of Osiris was Day 365, which it was necessary to add to the 364 days of a lunar year, and Horus completed the count by adding the period of slightly less than six hours to give an accurate year. There were temples and even cities dedicated to 'the Eight' and 'the Five'; for instance, the city of Hermopolis was actually called 'the Eighth', and its main temple was the 'Temple of the Eighth', the high priest of which was called, however, 'the great one of the five'. There was much more to it, naturally, too much for us to go into all the details here.

Baron Albert von Thimus believed that the Egyptian symbol of the *ankh* sometimes represented the musical fifth.[24] He also suggested that the symbol of the crossed arrows had musical significance. It is possible that the octave may be represented by the uraeus serpent on the brow, for Schwaller de Lubicz says: 'The reason for the choice of the serpent as the symbol for the principle of duality may seem strange, but everything in this animal is double, or dual, including its forked tongue and its sexual organs. It has a double penis, and the female has a double vagina; the testicles and the double ovaries of the higher animals are their vestiges.'[25] Some more specific evidence of the concept of the octave amongst the Egyptians comes from the magnificent publication and translation of papyri dealing with mythology by Alexandre Piankoff. In his Introduction, Piankoff explains:

'In the Theban theology [of the god Amun/Amon, in the new Kingdom period], Amon, the Hidden One, manifests first as the Eight primaeval gods: "The Eight gods were thy first form, until thou didst complete them, being One . . ." [a quotation from a Leiden papyrus] . . . In other words, the One manifests itself as a plurality of Eight, remaining itself the One. The same idea is encountered in the theology of Memphis [of the god Ptah, much more ancient, going back to the Old Kingdom, prior to 2800 BC]. Here the divine principle is Ptah . . . who manifests himself as Eight different forms of himself . . .' And Piankoff goes on to add that this extremely ancient tradition is 'Believed to be the oldest religious construction' of Egypt.[26]

This shows clearly that the 'eight-in-one' concept applied to the god Amun was borrowed from the much earlier scheme which described the god Ptah (whose cult was assimilated to that of Amun during the New Kingdom, and whose chapel at Karnak still survives intact except that the head of his seated statue is missing, having been chopped off in antiquity, probably by Christians). We thus see clearly that the 'eight-in-one', which is the description of the octave of the heptatonic diatonic musical scale – which has been conclusively demonstrated from cuneiform texts to have existed prior to 2500 BC in the Middle East amongst the Sumerians[27] – was a fundamental concept from the very beginning of dynastic Egypt. We may thus presume that the knowledge of the full harmonic tradition goes back to this era, together with the discovery of the Comma of Pythagoras.

The various calendars were all kept going side-by-side, and oaths were sworn never to cease to acknowledge the 'year' of 360 days, concerning which many elaborate religious rituals took place. George St Clair, lacking the concept of the Comma of Pythagoras, identified all these years, but could only conclude that they had been arrived at in succession and only retained by a stubborn conservatism of the Egyptian priests. This resulted in St Clair not being able to able to come to a full understanding of the situation; he had identified the elements but could not make out the overall pattern, because he lacked the *number*. He could not open the safe.

The truth was that the Egyptians did not arrive at all these different years in succession, abandoning one after another as they refined their calculations. They knew about and celebrated them all *simultaneously*. The fact that the short 360-day year results in feast days slipping round by an entire year in the short space of only 72 years was celebrated as the 72-year circumnavigation of the heavens by the sun god Ra, who is addressed by 72 names in the Book of the Dead.[28] Only the knowledge of the Comma of Pythagoras can explain why the Egyptians retained and honoured an obviously inaccurate 'year' of 360 days; they did this *because* it was inaccurate, but by being retained and compared with the accurate year, the Comma of Pythagoras could be computed. Otherwise the secret number might be lost and subsequent generations might never calculate it, so that one of the greatest secrets of the Universe might slip back into obscurity. (And in fact, that was what has happened until now.)

There are many such numerical symbols and calculations which occur, and to give many of them here would be confusing. But where this all

Figure 50. 'The Temple of the Eighth' – an engraving published in 1803 from a drawing of 1799 by Dominique Vivant Denon, showing the ruins of the Temple of Hermopolis in Upper Egypt, as it appeared at that time.
(*Collection of Robert Temple.*)

impinges upon ancient Egytian optics is that the many sacred 'Eyes' in Egyptian mythology all occur in various contexts which can only be interpreted within this schema; otherwise, they make no sense at all. Why are there so many 'Eyes of Horus', 'Eyes of Ra', 'Eyes of Osiris', 'Eyes of Isis and Nephthys', etc.? These 'Eyes' were all to do with optics, mostly solar images, occurring in the various different calendars! For instance, when the sun rose on an equinox or one of the solstices, it shone down the long corridor of an Egyptian temple oriented towards one of those three horizon points (the winter and summer solstice are the southernmost and northernmost points of sunrise respectively, and the equinoxes are the midpoint). The corridors were so long – as we have seen already at Karnak – that an image of the entrance was not projected, but rather the image of the solar disc appeared as a circle of light on the wall or screen of the inner sanctum. The circle of light would be seen for about two minutes before moving on. For those precious two minutes, either a High Priest would be present, or on a special occasion the Pharaoh himself would be present 'to be alone in the presence of the manifestation of his father Ra', as some inscriptions actually record.

There were a variety of such 'Eyes'. For one thing, each 'Eye' was double in the sense that it could appear in an inner sanctum somewhere in Egypt at both sunrise and sunset on the same day. (This is probably the origin of the legend that Pythagoras was seen in two different cities on the same day, which proved that he was a god.) But the solar 'Eyes' could be double in another sense, namely that the two extremes of Ra's position, at the two solstices, generated double sunrise 'Eyes' and double sunset 'Eyes'. And the precision of the true year involving as it does a calculation of an extra six hours (actually slightly less), this tiny portion of a day sometimes known as 'Horus' who was generated by the phallus of Osiris (which had been lost for the 364-day lunar year) and which represented Day 365, one could also speak on New Year's Day (the First Day of Thoth) of the appearance of an Eye of Horus rather than just the Eye of Ra. In fact, the same solar disc could be described as an Eye of Ra in one context and an Eye of Horus in another. The calendrical context could dictate the terminology relevant to the occasion. When the Eye of Ra became the Eye of Horus, the 'tiny gap' between the ideal and the real had been bridged, and the miracle of creation had occurred. Horus was 'the son' who was not so much born as re-born. The old had become new, the merely imagined had become real, the temporary had become eternal.

But the 'Eyes' which were projected by the sun onto the walls or screens, or even mirrors, of the inner sanctums of temples were not the only 'Eyes'. A large range of optical phenomena in ancient Egypt must now be sorted out. Even the 'obelisk flash' preceding sunrise could on occasion be referred to as an 'Eye'. The Egyptian obelisks were tipped with gold or electrum and the rising sun struck them before the light reached the ground's surface where people were standing. The way to be certain you could not blink and miss the moment of sunrise was to turn your back to the rising sun and observe the top of a nearby obelisk. (Even in 1999, observers of the total solar eclipse were advised in the newspapers to turn their backs on the sun and observe it as a pinhole-projection on a piece of paper.) A brilliant reflected light-flash would occur to herald the imminent sunrise, and you could then turn around and see the great event itself. We know about these functions of obelisks from ancient Egyptian texts, which I shall quote a little later on. The reason why the obelisks are not tipped with gold now, of course, is that it was all stripped off and melted down centuries ago by new rulers or simply by robbers during times of turmoil. The French have recently gilded the tip of their ancient Egyptian obelisk in the Place de la Concorde in Paris, possibly under Masonic influence.

Such use of obelisks would have been especially important at Heliopolis, the City of the Sun, which was on the east side of the Nile just north of modern Cairo. And this brings us to consider another strange thing about ancient Egypt – that traditionally obelisks were east of the Nile and pyramids were west of the Nile – Why was this? – And if sun-flashes from the tips of obelisks were so helpful, why were they only used east of the Nile and not all over Egypt? Well, for one thing, a sun-flash by an obelisk was only useful at sunrise, not at sunset, for obvious reasons! The east was correlated with sunrise and birth, whereas the west was correlated with sunset and death; hence, the huge necropolis on the Giza Plateau was west of the Nile. But what was the place of the pyramids in this religion of light? If the east had flashing obelisks, what did the west have? Clearly we have to investigate a little further. And on a trip to Egypt in 1998 I was able to discover one major 'light-trick' on the Giza Plateau caused by a shadow cast by the Pyramid of Khafre onto the south face of the Great Pyramid at sunset, reaching its maximum at the winter solstice.

Originally, the city of Memphis near the pyramids was noted for something called its *White Wall*. What was this? And let us look at the Great Pyramid for a moment: was there significance in the fact that between the autumn equinox and the spring equinox, the rising and setting sun illuminated the south face but not the north face, but that between the spring equinox and the autumn equinox it illuminated the north face but not the south face? Was this why such care was taken to face the three main Giza pyramids originally with white casing stones? In fact, what actual optical phenomena would have been manifested by the Great Pyramid at the time of its construction? Wouldn't it have been so brilliant in the sun that during the daytime no one could actually look at it? What would be the point of that? Also, what was going on at its tip? And what are the patterns made by the shadows of the Great Pyramid in relation to the other pyramids, and the Sphinx? My discovery of the winter solstice shadow (described at length in a moment) can only be part of the story. And how does all of this relate to the 'Eyes' which were not only solar discs seen in temples but were also crystal balls or crystal globes from which fire issued on the side opposite to

Figure 51. The two obelisks of Rameses II standing in front of the entrance to the Temple of Luxor. Only one now remains, for the other was removed in 1833 and taken to Paris, where it now stands in the middle of the Place de la Concorde. This engraving was made before its removal, and published in 1803 by Dominique Vivant Denon. Egypt has been despoiled of its obelisks for two millennia, for the ancient Romans removed far more of them than the modern Europeans did (there are 3133 Egyptian obelisks in Rome), and of those more recent ones, some were actually offered to Britain and France by the Pasha and not merely stolen. But despite the ancient pedigree of obelisk-collecting, we cannot consider this practice in any way respectable. It is very upsetting indeed to visit the ancient Egyptian sites and see gaps where the obelisks are supposed to be. No one had any business taking them away! (*Collection of Robert Temple.*)

the sun – the dancing serpent of fire, resembling the uraeus, the snake said to spit fire which is seen on the foreheads of all the pharaohs? We need to reconstruct the full schema of the ancient Egyptian theology of light and decode its multiple light-symbolism, which entered into much later esoteric sects such as Orphism and Gnosticism.

In November 1998, I was able to discover a fundamental shadow phenomenon connected with the pyramids. In Plate 30 I show the photo taken for me by my friend Mohamed Nazmy on 21 December, the winter solstice. This shadow is invisible in the other half of the year, but during the half of

369

the year when the south face of the Great Pyramid is illuminated, it creeps up until the solstice, and then down afterwards. And at its culmination, the shadow of the Pyramid of Khafre is thrown onto the south face of the Great Pyramid, transforming the triangle of that face into a very different triangle, by blotting out the south face's southeast corner. This dramatic shadow would have been far more striking when the pyramid was still covered in its white casing-stones, prior to their removal by the Arabs to build mosques in Cairo several hundred years ago. The Pyramid of Khafre was placed in just the right position on the Plateau to throw this Winter Solstice shadow onto the south face of the Great Pyramid. The shadow commences at the southwestern corner of the Great Pyramid's south face, so the purpose was clearly to truncate the face by altering the triangle.

The slope of the shadow at its culmination on the solstice is 26°, which is the same slope as all the descending and ascending passages inside the pyramid. It therefore serves as an exterior indicator of what is within.

This triangular shadow which is cast once a year upon the south face of the Great Pyramid has a very special significance. But in order to appreciate this, one has to be aware of a phenomenon which *can only be seen from the air* – the vertical bisection of the face and the 'hollowing-in' of the surface which were discovered by a British pilot flying over the Giza Plateau several decades ago, and which I discuss at length later in this chapter. (See the photo of this phenomenon in Plate 65.) The winter solstice shadow when taken as a triangle which stops mid-way across the face at this vertical line (which cannot be seen by the naked eye from ground level) and which rises from the base to the apex of the pyramid, forms a right triangle known as the *Golden Triangle*. This same Golden Triangle appears many times inside the pyramid, but this is its only known occurrence on the exterior.

A Flemish scientist named Hugo Verheyen and an earlier Dutch mathematician named H. A. Naber discovered occurrences of the Golden Triangle inside both the King's Chamber and the Grand Gallery of the Great Pyramid.[29] But first of all, what *is* the Golden Triangle?

The Golden Triangle is a right triangle whose smallest angle is 26° 33' 54". Its altitude is 1, its base is 2, and its hypotenuse is the square root of 5.[30] If you subtract the value of the altitude (1) from the value of the hypotenuse, you get a line segment remaining which is the Golden Section of the base. This triangle thus automatically generates its own Golden Section by the proportional relationship of its three sides, and it is the only triangle which does so. And this is the very triangle which is projected onto the south face of the Great Pyramid at the winter solstice.

The simplest occurrences of the Golden Triangle inside the Great Pyramid are found in the King's Chamber. All you have to do is draw a diagonal across the chamber from one corner to another and you have divided the chamber into a pair of Golden Triangles. The chamber was built with precisely the dimensions to enable this to be done. You can obviously

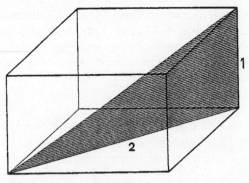

Figure 52. Hugo Verheyen's drawing of one of the several golden triangles manifested in the King's Chamber inside the Great Pyramid. The German Hermann Neikes and the Dutch physicist H. A. Naber were the first to discover the golden section in the Great Pyramid (in 1907 and 1915), and Verheyen has carried their studies much further. This is the same triangle projected onto the south face of the Great Pyramid at sunset on the winter solstice, as I discovered in 1998.
(From Hugo F. Verheyen, 'The Icosahedral Design of the Great Pyramid', in Istvan Harittai, editor, *Fivefold Symmetry*, World Scientific, Singapore etc., 1992, p. 349.)

do this on either the floor or the ceiling, and since you can draw the diagonal each time one of two ways, you can draw up to four Golden Triangles that way if you wish.

However, this is not all. The chamber's dimensions allow even more Golden Triangles to be inscribed within it. For you can draw a diagonal in the air from the floor to the ceiling with the base along the floor, and the invisible triangle drawn by this means in the air is also a Golden Triangle. See Figures 52 and 53. And you can draw up to four of these. So that means there are no less than eight Golden Triangles inside the King's Chamber.

But there is still more. See Figure 54 in order to recognize a Golden Triangle described by the ascending passage of the Great Pyramid and the Grand Gallery. Because the ascending slope is the correct angle, the distance from where the ascending and descending passages meet to the end of the Grand Gallery forms the hypotenuse of a Golden Triangle (and a vertical line dropped down from the altitude apparently indicates the eastern wall of the subterranean chamber as well). The Golden Triangle of the ascending passage *thus yields the length of the Grand Gallery as the Golden Section of the base*; this explains the length of the Grand Gallery, which has been generated according to the Golden Mean.

The Great Pyramid is thus riddled with Golden Triangles inside, and the winter solstice shadow is displayed annually outside as yet another of these unique triangles. We can also be certain that the point where the shadow intersects the apothegm (the vertical line bisecting the face), or in other words, the top of the shadow Golden Triangle's altitude, marks a precise spot which is of some importance. Either it indicates some further configuration

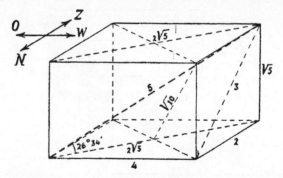

Figure 53. The second drawing of the golden triangle inscribed inside the King's Chamber of the Great Pyramid is believed to be this one by the physicist H. A. Naber which he published in 1908 in his book *Das Theorem des Pythagoras* (*The Pythagorean Theorem*), Verlag von P. Visser, Haarlem, Netherlands, 1908, Figure 29, p. 48, of which I have been fortunate to obtain a copy. (The previous year a similar drawing is believed to have been published by the mathematician Hermann Neikes in a rare German pamphlet which I have not seen.) Although Hugo Verheyen told me he had never seen this early book by Naber, he has a copy of Naber's rare Dutch book of 1915 on the golden section which inspired his own drawing in the preceding Figure 52.

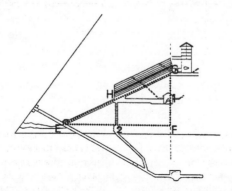

Figure 54. The Dutch physicist H. A. Naber, in a book published only in Dutch in 1915, first explained that the Ascending Passage inside the Great Pyramid is the hypotenuse defining a golden triangle. The so-called Grand Gallery has a length also defined by the major portion of the golden section of the base of the same golden triangle. In other words, if you divide the base of the triangle (here shown as line EF) in golden section and swing an arc upwards, the point at which it cuts the hypotenuse (i.e. the Ascending Passage) marks the commencement of the Grand Gallery. It is this same golden triangle which is projected on the south face of the same pyramid at the winter solstice, and the precise points indicated by it require highly detailed measurements and study, as they may indicate interior features, some of which may be currently unknown; these studies can only be made once a year on 21 December, and require considerable preparation. Anyone wishing to fund such a project should contact the author care of his publishers.

(Reproduced from H. A. Naber, *Meetkund en Mystiek*, Amsterdam, 1915, by Hugo F. Verheyen, in 'The Icosahedral Design of the Great Pyramid', as above, p. 350.)

372

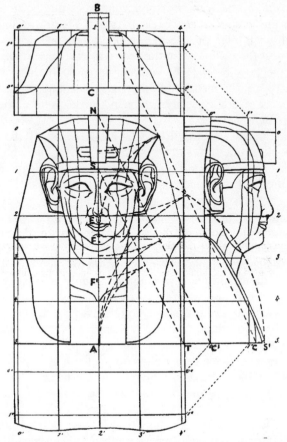

Figure 55. A typical Egyptian royal head laid out according to the classic canon of proportion, as found marked on various surviving examples. Everything is based upon the golden mean proportion, including golden triangles. This is Plate VI from Else Christie Kielland's fundamental book *Geometry in Egyptian Art*, London, 1955, p. 78. In order to understand the significance of this picture, the reader has to look at the various points marked with capital letters and follow the descriptions of the lines connecting them. The Egyptians always drew their plans with front and side views together like this (as we know from surviving papyri) as part of a whole plan of reducing three-dimensional reality to flat views which then became three-dimensional sculpture or wall carvings as the case might be. Here we have a head where the squares shown have actually been found inserted into the stone block (so that we know they are original). The height AN (the line joining A and N), giving the height of the head, is divided by the golden mean to give the point E, which lies under the nose. The line NB is equal to the line EN, so that the distance the face projects forward is equal to the minor golden section of the height of the head. The Egyptians then drew a golden triangle, ANC' where C' determines the positions of the squares in the profile view of the head. The minor golden section of the line AN then determines the half width of the head. Line AS is equal to line AS'. Line AS is divided by two other golden section cuts at points F and F'. Point F then determines the horizontal line of the headdress. Line FB is then also divided by a golden section cut which determines the point of the head touched by line BC and also the position of the symbol on the forehead. Each side of the dividing squares is equal to one third of the length AE. This rigorous canon was the basis of all Egyptian art, and gives it its immense power and presence and sense of transcendent harmony.

on the surface or, much more likely, it indicates the location of some key element in the interior of the Great Pyramid. These matters remain to be determined when more precise measurement becomes possible. Obviously one has to wait for a whole year after every missed opportunity, but my hope that the winter solstice of 1999 would bring an opportunity where many of the necessary measurements could be taken, enabling the decipherment of further aspects of this typically Egyptian puzzle, were dashed because of atmospheric haze.

The Scandinavian scholar Else Christie Kielland in 1955 published a brilliant book entitled *Geometry in Egyptian Art*, in which she reconstructed the canon of proportion used by the ancient Egyptians in all their art. In Figure 55 I reproduce one of her drawings, and the caption gives details of her analysis. Her evidence is all hard archaeological evidence, not mere speculation. The canon was based upon the golden mean proportion and golden triangles, so it is therefore only to be expected that golden triangles should riddle a structure so obviously important as the Great Pyramid. With the ancient Egyptian's evident obsession over thousands of years with golden proportions and golden triangles, the only surprise would be if the Great Pyramid had *not* manifested them, since such an omission would have been wholly out of character. And similarly, if any shape were going to be manifested on the exterior of the structure by a shadow, one would *expect* it to be a golden triangle. But just as people alive today cannot 'see' ancient lenses even when they are looking at them in display cases, so they cannot 'see' a golden triangle which is staring them in the face. (In any case, how many people alive today even know what a golden triangle is? Very few.)

What the ancient Egyptians thought they were doing is another matter. That is a subject for a long discussion which cannot take place here. The rigorous use of grids and a canon of proportion in all their art is paralleled by the application of the same techniques to the Giza pyramids. Unfortunately, this is a subject involving so much geometry and mathematics that few Egyptologists are prepared even to consider it, and they are also put off by the numerous enthusiasts whom they call 'pyramidiots' who get wildly carried away by numerical interpretation. The many 'pyramidologists' in the past who tried to relate the dimensions of the Great Pyramid to Biblical prophecies did a lot of damage to serious study of the mathematics and geometry of the Great Pyramid by dragging in their religious obsessions and contaminating the study. The irony is, however, that it was often only such people motivated by religious enthusiasm who were prepared to go to the trouble of obtaining the detailed measurements upon which a proper study can be based!

We now have the first real evidence as to why the Pyramid of Khafre was placed in its precise location *vis-à-vis* the Great Pyramid. If the location had varied even slightly, it would not have cast this winter solstice shadow upon the south face of its neighbour. Or it might have cast a shadow which cut across the Great Pyramid's south face in a manner which was not precise, without commencing at the bottom left-hand corner and neatly slicing the face in two by creating two new triangles in place of one. The Pyramid of Khafre, if situated further south, would have spilled its shadow upon the sand and it would have been lost. But the ancient Egyptians weren't ones to waste a good shadow when it could be harnessed and put to use.

So the winter solstice shadow was a stark signal, displayed upon the gleaming triangular white wall. Just as the sun went down in the West on the shortest day of the year, it gave a mammoth and spectacular public demonstration of the slope of all the interior passages of the Great Pyramid. Thereafter, the shadow would shrink away again and disappear until the next winter solstice returned.

When I mentioned in 1998 that I had discovered this shadow to Dr Zahi Hawass, Director of the Giza Plateau, he looked at me incredulous and for once was at a loss for words, while the cogs whizzed round in his head. Then he said thoughtfully: 'This is true, what you say.' He had 'seen' it many times in the years he has spent on the Plateau, but he had never *noticed* it. Now that I pointed it out to him, it 'clicked' in his head. He gave me permission to film it in the future for television.

The third Giza pyramid, the Pyramid of Menkaure, is too small to throw a shadow onto its neighbour the Pyramid of Khafre, and apparently has no involvement in shadow interplay with the other two pyramids.

I have found another golden triangle at the Valley Temple on the Giza Plateau. When I was walking up and down the 'ascending passage' which emerges from that structure onto the Causeway of Chephren, I had the distinct impression that the beautiful alabaster floor was sloping upwards at the familiar angle of 26°. I decided to test this. By this time, as a hardened golden triangulist, I had a child's plastic protractor in my pocket as if I were a schoolboy who might at any moment have to solve a geometry problem. And indeed I did need to solve a geometry problem! But this was not difficult. A small doorway and step to one side exists in the passageway, and I laid my protractor horizontal there and with a plastic credit card following the angle of the slope of the passage, it took only a moment to see that the angle of ascent of the passage was indeed 26°. With such rudimentary tools did I detect one of the secrets of the ancients: American Express to the rescue! – 'That will do nicely.' – One wonders whether the horizontal component of the golden triangle of which the Valley Temple's ascending passage is the hypotenuse may possibly exist in the form of a tunnel, and also whether anything might be found directly beneath the doorway at that level, where the triangle ends. This would seem to make sense, but the failure until now to realize that there was any coherent triangular structure implied has meant that nobody has ever thought of it before.

It is certainly interesting that both the Great Pyramid and the Valley Temple of Chephren contain interior Ascending Passages which ascend at

26°. What strikes me as odd is that nobody else ever noticed this, despite its being so very obvious. I do not have the length measurement of the Valley Temple passage; otherwise, I should compare its dimensions to those inside the Great Pyramid and see if there are any other correspondences.

There is a Descending Passage which descends at a slope of 26° at Saqqara. It dates from the Old Kingdom, either the end of the Fifth Dynasty or beginning of the Sixth Dynasty. It descends into the Mastaba of Neb-Kaw-Her (originally the Mastaba of Akhet-hotep), and was excavated by Selim Hassan in the 1930s.[31]

Golden triangles and slopes of 26° occur frequently in the tombs in the Valley of the Kings. See Plate 28 for my analysis of multiple golden triangles in a single wall painting, for instance. If one enters the Tomb of Rameses IX, one will see not only the famous 'backwards-leaning pharaoh' (see Plate 62) (now impossible to photograph because metal posts holding up the glass barriers are in the way!), one finds plenty of others in the same tomb. And there are at least two in the Tomb of Seti II. Once one starts looking for something, they seem to be everywhere. We never saw them before because we weren't looking for them.

The deceased pharaoh leaning at the angle of the golden triangle may have one other connotation which I should just mention. During the period of mummification, the king's body was put into natron salt (sodium carbonate, which occurs naturally in natron lakes in Egypt, and was gathered up in great quantities in ancient times). The natron had the effect of drying out and desiccating the flesh. Often the body would be left in natron for more than forty days, as part of the seventy-day embalming process. What may be significant is that the body was never laid horizontal during this process: embalmers' natron tables were always on a slope. I have not had the opportunity to lay my plastic protractor alongside such a natron table, but whether the angle was or was not the same angle of 26°, the fact that the dead pharaoh did actually recline at an angle while he was being prepared for the Afterlife probably featured in the symbolism, and would have been understood by the priests.

We already know that the base of the South Face of the Great Pyramid is 756.08 feet, according to Professor I. E. S. Edwards, the pyramid expert.[32] However, knowing this and the angle of 26° at the southwest corner of the shadow triangle is nevertheless insufficient to use trigonometry to find the other values we would like to know. I have looked through about 30 books on pyramid measures, without being able to find anyone who records the angles of the triangular faces of the Great Pyramid. Are these four faces isosceles triangles or equilateral ones? I cannot find anyone who tells us. If we had the angle of the southeast corner of the triangle, we could get the value of the side of the triangle which runs up the southeast edge of the pyramid. Then we could drop a perpendicular from the vertex of the shadow triangle at the top, and knowing the angle of 52° of the edge as we do, we would have the values of the other two angles as well as the value of one side. Thus we could find out the height above ground level of the top point of the shadow. It presumably has some significance for us. Doubtless this will be possible in the future on some occasion.

I have attempted an alternative method of determining the maximum height reached by the winter solstice shadow. I made a huge blow-up of the photo in Plate 30 and tried to count the masonry courses with a powerful magnifying glass. It ain't easy!

I believed I counted 49 courses, and at least one must have been obscured by the ground. If it be true that the maximum point of the shadow is really 50 masonry courses up, then it marks the very same masonry course on which the floor of the King's Chamber is found inside the pyramid, so that the shadow not only gives the slope of all the ascending and descending passages, but is a pointer to the location of the central chamber of the structure. And this is the very level where a horizontal section of the pyramid would have an area precisely half that of the pyramid's base area. However, an inspection in person in December 1999, seemed to indicate a point which was at about course 55 or 56, but I could not be certain of this.

It is also possible that the shadow gives the value of the natural constant known as *phi* (1.618), thus displaying the Golden Section along the edge of the pyramid. But this cannot be confirmed because it cannot yet be computed. It only looks as though it might be possible, allowing subjectively for the angular distortion of view. But as no reliable measurement is yet available, this remains speculation.

Clearly, the study of the winter solstice shadow is only beginning, and the opportunities to study it only occur once a year, at the rather inconvenient time of a Western holiday period. It may take some time to progress this situation. But at least we now know about the shadow, which is more than we did previously, and we are inching forward.

Others have studied pyramid shadows before me, but strangely they seem to have missed this one. Peter Tompkins in his extraordinary compendium *Secrets of the Great Pyramid* describes the work of two earlier students of the shadows, Robert T. Ballard and Moses B. Cotsworth. It is notable that neither of them was an Egyptologist. Egyptologists seem to be more interested in substance than shadow. It takes outsiders to think of these things.

Having first learned of Moses Cotsworth from the Tompkins book, I was fortunate to acquire a copy of his amazing work *The Rational Almanac*, signed by the author. An earlier version of this book had appeared in 1902,[33] and was the only version cited by Tompkins. But the full version of Cotsworth's work only appeared in 1905.[34] I don't know of anyone who has discussed this work in its full edition, which contains much more material on Egypt, and only Tompkins seems to have discussed its earlier edition. I can only presume that the book is so very rare that no one has seen it.

The Rational Almanac is a truly brilliant work, and Moses Cotsworth should be highly celebrated in the history of science. It is best to tell his story in his own words:

> Remembering that grandfather used to measure my height each birthday *by cutting its notch into the wooden pillar supporting the mantel-shelf* at the family fire-side, that formed my first conception of the record of passing years. I looked back upon those as 'my years' when growing and years seemed so long.
>
> Further back I could just call to mind in childhood how my great-grandfather used to tease me in our little walks, by finding from the length of his shadow when it was tea-time on Sunday. As one of the old agricultural labourers who had even to build their own houses with sods (not being able to buy bricks), he had never been able to afford a watch, and therefore had to resort to thus indirectly reading Time by shadows from nature's indications, as was generally done in country districts until cheap watches came within the reach of the labourers, some of whom in remote districts still [in 1905] use the 'Sun sighting' and 'Shadow-pin' guides to Time.[35]

I suspect that most readers today will find that their jaws involuntarily drop when they read this. You cannot find a countryman in the whole of England today (2000) who can tell the time by a shadow. All this is lost, like a dream. And over the many years that I have lived in the English countryside, I have never met a farmer who could even tell one star from another. So completely have farmers today become divorced from the phenomena of nature.

When Moses Cotsworth was grown up he developed a severe throat disease, and was ordered by his doctor to travel to a dry country to save his health. He decided to turn his adversity to advantage, and travelled to Egypt in 1900. The Egyptologists of those days were not the haughty type. Cotsworth, an almanac enthusiast with no university education, was welcomed with open arms by the distinguished French Egyptologist, Professor Gaston Maspero, then head of the Egyptian Antiquities Department, and also by Sir Flinders Petrie who was digging at Abydos. Both tried to help him, as Professor Charles Piazzi Smyth had already done in Britain, to try to reconstruct the lost Egyptian shadow-science.

Cotsworth became convinced that the Giza pyramids were erected 'to serve as a perfect almanac for registering the seasons and the year'. He had already befriended the greatest of the pyramidologists, Professor Piazzi Smyth, Astronomer Royal for Scotland and author of many volumes on the subject, and after Smyth's death he bought all of his books and papers at auction. (How I wish I could find that collection myself!) He rejected Smyth's Biblical obsessions (Smyth thought the Great Pyramid was connected with Biblical prophecies), but he used Smyth's wonderfully accurate data and measurements to study the way in which the pyramids and obelisks could throw useful shadows.

Cotsworth actually discussed the winter solstice shadow thrown by the Great Pyramid itself upon the northern pavement (he calculated a shadow length on the ground of 268 feet), without even thinking of – much less knowing of – the shadow cast upon the Great Pyramid's south face. Presumably he was so busy studying and measuring one shadow that he neglected to walk around to the back of the structure to observe that there was another being cast out of sight on the opposite face.

In fact, so close did Cotsworth come to noticing the winter solstice shadow which I found in 1998, that he actually published a photo of himself on a camel beside the Sphinx, with the south face of the Great Pyramid in the background upon which a partial and pointed shadow cast by the adjoining pyramid may be seen, and he describes it in the caption as 'the pointed Shadow of the 2nd Pyramid cast on the 6th December, 1900, at 5:30 p.m., from a distance of about $^1/_3$rd Mile, or 550 yards.' And in the accompanying text he adds: 'This photograph shows how even Sunset Shadows near the Winter Solstice could be used, and as the 2nd and Great Pyramids are situated almost exactly on the same diagonal line . . . they may have been so used to register Sunset Shadows.'[36] Isn't it amazing that

M. B. COTSWORTH, Acomb, YORK, England.

Figure 56. A portrait photo of Moses B. Cotsworth, which he published in his book *The Rational Almanac*, York, England, 1902 and 1905, p. 450.

379

Cotsworth came so close but still missed it? If he had stayed there for another half hour or so, being present actually at sunset rather than going back to return the camel and have his supper, he would have discovered the winter solstice shadow 99 years ahead of me.

The pyramid shadows in which Cotsworth was most interested were the equinox shadows, by which he believed the precise length of the year was ultimately determined. Cotsworth pointed out, quite correctly, that the northern pavement abutting the Great Pyramid was a shadow-floor whose blocks were laid alternately rather than square on, to facilitate shadow measurements on successive days. Alternate block-laying provides twice the number of points of intersection for the measurement of overlaid shadows, and gives a doubly effective measuring-grid. I reproduce Cotsworth's diagram of these blocks in Figure 57.[37] This was one of his countless brilliant observations. The paving blocks were cut in what he called 'the 4.45 foot gauge pattern'. That is, the junctions of intersection were 4.45 feet apart, and the tip of the pyramid shadow varies by 4.45 feet every successive day. So the junctions of the stones matched the successive daily points of the shadow tip as it moved throughout the months!

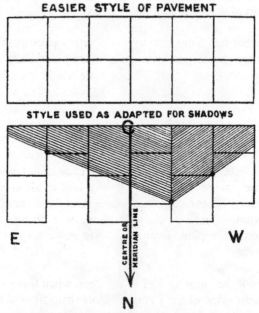

EASIER STYLE OF PAVEMENT

STYLE USED AS ADAPTED FOR SHADOWS

E   CENTRE OR MERIDIAN LINE   W

N

Figure 57. Moses Cotsworth's diagram of the alternate block pattern of the northern pavement beside the Great Pyramid, showing how the daily measurement of solar shadows was facilitated in Old Kingdom times. Cotsworth worked out that the paving block joints were 4.45 feet apart and the pyramid shadow moves its tip 4.45 feet per day, from joint to joint. The paving floor thus functioned as a daily calendar, with each shadow location identifying a specific day of the year. In reality, this drawing is greatly simplified, since the real blocks do not have this regularity which is shown here in a schematized form.

(From Moses B. Cotsworth, *The Rational Almanac*, York, England, 1902/1905, p. 67.)

However, the system was even more sophisticated than that. The shadow movements on the northern shadow-floor of the Great Pyramid automatically accounted for the phenomenon which we deal with by creating 'leap years', namely the fact that each year is not an even number of days but adds a fraction of a day. This was indicated by the fact that every year the shadow-tip on 20 March advanced along the gauge by about one extra foot. This material appears only in the 1905 edition of Cotsworth's book, as interleaved pages inserted between pages 78 and 79 of the old printed sheets; the paper is of a slightly different colour.

Tompkins's comments are interesting:

To support his observations, Cotsworth made a series of photographs of these shadows as they grew shorter towards the vernal equinox. To his delight he found that the paving blocks had been cut in widths very close to the 4.45-foot gradation by which each noonday shadow succeeded the former as they approached the vanishing point in March [at the spring equinox].

It was only thus, says Cotsworth, 'that the ancient priests could have established by physical observation of the shadow on the flagstones, the precise length of a year to .24219 of a day.'[38]

I don't know what has happened to Cotsworth's photographs, books and papers, but if they are deposited in some worthy Yorkshire library, I hope one day to find them, especially as they also would include all of Piazzi Smyth's as well. Cotsworth made many models of pyramids and cones to study their shadow-casting patterns, and drew many amazingly elaborate projections and diagrams. Presumably these are all preserved somewhere – but where? I reproduce in Figure 58 Cotsworth's diagram of the shadow patterns made throughout the year by the Great Pyramid.[39]

According to Peter Tompkins, Professor William Kingsland 'pointed out that some of the paving stones are actually laid at all kinds of irregular angles and corners; but the corners of these stones are clearly cut out to fit the adjoining stone – indicating, if anything, an even more sophisticated geometric pattern.' Tompkins then goes on to add a very important observation of his own:

To make up for the summer half of the year, when there was no shadow on the northern slope of the Pyramid, Cotsworth figured that the priests could have subdivided and tabulated the intervening months.

In this he failed to realize that the southern face of the Pyramid, being highly polished, could throw a triangle, not of shadow, but of sunlight onto a southern pavement during the summer months, quite as definite as the winter shadows thrown on the northern side.

From May to August the south face would cast a triangular reflection of the sun onto the ground which would shorten as it approached the summer solstice, the shortest being at noon of the solstice, lengthening again till noon of the last day of summer.

Noon reflections would also be projected every day of the year from the east and west faces. But this was to remain for David Davidson to establish.[40]

We should not be dismissive of the use of the shadow of the Great Pyramid for such purposes. By implication this has been found acceptable to others than Moses Cotsworth. The historian of science Otto Neugebauer, who was never known to stray into anything resembling a fringe, published an important paper in 1980 with diagrams explaining how the shadow of the Great Pyramid could be used to determine true geographical north to high accuracy.[41] Although Neugebauer's comments are brief in the extreme and he mentions nothing about pavements, it is obvious that for the shadow to have been effective in the way that he describes, a perfectly flat paved area such as that north of the Great Pyramid is a requirement. He therefore accepts all of that by implication.

We can confidently agree with Cotsworth in his general view of the Great Pyramid:

> . . . the Great Pyramid was erected for what I believe to be its *first great purpose of constantly showing the true time to all around*. Its position at the Southern apex of the large triangular delta-tract . . . comprising the most fertile, extensive, and populous lands of Egypt, enabled its vast bulk and towering height of nearly 500 feet to be seen over that vast level area, as a clock-point to gauge the Sun's position; whilst the clear, dry climate helped the reflection of the Sun's rays from its polished sides, thereby showing with true gradations the time of day to all the people, the bulk of whom were slaves requiring food, etc., on a large scale at organized times.[42]

We know from classical sources that the shadows cast by the Great Pyramid were studied intently in antiquity. An account of this dating to about 585 BC is preserved by Pliny [first century AD]:

> The method of measuring the height of the pyramids and of taking any similar measurement was devised by Thales of Miletus, the procedure being to measure the shadow at the hour at which its length is expected to be equal to the height of the body that is throwing it. Such are the wonders of the pyramids . . .[43]

It is generally accepted that Thales, one of the 'Seven Wise Men' of Greece, whose work is lost and known only through quotations, adapted the Egyptian sciences of geometry and trigonometry for use by the Greeks. Since Thales was alive in 585 BC at the time of a solar eclipse which he

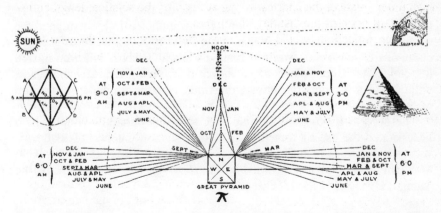

Figure 58. A drawing by Moses Cotsworth showing the monthly movement of the shadows cast by the Great Pyramid at 6 a.m., 9 a.m., noon, 3 p.m., and 6 p.m. At noon on the winter solstice, the shadow reaches its greatest elongation to the north. Because Cotsworth was so busy observing this phenomenon, he missed the more dramatic winter solstice shadow published for the first time in my photo in Plate 30, which takes place on the other side of the Great Pyramid, so that one cannot watch both at once. Cotsworth stresses that he has purposely exaggerated the shadows here, and that the diagram is only a rough one to give the idea. Above the pyramid diagram we see the angle subtended between the earth's equator and the Great Pyramid (shown as a small black triangle on the surface of the globe) as seen from the sun.
(From Moses B. Cotsworth, *The Rational Almanac*, York, England, 1902/1905, p. 60.)

supposedly foretold, we have at the very least direct evidence of the close study of the Great Pyramid's shadow during the Saite 26th Dynasty (ended 525 BC) of the Third Intermediate Period, prior to the arrival of the Persians in Egypt. It was during the Saite period that many Greeks settled in Egypt, and many also fought as mercenary soldiers there. It was clearly in this congenial and welcoming atmosphere that Thales was able to visit Egypt and learn something of its science and mathematics. But no one can doubt that the science of shadows had been practised in Egypt from the very beginning, and Thales was merely the first to tell it to the Greeks. As for the specific shadow mentioned in the text, it would presumably have been 481 feet long (or whatever original height of the pyramid one accepts). But where would this shadow fall? At what time on what day? Clearly it had significance – but what significance? Here again is something for us to calculate, and which may even offer an explanation as to why the Great Pyramid has the height that it has.

Something which needs to be mentioned about solar shadows is that the sun is not a point-source of light, but a disc. It therefore does not give a precise cut-off at the edge of its shadow because the disc itself is extended. The Egyptians hardly needed reminding of this, since they even had a special name for the disc of the sun – they called it Aten. And as is well known to

383

The Crystal Sun

a very large section of the general public, the heretical Pharaoh Akhenaten (who changed his name from Amenhetep/Amunhotep IV) worshipped the Aten specifically. He was so keen on the Aten, in fact, that he effaced the name of the god Amun from the temple walls at Thebes, and even moved his capital to a new place where he could worship the Aten in peace, without a lot of annoying priests of Amun hanging around making him nervous.

The need to try to get a precise edge to a fuzzy shadow is one which necessitated the use of something called a 'shadow-catcher'. This device was well described by a Chinese astronomer named Kuo Shou-Ching (Guo Shou-Jing in Pinyin), as recorded in *The History of the Yuan Dynasty* (the Mongol Dynasty, 1260–1368 AD):

The shadow definer is made of a leaf of copper 2 inches wide and 4 inches long, in the middle of which is pierced a pin-hole. It has a square supporting framework, and is mounted on a pivot so that it can be turned at any angle, such as high to the north and low to the south (i.e. at right angles to the incident shadow-edge). The instrument is moved back and forth until it reaches the middle of the (shadow of the) cross-bar, which is not too well-defined, and when the pin-hole is first seen to meet the light, one receives an image no bigger than a rice grain in which the cross-beam can be noted indistinctly in the middle. On the old methods, using the simple summit of the gnomon [tall shadow-pillar, like an obelisk], what was projected was the upper edge of the solar disc. But with this method one can obtain, by means of the cross-bar, the rays from the centre of the disc without any error.

This passage was translated by Joseph Needham, since *The History of the Yuan Dynasty* does not exist in English (although it should do! – any rich people out there to fund it?). Joseph then commented as follows:

This was long misunderstood. Gaubil, Wylie, and even Tung Tso-Pin, thought that the instrument was placed at the top of the gnomon, but Maspero showed rather convincingly that on the contrary it was moved along the horizontal graduated scale and had the effect of focusing, like a lens, the image of the cross-bar. That Kuo Shou-Ching should have utilized the principle of the pin-hole is not at all surprising, since, as will be seen in the Section on physics, it had been familiar to Chinese scientists at least three centuries earlier [i.e. the tenth century AD], and indeed the camera obscura may have passed from them to the Arabs. There is, moreover, contemporary supporting evidence for Maspero's interpretation, in a remark by the astronomer Yang Huan (died 1299 AD).

The observations of Kuo and his assistants were collected in a book with the title . . . *Studies on the Gnomon Shadows at the Two Solstices*, but it has long been lost, and the calendrical chapters of the *Yuan Shih*

[*History of the Yuan Dynasty*] are now our only resource. Laplace himself considered the work with the 40 ft. gnomon in the 13th century AD as perhaps the most accurate which had ever been done on solstice shadows.[44]

I have discussed these matters with Professor Allan Mills of the University of Leicester in England, and he has made some interesting refinements to the concept of the 'shadow-catcher'. However, to go into further detail would take us too far afield. Suffice it to say that methods of refining the edges of solar shadows were necessary, and indeed the ancient Egyptians might have used a lens, as described above, rather than a pin-hole device, for all we know, since they had them available.

With regard to the subject of light and shadow, it is instructive to look at some classical references to the Egyptian pyramids and obelisks for some interesting clues. First we turn to Pliny, and something he says about obelisks:

Monoliths of this granite [from Aswan] were made by the kings, to some extent in rivalry with one another. They called them obelisks and dedicated them to the Sun-god. An obelisk is a symbolic representation of the sun's rays, and this is the meaning of the Egyptian word for it.[45]

My old friend Professor Eichholz gives a good footnote at this point, having done his homework:

Pliny is right. *Tekhen* means both 'sunbeam' and obelisk.[46]

Pliny has some further interesting comments about obelisks, and what he says goes a long way to substantiate the ideas of Moses Cotsworth about a shadow-floor beside the Great Pyramid, since it provides evidence that the Egyptians did this with their obelisks, as an obelisk moved to Rome was set up according to their principles:

The one [obelisk] in the Campus was put to use in a remarkable way by [Emperor] Augustus of Revered Memory so as to mark the sun's shadow and thereby the lengths of days and nights. A pavement was laid down for a distance appropriate to the height of the obelisk so that the shadow cast at noon on the shortest day of the year [once again the winter solstice comes into prominence] might exactly coincide with it. Bronze rods let into the pavement [this is a bit obscure, and these rods may have been very small markers embedded in the stone, not upright] were meant to measure the shadow day by day as it gradually became shorter and then lengthened again. This device deserves to be carefully studied, and was contrived [doubtless following Egyptian principles] by the mathematician

385

Novius Facundus. He placed on the pinnacle a gilt ball, at the top of which the shadow would be concentrated, for otherwise the shadow cast by the tip of the obelisk would have lacked definition.[47]

Here we see the recurrence of the fuzzy edge-of-the-shadow problem, and learn that Novius Facundus tried to overcome it by placing a golden ball on the tip of the obelisk. A shining golden tip for the obelisk was by no means an innovation of his own, however, since all Egyptian obelisks except for the miniature ones used in cemeteries had them, as I shall describe in a moment. But the fact that Novius Facundus used a *globe* is interesting, because as we shall see shortly I believe that in Egypt sometimes a crystal globe was placed on the tips of structures for similar reasons, and that refracted light rays were part of the scheme of the designers.

Another classical author, Ammianus Marcellinus (fourth century AD), who is rarely read despite the fascinating nature of his writing, records an important detail about the pyramids:

And huge as they are, as they taper off gradually, they throw no shadow, in accordance with a principle of mechanics.[48]

What Ammianus was referring to was the disappearance of the shadow of the Great Pyramid on the northern shadow-floor at the equinox, which enabled the length of the year to be computed. (The shadow to the north of the pyramid vanishes when the sun is due east, the only shadow then being cast due west.) He correctly reported a detail of which he had been told, without understanding it himself. Ammianus was rather intrigued in general by the notion of something throwing no shadow, and he gives a much clearer account of this in his account of Upper Egypt:

There is also Syene [modern Aswan], where at the time of the summer solstice the rays surrounding upright objects do not allow the shadows to extend beyond the bodies. And if anyone fixes a post upright in the ground, or sees a man or a tree standing erect, he will perceive that their shadow is consumed at the extremities of their outlines. This also happens at Meroe, which is the spot in Ethiopia nearest to the equinoctial circle, and where for ninety days the shadows fall in a way just opposite to ours, on account of which the natives of that district are called Antiscii [from *anti*, opposite, and *skia*, shadow].[49]

In the third century BC the Greek scientist Eratosthenes had attempted to measure the size of the earth by studying the lack of shadow in a deep well at Syene, and it is interesting to see that 700 years later, the folk at Aswan had used this incident to puff up interest in their town, and doubtless the enterprising locals gave demonstrations to Roman tourists to earn some baksheesh.

An interesting text survives from the time of the 19th Dynasty Pharaoh Seti I (1291–1278 BC) describing the use of a shadow clock. This text is carved in the stone of the Oseirion at Abydos, known to Egyptologists as 'the Cenotaph of Seti I', since they now like to insist in the very name they officially use for it that it was built by Seti I at the same time as his large Temple of Osiris adjoining it.[50] Here is part of the text, in its revised translation by E. M. Bruins (which corrects Frankfort's translation):

> The hour of the day, beginning with fixing the place: Determining the hours . . . Determining the hours by means of a shadow clock, whose scale-bar is 5 palms in its length, the height with a top-bar-strip of 2 fingers in its height on top of the shadow clock. . . . When you have adjusted this shadow clock in accordance with the sun, its end being to the east, that is to say the end on which the cross-bar is mounted the shadow of the sun will be correct on this shadow clock.[51]

It is certainly always marvellous when a real ancient text comes to light dealing in some way with phenomena concerning which one is often otherwise reduced to speculation from physical remains.

We need now to look more closely at the Egyptian granite obelisks, which are assumed to have arisen from the earlier gnomons which had been made of wood. In Plate 25 we see an interesting bit of synchronicity. I was at Karnak, observing an obelisk (no, it didn't move!), and noticed that it had a carving of the hawk of Horus at its top. And just then, a real hawk flew along and perched on the tip of the obelisk above the carving of himself, and sat in the same position. I was able to get a photo of this amusing coincidence.

If we look at the Egyptian language, we find that the word *hui* means both 'light, illumination' and 'apex of an obelisk'. And this is not by chance. For the tips of the obelisks were always covered in gold or gold alloy to reflect the sun and cast their own rays of illumination far and wide. The obelisks literally had tips of light.

Speaking of the obelisks of Queen Hatshepsut of the 18th Dynasty (1498–1483 BC), Labib Habachi says:

> Apart from the usual decoration of the pyramidion [the tip], there are on the upper half of each face of each obelisk eight scenes on either side of the customary column of inscription. Each scene contains a figure of the queen or her stepson [and nephew] Tuthmosis III in adoration of or making offerings to Amun-Re. Not only the pyramidion but the scenes were adorned with electrum, so that almost the entire upper half of the obelisk gleamed in the sun. The damage suffered by these obelisks was not caused in an attempt to obliterate the name of the queen [as happened elsewhere]; rather they suffered from the attacks of the agents of Akhenaten (1379–1362 BC), who removed the name and image of Amun-Re.[52]

Habachi then goes on to quote the famous inscription, which was first published in English by Wallis Budge in 1902 in Volume IV of his wonderful *History of Egypt*, in the section on Queen Hatshepsut.[53] Twenty-four years later, Budge republished the text in his book *Cleopatra's Needles and Other Egyptian Obelisks*, which is conveniently available in a modern paperback.[54] I shall quote from the latter, more complete and revised, translation by Wallis Budge. But first it is important to explain what *tchām* is. This is a very mysterious word, symbolized by a strange-looking staff normally considered to be a sceptre. The 'sceptre' has a bifurcated bottom and a 'head' which looks like it might be a jackal's head or the head of the Seth-animal (identified at last by Richard Hobban, as explained shortly), but which in any case slopes downwards. This sceptre was certainly associated with shadow-study and surveying. It is also connected mythologically with the Sons of Horus – mythical founders of Egypt – and the god Anubis, who often carried it (see Plate 19). But primarily, it was the sceptre or staff of the god Ptah, who was rarely seen without it. It was fitting that the sceptre should be associated with Ptah, since he was the god of the celestial pole, and the sceptre was used in studying shadows to find true north. The reason why Ptah is portrayed wrapped tightly in a shroud, with only his hands (holding the sceptre) and feet protruding, is that this symbolizes his being endlessly 'wrapped around by the sky', which constantly revolves around the pole.

The *tchām* sceptre is also, and in fact more commonly, known as the *uas* or *was* sceptre. As Egyptian history progressed, it became increasingly common as a symbol used in tombs, and it often appeared merely for its decorative value in temple carvings of late date, as if it were a *fleur de lys*. The region of Egypt in which Thebes was situated was called *Waset*, and used this sceptre as its symbol, decorated additionally with a feather and a ribbon.

The word *tchām*, incorporating the hieroglyph of this same sceptre, refers to an unknown precious metal. Rather than busy ourselves with speculation as to what the original metal intended by the name may have been, we are concerned here only with its use by the time of the New Kingdom when it appeared in obelisk inscriptions. By that time, it was used to describe the metal which was placed on the obelisk tips by the pharaohs. Since all such metal has long since disappeared, we do not know what it was exactly, except that it contained gold and was immensely valuable, especially in such quantities. It may have been a mixture of gold and silver – what is called electrum – or it may have been a mixture of copper and gold. On the other hand, it may have been a particular type of gold which was especially shiny and reflective. Here is what Wallis Budge says about this problem:

> . . . even when the obelisk was set up and polished and inscribed, the work in connection with it was not finished, for the pyramidion had to

be supplied with a metal casing, or cap. . . . when [Pharaoh] Thothmes I [1503–1491 BC; 18th Dynasty] . . . set up his two great obelisks before the double door of the house of the god, he covered their pyramidions with casings made of a metal which the Egyptians called *tchām* [he here gives the hieroglyphs, with the sceptre sign]. This word has been translated by 'gold', 'electrum', 'white gold', 'gilded copper', but no one knows what the exact constituents of the metal were. It can hardly have been gold, for the common word for gold is *nub* . . . on the other hand, *tchām* may be an old, and perhaps a foreign, word for gold. Much of the gold ore found contains silver, and when the proportion of silver was one-fifth the ore was called 'electrum' (Pliny, *Natural History*, XXXIII, 23); an artificial electrum was made by mixing silver with gold. It is probable that *tchām* was a kind of natural gold which was found in the Sudan and was called '*green gold*'. In any case it was capable of a very high polish and reflected the light almost as brightly as quicksilver. It was used for the casings of the tops of obelisks throughout the XVIIIth and XIXth and following Dynasties . . . Of the style and thickness of such a casing we know nothing, but a great deal of metal must have been needed for its construction, for Queen Hatshepsut says about her obelisks, 'I allotted for them refined *tchām* [which] I weighed out by the *heket* measure, like sackfuls of grain.' . . . in other words, she used the precious *tchām* not by the pound but by the hundredweight. These words suggest that the casings of the pyramidions of her obelisks were made of thick plates of *tchām*; that they were of considerable value is proved by the fact that no trace of them has ever been found. It is probable that they were removed or stolen during the early years of the reign of the 'heretic' king Amenhetep IV [who changed his name to Akhenaten].[55]

There are reasons to believe that this New Kingdom tradition of plating the tops of obelisks with the shiniest possible metal, to facilitate optical reflections, derives from a much earlier tradition in the Old Kingdom period, when similar plates of metal were used at the tops of pyramids rather than obelisks. But we shall be returning to pyramids. For the moment, let us read some of the inscription of Queen Hatshepsut on her obelisks, in order to see how she understood the importance of the metal casings. She commences her inscription with a dazzling description of herself as a divine being, far too long for us to bother with here, but which includes a description of her as 'the Horus woman'. At the very end of this enormous paean of praise for herself, she culminates by calling herself:

. . . the woman who is the *tchām* of kings.

She then goes on to describe her construction and erection of her pair of obelisks at Karnak:

She made [them] as her monument to her father, Amen [Amun], Lord of
the Thrones of the Two Lands [i.e. Thebes], President of the Apts (i.e.
Karnak). She made for him two great obelisks of the lasting (or solid)
granite of the region of the South (i.e. the granite quarries at Aswan).
The upper part[s] of [them] are of *tchām* of the best of all the mountains,
and they can be seen [from afar both upstream and downstream?]. The
Two Lands (Egypt) are bathed in light when Athen [Aten] (i.e. the solar
Disk) rolleth up between them as he riseth up on the horizon of heaven.
I have done this because of [my] loving heart for Father Amen. . . . My
heart urged me to make for him two obelisks with *tchām* coverings, the
pyramidions (i.e. pointed tops) of which should pierce the sky . . . I made
them for him in rectitude of heart, for [he is] thinking of every God. I
longed to make them for him, plated (?) with *tchām* metal; lo! I laid their
part (or, half) upon their bodies [presumably she means she covered the
tops with the metal]. I kept in mind [what] the people would say – that
my mouth was true because of what came forth from it, for I never went
back on anything that I had once said. Now hearken ye to me. I gave to
them (i.e. the obelisks) the best refined *tchām*, which I measured by the
heket (bushel?) as if it had been ordinary grain in sacks. My Majesty
allotted to them a larger quantity of *tchām* than had ever been seen by
the whole of the Two Lands (i.e. Egypt). This the fool as well as the wise
man knoweth well. . . .[56]

Her nephew, Pharaoh Thothmes III, also known as Tuthmosis III
(1479–1424 BC), erected two obelisks of his own at Karnak. Just as
Thothmes himself was a small man less than five feet tall, so his obelisks
were smaller than those of his aunt. His obelisk inscription similarly states:

The son of Rā, Thothmes, crowned with crowns, set it up in the Apts
[Karnak], and made for it a pyramidion of refined *tchām*, the splendours
of which illumined Thebes, . . .[57]

Readers who live in England will be interested to know that *tchām* is
mentioned in the inscription which appears on the Egyptian obelisk which
stands beside the River Thames, which we colloquially call 'Cleopatra's
Needle', although it had nothing whatever to do with Cleopatra. This
obelisk once stood at Heliopolis, northeast of Cairo, and was also erected
by Pharaoh Thothmes III. It is one of a great many obelisks carried away
from Egypt as trophies to other countries, a bad habit which began with the
ancient Romans (there are 13 Egyptian obelisks in Rome!). The inscription
on 'Cleopatra's Needle' includes these comments:

He [the Pharaoh] set up a pair of great obelisks (*tekhenui urui*), the
pyramidions (*benbenti*) of *tchām*, at his third time of the Set [Sed]
Festival, through the greatness of his love of Father Tem.[58]

The twin of this obelisk, which once stood beside its brother-obelisk at Heliopolis, stands now in Central Park in New York and says:

> He [the Pharaoh] set up two great obelisks [with] pyramidions of *tchām*. The son of Rā, Thothmes, . . . the ever-living, did [this].[59]

It is sufficiently obvious by now that the obelisks of the New Kingdom period were designed to incorporate immensely expensive and spectacular optical effects, procured at a cost which Queen Hatshepsut boasted was greater than any that went before, at least in the New Kingdom. Her obelisks were designed by her vizier and – it is thought – her lover, whose name was Senmut. Senmut's tomb is notable for its astronomical ceiling (which also portrays an actual obelisk/gnomon!), and he was an architect and an intellectual to whom optical effects would have been very familiar. Although gold-plated pyramidions for obelisks existed before him, he was probably responsible for the extreme prominence given to them by his Queen, and the enormous cost lavished on procuring the necessary plates of gold.

Figure 59. Detail from a New Kingdom funerary papyrus. On the left the embalmer god Anubis presents the mummy of the deceased, whose widow laments him on her knees, clasping his legs in her distress. On the right, the tomb awaits. The two Eyes of Ra are on either side, representing the two extreme positions of the Sun God at the winter and summer solstices (as observed by projected images through the 'horizontal telescope tubes' of the great solstice temples such as Karnak). And between them is the solar symbol of the gold-tipped pyramidion atop the pyramidal roof of the tomb. Thus we see that during the New Kingdom period, non-royal individuals in their small ways attempted to copy the royal obelisks of their time in the more traditional mode of the older gold-tipped pyramids.

Martin Isler has done very important work on the subject of shadows in ancient Egypt, and like myself has had little choice but to fall back on Joseph Needham for his accounts of what went on in China, to offer some comparisons and help achieve better understanding of the phenomena. Inevitably, Isler ended up considering the accounts of the *History of the Yuan Dynasty*! What I find particularly exciting about the work of Isler is that he and I independently came to the same conclusion about the true nature of the wand with a bifurcated tip which is often seen in Egyptian iconography. It may be seen in Figure 61. For ease of reference, let us coin a name for it and call it the bifurx. I had already concluded that it was a sighting-device when I first turned to Isler's writings and saw that he was convinced of the same thing. He works out in great detail the use of the

Figure 60. On the left is the obelisk which now stands in Central Park in New York City, engraved as it looked when it was standing at Alexandria in Egypt, prior to its removal to America in 1880. It is also called 'Cleopatra's Needle', like its former twin, the obelisk now standing beside the River Thames in London; the two originally stood as a pair either side of the great entrance to the Temple of the Sun at Heliopolis (a building now vanished) near Cairo. The Roman Emperor Augustus moved them to Alexandria in the first century BC, and Lieutenant Commander H. H. Gorringe of the US Navy moved this one to New York. (The other 'Cleopatra's Needle' was moved to London in 1878.) This obelisk weighs 220 tons. It was originally erected by the Pharaoh Thothmes III (died 1425 BC), nephew of the Pharaoh Queen Hatshepsut. (Pompey's Pillar also seen here is a Roman monument at Alexandria in Egypt. In fact it has no connection with Pompey, having been erected by the Emperor Diocletian in the late third century AD to celebrate a victory.)
(Collection of Robert Temple.)

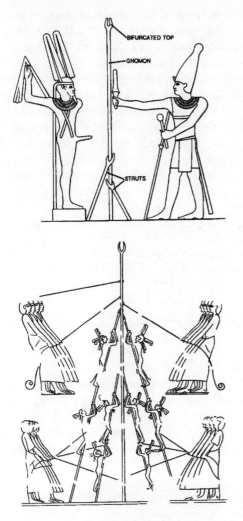

Figure 61. Two ancient Egyptian representations of the bifurx, reproduced by Martin Isler. Above, the god Min (who lacks an arm but makes up for it with another member) faces a bifurx before which stands the pharaoh, on the occasion of the Festival of Min. Below, an extremely high bifurx is being erected and stabilized by many people with ropes.

bifurx as a gnomon for catching the sun's shadow because of the forked tip. This eliminates the need for a 'shadow-catcher' pin-hole device, since the gnomon's tip – far more effective than a golden globe – acts as a kind of pin-hole itself. Isler's work is so brilliant and imaginative that one wishes there were more people like him around. My own interest in the bifurx was as a sighting-device for surveying; I had not thought of its use as a gnomon. Isler reproduces several ancient Egyptian scenes which show the bifurx prominently erected as a gnomon, none of which I had seen before. He doesn't say where they come from or what their dates are, which is rather frustrating. Of one huge bifurx-gnomon depicted as being raised by a large group of men, Isler says:

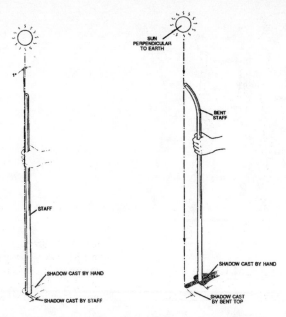

Figure 62. Martin Isler's drawings showing the reason for the curved top of a shadow-staff, such as that held by the pharaoh in the previous illustration.

I believe this pole is a gnomon, indeed one that has the special quality of distinguishing the meridian shadow from all others. As mentioned, this is the most important shadow of the day, because a comparison of the relative length of this shadow at local solar noon gives the changing altitude of the sun above the horizon. It is this height by which the time of the year can be judged.

And later on he gives this interesting information, in the light of what we have recently considered:

Supporting evidence in Egypt for measuring or counting shadow lengths also exists in a Middle Kingdom prophecy in which there is a reference about the solar eclipse in the following words: 'One cannot perceive when midday will be if one does not count the shadow.'[60]

In addition, Isler points out that in the Old Kingdom of Egypt, staffs with curved tops also can be used 'to give a clear and measurable shadow'. A statue of Pharaoh Amenophis II of the 18th Dynasty (1453–1419 BC) actually holds such a staff with clearly marked, evenly spaced rings on its shaft which constitute a shadow measuring-scale. We shall come back to these things when we consider ancient Egyptian optical surveying, which provides the only conceivable explanation for the construction of the Giza pyramids.

Figure 63. A drawing reproduced by Martin Isler showing Pharaoh Amenophis (Amun-Hotep) II holding a staff with a curved top for measuring shadows, and a measuring scale inscribed along its length.

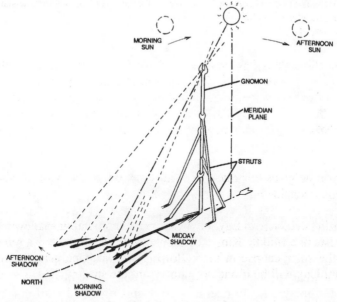

Figure 64. Martin Isler's drawing showing how a bifurx gnomon can be used to detect the meridian line and hence establish true north and south. The moving sun causes the shadow form to change its shape during the course of the day, and it is only at noon when the sun is on the meridian line that the shadow tip is fully-forked. When that occurs, the shadow of the entire pole culminating in the forked tip is a true north–south meridian line. The 'light-offering' at Karnak seen in Plate 20 similarly involves a specific shape appearing for only a few minutes a day – the feather only appears when the 'light-offering' hits the incense tray. Before and after, the image is not of a feather at all.

Before we leave *tchām* behind, we need to return to the *tchām* sceptre, or as most people refer to it today, the *was* sceptre. The ingenious Martin Isler has reconstructed the technique of its use as a shadow-definer. Whereas I called the staff with a bifurcated top a bifurx, there is already a term for a staff with a bifurcated bottom. It is called a *bay*. Isler describes and prints drawings to demonstrate how the bay was used to render the tip of a gnomon's shadow precise. One simply placed the bottom of the bay on the ground at the end of the gnomon's shadow – which would have been slightly fuzzy – and the notch at the bottom of the bay gave a precise defin-ition of the true tip of the gnomon shadow. The effect is somewhat similar

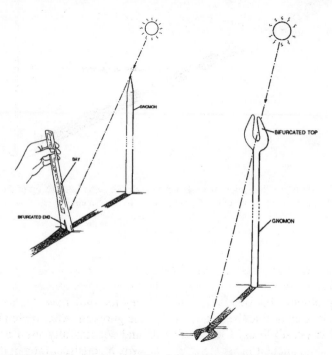

Figure 65. Martin Isler's drawings showing, left, a bay, and, right, a bifurx.

to what happens with a pinhole. Now that I am presbyopic (long-sighted) and have to wear spectacles for reading, if I don't have my spectacles with me and absolutely have to read a word, I curl my hand until only a tiny pinhole can be seen through, I then put my cupped hand to my eye and look through the middle and the word is in focus. In fact, this trick can be used for looking at a faraway stage, even when there is nothing wrong with one's distant vision. If you want to see the actor's face better, cup your hand and he suddenly becomes sharper. The notch in the bay is similar in its effect, and brings the shadow tip to a sharp definition. Here is what Isler says of this:

396

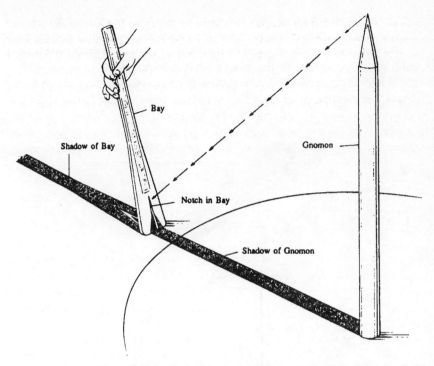

Figure 66. Martin Isler's drawing (obviously not to scale) showing how the tip of the shadow of an obelisk can be rendered precise rather than fuzzy by the 'shadow-catcher' with a forked bottom known as a bay. The *uas* sceptres carried by many of the Egyptian gods were bays, as for instance that held by the god Anubis in Plate 19.

We can reasonably assume that if the Egyptians made use of the gnomon to indicate time of day, or direction, they would have experienced the same problems that others did: that is, they too may have had need of a device to help define the shadow tip of the gnomon. After reviewing the available possibilities, I have selected and successfully used a device based on an ancient instrument called a *bay*. It consists of the middle rib of a palm leaf which is slotted at the broader end, and inscribed, 'indicator for determining the commencement of a festival and placing all men in their hours.' [This is an inscription in hieroglyphics on a real specimen.]

The bay has generally been considered an instrument for sighting the stars; however, judging from the specimen preserved in Berlin, Zaba felt it would not be possible to do so with precision, probably because the slot is irregular and asymmetrical. However, if instead of peering through the notch at an object, as is generally supposed, it is placed notch-down and angled to frame the shadow tip as it impinges the surface, it seems to help reduce the fuzziness by blocking the amount of light around the shadow and the reflection off the surface. Neither the

397

shape nor symmetry of the notch is important, as equal success is achieved with a wide range of notches. As shown in fig. 5 the bay is easily positioned at the tip end of the shadow, for it can be clearly seen falling on the surface of the bay facing the gnomon. Drawings of how the shadow tip appears before and after the bay is used are shown in figs. 6 and 7 respectively.[61]

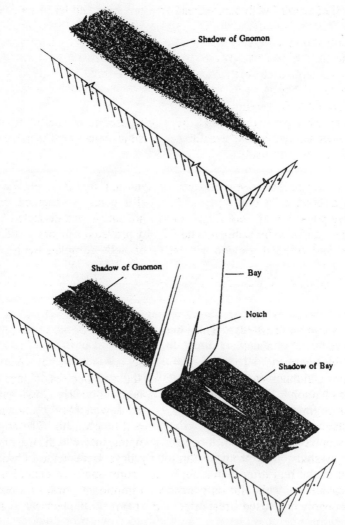

Figure 67. Martin Isler's drawings showing how a shadow tip is rendered precise by a bay. Above, the fuzzy or undefined shadow tip of an obelisk or gnomon is too vague to make a precise reading on a scale in order to achieve the precision which ancient astronomers required. Below, using a bay, a needle-sharp precision is obtained through the pinhole effect where the obelisk's shadow tip is focused in the tiny gap of light which passes through the fork, and is highlighted within the shadow of the bay itself so that the observation can be seen in bright sunlight.

The strange thing is that although Isler has figured all this out about the notched palm, and published various drawings showing the notch, he has apparently not realized that the shape he is depicting is also that of the *was* sceptre, or *tchām* sceptre!

F. Griffith in 1898 attempted to distinguish between the *tchām* sceptre and the *was* sceptre and concluded that the *tchām* sceptre had a twisted handle, but was otherwise the same as the *was* sceptre, which he described as 'A kind of sceptre with canine head, the ears long and laid back.' He did not bother to mention the forked bottoms of the two sceptres, having presumably thought that detail insignificant. He did, however, point out that the name for Thebes was *Waset* (*Uaset*), and its hieroglyph was a *was* sceptre with an ostrich feather tied to it.[62] Since there was probably more *tchām* metal gleaming in the sun at Thebes than anywhere else in Egypt, this turned out to be serendipitous.

It cannot be a coincidence that the sceptre used to define the tip of the shadow of an obelisk bears the same name as the shiny metal which capped the tip of the obelisk itself.

The *was* sceptre has been brilliantly identified by the anthropologist Richard Lobban as a bull's penis. The bull's penis represented 'primal generative power' in ancient Egyptian symbolism. It was dissected by the Egyptians – and also by Lobban, who thereby proved his theory – and when stretched and dried it yielded the 'head of Set', complete with square upright ears, and even terminated in a bifurcated base. These penises from deceased sacred bulls were dissected, laid out, salted, and dried, and went as hard as staffs. (Lobban says his has kept well for six years.) He has published photos which are wholly convincing. I reproduce these in Plate 56. He comments that 'Nineteenth -and Twentieth-Century prudery has blocked serious consideration of the phallus as an object of historical and religious enquiry.'[63] That is certainly true, and it is dismal when visiting Karnak and other sites to see so many of the erect penises chipped away from the pharaohs. That was apparently done by the early Christians, but Victorian engravings all had the penises erased as well. (My position is that a dead pharaoh should be allowed to have sex if he wants to.) The origin of the *was* sceptre as a sacred bull's penis is complementary to the use of a bay for shadow-study. It is probable that many bays were made of wood in imitation of the real dried bull's penis, and some made of ceramics have been excavated as well. But on occasion an important priest or a pharaoh would probably have used a real dried bull's penis for the purpose of studying the shadows.

It is very important that we have established all of this, because I propose to show that other strangely-shaped objects shown in the Egyptian iconography may also be related to optical phenomena, in particular the science of surveying, which had such sacred importance in laying out the foundations of the temples and other structures. In fact, some of the objects

I intend to discuss are actually seen conjoined with the *was* sceptres in frieze decorations. But first let us consider the case for optical surveying in ancient Egypt from a different point of view.

Before we do this we should just stop to consider what surveying is. If one were to attempt a definition, one could say that surveying is 'the science of determining the positions of points on the earth's surface'. However, this includes points up and down and as well points from side to side. In other words, surveying takes places in three dimensions, not just on the surface. One of the main functions of surveying is to tell how high things are. It is not always possible to climb up to the top of a cliff and drop down a tape measure; sometimes you have to use surveying instead, in which case you can measure the height of a cliff just standing where you are on the ground, as long as you measure the distance *to* the cliff. Then it is all calculated using triangles and the science of angles, known as trigonometry.

The main thing you have to do is get level. That is, your instrument must be level. Today we use spirit-levels with bubbles floating in them. When the bubble is in the middle you are level. Then we measure the distances on the ground when we can with tape measures. Then we have to do *sighting*. You get your line of sight correct and then you read off the angle. (There are different ways of doing this, some simple, some complicated, and various types of instruments can be used.) You then look the angle up in a table and get the sine, or the cosine, or whatever it is you need for the particular measurement you want to make, and you plug that value into your simple equation. You then solve the equation for the value that is still missing and you get your answer: it might be the height of the cliff, for instance.

A surveying instrument needs a small telescope in order to achieve real accuracy. When it has this telescope it is called a theodolite. When you do your sighting, you do it through the telescope instead of just through a hole in an empty tube, and because you can thus see your target better, your accuracy is far greater. The point about the pyramids at Giza in Egypt is that they are so accurately surveyed that only theodolites were capable of achieving such precision. No one could have done it without the use of lenses, as we shall see. It is a simple physical impossibility for the pyramids of Giza to have been built without optical surveying instruments.

We return now to Robert T. Ballard, whom I mentioned earlier as being the other great shadow enthusiast besides Cotsworth. He was a chief engineer of the Australian railways, and in the 1880s he observed the pyramids of Giza from a passing train and had the following idea, as Peter Tompkins explains:

> From the constantly changing relative position of their clear-cut lines against the sky, Ballard realized that the pyramids could serve as excellent theodolites [presumably markers rather than theodolites are meant

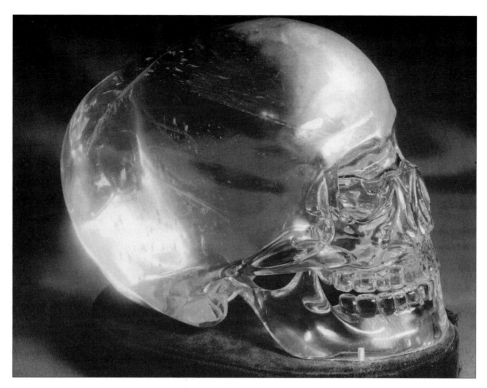

Plate 32

Plate 33

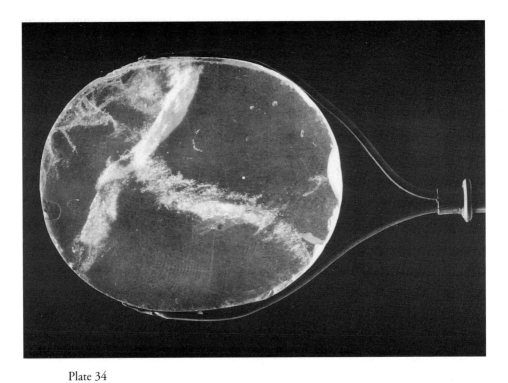

Plate 34

Plate 35

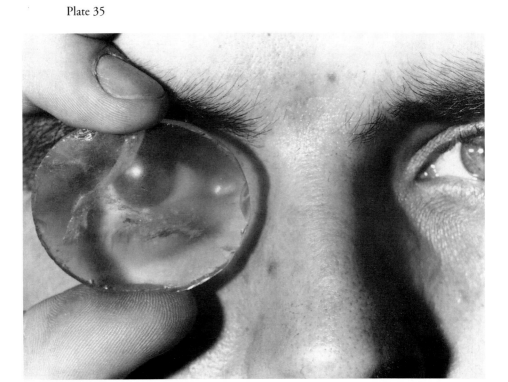

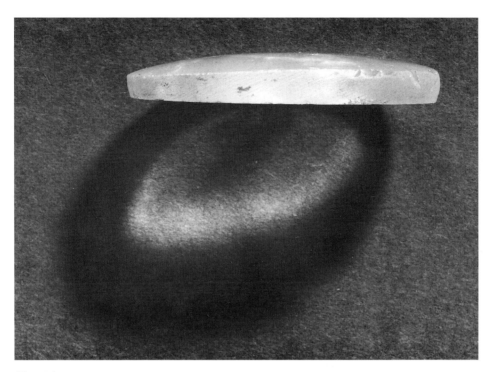

Plate 36

Plate 37

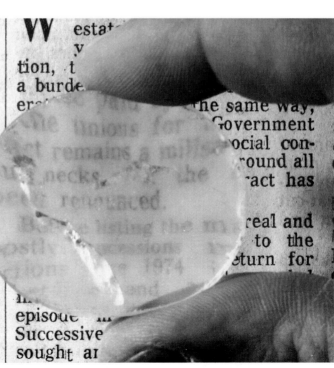

Plate 38a, b, c

Plate 39

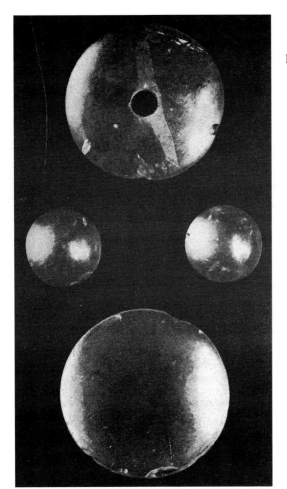

Plate 40

Plate 41   Plate 42

ATHENS ARCHAEOL[...]CAL [...] SEUM

ROOM 4 (M[...]aean)

[...]ai[...] [...]stal [...] 2 items[

Plate 43

Plate 44

Plate 45

Plate 46

Plate 47

Plate 48

Plate 49

Funde und
im Be.
Archäologische B

Plate 50

Plate 51

Plate 52

Plate 53

Plate 54

Plate 55

Plates 56a, b, c

Plate 57

Plate 58

Plate 59

Plate 60

Plate 61

Plate 62

Plate 63

Plate 64

Plate 65

BLACK AND WHITE PLATE SECTION CAPTIONS

PLATE 32

'The Skull of Doom'. This was the first ancient rock crystal artifact I ever encountered, when I was in my teens. It was discovered at the Mayan site of Lubaantun in British Honduras by Miss Anna ('Sammy') Mitchell-Hedges, during her adoptive father's excavations there in the 1920s, when she was about the same age as I was when I 'met' the Skull. It is life-size, with a detachable jaw. Sammy let me place it on my right shoulder and compare it with my own head, which she said it matched so well we could have worn the same hat size. – 'The Skull *likes* you,' she added, eerily. – And it was this strange encounter (described in Appendix One) which indirectly led to my writing this book, for I told Arthur Clarke about it, and he ended up using the Skull as the motif for all his television series; in return for telling Arthur and his friend Derek Price about this mysterious object, Derek then had to 'match' my story, so he told me about the Layard Lens in the British Museum, and my researches into ancient optical technology began.
(Photo by C. E. May & Son, Reading, courtesy of Miss Anna Mitchell-Hedges, who gave it to me in 1963.)

PLATE 33

Stanley Kubrick (left) and Arthur C. Clarke (right) on the set of *2001: A Space Odyssey*, in 1966, the year I met them. I have had this photo since that time in my collection, having obtained it from the publicist at the studio during the shooting. (I don't believe any other copy of the picture survives.) If I had not 'visited outer space' at MGM Studios in 1966 and met Arthur, this book would never have been written, as I explain in Chapter One. Stanley has now genuinely entered the weightless condition, which beckons to us all eventually.
(Photo courtesy of MGM Publicity, 1966.)

PLATE 34

This is the original old photo of the Layard Lens commissioned by the optician W. B. Barker, President of the London College of Optometrists, in 1929 and first published by him in 1930. Thus, it has always been optical scholars who have pushed the British Museum into taking photographs of this object, whereas the archaeologists left to their own devices have tended to ignore the Lens.
(Copyright unknown whether W. B. Barker, the College of Optometrists, or The British Museum.)

PLATE 35

The Layard Lens perfectly fits the human eye socket, as I sought to demonstrate in this photo which I commissioned in 1979 at the British Museum, with the Lens held up to the eye of a photographer's assistant. *(Photo copyright © 2000 by Robert Temple.)*

PLATE 36

The Layard Lens seen from the side. I commissioned this photo at the British Museum in 1979, and the regular 45° striations along the rim may be clearly seen. These were meticulously and deeply cut, to enable this lens to be as firmly as possible mounted in a surrounding band. The labour taken to produce these scourings was very extensive. The Layard Lens was thus probably originally mounted in gold, like the Nola Lens, and the gold was stolen either in antiquity or by the digger who found the object for Layard. (The Nola Lens also had its gold mounting

stripped off and sold by the digger.) Also visible in this photo are the chips at the top of the rim where someone has tried very hard to prise the lens from its mounting.
(Photo copyright © 2000 by Robert Temple.)

PLATE 37

The irregular magnification of the Layard Lens is clearly shown in this photo I commissioned in 1979 at the British Museum, with the Lens held over a newspaper. The lens was ground toroidally, so that its magnification purposely varies across its surface. It appears to have been ground to accommodate an individual case of astigmatism. It would be possible to go out into the street today and find somebody whose astigmatism would perfectly match this lens, if one took long enough. We must presume that the correction for astigmatism was arrived at empirically by trial and error, rather than from an optical theory advanced enough for this to be accomplished in one attempt. However, the extended labour and the amount of rock crystal necessitated for a trial and error method are so vast that the lens must have been made for a potentate to whom expense was no object. Since it was found in the throne room of a king, in the ruins of a palace, this seems to be the answer.
(Photo copyright © 2000 by Robert Temple.)

PLATE 38

The pre-dynastic ivory knife handle from Abydos in Egypt with microscopic carvings (the carvings are also reproduced in Figures 8 and 9). This object, excavated by Günter Dreyer, dates to 3300 BC, and is the oldest known evidence of the use of magnifying lenses in the world. The human figures are bearing tribute, and they include Canaanites from Palestine. Each person's head is less than one millimetre across, and Dreyer had to clean them of dirt with the point of a pin.
Photos courtesy of Günter Dreyer and the German Institute of Archaeology at Cairo.

PLATE 39

The Mainz Lens, of Roman date, excavated in the midst of a Roman glassworks at Mainz in Germany in 1875 by Baron von Sacken. It is now fragmentary and survives today in three pieces. It was apparently discovered whole and was still intact in 1913 when examined by the physicist Ernst Mach. How the lens came to be smashed and how it ended up in a museum in Vienna are unexplained, as in 1913 it appears to have been in the private collection of Professor R. von Schneider and undamaged. It was photographed for the first time at my request.
(Photo courtesy of the Kunsthistorisches Museum, Vienna.)

PLATE 40

Four of the Trojan lenses excavated by Schliemann at Troy. The top one has a perforation in the centre through which an engraver could insert his tool, while the lens would magnify all around. This was the only photo published of any of the 49 plano-convex Trojan lenses prior to the rediscovery of the Trojan hoards in Russia in the mid-1990s, where they had been secretly taken from Berlin by the Red Army after the Second World War and concealed along with the famous Trojan gold. Most of the Trojan lenses have now been beautifully photographed in colour – each described tentatively as a 'lens' in quotation marks, implying doubt – in *The Gold of Troy: Searching for Homer's Fabled City*, by Irina Antonova, Vladimir Tolstikov, and Mickail Treister, Thames and Hudson, London, 1996, although only the most basic measurements are given there, and no proper study of them has been made. I was unable to gain access to the collection, and could not even obtain a reply from the relevant Russian authorities to my enquiries. (Many years previously, under the old regime, the authorities in East Berlin lied to me several times and insisted the lenses had been destroyed by wartime bombing.) This photo was published by Hubert Schmidt in his catalogue *Heinrich Schliemann's Sammlung Trojanischer Altertümer (Heinrich Schliemann's Collection of Trojan Antiquities)*, Berlin, 1902, with the pieces numbered 6065–6106, 6112–6114, and 6119–6120, described on pp. 243–4. (Piece 6120 is the perforated lens.) The lenses were also discussed by A. Götze in

Wilhelm Dörpfeld, ed., *Troja und Ilion* (*Troy and Ilium*), Athens, 1902, pp. 339–40. The optician Harry L. Taylor wrote about them in 'The Trojan Lentoids', *British Journal of Physiological Optics*, Vol. V, No. 1, January, 1931, pp. 59–63, and also reproduced this photo. The only other discussion of them was by Richard Greef, in his booklet *Die Erfindung der Augengläser* (*The Invention of Eyeglasses*), Berlin, 1921, p. 25; he had discussed them with Professor Hubert Schmidt and seen them in the museum at Berlin, and he informs us that most of the lenses were in the opinion of Schmidt once mounted in brass. As usual, however, Greef in his desire to dismiss all evidence of ancient optical technology, dismisses the lenses as 'ornamental or decorative specimens'. What people like Greef never seemed to think of is that transparent jewellery has never been of great appeal at any time in history, since you can see through it and not notice that it is there! The purpose of jewellery is to be seen, not to be unseen. Nor can Greef explain why these invisible ornaments would have been so laboriously polished from rock crystal in the perfect forms of magnifying lenses. The Greef hypothesis also necessitates the failure by the craftsmen to notice that their mere 'ornaments' magnified, which means that they would have had to grind and polish them all with their eyes closed, lest they see that they were producing magnifying glasses. It would seem that Richard Greef would have felt at home in the state of Kansas in 1999, denying the theory of evolution in all confidence. We await momentarily an edict of the Kansas Board of Education declaring that ancient lenses are not specifically mentioned in the Bible.

PLATE 41
A glass lens from Tanis in Egypt excavated by Flinders Petrie in 1883–4. It is of Roman date, approximately second century AD. Such lenses were mass-produced by the Romans at that time throughout the Empire. This lens and another fragmentary one from Tanis are preserved in the Department of Egyptian Antiquities of the British Museum. Front view.
(Photo courtesy of the British Museum, London.)

PLATE 42
Side view of the intact Tanis Lens, showing the flat base and perfectly convex top of this plano-convex specimen. Object 22522 in the Department of Egyptian Antiquities.
(Photo courtesy of the British Museum, London.)

PLATE 43
One of the rock-crystal Mycenaean lenses in the Athens Archaeological Museum which I studied, and which until then had been 'invisible', although prominently on display in the Mycenaean Room.
(Photo by Robert Temple)

PLATE 44
Karanis Lens 5970, preserved at the Kelsey Museum, University of Michigan, USA. The glass has been badly cracked by pressure underground. Also of Roman date, *circa* 100 AD, and excavated at Karanis in Egypt between 1924 and 1929.
(Photo courtesy of the Kelsey Museum, University of Michigan.)

PLATE 45
One of the amazing concave crystal lenses excavated at Ephesus in Asia Minor, the coast of present-day Turkey. The lens may here be seen reducing the size of images by 75% (power of *minus 3X* without the slightest distortion). Concave lenses are for myopic (short-sighted) people. This is the only substantially intact concave lens in the British Museum; the rest are scattered all over Greece, the islands, and Turkey. About forty are known altogether. This is Object Number 1907.12–1.472 in the Department of Greek and Roman Antiquities. It is spectacularly clear, lustrous and transparent but for a few tiny specks of dirt on the flat base. This lens has severe chips and gouges effecting the rims but not damaging the centre or interfering with the optical qualities. I have named this type of lens a Concave Standing Lens, since it can stand on its flat

base and reduce images by 25%, but its power of reducing images is threefold when raised slightly above the surface. This lens is perfectly round (2.98 cm diameter constant for surviving portions of the top; the base diameter is 2.48 cm, again constant for surviving portions). The lens is 1.3 cm thick but the superior surface has a concave depth reaching a maximum of 3 mm. The crystal internally remains unflawed and absolutely perfect in its clarity; the chips and gouges on the rims seem to have occurred as the result of a variety of blows or pressures of weight underground or during excavation.
(Photo by Robert Temple)

PLATE 46

'Oh dear, what *will* he think of me?' – Some things don't change, and mirrors are amongst our most urgent necessities.
(From the Gazette Archaeologique, *Paris, 1878, Plate 10; statue from Tanagra.)*

PLATE 47

Ioannis Sakas on the fateful day of November 6, 1973, at Piraeus Harbour near Athens. He stoops down to secure the mooring of a small wooden boat beneath him, which will shortly be destroyed by fire according to the optical techniques of Archimedes. Behind him are arrayed the large mirrors held by some of the seventy sailors of the Greek Navy who will jointly reflect the rays of the sun onto the same focal point – the side of the wooden boat. Within seconds of the signal to begin, the boat began to smoke, and within three minutes it burst into flames and was consumed by fire. The average distance of each sailor from the boat was 55 metres. This was the only modern recreation of the feat of Archimedes of the third century BC. It was reported round the world at the time, but most reports contained inaccuracies.
(Photo courtesy of Ioannis Sakas)

PLATE 48

Ioannis Sakas at his home near Athens in March, 1998. He is the only living person who has recreated the feat of Archimedes, who burnt part of the Roman fleet at Syracuse in the third century BC by the use of a group of burning-mirrors. Sakas arranged for seventy sailors of the Greek Navy holding special mirrors to focus the rays of the sun on a boat in the Piraeus, and it burst into flames within three minutes. The average distance from a mirror to the target was 55 metres.
(Photo by Robert Temple)

PLATE 49

One of the many tiny mass-produced Roman glass globes which survive in Roman collections in a variety of European museums. This one is in the Bonn Museum. I was able to fill it with water, as described in the text, and even the feeble light of a desk lamp with a 60-watt bulb came to a powerful focus, as may be seen here. Actual sunlight would have ignited a fire very rapidly. I was unable to take the object outside for a photo. The water, once put in, is trapped by surface tension and will not escape through the pinhole opening even if the globe is shaken violently. (It has to be dribbled out with a pin.) These little burning-globes could fit readily in a pocket, and would not get it wet. If they were broken they were cheap to replace. Anyone on a sunny day could use these to light a fire or to cauterize a wound. They were especially popular for such medical purposes.
(Photo by Robert Temple)

PLATE 50

The tiny Roman glass globe which I filled with water in the Bonn Museum in Germany. It can readily be seen that these pocket-objects made handy and powerful magnifiers. They were widely distributed throughout the Roman Empire, could be carried anywhere and cheaply replaced. The poor lighting conditions reduced the visibility of the magnified image in this

photo, which is actually clearer than appears here. The glass is also somewhat discoloured through age.
(Photo by Robert Temple)

PLATES 51 AND 52
These two burning mirrors, which are kept in the warehouse of the Conservatoire des Arts et Métiers (Paris), are attributed to Buffon. The mirror, composed of 48 small flat mirrors, would have been made in 1740; the round mirror dates from 1741. Buffon had made several other mirrors of this type. The most famous is that which he used for his experiments of 1747; it was made up of 168 flat glass mirrors (*glaces*) measuring 6x8 inches each (about 16 cm x 21.5 cm). For example, he wrote that 'on the tenth of April in the afternoon, with a clear enough sun, one set fire to a plank of tarred fir at 150 feet (about 50 m.) with only 128 mirrors; the conflagration was very sudden, and it was in the whole area of the focus, which was about 16 inches in diameter (about 45 cm) at that distance.' Or again, the focus being at 20 feet away, 'with 45 mirrors, one melted a large tin bottle which weighed about 6 lb; and with 117 mirrors one melted some little bits of thin silver and brought to a red heat a plate of sheet metal.' Buffon knew that it is impossible to make a perfect burning-mirror, the reason being, as Descartes had already remarked, that the apparent diameter of the sun is not negligible (about 32 minutes of arc). Whatever the form adopted, the focus will be imperfect, 'dispersed', and more especially imperfect as the focal distance is longer. 'The achievement of [Archimedes at] Syracuse has indeed been able to be realized . . . I must render to Archimedes and to the ancients the glory which is their due . . . it is certain that Archimedes had been able to do with metal mirrors that which I have done with glass ones.'
(Musée des Arts et Métiers, Paris. Miroir à foyer variable de Buffon.)

PLATE 53
An early 'magno-illuminator': one of the ancient British lenses, 60869-A, in the Natural History Museum, London. This is the one which condenses ambient light upon the magnified text, illuminating it at the same time as it magnifies it by 2 $\frac{1}{2}$X to 3X. In a dim room, one can more or less double the illumination of the portion of the text one is reading by placing the lens upon it. In this photo, this added illumination may be seen in the upper left corner of the lens. Made of ground and polished rock crystal, this round biconvex lens has a superior surface which is a dome, but a base which tapers to a central point. Its maximum thickness is 1.83 cm and its diameter varies between 2.58 and 2.63 cm. The rim is heavily chipped, demonstrating that the lens was once mounted in a metal band. The lens is totally transparent. The base has several serious deep scratches and striations and is fairly heavily abraded; the central point is severely worn from constant use, abraded and with ingrained dirt. There is only light abrasion on the superior surface. See Appendix Eleven.
(Sir Hans Sloane Collection, Natural History Museum, London, Photo by Robert Temple)

PLATE 54
Dr John Woodward (1665–1728), a contemporary portrait in oil by an unknown artist. This now hangs with his collections in the Sedgwick Museum of Geology at Cambridge. Some of the British crystal lenses are in this collection; see Appendix Five.
(Contemporary portrait in the Sedgwick Museum. Photo by Robert Temple)

PLATE 55
An aerial view of the temple of Amun at Karnak, showing the vast size of the edifice and the light-corridor more than 500 yards long. Photo taken in the early 1900s.
(Photo courtesy Abbdullah Gaddis, Luxor, Egypt)

PLATE 56

A photo taken by anthropologist Richard Lobban of a stretched and dried bull's penis, showing the typical square 'ears' and 'face' of the ancient Egyptian god Set. Inset is a photo by Lobban of the bifurcated base of such a penis; the god Set was often portrayed with such a bifurcated 'tail'. Lobban thus appears to have discovered the basis for the iconography of this god, which has always puzzled Egyptologists because no known real animal resembled the god. See adjoining Plate 56b for a typical depiction of the god. This bull's penis is also the inspiration for the *was* sceptre of the Egyptians. Plate c shows a close up of the bifurcated end of the penis. *(Photos by Richard Lobban.)*

PLATE 57

A priest of Isis, carrying an *ankh* – the sign of life – in his right hand, walks in sacred procession holding before him in his left hand a *tcham* sceptre, also known as a *uas* sceptre. It has the 'canine head' with the sloped ears and the bifurcated base used for shadow study. Behind the priest is also a long pole with a bifurcated base for shadow study. The motifs of sacred surveying are thus prominently displayed. From the temple at Philae in Upper Egypt. *(Photo by Robert Temple)*

PLATE 58

A wall carving at the Temple of Hathor at Denderah in Upper Egypt. Here we see the *ankh*, symbol of life, animated and possessing two arms. In each hand it grasps a *was* staff, each with the bifurcated bottom used for defining the tips of shadows cast by obelisks; the curved top had a similar use. The two weights suspended from each elbow show a method of obtaining a level in surveying which differs from the modern method of a spirit bubble. It is possible that the *ankh* itself was a sighting-device originally, and like the *was* staff, was known to the uninitiated only as a decorative religious symbol. *(Photo by Robert Temple.)*

PLATE 59

A closeup view of part of the famous Pyramid Texts in the pyramid of the Pharaoh Unas (sometimes called Wenis, 2356–2323 BC) of the Fifth Dynasty. These are the oldest of the Pyramid Texts and thus the oldest surviving religious writings in the world. In the centre of this photograph, the name of Unas appears in the elliptical loop known as a cartouche; the hare with the long streaming ears represents the letter 'U', the wavy line represents the letter 'N', the reed at the bottom right is the letter 'short A', and the sign at the bottom left which some think is a picture of a chair-back represents the letter 'S'. The texts in this chamber speak of the mysterious meteoritic iron which fell from the floor of heaven. *(Photo by Robert Temple)*

PLATE 60

The 'light-well' in the Valley Temple at Giza, beside the Sphinx. This photo was taken by Professor Charles Piazzi Smyth in 1865, but he never published it. It was amongst Piazzi Smyth's papers purchased after his death by Moses Cotsworth, who then published the photo in his own book, *The Rational Almanac*, York, England, 1902, p. 176. Taken at noon, the photo shows the total absence of shadow on the north wall, and total absence of light on the east and west walls, indicating the perfect alignment of the building. See the main text for the full captions to this photo.

PLATE 61

This block of stone was spotted in 1998 by Robert Temple lying on scrubland within the temple precincts of Karnak, some distance south of the Temple of Amun. It shows the chiselled north-south and east-west alignment lines cut into the floor of one of the Karnak temples by the surveyors at the time of laying its foundations. Its true nature has not been recognized by the archaeologists, who have never bothered to salvage it from the rubble. A photo of a similar chiselled alignment stone has been reproduced by Schwaller de Lubicz, as Plate 85 (attached to Chapter 40) in his study of the Temple of Luxor, *The Temple of Man*, Inner Traditions Publishers, USA, 1998. Schwaller was the one who originally spotted the Luxor chiselled alignments, which define the axes of the Temple and were inscribed in the underfloor of the Sanctuary of Amun's Barque. They had been concealed under the superimposed finished flooring of the temple. This newly-identified Karnak alignment stone shown here actually shows the crossing of the two fundamental alignment lines, and is a priceless relic of ancient Egyptian science which should be preserved in a museum and given its due recognition. Archaeologists please note!

(Photo by Robert Temple.)

PLATE 62

Many people have wondered about the strange scene on the left in this wall painting from the tomb of Pharaoh Rameses IX (1126–1108 BC) of the Twentieth Dynasty. We see the pharaoh leaning back in what is surely not just a callisthenic exercise, while above him the sun is seen being pushed above the horizon by the scarab beetle. – What is going on? – The answer may be discovered by taking a plastic transparent protractor, such as any child uses at school, with its central point at the spot where the pharaoh's fingertips touch the line. From this we see that the line from that point touching the king's bottom and his heel makes an angle of 26° and thus constitutes the hypotenuse of a golden triangle. It is this very triangle which is projected onto the south face of the Great Pyramid at sunset on the winter solstice, as I discovered in 1998, and which may be seen in Plate 30. I have never come across any comment anywhere by an Egyptologist recognizing that the pharaoh's position here forms a golden triangle. In Egyptian tradition, the three sides of a right triangle (and the golden triangle is a right triangle defined by the golden ratio) were identified with Isis, Osiris, and Horus, with the hypotenuse being called Horus. Here, therefore, the deceased king becomes a Horus and is resurrected to eternal life – as shown by his becoming a hypotenuse of a golden triangle. The king's erect phallus has been eradicated from this painting, but a white stripe may be seen where it once was painted. If we drew such a pharaoh along the line of the shadow on the Great Pyramid, it is interesting to speculate to what the king's erect phallus might point: at a location within the pyramid, or at a star?

PLATES 63 AND 64

A Delian Eye of Horus? Light being reflected from a pyramidion? The sun at noon above a pyramid? – As described in the main text this mosaic was excavated on the sacred Greek island of Delos, in the vestibule of the House of the Dolphins. It was published as Figure 68 in Marcel Bulard, *Peintures Murales et Mosaiques de Délos (Paintings, Murals and Mosaics of Delos)*, Vol. 14 of *Monuments et Mémoires Publiés par l'Académie des Inscriptions et Belles-Lettres*, Paris, 1908. (Figure 69 shows a similar design from a fragment of a lamp excavated at Delos.) Bulard was in no doubt whatever of the foreign origin of this symbol, and viewed it as either North African or Phoenician. He points out that the mosaic of the peristyle of this same house is recorded as having been the work of an artist originally from the town of Arados, 'which is perhaps Arados of Phoenicia'. He adds: 'The House of the Dolphins should be viewed as a place apart amongst the Graeco-Roman houses of Delos, owing to its Oriental influences' (p. 194, Bulard). Since Bulard cites Edouard Meyer as mentioning that this sign is frequently found in the Punic sanctuaries of North Africa, and believes it to be of Egyptian origin, it is likely that the concept of the pyramidion as an Eye of Horus was widespread all along that coast, but has not been recognized for what it is. The subject of the spread of Egyptian religious influences westwards along the coasts of Libya, Tunisia, Algeria, and Morocco, is something which has never been fully studied, and the well-known occurrence of Isis chapels all over the Roman world is another indication of the Egyptian religious influence – however diluted and superficial by that time – which spread across the entire Mediterranean under the Roman emperors.

PLATE 65

The crucial aerial photograph by Brigadier General Groves, first published in 1929, showing the vertical bisection of the south side of the Great Pyramid (the upper one in this photo) by a mysterious 'hollowing-effect' planned by the original builders, but which cannot be detected from the ground. The winter solstice shadow on this same south face, which I discovered in 1998, forms the hypotenuse of a golden triangle with this vertical line. In fact, the Great Pyramid has eight sides, not four, but the naked eye cannot discern this from ground level. The 'hollowing-effect' is so slight that it does not exceed 37 inches on any face of the structure. The half of the south face which is here seen in darker shadow would have given an 'equinox flash' at sunrise on the days just preceding and following the spring and autumn equinoxes, when the Great Pyramid was still covered with shiny white reflecting limestone. Neither the solstice shadow nor the equinox flashes have previously been recognized. See Chapter Nine for a full account of these phenomena.

(Photo by Brigadier General P. R. C. Groves, reproduced from the frontispiece of David Davidson, The Hidden Truth in Myth and Ritual and in the Common Culture Pattern of Ancient Metrology, *Leeds, 1934.)*

here] for a land surveyor, enabling him to triangulate the land anywhere within sight of the pyramids.

The land of ancient Egypt was parcelled out in small lots to individual priests and soldiers, the boundaries of which would regularly vanish with the flooding of the Nile [this happened once a year and the inundation often lasted for three months].

By means of the pyramids, not only could the surrounding country be quickly resurveyed, but boundaries destroyed by the Nile could be readily restored.

From the silhouettes of the pyramids, the engineer realized that lines could be obtained as perfect as can be laid out nowadays with all of our modern instruments. With a string and a stone held in the hand and the clear-cut point of a pyramid 20 miles away against the ball of the sun 90 million miles away, the error in such a line would be trifling.

What's more, the same building could also be used with either moon or stars.

Knowing the latitude of the pyramids, survey lines could be shown all the way to the coast of the Delta – with nothing more than a string and a weight. . . . Ballard figured that the simplest portable survey instrument would be a small scale model of the Pyramid of Cheops in the center of a circular graduated board marked like a compass. When the north end of the card was pointed toward the north, and the faces of the model turned to indicate the same light and shade displayed by the Great Pyramid, the surveyor could simply read off the angle of bearing.[64]

In his book *The Solution of the Pyramid Problem* published in 1882,[65] appear many drawings of the Giza pyramids with different shadow patterns.

We will be considering surveying by the ancient Egyptians a little later, and it certainly took place with more than a string and a weight. Indeed, the whole point is that they used telescopic lenses.

Way back in August 1976, this was brought to my attention by Professor José Álvarez Lopez, a physicist from the University of Cordoba in Argentina. I met him in that year in New York City, and as he spoke English we were able to have long talks. Whenever we had difficulty understanding each other, his friend Christina translated beautifully. Professor Lopez had published seven books in Spanish of which he gave me copies of two. The first was called *Misterios Egipcios* (*Egyptian Mysteries*).[66] I am handicapped by not being able to read Spanish, so can only gaze at the photos, drawings and diagrams of pyramids, obelisks, etc., and wonder.

His second book was entitled *El Enigma de las Piramides* (*The Enigma of the Pyramids*).[67] But in this instance, Lopez gave me a photocopy of a complete English translation of the book in typescript.[68] Before I refer to Lopez's optical comments, I will point out that he mentions a prohibition against the use of iron tools in building Solomon's Temple at Jerusalem. He refers to I Kings 6,7 in the Bible, where we read: 'In the building of the house, only blocks of undressed stone direct from the quarry were used; no hammer or axe or any iron tool whatever was heard in the house while it was being built.' In the light of our discussion of iron in the last chapter, this will be found of interest. Lopez mentions this in the context of these intriguing remarks:

> An additional point we must observe is . . . [there was] a sort of taboo . . . [concerning] the use of iron. Today, we know that the wheel and iron were both known in Precolumbian America but that they were not used. [In fact, the use of wheels by the Maya for children's toys is well known to archaeologists, but the Maya evidently refrained from its use for more serious matters because of a taboo.] Furthermore, as we shall see later on, archaeology has established a connection between iron and the Egyptian pyramids although the presence of this metal in the pyramids has been deliberately disguised. By way of explanation of this cultural phenomenon, we can recall the Biblical passage (Kings 1:6:7) that forbids the use of iron tools in building Solomon's Temple. The stones to be used were to be finished and dressed at a place far from the temple site . . . Reinforcing these associations, archaeologists have observed that the stone blocks of the Great Pyramid were finished in workshops far from the pyramid itself and that these blocks did not receive any kind of further dressing 'in situ'. The relationships are evident although their meaning escapes us.[69]

This subject is doubtless connected with the subject of meteoritic iron and 'thunderstone' lore.

In his English Introduction (which does not appear in his Spanish edition), Lopez makes his first comments relating to optical matters:

> The perfection of its technology is reflected in every element of the Great Pyramid. One of the many examples that illustrates this feature is the [white] marble casing that originally covered the whole pyramid, giving it four magnificent triangular mirrors of many acres of extension each. [A small number of these blocks remain.] . . . The perfect optical cutting of these blocks has surprised archaeologists. According to the studies of [Sir Flinders] Petrie, the error of parallelism of the edges of these blocks of 16 tons each is less than 0.002 cm/metre, a precision of the order of our most advanced optical devices. The surfaces of the blocks are perfect planes with an error of 50 micra. The dihedral right angle has an error of less than 5 seconds.
>
> Each one of these 25,000 blocks was a masterpiece of optical precision comparable to the 5 meter mirror of the telescope of Mount Palomar (USA).
>
> Drills are another example of this highly advanced technology. According to the studies of Prof. Petrie and Prof. Baker, the Egyptian

drills had a degree of penetration of hard stone 100 times stronger than the best drills of the modern oil industry [these comments by Petrie were made several decades ago, and this has presumably changed somewhat]. As Prof. Baker pointed out, a modern engineer capable of duplicating the ancient drills would not only become rich but would revolutionize modern industry as well.

About halfway through his book, Lopez first refers to the likelihood that the ancient Egyptians possessed optical instruments:

As far as the instruments employed by the Egyptians in their observations, we know only the *merkhet* or rod of the 'Observer of the Hours' and the *bay* which consisted of a palm rod with a V-shaped notch in the top part. [Lopez did not anticipate the insights of Martin Isler, who realized that the true importance of the bay was that the notch was placed at the bottom and rested on the ground.] This was used to measure the hours of the night by the height of the stars. It is immediately clear that with these instruments alone the Egyptians could not advance much in their astronomical knowledge. They must at least have possessed one other instrument to add to the *merkhet*, since these types of observations require a *lens* and an *eye-piece*. But in this respect, we know nothing more about the Egyptians or the Chaldaeans.

Lopez of course knew nothing of the physical evidence for the existence of telescopes in antiquity, nor was I able to enlighten him in 1976 on this question yet myself. He continues to draw inferences about ancient telescopes in his remarks which immediately follow:

On the other hand, we know several Mayan codices (cf. [S. G.] Morley [*The Ancient Maya*, 1946]) that represent both observatories and observers, such as the *Bodleian Codex*, the *Nutall Codex*, and the *Selden Codex*. An eye above an X appears in all of these codices and in the *Bodleian Codex*, besides this *eye-piece*, there appears a star above a V. Various astronomers were consulted on the significance of this X with an eye and this V with a star. They immediately interpreted the symbols, for modern instruments of observation usually have a reticle (crosshairs) in X in the *eye-piece* and a reticle in V in the *lens*.

All expressed surprise when told that these representations were Mayan. It was also pointed out that for observation with the naked eye the most efficient system was that of the *alidades* [a ruler combined with a telescope or sight slit as part of a simple surveying instrument] and *pinules* [the two sights at the ends of an alidade] of the old astronomers, and thus the Mayan system of observation could not function in the absence of optical instruments. Why, then, did the Maya represent observational methods which they could not employ? [i.e., on the usual assumption that ancient lenses did not exist, they could not be employed]. When we survey the science of the ancients, we constantly encounter questions of this nature. For example, why did the Chaldeans represent Saturn (Nisroch) wrapped in a ring? Saturn's ring cannot be seen with the naked eye.

But all of these problems are overshadowed in both historical and scientific interest by the Egyptian calendar . . . [and] their astronomical cycle of 365.2500 days . . .[70]

The telescopes of antiquity would certainly have been able to show the rings of Saturn. We must presume that all of the ancient cultures known to have possessed telescopes would have known of the rings. Lopez was right to have his suspicions.

A little later on, Lopez has an entire section entitled *Optica* (Optics). Here he makes further comments:

The Egyptian capacity for mensuration [measurement] cannot be considered as an isolated happening in the midst of a general ignorance about science and technology. . . . it is impossible to carry out precision measurements without having at the same time a vast knowledge of optics . . . We will not find anywhere in the Greek or Roman worlds anything comparable to the precision of the measurements achieved by the Egyptians. Consequently, it must be inferred that the scientific knowledge of the Egyptians was very much above that possessed by the Greeks and Romans. . . . a preoccupation with exactness in measurement was as obsessive with Egyptian technologists as it is with any modern physicist or astronomer. . . . Unfortunately, our lack of scientific documents is so great that a study of specific aspects of that science is impossible. Nevertheless, in the case of optics, there are some observations that can . . . be applied to the Egyptians. Thus, in relation to the necessity for a knowledge of the magnifying glass in order to carry out precision measurements, we have the . . . problem . . . as to whether or not they had any knowledge of the magnifying glass.

In general, historians of science have denied the Greeks and the Romans any knowledge of the magnifying properties of lenses and mirrors. . . . it is worthwhile to recall that passage in Aristophanes' *Clouds* where Strepsiades advises Socrates to burn his promissory notes from a distance, availing himself of a magnifying glass. . . . Are we to believe that optical scientists ignored facts that were known to the people?[71]

It is important to remember that Lopez was a physicist and a Professor in the Institute for Advanced Studies of his university, and that as a practising scientist, he saw things from the practical perspective. Thus, if the historians of science insisted on something which he, as a practical scientist, thought nonsense, he trusted his own judgement in preference to any 'authority'. This is as it should be.

Much later in his book Lopez returns to optics:

> When we studied, in Part II, the technological aspects of the dressing of the marble blocks that once covered the Great Pyramid, we established a comparison between the 'opera magna' of modern precision technology – the mirror of the telescope at Mt Palomar – and the 25,000 optical prisms of the facing [of the Pyramid] weighing 16 tons, each of which represented, by itself, a task (in optical finish) equivalent to that of the famous mirror [at Mount Palomar].
>
> This immense micrometric task – according to the exactness of the planes of each unit and the exact correlation between them observed by Petrie – would have produced four plane mirrors of optical precision, each one with a surface of 1.7 hectares. If this work hadn't been destroyed [by the Arabs], today the pyramid would be a monumental 'optical instrument' – something as yet unimaginable for opticians of the Cosmic Age.[72]

His conclusion about the building technology of the pyramid-builders is expressed in the final sentence of Appendix One:

> The hypothesis which does the least amount of violence to our present scientific knowledge is to accept the fact that the Egyptians possessed high-precision optical instruments.[73]

Lopez published this book 11 years before he and I met, and in the interval he had given a lot more thought to these questions. A considerable proportion of the hours he and I spent talking in New York were devoted to his trying to persuade me that the pyramid-builders had optical surveying instruments, which were essentially theodolites of some kind. He had worked out a lot of further details and had more figures than appear in his book. He was a small, intense man of enormous energy who was passionate about his discovery and wanted to tell the world about it. But he didn't know how. He reeled off number after number giving details of 'impossible' precision attained in the construction of the Giza pyramids, and said that *it was all physically impossible without optical surveying instruments*. And here I am now, attempting to tell the world about it too.

I owe entirely to Lopez my awareness of the need for precision optical surveying in ancient Egypt. It was because I knew it had to be there that I persevered in searching for truly ancient lenses – not just Graeco-Roman ones, but really ancient ones in Egypt. I fretted and fretted about this until one day, *bingo!* – I realized that it was the Old Kingdom crystal *eyes* that *proved* the technology existed. I had long been familiar with the similar crystal eye in the famous 'Bull's Head Rhyton' excavated by Sir Arthur

Evans at Knossos on Crete; that Minoan lens is a convex meniscus lens (convex on top, concave on the bottom) which magnifies the pupil painted behind it, to give a vivid impression of life. So when I finally encountered the Old Kingdom crystal eyes in human statues (see Plates 14, 15, 16 and 17), and even discovered that the statue of King Zoser of the Third Dynasty (Plate 18) had had such eyes but they had been removed by ancient robbers, according to I. E. S. Edwards,[74] I knew that there was irrefutable proof that the technology existed for the manufacture of the highest-quality ground and polished crystal magnifying lenses. These existed at least by the beginning of the Third Dynasty, *circa* 2686 BC! But as I have also pointed out earlier, and shown in Plate 38 and in Figures 8 and 9, there is unmistakable evidence of the use of magnifying lenses at Abydos in Egypt no later than 3300 BC, in predynastic times.

Figure 68. A 19th-century engraving of the ancient wooden statue known quaintly as the 'Sheikh el Balad (or Beled)' – the name given to him by the workmen who cleared his tomb because he resembled the head of their village who bore that name. In fact, in the Egyptian Museum in Cairo, where the statue stands today, there is a man who currently works selling postcards in the gift shop, who also resembles the statue. This is a cause of great merriment amongst the staff, who call him 'the Sheikh' and tease him about 'his statue'. He laughed and was pleased that my wife and I 'recognized' him. We don't know whether these resemblances are just because there are lots of jolly chubby Egyptian men who have all looked alike for millennia, or whether the original fellow has been multiply reincarnated. The ancient man's real name was Ka-aper, but so far that name has not caught on in modern times. Any moment now, perhaps an enthusiast will adopt it. Ka-aper lived in the Fifth Dynasty (approximately 2500–2300 BC, with some uncertainties about precise dates), and this statue was excavated from his tomb at Saqqara. (The feet and the walking stick are modern restorations.) Ka-aper has magnificent rock-crystal eyes which are perfectly ground and polished plano-convex lenses of the highest quality. They may be seen in the photos which I took of Ka-aper's face in Plates 14 and 15.
(*Collection of Robert Temple.*)

Lopez's comments about the four faces of the Great Pyramid as they would have appeared when they were new (or even when they were old, for that matter!) are highly suggestive. Actually, a strange feature of those faces was discovered originally by the great Egyptologist Sir Flinders Petrie. As Peter Tompkins describes it:

> Petrie, with his meticulously careful measurements, had managed to observe a definite hollowing of the core masonry on each side [face] of the Pyramid. The accuracy of this observation, normally invisible to the human eye, was revealed in Petrie's lifetime in a dramatic aerial photograph taken accidentally at a specific time and angle by Brigadier P. R. C. Groves, the British prophet of air power. A similar line along the apothegm [vertical line up the middle of the face], visible in an etching by Napoleon's savants, had been ignored for a century.[75]

Also visible in the very same etching, and ignored by everybody until now including myself, is the shadow cast across the south face of the Great Pyramid sometime not far from the winter solstice (see Tompkins's book, Chapter 9, p. 109, for a reproduction of this old etching). It was only after I 'discovered' the shadow (see Plate 30) in Egypt that I came back to England and 'saw' it in the old picture. Naturally no one else had ever 'seen' it either, not even the man who had drawn it, probably. So much for empirical theories of perception!

On the same page – 109 – of Tompkins's book, and in some other pyramid books as well, is the famous photo by Brigadier Groves, who is often called Captain Groves (presumably he was a captain at that time and a brigadier later). The photo was taken late in the day, apparently in the late spring or early summer, at a moment when the sun was at a particular point in the sky where the eastern vertical half of the south face of the Great Pyramid could just catch a tiny bit of sunlight (apparently reflected across from the north face of the Pyramid of Khafre rather than caught from the sun directly, since the result is a softening of the shadow rather than a full illumination). The south face of the Great Pyramid is seen to be bisected vertically in a most striking manner. This light effect cannot have lasted for long, and it reminds me of the luck which my wife and I had at Karnak in seeing the 'light-offering' described earlier, and which lasted for less than three minutes. This striking photo by Groves has never been repeated, possibly because not many people are allowed to fly over Giza. But it shows in a way which transcends mere words how the faces of the Great Pyramid were really each constructed of two right triangles back-to-back, and were not built as the four large single triangles which they seem to be. This phenomenon, where they 'dip' slightly in at the centre, along the vertical line which bisects the faces, is what the clever Petrie discovered because his measurements were so precise.

It was by calling attention to this detail that the pyramid scholar David Davidson vindicated the claim by Professor Charles Piazzi Smyth, as mentioned earlier, that the perimeter of the Great Pyramid gives a measurement which indicates the true length of the year as 365.24 days. The hollowing effect is so slight that it doesn't exceed more than 37 inches on any face![76]

David Davidson was the first person to publish Groves's aerial photograph, in a newspaper called *The Morning Post*, on 2 October 1929. In 1934, Davidson privately published his third book about pyramids in 1934, entitled *The Hidden Truth in Myth and Ritual*, and Groves's photo was used as the frontispiece plate.[77] I have been fortunate to acquire a copy of this extremely rare book. I have reproduced the celebrated photo as Plate 65. Chapter 6 of this work is devoted to a discussion of the 'hollowed-in surfaces' of the Great Pyramid. It was certainly Davidson who first recognized their significance. He gives a precise value of the hollowed-in effect as 35.76278 inches depth. Here are some of his comments:

> The hollowing-in of the four core escarpments was a feature that was first observed and measured by Sir Flinders Petrie [who called it 'a striking feature' but did not recognize its significance], who, however, supposed that the observed effect was due to a specially channelled groove up the centre of each core escarpment. A study of his sightings from the top platform, however, showed this view to be untenable, since such a groove as Petrie supposes would have sheared the arris edges of the core near the top. On the other hand, the writer's interpretation of Petrie's data has been confirmed by an air-photograph of the Gizeh pyramids taken shortly before sunset, by Brig. Gen. P. R. C. Groves, C.B., C.M.G., D.S.O. The photograph is reproduced by Brig. Gen. Groves' kind permission, on the Frontispiece. . . . it should be understood that the hollowing-in of the core-escarpments is, proportionately to the vast surfaces of the escarpments [the faces of the pyramid], too minute to be perceived by the eye. It was only owing to the astonishing accident of propitious time and suitable position of camera synchronizing that the feature was revealed on Brig. Gen. Groves' photograph.[78]

One of the most interesting books ever written about the pyramids is *The Egyptian Pyramids: A Comprehensive Illustrated Reference* by the late J. P. Lepre, who died young in an accident in the 1990s, having published his extraordinary book in 1990.[79] Lepre made the most careful observations and measurements of certain particular aspects of the Great Pyramid which have ever been done, and he spotted many things which previous investigators had overlooked. He did not advocate any unusual theories, and was inclined towards orthodoxy. But he had an *unorthodox eye*. Lepre discusses the faces of the Great Pyramid and their hollowing-in effect. He leads into this by quoting James Baikie in 1917:

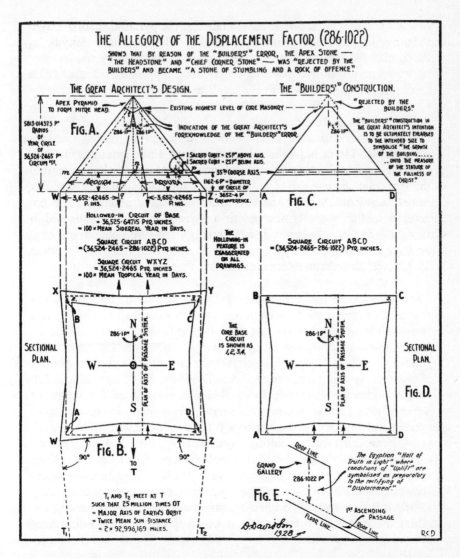

Figure 69. One of the many complex illustrations from David Davidson's book *The Hidden Truth in Myth and Ritual and in the Common Culture Pattern of Ancient Metrology*, Leeds, 1934, p. 50. The hollowed-in aspect of each of the four sides of the Great Pyramid is here shown twice, purposely greatly exaggerated for visibility, in the two square plans to left and to right. Davidson had a theory that the measurements associated with the hollowing-in of the faces when expressed in a measure called 'the pyramid inch' added just enough of a tiny fraction to the base measurement of the structure for the total to correlate with the exact number of days in the year. We do not need to concern ourselves with this elaborate theory of Davidson's (for which his own book should be consulted). The important point is that he intuited that the hollowing-in of the faces was highly significant in some way, although he had no knowledge of the winter solstice shadow, and thus could not realize that only by means of the hollowing-in could the golden triangle be produced and the 'equinox-flash' occur (it is described in a moment).

417

The size of this vast monument is not, however, its only claim to notice. The fineness of the workmanship, the skill with which the building has been planned and oriented, and the precision of its levels, are all most extraordinary – 'equal to optician's work of the present day', says Petrie, 'but on a scale of acres instead of feet or yards.'

One very unusual feature of the Great Pyramid is a concavity of the core that makes the monument an eight-sided figure, rather than four-sided like every other Egyptian pyramid. This is to say, that its four sides are hollowed in or indented along their centre lines, from base to peak. This concavity divides each of the apparent four sides in half, creating a very special and unusual eight-sided pyramid; and it is executed to such an extraordinary degree of precision as to enter the realm of the uncanny. For, viewed from any ground position or distance, this concavity is quite invisible to the naked eye. The hollowing-in can be noticed only from the air, and only at certain times of the day. This explains why the concavity was never discovered until the age of aviation. [In fact, he seems to have been unaware of the earlier discovery by Petrie and also he seems never to have heard of David Davidson, for he nowhere mentions him.] It was discovered quite by accident in 1940 [this is an error, since the photo was first published in 1929], when a British Air Force pilot, P. Groves, was flying over the pyramid. He happened to notice the concavity and captured it in the now-famous photograph. [See Plate 65. By this time, the fact that Davidson had first published the photo and drawn attention to the hollowing-in of the faces which it showed had been conveniently forgotten by most people, and Lepre presumably never even knew about it.] The white finish or cover stones still seen on the bottom course once sheathed the entire pyramid, but were subsequently stripped from the monument for latter-day building projects in Cairo and at other pyramid fields. These casing stones, of which only a few remain at the first course of masonry, were originally fitted together with such unerring precision that the jointing between them was barely discernible to the naked eye, resembling hairlines rather than joints of masonry.[80]

There were 144,000 of these casing stones separated only by hairlines!

Although many people might think that the few casing stones left at the top of the Pyramid of Khephren are very weathered now and incapable of reflecting any light, they still did so as recently as the early 19th century. Edmé-François Jomard, one of the scholars who accompanied Napoleon to Egypt, wrote of that pyramid: 'It still possesses a portion of its polished casing, which reflects the rays of the sun and declares its identity to people at a vast distance.'[81]

A 'sun-flash' would have been generated when the Great Pyramid was still gleaming white by this mysterious and all but invisible concavity or hollowing of the faces. I believe such flashes would have happened at sunrise and sunset just prior to and just after the two equinoxes. Since the Great Pyramid is oriented precisely to the geographical poles, its eastern and western faces face due east and west. That means that just before and just after the sun was rising from the due east and setting in the due west, which it does twice a year at the Spring Equinox and the Autumn Equinox, the western vertical halves of the north and south faces would have 'flashed' with the sunlight at sunrise, and at sunset the eastern vertical halves of the north and south faces would have 'flashed' with the sunlight. It is possible that in both cases the 'flashes' would have been deeply golden in colour. On the actual days of the equinoxes themselves, the sun-flashes would have vanished, to be resumed again two or three days later. The cessation of the flash would prove the equinox had arrived, since the sun was then briefly absolutely dead-on.

I believe the golden-tipped obelisks of the New Kingdom were an attempt to emulate this phenomenon of the solar flash, especially at sunrise. In the New Kingdom the pharaohs no longer knew how to build flashing pyramids, but they could build flashing obelisks. They must have felt uncomfortable if they found themselves at Memphis in the spring or in the autumn, seeing with their own eyes the tremendous 'approaching Equinox Flash' which emanated from the Great Pyramid and shone up and down the north and south of Egypt (though how far it reached to the south I cannot calculate, and it is doubtful that any distant illuminating flash in the northern sky would have been visible in Upper Egypt). For whenever they saw this, they were reminded of their own impotence to emulate it, and of the incapacity of their engineers even to understand how it was caused. (After all, the New Kingdom engineers could not see the hollowing-in effect with the naked eye any better than we can, and it is doubtful that they knew of its existence.) Is it any wonder that the frustrated pharaohs of the New Kingdom built flashing obelisks? It was all they could manage, and if they lavished gold on their tips, it was all the better to show just how 'flashy' the New Kingdom could be!

We have thus seen that the Great Pyramid manifested the approach of the two equinoxes with light flashes and the two solstices with shadows; the winter solstice was indicated by the shadow cast upon the south face by the adjoining pyramid (Plate 30), and the summer and winter solstice shadows were closely scrutinized on the special shadow-floor to the north of the pyramid, which was perfectly level and constructed in a graduated scale where the stones were fitted at precisely the intervals corresponding with the daily movement of the shadow tip (see Figure 57). This tip would, of course, have been precisely defined by priests using bays, otherwise known as *tchām* or *was* staffs.

The Great Pyramid was thus a great centre of light and shadow phenomena marking the four points of the year, and enabling the year to be defined with precision to 365.24 days, a length which was in turn embodied in the perimeter measurements.

But there is yet *another* way to look at the Great Pyramid as well: It can also be considered as a Great Eye looking skywards. To its designers, the pyramid itself seems to have been viewed as a kind of giant 'Eye of Horus'. This would also explain why they shared the same name, *Aakhu-t*. The Old Kingdom texts are full of references to the pupil of the Eye of Horus (in Egyptian the pupil is *ar* and the eye is *ar-t*; *Ar-t Ḥeru* is another name for 'Eye of Horus', since Heru is the Egyptian form of Horus). Here now we have to think like birds, as the ancient Egyptians seemed inclined to do – they were always saying things in the Pyramid Texts like 'I soar like a heron' in connection with rising from the pyramid. Imagine yourself in the sky above the Great Pyramid. You are looking down. The Egyptians seem to have thought that from this point of view the Great Pyramid was like a giant eye, with the pyramidion as its pupil, especially prominent when gleaming in the sun.

This also can explain the mysterious fact that the word *Aakhu-t* also means 'Horizon'. Only an aerial viewpoint can make this clear. Since the Great Pyramid is perfectly oriented to the geographical poles, the four faces of the pyramid are thus perfectly north, south, east, and west. So there you are, a bird flying above the Great Pyramid. You fly from east to west, and eventually you reach a point where the pyramidion, the solar symbol and 'pupil' of Horus's Eye, seems to sink below the western face of the pyramid, as if it were a glowing sun setting below the western horizon. You fly eastwards again and look back, and the pyramidion appears to rise above the western horizon. You can do this from any direction; there are four horizons, north, south, east, and west, all perfectly aligned and represented by the four faces of the pyramid. As soon as you reach any point near the apex of the pyramid, Horus is *in* his horizon – whichever horizon you choose by approaching from the direction opposite to it. This can explain the strange references in Egyptian texts to 'Horus *in* his horizon'. Whichever way you move above the pyramid, Horus is always rising and setting above or into one of his four horizons. What a marvellous symbol this is, then, of the totality of directions and of the omnipotence of the sky. For the Great Pyramid itself may be considered the ultimate Eye of Horus.

Another possibility is that the pyramidion was cased in highly reflective golden metal like the later obelisk tops. Perhaps the reason why the pyramidion is not there anymore is that during the First Intermediate Period, after the Sixth Dynasty and the end of the Old Kingdom *circa* 2195 BC, when Egypt entered a century-and-a-half of complete chaos and collapse of all government due to a catastrophic failure of the Nile floods, with people dying of famine in the fields and towns, the pyramidion was levered off its summit and fell to the ground so that robbers could strip it of its gold.

A pyramidion cased in mirror-like golden metal would once have flashed daily at sunrise, heralding heliacal risings of stars long before the sun came up, and visible for enormous distances. This is certainly a subject which needs further investigation, with calculations of the angles and times of the optical phenomena associated with such a pyramidion.

Earlier on, I mentioned that the ancient name for the city of Memphis was (translated) 'White Wall'. We are now in a better position to understand this strange name. The white wall was clearly a shadow-wall, whether at Memphis itself, or perhaps at the nearby necropolis of Giza. After all, each face of the two large Giza pyramids was a 'white wall'. So there was no shortage of white walls near Memphis! Furthermore, any wall facing due south was bound to be white in the daytime, for it would always be lit by the sun. There is some reason to believe that a major shadow-wall was a feature of the great Temple of Ptah, which was the central religious building at Memphis. Unfortunately, Memphis has never been fully excavated, and not much of it seems to be left in any case. But this doesn't really matter. We don't have to find and identify a white wall to know what a white wall is! In any case, not wishing to leave any reader disappointed, I reproduce in Plate 60 a rare photograph of a 'white wall' at Giza which is nothing to do with one of the pyramids. This 'white wall' is actually in a 'light-well' in the Valley Temple near the Sphinx. The photo was taken by Professor Charles Piazzi Smyth in 1865, but he apparently found no occasion to publish it. It represents the first evidence of a major shadow phenomenon at Giza discovered by a modern person.

This photo was amongst the papers of Piazzi Smyth purchased by Moses Cotsworth, and it was Cotsworth who first published it.[82] Cotsworth was able to describe the photo by its caption which Piazzi Smyth had carefully written and attached to the glass negative. It reads as follows:

North end of meridian granite chamber of King Khafre on Great Pyramid Hill [the Giza plateau], tested after 4,000 years for truth of astronomical orientation, and found sensibly perfect, in 1865.

A second caption then followed:

King Khafre's sun-shadow-well. Proof. – A camera having been adjusted over centre of south-wall, this photo was taken at the instant of noon by astronomical observation, and no more shadow will be found on the east, than on the west, wall; but full light on the north wall. – C.P.S., 1865.[83]

In other words, the north wall is a 'white wall', fully lit by the sun, whereas the east and west walls are entirely in shadow. This suggestive discovery must have done much to encourage Cotsworth's own researches into shadows on the Giza plateau. Naturally, Egyptologists know nothing of this evidence, which is never mentioned by them. But then, it is high time we all recognized the fact that Egyptologists are not capable of acting as the sole authorities on any scientific aspects of ancient Egypt, at least until such time as they add some scientific education to their training to enable them to tackle such subjects.

Let us now return to the subject of surveying, for without optical surveying the Great Pyramid with all its wondrous aspects could never have been built in the first place. We have already learned of Ballard's suggestions that the Giza pyramids themselves would have acted as wonderful back-sights for surveying the flooded fields for miles around – and in fact a flashing pyramidion would greatly have facilitated this.

We have also learned of the use of 'shadow-catchers' and the true significance of the staff with the forked base, carried as a sceptre by most of the gods at one time or another.

But the work which has been done so far by people such as Martin Isler relates chiefly to orientations and the foundations of buildings. They have rightly called attention to the many accounts and depictions of 'laying-of-the-cord' ceremonies, where cords are seen to be ceremonially stretched by

Figure 70. A fanciful English engraving of 1840 showing Arab astronomers observing the setting of a crescent moon from the platform on the top of the Great Pyramid – inspired by speculation that the Great Pyramid had in ancient times been an astronomical observatory. However, the engraving was prepared from a genuine sketch made in 1839 by an anonymous British artist who did it while really observing the moon setting from the top of the Great Pyramid, so that the general view is authentic.
(*Collection of Robert Temple.*)

the pharaoh to mark the site of a new temple. A faint and purely secular modern echo of this practice, but without any measuring implications, is the familiar 'laying of the cornerstone' ceremony for a new building. Whereas a foundation inscription used to be a grand and religious pronouncement by a pharaoh praising his god, a foundation inscription in our time is likely to say that a long-forgotten and transient alderman represented his municipal authority and made a feeble speech to which tepid applause put a merciful end.

The 'stretching-of-the-cord' is absolutely essential to any kind of surveying, of course. Let us pause for a moment to consider just what *is* necessary for surveying, and see if the ancient Egyptians had it. If they had lenses which they could use for rudimentary telescopes to do optical surveying, what was the rest of their gear?

The first thing you have to do if you want to survey anything is establish a level. If you can't do that, you can't go any further. Measurements which are not taken from a level base are useless. Could the Egyptians establish a level? Well, the immediate answer is of course they could, since the northern pavement adjoining the Great Pyramid for instance was perfectly level. But putting results like that aside, could they establish a level with the equipment which we know them to have possessed? In other words, is there any evidence of how they actually established a level? After all, today we use spirit levels – a bubble floats in a trapped ball of spirit and when it is centred, your device is level. But we don't believe the Egyptians had anything like that. They must have used another method. What was it?

In Plate 58 I reproduce a suggestive photo I took of a carving at the Temple of Denderah in Upper Egypt. This shows an *ankh*, the symbol of life, animated with two arms. From the elbows of these arms we see suspended two balance weights, one from each arm. This represents what I believe was the system of obtaining a level in use amongst the Egyptians. In effect, it was a double plumb-bob system, to ascertain that each side of the device being used was level. It is notable that the hands grasp *was* staffs, which is an indication of the true significance of the symbolism. The plumb-bobs may simply have been attached to either end of a flat board (a 'plane table' as surveyors would call it), to make it level, and sighting would have been done across it through a tube.

I believe we can take this indication, together with the extensive surviving evidence of plumb-bobs found by archaeologists, as indicating the nature of the process used by the ancient Egyptians to find a level. Having accomplished that, what did the Egyptians do next? What does any surveyor do next? He extends a baseline.

Here Martin Isler comes riding in on his white horse again, because he has reconstructed an ingenious system used by the ancient Egyptians to extend baselines for very long distances without sagging of the cord. He explains this in his article 'An Ancient Method of Finding and Extending a Direction', from which we have quoted before. First he reproduces one of

The Crystal Sun

Figure 71. Drawings of two Egyptian Old Kingdom wall carvings from about 2500 BC showing typical scale balances used for weighing at that time. An adaptation of this type of balance with a plumb bob at either end was used to find a level, as indicated in Plate 58 where the animated *ankh* has two balance weights hanging from either arm. The scale at the top has a central plummet as well, which is a plumb bob suspended to demonstrate that the scale is truly vertical and that the weighing is reliable, without a bias caused to either side by the scale leaning in either direction. The Egyptians had only balance scales prior to Roman times, and the steelyard scale which has a pan at only one end – the weighing scale still used by vegetable sellers all over China, except that it has now been banned by the Municipality of Beijing, and of which I have a large collection of different types (Chinese and Greek) with weights up to 30 kg – was only introduced to Egypt from Rome. Balance scales are shown in countless illustrations of the *Book of the Dead* and tombs, where judgement is rendered in the afterlife and the soul is weighed against a feather in the other pan.

424

the many scenes seen on Egyptian wall carvings of the pharaoh and the goddess Seshat using mallets to hammer two stakes into the ground at the foundation of a temple. The two stakes are bound together by loops of cord. He also quotes a typical inscription from the Temple of Horus at Edfu commenting on the scene:

'I hold the peg. I grasp the handle of the club and grip the measuring-cord with Seshat. I turn my eyes to the movement of the stars. I send forth my glance to Ursa Major [I believe the ceremony was taking place in the daylight, and this direction of the pole was indicated by an alignment visible to the pharaoh] . . . the cord was stretched by His Majesty himself, having the stake in his hand with Seshat: he untied his cord with He-who-is-south-of-his-wall [this may be an epithet of the sun, who is always in the south of the sky in Egypt, the wall perhaps being a shadow-wall], in perfect work for eternity, being established on its angle by the majesty of Khnoum. He-who-makes-existence-run-its-course stood up to see its shadow [this shows that we are definitely in the daylight, and not looking at the night sky], it being long in perfect fashion, wide in perfect fashion, high and low in accurate fashion, . . .'[84]

Isler then works out how the looped cords can be stretched very great distances without horizontal distortion, vertical sag being rendered irrelevant to the process. He reproduces several diagrams showing this. If the

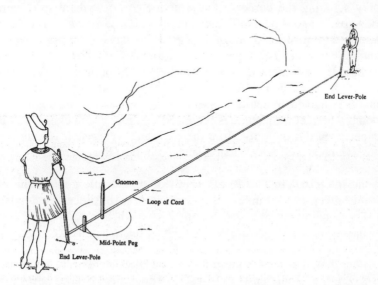

Figure 72. Martin Isler's drawing of a pharaoh and the goddess Seshet, goddess of construction and foundations, 'stretching the cord' for the site of a new temple. The cord is looped round the poles held in the hands of the two parties, and levered taut. The cord is kept straight, and horizontal distortion of the line is eliminated, by the insertion of pegs (of exactly equal diameter to the two poles) as shown.

poles shown in the wall carvings are regarded as the end lever-poles to pull a looped cord taut, what is needed is to have a couple of poles of diameter equal to the end ones erected elsewhere between the cords. This keeps the whole arrangement straight, so that any horizontal deviation can instantly be spotted. He says:

> During my trials of the Indian circle method, two points 40.3 cm apart were established: the south terminus was the base of the gnomon, and the north was the mid-point of where the shadow tip entered and emerged from the circle. By making the loop taut with the two end lever-poles, I have accurately and easily extended the distance to 131 m [430 feet!]. Although it could not be proved for lack of space, I believe the distance could have been greater without loss of accuracy. For these trials, the closely spaced peg and gnomon were placed near one end of the loop in order to observe the relationship of the cord and adjust it accordingly while holding an end lever-pole. Over this long distance, although the cord will sag, the accuracy will not be compromised; for its horizontal component will be unaffected.

> Although the Egyptian pictographs show only the loop or cord and end poles, these are the essential features when representing the 'Stretching of the Cord' ceremony; for it was also used when a gnomon was not present. The ceremony was shown in temples not noted for careful orientation, which indicates that it may also have been used for only squaring the corners of a structure. As described by [Reginald] Engelbach, and shown in fig. 73s, the base leg of a square is placed on a line, and the position of the other leg, which may only approximate a 90° angle, is marked. The square is then flipped over a common point, with its base leg still on the line, but on the other side of the point. The extending leg is once again marked, and the difference, if any, between the two marks is halved. When this bisection is aligned with the common base point, a perfect right angle is produced. . . . Engelbach claims that in no experiment did the error from the right angle exceed 1 1/2 minutes of arc, which is well within that displayed in the Great Pyramid . . .[85]

Anyone interested in the details of all of this should consult the many drawings given by Isler in his article, which show the processes clearly, and are very convincing. See also Figure 74, which is a reproduction of an ancient wall carving showing the loop being made taut between two poles.

The other thing needed for surveying was a knowledge of the geographical points of north, south, east, and west. We have already seen how this was determined with immense precision by the Egyptians. And since they did not use the magnetic points of the compass, they did not need to have any knowledge of maps of magnetic variation as a corrective factor in the way that modern surveyors would require.

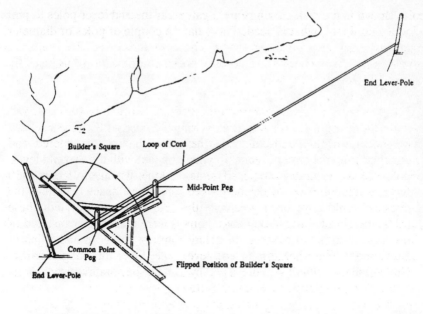

Figure 73. Martin Isler's drawing showing Reginald Engelbach's solution to the squaring of a corner and accurate 'stretching-of-the-cord' for a baseline without distortion. By using this device, precision equal to that of the Great Pyramid foundations could apparently be achieved.

Having established a level and a baseline, and knowing the points of direction to great precision, we know the Egyptians had the telescopic technology for sighting, and the only thing lacking is therefore a graduated scale to determine sighting-angles. What did they use for this? Modern theodolites prior to the era of electronics featured tiny telescopes mounted so that they could slide along magnificent brass arcs. I show a 1916 engraving of a 'modern' theodolite in Figure 76, with the letter 'N' beside the brass arc marked off in degrees, so that the reader can see what I am talking about. These arcs had angular degrees prominently indicated on them, and you could read off the degree measurements by leaving your telescope at its sighting-angle and looking at the side of the device to see where your pointer was pointing on that arc. This method incorporates the angular measure in the sighting-device itself, and is very convenient. But the alternative is to have the angular measure separate, somewhere in front of you. Such an idea may be very unfamiliar to us, and may even seem bizarre, since we are not used to such a notion. But I have been forced to look for some such devices because there is no evidence whatever that I know of to indicate that the Egyptians adopted the system which we use. And, once you have thought about it for a while, you realize that just because we use a system doesn't mean it has to be the only one.

I had to adopt a fresh attitude, and try and rid myself of preconceptions. So I began to think – what familiar but odd little device was there in ancient

Figure 74. The pharaoh Ptolemy XIII Auletes (80–52 BC) and the goddess Sefkhet-Abwy (a form of the goddess Seshet) use wooden mallets to drive stakes into the ground in order to stretch a looped cord taut between them. (Two tiny *djed* symbols meaning 'stability' and perhaps indicating surveying are seen in the middle of the loop.) This ceremony was sacred and was called 'the stretching of the cord ceremony'. This wall carving was found on the west wall of the Temple of Auletes at Athribis, near Sohag in Upper Egypt. The fragmentary inscription describes Sefkhet as 'establishing the angles (*kheses*)'. The inscription in front of the pharaoh says: 'Founding thy sanctuary like the horizon. Establishing it with the sacred mallet.' (From W. M. Flinders Petrie, J. H. Walker, and E. B. Knobel, *Athribis*, British School of Archaeology in Egypt, London, 1908, Plate 26, and p. 20.)

Egypt which we do not properly understand, which might be such a sighting-scale, or perhaps a stylized indication of one? And I settled on something I call the *tet*. See Figure 77. Here we see a strange notched object known in earlier days of scholarship as a *tet* or a *tchet*, but nowadays – using a newer transliteration system – known as a *djed*. (I still prefer to call it a *tet*.) In later times this peculiar object, which most Egyptologists admit represents something unknown, became a symbol of 'stability', and even became described as the backbone of the god Osiris. Huge *djed*-pillars bigger than a man are seen in wall carvings as being raised by the pharaoh in a special ceremony called 'the raising of the *tet*' or 'raising of the *djed*'. However, it is well recognized that all this came later, and that the origins of this strange object were nothing to do with any 'backbone of Osiris'. As

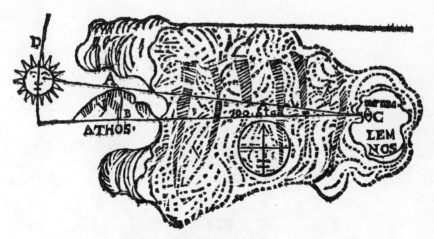

Figure 75. This quaint woodcut appears in Athanasius Kircher's *Ars Magna Lucis et Umbrae* (*The Great Art of Light and Shadow*), Rome, 1646; reprinted at Amsterdam, 1671. It shows the use of trigonometry to measure the height of Mount Athos on the Greek mainland from a theodolite on the Island of Lemnos. The distance between them (points B and C) is shown as 100 stadia. Point A is the top of the mountain, and D represents the angle, noted as the sun sets in the west over the mountain. The sun looks quite surprised to be observed just as he is turning in for the night.
(From p. 728 of the 1646 Rome edition and p. 644 of the 1671 enlarged Amsterdam edition.)

Manfred Lurker frankly acknowledges in his book *The Gods and Symbols of Ancient Egypt*:

> The djed-pillar is a prehistoric fetish, the meaning of which has still not been unequivocally explained. It may be a stylized representation of a leafless tree or a pole with notches in it. . . . it [eventually] became a general symbol of 'stability' and as such entered the written language. In the Old Kingdom at Memphis there were some priests of the 'noble djed', and the chief Memphite god, Ptah, was himself called 'noble djed'. The ritual of 'raising the djed pillar' began at Memphis; the king himself performed it by means of ropes and with the assistance of priests. . . . the erstwhile fetish became a symbol of Osiris at the beginning of the New Kingdom. Therefore the djed was regarded as the god's backbone.[86]

The associations of the *djed* with a pharaonic ceremony at a temple reminds us of the 'stretching-of-the-cord' ceremonies. Ptah being the god of the pole, finding true north was associated with him, and so an object sacred to him might be expected to have some surveying or measurement connotations. But what could these be?

The first thing to realize is that the *djed* has many forms of representation. It does not always appear alone, and a double-*djed* is very common,

429

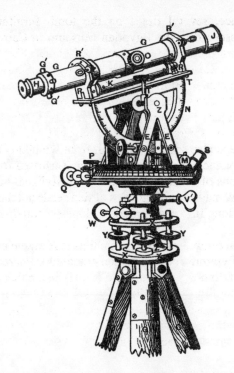

Figure 76. An engraving from 1916 showing an ordinary surveyor's theodolite of that time. The tripod was of wood, and all the other parts were of brass. The sighting-telescope rests on top, with the letters II and J at either end. It can be turned sideways or up and down. If turned sideways, its position is marked in degrees on a circular dial which can be seen here from the side in the middle of the engraving (beneath the letters P, D, and M). If turned up and down, its position is marked in degrees along the semi-circular arc which has the letter N beside it. This theodolite incorporates two spirit-levels at right angles to one another (one is the small tube marked K beneath the telescope, the other can only be seen here head-on as a small circle marked M, which is the end of a second tube) to assure that the instrument is level, but the ancient Egyptians used weights and plumb bobs for this purpose, of which very many survive in museums. We know how the Egyptians found a level, we know how they took their baselines with cords (from pictures and texts), we know that they had the lenses for the rudimentary telescopes, but the question remains: how did they measure the arcs? The answer seems to be that instead of doing so beside the telescope on graduated pieces of brass like the Victorian engineers, they did so remotely by sighting through evenly-graduated slits in a device of which the sacred *djed* is a stylized depiction. Figure 77 shows an ancient Egyptian picture of eyes peering through a slit in a *djed*. There are many such pictures, and another may be seen painted on the New Kingdom Papyrus of Pa-di-Amon. (See Figure 47, p. 60, in Vol. I, *Texts*, of Alexandre Piankoff, *Mythological Papyri*, Bollingen Series XL, 3, Pantheon Books, New York, 1957, 2 vols. The Papyrus is photographically reproduced as Number 10 in Vol. II.) Above the depiction is simply the inscription which translated reads: 'Osiris, Lord of Busiris [a city in the Delta sacred to the god], the Great God, Ruler of Eternity' (Vol. I, p. 114). The symbolism of the *djed* and Osiris-as-*djed* was so widespread in the funerary cults that it was used constantly without any direct reference whatever to its source or origins – subjects which mystify and have eluded all Egyptologists, as they frankly admit.

(Engraving taken from George Lionel Leston, *Practical Surveying*, 11th edition, London, 1916, Figure 89, p. 47.)

appearing, for instance, several times on the tomb furniture of King Tutankhamen, as I observed in the Egyptian Museum in Cairo. A *djed* is also often portrayed as animated, with arms and hands, like the *ankh* in Plate 58. And the *djed* device is a standard element incorporated in the sceptre of Ptah, and is embodied into Ptah's *was* staff.

I became more and more intrigued by the different forms of *djed*. And then I discovered what may possibly be the earliest known depiction of the *djed*, from the reign of Pharaoh Zoser (2668–2649 BC) of the Third Dynasty, whose statue is also seen in Plate 18, from which his crystal eyes have been removed by ancient robbers. But I was surprised to notice that these original depictions of the *djed* were not at all stylized, but appear to be natural and realistic, made out of bundles of tied reeds notched at the top and with four rows of long flat reeds stretched along several *djeds* in an arc. See Plate 26.

This beautiful mural of blue-green ceramic tiles is from the underground chambers of the Step Pyramid at Saqqara, constructed for Pharaoh Zoser by his vizier and architect, Imhotep. It is now on display in a rather dark corner of the Egyptian Museum in Cairo, where I was able to take a photo of it using a very long time exposure. As can be seen from the photo, this mural bears the design at the top of a multiple-*djed*. There are in fact 11 *djeds* in the design. The later depictions seem to have arisen from this rather homely and very natural one.

What *is* this multi-*djed*? Of course, we have no way of knowing for sure. Some archaeologists have assumed that it is just a rather peculiar type of high window. They seem to have no reason for this, nor can they say why it is shaped like that. The fact is, nobody knows what this is all about. If making a long, high arc of a window, why would anybody go to all the trouble seen here? Yes, it is a very pretty design. But we ought to know by now that when we see a very pretty design from ancient Egypt which is peculiar in some way, there is often 'something going on here'.

So I began to think that perhaps this was really some kind of sighting-device used for surveying, and the notches are meant to represent a means of taking angular measures. I stand with my sighting-scope on a pole looking through this arc, having already obtained my level and stretched my cord, and read off my angles in front of me by the notches. The fundamental device would be a double-*djed*, and the sightings would be taken through the slots extending from their notches between them. The multi-*djed* may be a more complex form, or it may be a decorative extension of the idea. The single *djed*, on the other hand, would not be a sighting-device, but would be a symbol extracted from the sighting-device. And the large *djed*-pillar would also be symbolic.

Perhaps something of this sort can answer the angular measure requirements of ancient Egyptian surveying. The stylized *djed* became one of the standard religious decorative symbols of Egypt for millennia, just like the *was* staff, and the two were often seen together. And when one begins to examine the frieze-motifs of the late Egyptian temples, one begins to see that the mysterious shapes are often connected in some way with survey-ing, foundations, and the 'achieving of stability' by correct orientation. In Plate X is a photo I took at Philae of a *djed* with a solar disc on top – an image of the sun presumably sighted and its angle of altitude measured with a *djed* – flanked by strange objects I cannot identify. Certainly Egyptian iconography is full of 'things we cannot identify'. I can offer a possible explanation for the strange tail of the 'Seth animal', that canine beast symbolizing the god Seth, which has only recently been identified, as we saw a moment ago. Seth (albeit here without his tail) is shown in Plate 56. In many depictions, however, this upright tail is prominently forked – a bifurx! Well, we know by now what that is, don't we? So perhaps that is one mystery solved. Seth, the god who in some respects represented the night sky and thus could be viewed as inimical to the forces of light, had a

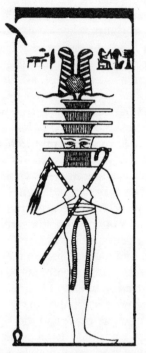

Figure 77. The *djed* pillar emerging from the body of the god Osiris, not as a backbone but as an extended 'head'. Perhaps the two eyes peeking through a hole or slat or observation-slit in the *djed* are meant to represent the use of the *djed* as a sighting-device. On the other hand, the figure could just represent the face of Osiris emerging from the symbolic *djed*, with no further meaning. We simply don't know for certain what the *djed* really was meant to represent. My suggestion that it may have been used in surveying sacred sites cannot yet be proved. But the occasional depictions of eyes peering through the *djed* are suggestive.

(A redrawing of Plate 25, Part 1, in Sir Gardner Wilkinson, *Supplement Volume, Second Series of Manners and Customs of the Ancient Egyptians*, London, 1841.)

bifurx for a tail, through which one could make astronomical sightings of the stars in that night sky.

And there is another aspect of Seth which may be intended to refer to the telescope. In a great conflict which took place between Seth and Horus, where Seth plucked out the eye of Horus, Horus grabbed Seth's testicles and tore them off. The eye was later restored to Horus, and the testicles were later restored to Seth. But what was this all about? If we think morphologically, what is it that the testicles represent? Forget about the notion of seed coming from them. They are a *pair of balls* – two small spheres. They may have been intended as a symbolic reference to the convex crystal lenses, any two of which in juxtaposition (and testicles are very much in juxtaposition) make a rudimentary telescope. Looked at like this, with a snout that was the same curve as the top of a sighting-staff, with a tail that was a bifurx, and with two balls which make a telescope – and representing the night sky as he did – Seth seems to be very much an optical creature. When no less than three physical attributes of a god can be reasonably interpreted as symbolic of optical instruments, we can safely conclude that somebody is trying to tell us something.

The Greek tradition of the Cyclops seems to relate to optics, as the large central eye of the Cyclops is a perfect symbol of a lens or crystal ball. The surviving details of the Cyclops legends amongst the Greeks are somewhat vague and disappointing. The original Cyclops were from an 'earlier generation' of mythological figures, preceding that of the Olympian gods. By the time of *The Odyssey*, they had become stock characters which could be utilized for storytelling purposes; what Homer has to say about the Cyclops named Polyphemus is of little mythological consequence. The earlier legends relating to the Cyclops connect them with massive stone walls and edifices, hence the name which we sometimes use for these: 'Cyclopean'. It was the Cyclops who built the walls of Argos and Tiryns, and of Midea and Mycenae for Perseus (mythical founder of Mycenae) – in other words, of the typical Mycenaean cities. Probably the Cyclops were a Minoan tradition. Even Polyphemus in *The Odyssey* is associated with massive stones and is a giant. Echoes of the megaliths are always heard when the Cyclops are mentioned.

Specific optical aspects to the Cyclops are that one of them was named Brontēs. And as we have already seen, this is a reference to thunderstones, since *brontē* means 'thunder'. But the association was even more specific than that, for it was the Cyclops who actually fashioned the thunderbolts for Zeus. And it was the thunderbolts which produced thunderstones, so what could be more obvious? And the Cyclops also made for Hades, the god of the Underworld, his prize possession – a 'helmet of invisibility' – which seems another optical allusion. It could refer to the fact that without optical

Figure 78. Three ancient depictions of a Cyclops. The two small Roman figures (*a* and *b*) were found at Naples and show the Cyclops as having two normal eyes, with a third eye in the middle of the forehead. These are late and decadent concepts of the Cyclops. Earlier Greek pictures of Polyphemus, the Cyclops who features in *The Odyssey*, show him with one giant eye only. There is a very good representation of Polyphemus having his eye put out on an archaic Greek pot in the Museum of Argos, but the light was so poor that I could not photograph it in its display case. The largest image above (*c*) is a traditional Greek idea of the Cyclops preserved in the Louvre, Figure 2259 (p. 1695) from the Daremberg-Saglio *Dictionnaire des Antiquités (Dictionary of Antiquities)*, Paris, 1877–1919, Vol. I, Part 2.

aids, many things were invisible. And I think that perhaps the association of the Cyclops with the construction of huge 'incomprehensible' early 'cyclopean' walls and cities may be connected with the use of optical instruments for surveying in prehistoric times.

This brings us back to the Eye of Horus. And in this connection, I reproduce in Plate 63 a photo of an extraordinary design found in a mosaic on the Greek sacred island of Delos by French archaeologists, and published in 1907. The design shows what appears to be the sun standing on the tip of a pyramid, with prominently reflecting rays shooting out to either side. In the light of what we have learned, this is a highly suggestive image, to say the least. Although the design is from a more recent culture than ancient Egypt, the remarks by the archaeologist are extremely interesting:

The symbol in the middle of the mosaic . . . is found many times on stelae [erect stone tablets] discovered in the Punic [Carthaginian] sanctuaries of North Africa; and in it one usually recognizes the more or less anthropomorphic representation of the Phoenician goddess Tanit. [They believe that the sun on top is a head, and the rays shooting out are arms, with the pyramid being a body in a dress! Can you beat that? It must be the most bourgeois misinterpretation of a sacred symbol I have ever heard.] According to M. Ed. Meyer, the meaning of the symbol is different; he sees in it a Phoenician and Syrian interpretation of an Egyptian sign [of the *ankh*], the hieroglyph for 'life'; this sign would have been considered as having a mystical virtue, and thus its use on amulets could be explained, as also on the stelae mentioned above. If this last explanation is the true one, we can understand better the use of the symbol in question on our mosaic. As a matter of fact, it is found in the vestibule of the House of Dolphins. . . . The mosaic of the peristyle of this same house is the work of an artist who came originally from the town of Arados, which is perhaps Arados of Phoenicia. . . . The House of Dolphins would then be a place apart among the Graeco-Roman houses of Delos, owing to its Oriental influences.[87]

It is certainly interesting to learn that the sign of a pyramid reflecting the rays of the sun from its pyramidion was widespread throughout North Africa and known also in Phoenicia. Phoenicia was an Egyptian territory during the New Kingdom (15th century BC), with Egyptian governors and Egyptian temples.

The sun on top of the pyramid may be considered an Eye of Horus. But then, as we have seen, the Great Pyramid itself was also an Eye of Horus. In fact, the whole of Egypt could also be called the Eye of Horus. This is pointed out at the end of his fascinating book *The Conflict of Horus and Seth* by J. Gwyn Griffiths. In his final paragraph he says:

Drioton has called attention to a hymn to Egypt in the Pyramid Texts [of the Old Kingdom]. The land is called *the eye of Horus*.[88]

It is difficult to imagine that the ancient Egyptians could possibly have known the details, but there is something extraordinary about the eyes of hawks and falcons. Anyone who has watched them can infer this, as it is so obvious that they hover at a great height and can see small rodents from higher than we could possibly do. In 1982 a report was published in the scientific journal *Nature* about anatomical studies done of the eye of the small falcon known as the kestrel. It was discovered that the kestrel's eye is designed in such a way that it magnifies images, and in fact the precise magnifying power is 1.33X.[89] Larger hawks such as those which represented Horus presumably have much more powerful eyes than this. The fact that a hawk's eye is thus a magnifier is rather eerie, considering the subject of this book, and that the hawk symbolized the god Horus. It means that the zoological Eye of Horus was a magnifying lens.

Another thing to consider, when realizing that the Eye of Horus may sometimes have been intended to mean a lens (or magnifying- and burning-globe), is that 'Eyes' in Egypt so often come in pairs. In the case of the Two Eyes of Rā, the two solstices were undoubtedly referred to in most cases, as I have already explained. But if by an 'Eye' a lens is referred to, then a pair of Eyes can obviously refer to a telescope. As I have also explained already, all you have to do if you have lenses is hold one up in each hand and look through them both at the same time, and you have a rudimentary telescope. So 'The Two Eyes' could be a way of referring to rudimentary telescopes in Egypt. And in this connection there is one other important point which I must make. Everyone was believed to have a 'double', known as a *ka*. This led to the concept of the *eidōla* in Greece, with all of its optical connotations, as I have already explained at length. But let us think for a moment about the Egyptian hieroglyph for *ka*. It consists of a pair of raised arms. Now, why should this be? Most people presumably just assume that the raised arms indicate an act of worship or something of the sort. But why should they? What has a *ka* got to do with acts of worship?

On the other hand, there is a possible optical explanation for the hiero-glyph of the *ka*, meaning a person's 'double'. If you look through a rudimentary telescope, the image you see will be inverted unless you use a third lens known to us as a 'rectifying lens' to flip the image right way up again. Imagine the awe which must have been inspired in ancient peoples at this phenomenon of the inverted image seen through their rudimentary telescopes of two lenses! What would they make of it?

If you look through a rudimentary telescope at a man standing in the distance (as in connection with the act of surveying you would have to), he would be upside-down. *His arms would be pointing upwards.* Can this be the origin of the hieroglyph for a person's 'double'? Considering that the Greek optical tradition drew so heavily upon this original concept, we are encouraged to think in terms of optical associations. And the suggestion is therefore well worth making, in case any overt evidence relating to it might ever come to light or, indeed, might already be known but not compre-hended at the moment.

Attempting to decide what the Eye of Horus really was exactly is one of the most difficult feats in Egyptology. Practically everything at one time of another was described as an eye of Horus. If one reads through the Pyramid Texts, in the sections of offerings to the deceased pharaohs, one quickly realizes that the phrase 'eye of Horus' is synonymous with 'sacred offer-ing'. Calling a loaf of bread or a joint of meat an 'eye of Horus' was a bit like calling a pretty girl 'a real Venus', which used to be common a few decades ago before classical education ceased to exist. An Italian might say of a beautiful girl that she is a Madonna. By saying that, he does not mean that the girl has just given birth to Jesus, he is speaking metaphorically. And when we say someone is 'angelic', we do not mean he or she has wings but that he or she is extremely good. So when someone brought his ducks and geese to offer to the deceased pharaoh, those birds were referred to as veritable 'eyes of Horus'.

The various translations of the Pyramid Texts are mostly in a real jumble. The separate portions are called 'Utterances'. But the numberings of the Utterances do not necessarily make any sense. In the Pyramid of Unas, for instance, Utterance 221 is followed by Utterance 118, and Utterance 133 is followed by Utterance 16. Confronted with this confusion, I introduced myself to the Pyramid Texts in a very sensible way which I recommend to others. Alexandre Piankoff did a translation only of the Pyramid Texts which appear in the Pyramid of Unas at Saqqara;[90] this was the earliest pyramid to have any texts, so one is starting at the beginning. He gives the texts in the sequence in which they are found, in the entrance to the antechamber, in the antechamber, in the passage to the sarcophagus chamber, and finally culminating in the sarcophagus chamber itself. This is how he presents them – just as they appear on the walls. I have sat in that pyramid for some hours, and so when I read those texts I know exactly what wall they are on. This is the best way to start – the sequence is important. Follow the texts from room to room in the earliest structure in which they occur. They are the oldest surviving religious texts in the entire world, and thus worthy of the deepest attention. Later, one can read the additional Pyramid Texts as they occur in the compendia where they are presented in such a jumble. See Plate 59 for a photo of part of the Pyramid Texts in the Pyramid of Unas.

One of the most surprising things about the texts in the Pyramid of the Pharaoh Unas is the total exclusion of the god Ptah from all mention and consideration. Since he was the chief god of Memphis, which is within sight of Saqqara, this is highly peculiar, to say the least! The 'Memphite Theology' of Ptah is ignored as if it didn't exist. One wonders how this is possible, considering Ptah's main sanctuary in Egypt was only just down the road and his priests must have been all over the place at the funeral. Perhaps a form of taboo was being observed in Ptah's own precincts, by refraining from mentioning his name.

As soon as one enters Unas's tomb, one is informed that 'Unas is a Horus'. (Utt. 503) Shortly afterward, we are told 'Unas brings the green brilliance to the Great Eye.' (Utt. 509) And then: 'Unas is the bull of the double brilliance in the midst of his eye.' (Utt. 513) That is before we even get into the antechamber. There we are told that 'Unas will come with a face like this Great One, the Lord of the lion helmet who became powerful through the injury of his eye. Then he will cause the fire of his eye to encompass you . . .' (Utt. 255) And also: 'Unas's shelter is in his eye, the protection of Unas is in his eye. Unas' victorious strength is in his eye, the power of Unas is in his eye.' (Utt. 260) We learn also that 'They stand fast, the two *Djed*-pillars . . .' (Utt. 271), which confirms what I believed about the early *djeds* occurring in pairs.

The actual phrase 'Eye of Horus' is not mentioned until we enter the passage to the sarcophagus chamber, where the very first statement is: 'This is here the hard eye of Horus. Place it in thy hand that thou mayest be sure of victory and that he [Seth] may fear thee!' (Utt. 249) Shortly afterwards, the confusing statement occurs: 'He comes against you, Horus with blue eyes. Beware of the Horus with red eyes, whose anger is evil, whose power one cannot withstand!' (Utt. 246) A variety of offerings are then made, which are called eyes of Horus.

In the sarcophagus chamber itself we are informed of Unas that 'thou art indeed Horus who fought to protect his eye.' (Utt. 221) The dead pharaoh is identified with Osiris, who is viewed as the lord of the Underworld. He is even addressed as 'Osiris Unas'. We are told: 'Osiris Unas, I give thee the Eye of Horus that thy face may be adorned with it . . .' (Utt. 25) It is perfume, and it is obviously a perfume oil applied to his face. Similarly, a libation called Eye of Horus is offered to him next. (Utt. 32) Many more eyes of Horus are then offered. Often some descriptive words are added about the Eye, such as 'which was snatched from Seth', 'which was rescued for thee'.

These references are to the famous myth that Horus and Seth had a great combat. Seth plucked out the Eye of Horus, and Horus pulled off Seth's testicles. Later the gods arrange peace and restore the missing parts, and the sacred mutilations are soothed and healed, but another version has it that the Eye of Horus was snatched from Seth by the god Thoth and restored to Horus by him against Seth's will. Sir Peter Renouf translates an inscription from Edfu:

Asten [Thoth], who restored the Eye of Horus to its Lord, who preserved the Eye from suffering harm, who made fast the Eye in its place, and who pacified Horus with his Eye.

Renouf then comments on this text by saying:

The different synonyms designating the Eye are important as showing that the word is here used in the sense of the *daily* light of the sun. . . . The priestly title 'holder of the Eye' is like all such titles, that of the divinity whom the priest personates. The god himself is hieroglyphically represented by the sign of an ape [of Thoth] holding the Eye.[91]

Sir Peter Renouf wrote five pages attempting to explain the different Eyes of Horus, Eyes of Ra, and so forth, in his translation of the *Book of the Dead*.[92] But he only succeeded in convincing anyone reading his account how hopelessly confused this mass of tradition really was! There are no simple explanations to all of this. Egyptian mythology will not crack at the first assault, or even the ten-thousandth. It is more robust than that. If we think we are clever, the Egyptians were cleverer. They are like someone who designed a computer programme so advanced that we can't hack it.

Nonetheless, there is evidence that the Eye of Horus is ultimately something that is counted and measured. We are told in *The Book of Opening the Mouth:*

> I am Thoth, who journeyeth at the two seasons to seek for the Eye of its Lord. I have come, I have found the Eye, I have reckoned it up for its Lord.[93]

What kind of Eye can be 'reckoned up'? And why by Thoth?

An ancient medical papyrus tells us this extraordinary information:

> Spell for the *debeḥ*-measure when it is taken to measure a medicament. As for this measure with which I am measuring this medicament, it is the measure with which Horus measured his eye, it being examined and found living, prosperous, and healthy. This medicament is measured with this measure . . . it is the eye of Horus which was measured and examined.[94]

Clearly what is being referred to is either a shadow or a time. If a shadow, then it is time which in turn is measured by it. In either case, the calendrical obsessions of the Egyptians are being referred to. They had to have the precise length of the year, and they must either measure pyramid or gnomon shadows, or they must measure the position of the 'eye' cast upon the wall, or screen, or mirror in the inner sanctum of the temple whose long corridor was, as Sir Norman Lockyer liked to call them, a 'horizontal telescope' aimed not at the meridian but at the horizon.

We have seen earlier that the fraction of a day, .2424 of a day (or more exactly .242392 of a day), which must be added to 365 to make an accurate year, was associated with Horus. *This* was the 'mutilated' Eye of Horus, which was plucked out and rendered incomplete, before being reinstated. For it was not a 'complete Eye', but a mutilated Eye. And it was such a mutilated Eye that its precise numerical value had to be 'reckoned up' with great care because it was not an integral number but a fraction.

Thoth was the god of the Octave, since 'the Eight of Hermopolis' were known as 'the souls of Thoth'. And it was his multiple, 128, which fell short of the number 129.75 which was the multiple of 'the Five' (the fifths), who were also born at Hermopolis. We know from an ancient inscription that the name of the High Priest of Thoth was 'the great one of the five'. Hermopolis was, as Thoth's cult centre, therefore the location where 'the Five' and 'the Eight' were arithmetrically reconciled. This gave the magic number of the Comma of Pythagoras. And in order to come to the Comma of Pythagoras by the calendrical route as well, the mutilated Eye of Horus was required, the extra .2424 of a day – calculated from an equally 'mutilated', i.e. fractional. shadow-reading. It must be added to 365 to give the number which would also give the 'greatest secret of the Egyptians', their *tiny gap*.

Thoth was the mathematician and astronomer of the gods. He must 'reckon up' the difference between *the eights* and *the fives*. He must also reckon up the difference between 360 and 365.2424, which he could only do if he 'held the Eye of Horus in his hand', i.e. held its tally, having reckoned that up. The Eye of Horus was essential, and without its mutilation into a fraction there could not be an accurate year.

As George St Clair so rightly concluded:

When Thoth holds up the symbolic eye he means to say that he shows the true length of the year.[95]

Figure 79. The god Thoth holds the Eye of Horus in his hands, having 'reckoned it up'. In fact, the image may actually represent the priest who bore the title 'Holder of the Eye' wearing a Thoth headdress, and symbolizing Thoth holding the Eye. In harmonic terms, Thoth was the god of the octave, and he needed to hold the Eye of Horus in order to get from 128 to 129.75 where he could 'meet' the spiral of fifths. The Eye of Horus thus represented 'the tiny gap' known as the Particle of Pythagoras, which also gave the necessary 5.2424 days to go from the 'ideal' year of 360 days to the true year. The Eye of Horus was 'mutilated' because it was not an integer or even fraction, and hence it had to be 'reckoned up'. By 'restoring' the Eye, the true length of the year was calculated, upon which the entire Egyptian sacred calendar depended. (Reproduced from Sir Norman Lockyer, *The Dawn of Astronomy*, London, 1894, p. 232, who gives no source.)

In Egypt, optics served the greatest compulsion of that ancient country: keeping accurate time. As the population of Egypt grew, only the precise timing of the many agricultural events, of the rise of the Nile, and of the festivals which kept the gods happy, could feed the Egyptians and allow them to prosper.

In the Bible there is a strange statement: 'If thine eye offend thee pluck it out.' The Egyptians' Eye certainly didn't offend them, but they had to pluck it out, or they might have starved.

Finally, in explaining the Eye of Horus, we can come back to 'the greatest secret of the Egyptians' by yet another way. The Eye was sometimes portrayed as what is called the *udja* eye. This curious design of an eye with an eyebrow and assorted bits and pieces of stylized design gives every appearance, at first glance of being simply an elaborate example of an artist getting carried away. The fact that it is repeated countless times in Egyptian art for thousands of years might just seem to the superficial observer an instance of the extreme conservatism of the Egyptians. Well, in a way, that is indeed the case. But not in the way you might think.

It was the Egyptologist Möller who first noticed that the Udja Eye was composed of a collection of mathematical hieroglyphic signs stuck together to look like an eye. The signs were all mathematical ones, and each one represented a particular arithmetical fraction. We may see this clearly in Figure 80, a drawing which has been reproduced by many authors since at least 1923, when T. Eric Peet discussed it in his book on *The Rhind Mathematical Papyrus*.[96]

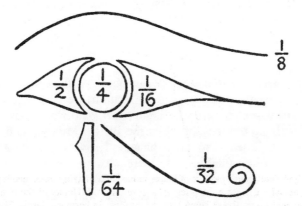

Figure 80. The Udja Eye, or Eye of Horus compounded of hieroglyphic signs for fractions. The eyebrow has the value of 1/8, the iris of 1/4, etc. The total adds up to only 63/64 – a 'mutilated' or incomplete Eye. The inverse of this fraction gives a close approximation to the decimal value of the Comma of Pythagoras. No one in modern times seems to have grasped the true significance of the Udja Eye, which is to represent that secret number. The number can also be considered as arrived at by dividing a whole Eye by a mutilated Eye, if we take a whole Eye as 64 and a mutilated Eye as 63. Thus, the ultimate optical symbol of the ancient Egyptians is in fact a direct expression of their most secret number.

It was very quickly realized that if you add up all of the fractions which have been brought together to compose the Eye, you fall short of unity. Taken together and added up, they only come to a total of 63/64. There is a tiny fraction of 1/64 missing. This intriguing detail has had the effect of distracting absolutely everyone from the true importance of the fractions and of the Eye. None of the discussions of the Udja Eye which I have seen gets the real point, and they all emphasize this matter of the 'incomplete eye'.

If, however, you know the answer in advance, then you can see it. It is not the fraction 63/64 which is important at all, but its inverse: the value 64/63! In order to obtain the Eye's true significance, you have to start with a unitary value of 64 and then divide it by the fractional value of 63 indicated by the hieroglyphic components. This is 'thinking like an ancient Egyptian' and not like a modern. It means dividing a whole eye by a 'mutilated' eye. The process is even described in a Middle Kingdom text: 'I know what was injured in the eye . . . on the day when its parts were reckoned, . . . the complete half which belongs to him who reckons its parts, between the full and the injured eye.'[97]

If you then divide out the result of 64/63, guess what you end up with? This converts the figure to a decimal which is clearer to us. The result is: 1.015! It is an approximation to the value of the Comma of Pythagoras which is passably accurate for such a simple fraction, and is the closest approximation one can get to the Comma expressed in terms of common fractions of daily use. The Udja Eye is therefore nothing less than a direct statement of the Comma of Pythagoras. But, like the many ancient lenses in the world's museums, it is 'invisible' as such, since no one has ever noticed.

* * *

Thus it is that we come to the end of our quest. At the very beginnings of optical technology in the history of civilization, we have finally encountered that most urgent motive of all: survival. Who would have imagined that talk of a single old lens sitting in the British Museum and said to be Assyrian could have led us so far? A lunch in London in the 1960s, a determination to 'look into that' because there was something that didn't fit – more than three decades later we have ended up at the Great Pyramid in the company of the Egyptian gods. Not a bad adventure, don't you agree?

But in closing, we should take to heart a major lesson we have learned so far. We see clearly now how astonishing were the advances made by the ancient Egyptians in optics, astronomy, arithmetical calculations, trigonometry, and various aspects of geometry. We have penetrated some of their innermost secrets, but we must not assume that we know them all. The Egyptians were clearly far more advanced in science than anyone has previously realized. And from this it follows that they may have known other things which we have not yet guessed. Nor have we necessarily exhausted the implications of our discovery that the Comma of Pythagoras applies to astronomy and cosmology just as much as it does to music. We could say, after all, that we have now discovered the true key to that elusive Pythagorean enigma, *the harmony of the spheres*. Celestial orbits display the same precise number as the piano keyboard (or lyre, if you are an ancient Egyptian), which is generated by the fact that the octave and the fifth in music don't quite 'fit'. And this turns out to be fundamental to the deep structure of the Universe.

Let us ask ourselves, therefore: If the ancient Egyptians knew that, what else did they know? And also, what is the significance of the fact that some of the finest-quality lenses ever made before 1900 AD date from 2600 BC in the Old Kingdom period of Egypt? And what is the significance of the fact that after the Old Kingdom of Egypt there seems to have been a *decline* in technology until modern times? Can it be that our presumption of the steady progress of humanity is an illusion? If so, it is still not too late to correct for our astigmatism. I hope this book has been something of a *visual aid*.

Notes

1. Lockyer, J. Norman, *The Dawn of Astronomy: A Study of the Temple-Worship and Mythology of the Ancient Egyptians*, Cassell, London, 1894. This book does exist in a modern photographic reprint edition which I have not personally seen.
2. *Ibid.*, pp. 99–112.
3. Heilbron, John L., 'The Sun in the Church', in *The Sciences*, New York Academy of Sciences, New York, Vol. 39, No. 5, September/October 1999, pp. 29–35.
4. Heilbron, John L., *The Sun in the Church: Cathedrals as Solar Observatories*, Harvard University Press, USA, 1999.
5. de Lubicz, Schwaller, *The Temple of Man*, translated from the French *Le Temple de l'Homme* by Deborah and Robert Lawlor, Inner Traditions, Rochester, Vermont, USA, 1998, 2 vols. See Vol. I, p. 463 for the empty box of cloths on one side of a wall being filled with cloths on the other side of the wall, *through the stone*.
6. Raslan, Mohamed Awad M., 'Academic and Applied Paper on the History of Architecture: The Causeway of Ounas Pyramid', in *Annales du Service des Antiquités de l'Égypte*, Vol. LXI, Cairo, 1973, pp. 151–69. Figure 8 opposite p. 158 is the foldout drawing of the light slit, with rays indicated and the maximum angles of sunlight.
7. *Ibid.*, pp. 157–8.
8. Brenda became more and more famous for her paintings, and made a triumphal tour of America, exhibiting and painting all the rich and distinguished families. It was on this trip that she first befriended Lucretia Garfield, widow of the assassinated American President James Garfield (died 1896). I have letters and photos of Mrs Garfield, which are fascinating historical mementos. As the widow of a President, Mrs Garfield did not have to use postage stamps like ordinary mortals, but wrote her name in the top righthand corner of the envelope, and that was considered sufficient postage – what one might call an extreme philatelic curiosity. One of Brenda's most brilliant paintings was a sensitive and soulful portrait of Lucretia Garfield, which she gave to me just before her death to give to the White House (who had no portrait of this First Lady). This gift was made at my suggestion, and Brenda was thrilled to follow through with it. I delivered the miniature to the

American Embassy in London and after some delay it was taken by hand to the White House by a diplomat, where it was hung in the Blue Room – although under the Clintons it has been kept in a box in the Curator's office safe, as my wife and I discovered when we dropped by the White House to see it in October 1999.

Between the time when Brenda gave me the miniature of Mrs Garfield and the time it arrived at the White House, Brenda died. I was not immediately informed, and the first I learned of her death was when a policeman turned up at the door of my flat in London saying that he had been informed I was in possession of valuable stolen goods belonging to the late Brenda Francklyn, who had already been buried, and demanded that I hand over the portrait of Mrs Garfield or go to jail. The executors of the will demanded the portrait of the American First Lady.

And so it came about that the American Government and I became co-defendants in a legal action where, I am pleased to say, the American Government paid the legal bills! After a considerable time, the executors realized that the White House was never going to part with the portrait which was now viewed as a precious part of America's national heritage, and they finally gave up. But I was amazed at how long they went on. There were, of course, letters signed by Brenda authorizing my action, and so forth, but this made no impression upon them.

Pat Nixon was absolutely thrilled and invited me to the White House as a special guest at a gala party, the largest and most glamorous the Nixons ever threw, on 15 May 1972, on the occasion of the opening of the Blue Room, where the star attraction was the painting which Pat Nixon had discovered of Lucretia Garfield. I'm sure she intended to thank me and Brenda publicly. At that time Olivia and I were so broke we couldn't have afforded to pay for a taxi to the airport, much less fly to America, so we had to take a raincheck. I seem to recall reading about the party and seeing photos of famous guests in *Time* or some such magazine. The numerous letters I received from the White House at that time came to the attention of my neighbours, through nervous postmen not being able to deliver them and handing them to people who could hand them to me. This led to a widespread conviction that I was a secret agent planted in Britain by Richard Nixon personally, and my mission was so special that the President had to write to me personally about it from time to time – indeed, rather too often for my neighbours' comfort. After all, what could my mission be if the President had to keep taking time off from world affairs like that to send me all those letters? I must be up to something awesome.

Brenda's executors disposed in a way I was never able to discover of one of her other priceless possessions. Some of Brenda's dearest friends were the Khevenhüller girls – sisters who were Austrian princesses and lived in so many castles before the First World War that no one can remember them all today, even though various descendants still inhabit some of them. I have many letters and photos of this charming family, who were so affectionate and loving to their 'dear Brenda', who was like another sister to them. The youngest of these princesses before she died left to Brenda one of her most precious objects, which had been given to her forebear (I believe her grandfather), who had been the best friend of Maximilian, the Emperor of Mexico. When Maximilian was taken to the firing squad for execution, only one friend remained with him, the young aristocrat Khevenhüller. Maximilian said: 'You are the last friend to stand by me, and I wish I could give you something as a token of my love and gratitude, but I have nothing to give.' But then he remembered that he still had round his neck his lucky fire-opal cross which he had never taken off for years. It was clear that within minutes he wouldn't be needing it any more. So he removed it and handed it to Khevenhüller, saying: 'This is the only thing I have left in the world. Keep it and remember me by it.' He was then shot.

Brenda knew the story, which she had been told many times, and imagine her surprise when she was given Maximilian's fire-opal cross, which she treasured beyond all other things. I knew she had left it to the British Museum in her will, and I thought it rested there safely. Then the film director Fred Zinnemann, whom I knew fairly well at one stage, hoped to make a film about the Emperor Maximilian (in fact he never could raise the finance). So I said to Fred, who I knew had a passion for accuracy, why not make an exact copy of Maximilian's fire-opal cross and have the actor in the film wear it all the time? Fred was excited by this, and at his request I wrote to the British Museum inquiring how we could arrange to copy the cross. But I got a letter back saying they had indeed been offered an opal cross by a Miss Francklyn, but had returned it to the executors, as they had far too much jewellery already. (Will-makers beware!)

So I suppose the fire-opal cross is now lost in the anonymity of some antique shop window somewhere, or someone is wearing it to parties unaware, as I don't believe the executors knew its background, and no one will ever know the terrible emotional scene when its owner handed it to his last friend on his way to his death. It is said death brings oblivion, and in this case I fear it is true.

9. Eddington, Sir Arthur, *Fundamental Theory*, Cambridge University Press, 1953, pp. 4 and 105.
10. Temple, Robert K. G., *The Sirius Mystery*, revised edition (50 per cent new material), Century, London, 1998, p. 24.
11. An interesting early reference to the Comma of Pythagoras by a classical scholar was by the German, August Boeckh, in 1819. In his little book *Philolaos* of that date, dealing with Pythagorean knowledge, Boeckh gives the ratio 531441 divided by 524288 as defining the tiny interval described as the Comma of Pythagoras. (Boeckh, August, *Philolaos des Pythagoreers Lehren nebst den Bruchstücken Seines Werkes*, Berlin, 1819, p. 79.) He does not carry out the division, but the result is 1.01364.
12. Barbera, André, *The Euclidean Division of the Canon: Greek and Latin Sources*, University of Nebraska Press, USA, 1991, pp. 23 and 28.
13. Garland, Trudi Hammel, and Kahn, Charity Vaughan, *Math and Music: Harmonious Connections*, Dale Seymour Publications, Palo Alto, California, USA, 1995, p. 62.
14. Barbera, *op. cit.*, Greek text on pp. 146 and 148, English translation on pp. 147 and 149. The text is repeated in the later work by the third-century AD Neoplatonist Porphyry (232–301 AD), in his *Commentary on Ptolemy's Harmonics 1.5*; this Greek text is found in Barbera, pp. 214 and 216, with English translation on pp. 215 and 217. The Latin translation of the same passage by Boethius (480–524 AD) in his *De Institutione Musica*, 4, 1–2, is on p. 256 and the English translation on p. 257. The Greek text of the original work has further comments on pp. 164, 166, 168, and 170, translated into English on pp. 165, 167, 169, and 171, as follows: 'The diapason [the octave; this Greek word has the literal meaning 'extending through all the notes' and was the name chosen for the octave instead of the alternative, *diocto*] is less than six tones. For the diapason was proved to be duple [having a ratio of two to one, i.e. a doubled frequency], and the tone sesquioctave. Six sesquioctave intervals are greater than a duple [doubled] interval, therefore, the diapason is less than six tones. . . . The tone will not be divided into two equal tones [i.e. there is no true semitone] nor into more. . . . Therefore, the tone will not be divided into equal intervals.'
15. Levin, Flora R., *The Harmonics of Nicomachus and the Pythagorean Tradition*, American Classical Studies, Number 1, American Philological Association, Pennsylvania State University, USA, 1975.
16. *The Manual of Harmonics of Nicomachus the Pythagorean*, translation and commentary by Flora R. Levin, Phanes Press, Grand Rapids, Michigan, USA, 1994.
17. *Ibid.*, p. 136.
18. *Ibid.*, p. 41.
19. *Ibid.*, p. 81, n. 14.
20. Temple, Robert K. G., *China: Land of Discovery and Invention*; alternative title: *The Genius of China*, various publishers, originally appeared in 1986, now published by Prion Books, London, same pagination in every English language edition; see pp. 209–13.
21. Treating the number 136 as a coefficient, I might also point out the following with regard to some of the nuclear particles: the mass of the positive pion or pi meson is 273, which is 136 x 2 (plus 1), the mass of the positive K meson is 968, slightly less than 136 x 8, the

proton has a mass of 1836 and the neutron of 1840 – they are both near to 136 x 13, barring a small fraction. If one accepts that the neutrino really has zero mass, one can envisage the possibility of a series of particles of ascending mass described by the Fibonacci Series (a famous series of numbers arising from the Golden Mean Proportion) 0, 1, 2, 3, 5, 8, 13, multiplied by the coefficient 136. Since we seem to have particles which would correspond to the numbers 0, 2, 8, and 13, the way to test for the validity of the idea is to look for the missing particles of mass 1 x 136, 3 x 16, and 5 x 136.

Additionally, the mass of the sigma particle is equal to the mass of the lambda particle plus 136, and the mass of the xi particle is equal to the mass of the sigma particle plus a little less than 136 x 2. As for energy levels, the energy of the pion or pi meson is approximately 136 meV. The energy of the xi particle is 1318 meV, and if you subtract 136 from that you get almost exactly the energy of the sigma particle, and if you subtract twice 136 x 2 from that, you get almost the energy of the proton and neutron. And if you subtract 136 x 3 from that you get almost exactly the energy of the K meson. These numbers 1, 2, and 3 are also in Fibonacci series, or may be looked upon simply as what is called an arithmetical progression (only the occurrence of the next term in the series would make it clear which). I mention these observations, which may or may not have value, in case they are helpful to people interested in such things, and because they may indicate the appearance of the numerical coefficient of the Particle of Pythagoras at the nuclear level.

22. In order to stick it in an equation, the Particle of Pythagoras must be given an algebraic symbol, which until now it has not had. So I propose P, a capital letter P with a horizontal bar drawn across its stalk, which would be pronounced 'pee bar'; its square would be P^2. The Comma of Pythagoras would not have its own symbol but would be expressed as $(P + 1)$, unless of course that were found too cumbersome, so that a single symbol was preferred, in which case we could perhaps draw a second bar over the top of the original symbol.

23. St Clair, George, *Creation Records Discovered in Egypt: Studies in the 'Book of the Dead'*, David Nutt, London, 1898.

24. von Thimus, Albert Freiherr, *Die Harmonikale Symbolik des Alterthums*, Cologne, 1868, reprinted by Georg Olms Verlag, Hildesheim, 1988, 2 vols, Vol. I, pp. 96–7.

25. Schwaller de Lubicz, R. A., *The Temple of Man*, translated by Deborah and Robert Lawlor, Inner Traditions, Rochester, Vermont, USA, 2 vols, Vol. I, p. 466.

26. Piankoff, Alexandre, trans. and introduction by, *Mythological Papyri*, Bollingen Series XL, 3, Pantheon Books, New York, 1957, 2 vols (the second consists of photographic reproductions of the papyri), Vol. I, *Texts*, p. 12.

27. Crocker, Richard L., and Kilmer, Anne, Letter to the London *Times*, 15 April 1974; also article about their discoveries in the London *Times*, 7 March 1974. See also their record album and booklet done with Robert Brown, *Sounds from Silence: Recent Discoveries in Ancient Near Eastern Music*, Bit Enki Publications and records, California (BYNK 101), *circa* 1976.

28. St Clair, *op. cit.*, p. 158, with references also to Wallis Budge, the *Book of the Dead*, and Renouf in his footnotes.

29. Verheyen, Hugo F., 'The Icosahedral Design of the Great Pyramid', in Hargittai, István, ed., *Fivefold Symmetry*, World Scientific, Singapore, New Jersey, London and Hong Kong, 1992, pp. 333–59. The further geometrical discussion by Verheyen is essential reading for any serious student of these matters, but I omit a full account of the icosahedral interpretation and many other details as being both too technical and too lengthy for inclusion here.

30. *Ibid., passim.*

31. Hassan, Selim, *Excavations at Saqqara, 1937–8*, 3 vols, reedited by Zaky Iskander, Antiquities Department, Cairo 1975, Vol. I, *The Mastaba of Neb-Kaw-Her*, p. 56. (See also p. 5 for date.)

32. Edwards, I. E. S., *The Pyramids of Egypt*, revised edition, Viking, London, 1986, pp. 105–6.

33. Cotsworth, Moses B., *The Rational Almanac*, privately printed at York, England, 1902. This edition was superseded by the one of 1905.

34. Cotsworth, Moses B., *The Rational Almanac: Tracing the Evolution of Modern Almanacs from Ancient Ideas of Time, and Suggesting Improvements*, enlarged edition with interleaved pages inset after pages 78 and 154, as well as additional sections added, privately printed at York, 1905. This edition runs to more than 500 pages, with various separate paginations.

35. *Ibid.*, p. 6, Introduction pagination.

36. *Ibid.*, p. 273, main pagination.

37. Reproduced from *Ibid.*, p. 67, main pagination. Cotsworth published 180 illustrations, but they are all unnumbered.

38. Tompkins, Peter, *Secrets of the Great Pyramid*, Harper & Row, New York, 1971, pp. 122–4.

39. Taken from Cotsworth, 1905, *op. cit.*, p. 60, main pagination.

40. Tompkins, *op. cit.*, pp. 124–5.

41. Neugebauer, Otto, 'On the Orientation of the Pyramids', in *Centaurus*, Vol. 24, 1980, pp. 1–3.

42. Cotsworth, 1905, *op. cit.*, pp. 7–8, main pagination.

43. Pliny, *Natural History*, Book 36, Chapter 17, translated by D. E. Eichholz, Loeb Classical Library, Harvard University Press, USA, Vol. 10, 1971, p. 65.

44. Needham, Joseph, and Wang Ling, *Science and Civilisation in China*, Volume 3, *Mathematics and the Sciences of the Heavens and the Earth*, Cambridge University Press, 1979, p. 299.

45. Pliny, Book 36, Chapter 14, *op. cit.*, p. 51.

46. *Ibid.*, 50, note b.

47. *Ibid.*, Book 36, Chapter 15, p. 57.

48. Ammianus Marcellinus, *The Roman History*, XXII, 15, 29, translated by C. D. Yonge, Bohn's Library, London, 1862, p. 311.

49. *Ibid.*, XXII, 15, 31, p. 312.

50. Sir Flinders Petrie believed that the Oseirion, fabled to be the burial place of Osiris, was contemporary with the Valley Temple at Giza and at least 1,200 years earlier than the time of Seti I. But Henri Frankfort, who wrote the excavation memoirs of the building for the Egypt Exploration Society, stridently rebutted this view. Since then it has been considered 'uncool' to insist upon the Oseirion being early. I have taken more than 50 photos of it, which I have had ample time to ponder. I have read the passionate statements of Henri Frankfort, as well as the full report on the original dig published by Margaret Murray, who did the initial excavations of the Oseirion with Petrie's wife. Murray, Margaret A., *The Oseirion at Abydos*, Egyptian Research Account, Ninth Year, 1903, reprinted by Histories & Mysteries of Man Ltd., London, 1989. I have to say I agree with Petrie. I have additional reasons for thinking this, but this is no place for a discussion of a subject as extended as that. The inscriptions cut into the stone of the Oseirion look to me like later work – afterthoughts – and they are not cut deep enough to be original in my opinion. I also cannot accept that this megalithic construction was built at the same time as the Temple of Osiris, which is in such a totally different style. But for the purposes of dating the text about the shadow clock, everyone can be in happy agreement and accept that it is from the time of Seti I in the early 13th century BC.

51. Bruins, E. M., 'The Egyptian Shadow Clock', in *Janus*, Vol. 52, pp. 127–37. I am grateful to Professor Allan Mills for giving me a photocopy of this fascinating article, though I have no date for it.

52. Habachi, Labib, *The Obelisks of Egypt: Skyscrapers of the Past*, The American University in Cairo Press, Cairo, 1988, pp. 61–2.

53. Wallis Budge, E. A., *A History of Egypt*, Volume IV, *Egypt and Her Asiatic Empire* (this volume covers the period from Queen Hatshepsut to the end of the Amarna period), London, 1902, pp. 16–18.

54. Wallis Budge, E. A., *Cleopatra's Needles and Other Egyptian Obelisks*, originally

published at London in 1926, Dover paperback reprint, New York, 1990. The inscription on the obelisk of Hatshepsut is given in hieroglyphs and translation on pp. 111–24.

55. *Ibid.*, pp. 36–8.
56. *Ibid.*, pp. 111–22.
57. *Ibid.*, p. 155. I have used the word *tchām* here, as the hieroglyphic word clearly appears in the text above the translation, despite the fact that Budge did not use it in the actual translation on this occasion as he did earlier.
58. *Ibid.*, p. 168.
59. *Ibid.*, p. 172.
60. Isler, Martin, 'The Gnomon in Egyptian Antiquity', in *Journal of the American Research Center in Egypt*, Vol. 28, 1991, pp. 155–85. I am indebted to Professor Allan Mills for this reference.
61. Isler, Martin, 'An Ancient Method of Finding and Extending Direction', in *Journal of the American Research Center in Egypt*, Vol. 26, 1989, pp. 191–206. The quote is from pp. 198–9.
62. Griffith, F. Ll., *A Collection of Hieroglyphics: A Contribution to the History of Egyptian Writing*, Sixth Memoir of the Archaeological Survey of Egypt, Egypt Exploration Fund, London, 1898, p. 59.
63. Lobban, Richard A., Jr, 'A Solution to the Mystery of the *Was* Sceptre of Ancient Egypt & Nubia', *KMT*, Vol. 10, No. 3, Fall 1999, pp. 68–77.
64. Tompkins, *op. cit.*, pp. 117–19.
65. Ballard, Robert T., *The Solution of the Pyramid Problem*, Wiley, New York, 1882.
66. Lopez, José Álvarez, *Misterios Egipcios, segunda edicion* (second edition), Coleccion Horus, Editorial Kier, S.A., Buenos Aires, Argentina, 1974. (The first edition was 1973.)
67. Lopez, José Álvarez, *El Enigma de las Piramides* (*The Enigma of the Pyramids*), *novena edicion* (new edition), Coleccion Horus, Editorial Kier, S.A., Buenos Aires, Argentina, 1975. (The first edition was 1965.)
68. He asked me if I could help him find an English-language publisher. We also had long conversations about the matters raised in the book. I never saw Lopez again after I left New York shortly afterwards, and although I wrote to him, I had no replies, and when I tried to phone him a few times in Argentina, I only got women who spoke no English, from whom I could learn nothing. All my efforts to remain in contact having failed, I have to report that from my point of view, Lopez has most unfortunately 'disappeared', and I do not even know whether he is alive. Nor did his friend Christina remain contactable shortly afterwards at her number in New York, or leave any forwarding number or address, so I have never been able to follow up on questions I would have liked to ask Lopez about his ideas. I was merely left with the fascinating typescript in English, from which I now will quote, attempting to identify the passages in Spanish and give page references to them if I can.
69. I cannot locate this passage in the Spanish text; three paragraphs previously, the continuity of the English with the Spanish ceases.
70. Lopez, *Piramides*, pp. 89–90. Three Mayan and one Chaldaean illustration are on p. 90.
71. *Ibid.*, pp. 92–5.
72. *Ibid.*, p. 172.
73. *Ibid.*, p. 200.
74. Edwards, *op. cit.*, p. 43.
75. Tompkins, *op. cit.*, p. 108.
76. *Ibid.*, p. 110.
77. Davidson, David, *The Hidden Truth in Myth and Ritual and in the Common Culture Pattern of Ancient Metrology*, privately published by the author at Leeds, England, September 1934.
78. *Ibid.*, pp. 51–2.
79. Lepre, J. P., *The Egyptian Pyramids: A Comprehensive Illustrated Guide*, Jefferson, North Carolina, 1990. This book (ISBN 0–89950–461–2) is still available from the publisher, McFarland & Company Inc., Box 611, Jefferson, North Carolina 28640, USA.

80. *Ibid.*, p. 65.
81. Quoted in Georges Perrot and Charles Chipiez, *A History of Art in Ancient Egypt*, translated by Walter Armstrong, Chapman and Hall, New York, 1883, 2 vols, Vol. I, p. 240, note 1.
82. Cotsworth, *op. cit.*, p. 176 of main pagination.
83. *Ibid.*
84. Isler, 'Ancient Method', *op. cit.*, pp. 203–4.
85. *Ibid.*, pp. 204–6.
86. Lurker, Manfred, *An Illustrated Dictionary of The Gods and Symbols of Ancient Egypt*, Thames and Hudson, London, 1995, pp. 46–7.
87. 'Peintures, Murales et Mosaiques de Délos' ('Paintings, Murals, and Mosaics of Delos'), in *Monuments et Mémoires de Délos* (*Monuments and Memoirs of Delos*), Paris, Volume 14, 1907, pp. 192–4, and Figure 68 (another similar representation may be seen in Figure 69).
88. Griffiths, J. Gwyn, *The Conflict of Horus and Seth from Egyptian and Classical Sources: A Study in Ancient Mythology*, Liverpool University Press, Britain, 1960, p. 148.
89. Hirsch, Joy, 'Falcon Visual Sensitivity to Grating Contrast', *Nature*, Vol. 300, No. 5887, 4 November 1982, pp. 57–8.
90. Piankoff, Alexandre, translated with commentary by, *The Pyramid of Unas*, Vol. 5 of the series *Egyptian Religious Texts and Representations*, Bollingen Series, Vol. 40, Princeton University Press, USA, 1969.
91. Renouf, Sir Peter le Page, *The Book of the Dead*, continued and completed by E. Naville, Vol. IV of *The Life-Work of Sir Peter le Page Renouf*, Paris and Leipzig, 1907, p. 130.
92. *Ibid.*, pp. 236–40.
93. *The Book of the Opening of the Mouth: the Egyptian Texts with English Translations*, translated by E. A. Wallis Budge, Kegan Paul, London, 1909, 2 vols, Vol. I, p. 208. (The Seventeenth Ceremony on Entering the Shrine.)
94. Griffiths, *op. cit.*, p. 34.
95. St Clair, *op. cit.*, p. 375.
96. Peet, T. Eric, *The Rhind Mathematical Papyrus: British Museum 10057 and 10058*, introduction, transcription, translation and commentary, University Press of Liverpool, and Hodder and Stoughton Ltd., London, 1923, pp. 25–6.
97. Piankoff, Alexandre, *The Tomb of Rameses VI*, 2 vols, Vol. I: *Texts*, Bollingen Series, Pantheon Books, New York, 1954, p. 38.

Appendix One

The Skull of Doom

In the summer of 1963 I spent a couple of days with Miss Anna Mitchell-Hedges, known to one and all as 'Sammy', the name given to her by her adopted father when she was a girl. At that time Sammy was living in Reading, England, and had not yet moved to Kitchener, Ontario. She had a very large rambling house but she wanted me to see her previous residence, Farley Castle, a late folly which she told me had previously belonged to 'Simon the Red, the King of the Gypsies'. She swore it had a mysterious underground tunnel. When she took me round Farley Castle, there was a conservatory attached to the house where a camellia tree was blooming. She picked a red camellia and gave it to me, asking me to press it and keep it forever. I still have it.

Sammy lived with her secretary Cynthia Fowles in the Reading house which was stuffed with antiques and bizarre objects. Sitting prominently on the top of a mediaeval oak table or chest in the main sitting room was a small blunderbuss. I naturally picked it up, and as I did so, Sammy looked on benignly with her quiet approving smile. My friend Prince Friedrich (Prince Friedrich Ernst von Sachsen-Altenburg, the guardian and advisor of Anna Anderson, who claimed to be the Russian Grand Duchess Anastasia) was standing next to me watching curiously. I noticed a strange little metal catch on the blunderbuss, and released it. Instantly, a sharp blade flipped out and came whizzing down directly in front of my chest, nearly slicing my shirt in half. I jumped with alarm, and Prince Friedrich was in a state because he thought I had been disembowelled, which I almost was! 'Good God!' I shouted. Sammy said in an unperturbed voice: 'Yes, do be careful, everyone nearly kills themselves with that blunderbuss. I really should warn people, I suppose.' 'But it's like a switchblade knife!' 'Yes, it always surprises people. It was one of the things collected by my father. It's a bit of a test for visitors, he used to say.'

Prince Friedrich and I stayed the night with Sammy. Cynthia brought me a tea tray in the morning when I was still in bed, the first time I had ever been exposed to that charming British country house habit, which greatly astonished me at the time. We were driven there and picked up the next day by my friend Michael Scott, who had just then bought his VW van, of which he was immensely proud. He was equally proud of the M4, which had just been constructed, and along which he was tentatively making his way, as it was strange to him. 'It's called a *motorway*,' he said. 'And look over there, you can actually see Windsor Castle from the road.' We all looked at Windsor Castle, and indeed it was there as he said; he was not imagining things even though he only had one eye. I still have a photo of all of us – Sammy and Cynthia, Sammy's niece Solange, Michael, Prince Friedrich, and myself – standing in front of the house in Reading, smiling. It was the summer of 1963, when there were only three days of full sun in England. It was the day when I encountered my first ancient crystal artifact.

Sammy is still alive and she is now very famous. For she is the owner of the 'Skull of Doom', which she found in the ruins of Lubaantun, a ruined Mayan city in the jungles of British Honduras, which her father discovered and excavated. Sammy as a young girl helped clear the jungle growth from the ruined temples, and while she was doing that she told me she saw something glistening in the side of one of the ancient stone structures. She hacked away to get at it, and found the Skull of Doom amongst the stones and rubble. A ray of sunlight had been at the right angle to strike it at that moment. It was a skull of rock crystal carved in the shape of a human skull, complete with detachable jaw. (*See Plate 1.*) It was evidently an ancient Mayan artifact, although it was curious that it was not actually buried in a grave. Its only archaeological provenance is that it was found in a ruin at Lubaantun, a ruined city which had been lost for centuries. But whether the local Indians knew the site and may have concealed the skull there as a supposedly safe place to keep such a sacred object – and whether they occasionally used it for secret religious ceremonies – we will never know. Perhaps it had been concealed since antiquity. I have never been quite easy about this. Why would the crystal skull be concealed in the side of a crumbling structure? I believe Sammy speculated that it had been hidden by Mayan priests who fled the city and may have continued to use it as a ritual object after the collapse of the city as a residential centre, when they were able to make surreptitious return visits on special occasions. In other words, it would have been in use at the time of the collapse of the city. On the other hand, perhaps no one had ever returned. But it appears that it was meant to be accessible to those who knew its place of concealment, like a secret treasure.

Sammy showed us the Skull of Doom, which she kept in a velvet-lined box with little front doors which folded shut. Both Michael Scott and Prince Friedrich gave forth sighs at my audacity when I asked Sammy if I could pick it up. Sammy, who was nothing if not laid back, said of course. I picked up the skull, which was the first rock crystal object I had ever touched, and the first thing I noticed was that despite the warm day, the skull was cold and was sweating. 'Yes, crystal sweats,' Sammy explained. I set the detachable jaw down, as one could not really handle the two objects conveniently at the same time, and Michael and Prince Friedrich gingerly picked the jaw up – I remember Michael touching it with delicate fingers of awe as if he were handling the Holy Grail and feeling guilty about it. Michael always did everything with tentative reverence, and inevitably swallowed his sentences apologetically when he spoke, in that self-effacing manner of English gentlemen of a bygone era.

I inspected the Skull of Doom very carefully, with mounting incredulity. As I did so, Sammy assured me of its anatomical perfection – it was a perfect match for a human skull – and said she had been told by experts that it must have been polished using grains of sand and would have taken many years to make. She gave some large figure for the number of man-hours, which I have now forgotten. I think she had been given an estimate that three human generations would have been required to perfect such an object in such hard material as crystal, with primitive tools. Certainly the skull is polished to a high degree of perfection, to match the impeccable precision of its shape – it is as smooth as silk. I played with putting the jaw in and out. Then I placed the skull on my shoulder and jostled it there. It seemed very friendly, and felt quite natural. I said to the others: 'How does it compare with the size and shape of my own head?' Michael Scott intoned with superstitious dread: 'It's exactly the same size as your own head, and looks as if it could have been made as a copy of your skull.' Prince Friedrich said: 'Yes, the resemblance is really very remarkable.'

Sammy said: 'Maybe you have come back to visit the Skull, having known it before. It seems to like you. Most people get the opposite reaction. The Skull is very powerful. It can kill. That is why it is called the Skull of Doom. But it is not evil. It is neutral, just as Divine Justice is neutral. It does not like many people. You must have been a priest of some kind in another life.' Sammy was inclined to mystical views about the Skull, and she confessed to me that since the Cuban Missile Crisis she had been holding the Skull in her hands at night and going into deep meditation and 'wishing Castro dead', hoping the Skull would kill him. But unfortunately the Skull never saw fit to do that. However much she hated Castro, Sammy was not a negative person, and most of her meditation sessions with the Skull in her hands were gentle ones where she prayed for the peace of the world.

When I told Arthur Clarke and Derek Price about the Skull of Doom, they were all agog – they had never heard of it. I remember Derek raising a sceptical eyebrow when he heard about Simon the Red the King of the Gypsies, and I must confess, I have no idea whether Sammy was serious about that. But she seemed entirely in earnest, I believed her, and I think it was all true. She said he collected tithes from lots of gypsies and was their informal 'head of clan', which is how he got the money to buy the Castle.

Sammy had other surprises up her sleeve, for she was also owner of the world's largest emerald. It was on the *riza* (gold covering) of the Black Virgin of Kazan Icon, which her father had obtained from Russia. I didn't see it because it was in a safe in America. This Icon was credited in Russian folklore with having turned back Napoleon, since some Orthodox priests had been holding it and praying to it at the time Napoleon couldn't go on any more in his Russian campaign; thus the Black Virgin was given the credit for defeating the French invasion. Sammy's father had been a friend of a poor starving Russian before the Revolution, whom he kept alive with handouts; the man's real name was Leon Trotsky. He had also made most of his money beating J. P. Morgan at poker, and had been a friend of Duveen and other top art dealers, through whom he acquired many impossible objects such as the Black Virgin. But to continue with stories about Sammy's father would be too distracting, so we shall leave him to his own reveries in the Land of the Dead, where he has now been joined by Prince Friedrich and Michael Scott, who I am sure have looked him up with alacrity.

My tale of the Skull of Doom made a great impression on Arthur Clarke. Within only a few years, he was to adopt a photo of it as his personal logo for his television programmes about strange artifacts. And *Arthur C. Clarke's Mysterious World* would feature episodes all beginning with a shot of a spinning Skull of Doom – still to be seen in their endless repeats on the Discovery Channel. Indeed, in the very first episode which he ever made, Derek Price himself appears – so that seeing that really takes me back to when we all used to sit and chat together about these things.

Appendix Two

Named Lenses

THE MAINZ LENS

It took me many years to find 'the Mainz Lens' which had been mentioned by various optical writers in a casual manner, without saying where it was. The reason I had such trouble was that it was not in Mainz, a charming little town on the River Rhine – in fact, it was not even in Germany at all. After writing to many German museums, I eventually found it in Vienna. It is today in the Antiken-Sammlung of the Kunsthistorisches Museum there (Object AS. XI. 835; see Plate 39). It was excavated in 1875 in the midst of a Roman glass works at Mainz, but how it came into the possession of an Austrian museum is not explained. The Vienna Museum catalogue merely says it was 'acquired'. A one-paragraph archaeological report, published in German in 1879 by Baron von Sacken, described the lens as follows:

> In the midst of a Roman glass works was found a biconvex lens of 5.5 centimetres diameter, severely oxidized, and here and there iridescent, which without the slightest doubt was worked into this form to serve as a magnifying glass. If one considers such products of Roman art, especially the often incredibly minutely cut stones, the conviction thrusts itself upon one that they could scarcely have done such work without the assistance of magnifying apparatus; according to the usually accepted view, water drops were used for this purpose.[1]

Joachim Marquardt noticed von Sacken's report and in 1886 mentioned the Mainz Lens along with four others in a footnote to his famous work, *Das Privatleben der Römer* (*Private Life of the Romans*).[2] He said that lenses were definitely ground in antiquity, and four surviving ones had been found: the Mainz Lens, the Cuming Lens, the Nola Lens (described in Chapter One), and the Pompeii Lens (for the other two, see my accounts of them which follow). Of these, he said that the Mainz Lens and the Nola Lens 'could scarcely be anything other than lenses', and he points out that the German poet Lessing had already mentioned the possibility that the ancients were familiar with magnifying glasses back in the 18th century. (I

455

discuss Lessing elsewhere. I have translated his writings on optics for the first time into English, and they are in Appendix Three.) He also notes that the Roman author Pliny (first century AD) had discussed crystal spheres being used as burning-globes. Marquardt was friendly to the idea of ancient lenses, and sharp-eyed enough to have spotted reports of four of them in three different languages.

The next person to mention the Mainz Lens was Emil Bock, in his pamphlet of 1903, *Die Brille und Ihre Geschichte* (*Spectacles and Their History*). He merely repeats what Marquardt said in his footnote but adds a comment about the Layard Lens.[3]

In 1908, Professor A. Kisa, drawing on von Sacken and Marquardt, referred to the Mainz Lens in his book *Das Glas in Altertum* (*Glass in Antiquity*), saying: '. . . certainly the objects found at Nola and Mainz are magnifying glasses', and gives the references.

Also alerted to its existence by Marquardt's book, the famous physicist Professor Ernst Mach examined the Mainz Lens personally in 1913 'through the kindness of my colleague, Professor R. v. Schneider' (while neglecting to say where it was!) and concluded it was indeed an ancient reading glass or burning glass. He gave measurements of 1.8 mm for its marginal thickness and 5.9 mm for its axial thickness. He found it to have a refractive index of 1.5. Although the glass had gone opaque by 1913, Mach easily computed the focal length at about 18 or 19 cm. Mach mistakenly believed the lens to have been found in a grave at Mainz, whereas it was actually found in a glassworks, as von Sacken had clearly informed us.[4,5]

In 1935, Wilhelm Theobald mentioned the Mainz Lens in passing (three words plus its diameter), once again taken obviously from Marquardt's footnote.[6]

The historian of science, R. J. Forbes (whose inaccurate description of the Layard Lens we have already seen in Chapter One), in 1957 gave the Mainz Lens an 11-word description – but even that is in error, for he says the lens is plano-convex (flat on the bottom and curved on top), whereas it is really biconvex (curved on both bottom and top), which shows that he certainly never saw it and took little trouble to ascertain the facts. He did not bother to get a copy of von Sacken's report, as it is not mentioned in his references.[7]

During the time I was trying to track down this missing lens, I received a typical response (for the period 1980) from one archaeologist who seemed somewhat alarmed that I was looking for an *ancient lens*. Dr Decker, Head Curator of the Mittelrheinisches Landesmuseum at Mainz, wrote to me on 18 June 1980, saying the following:

We received your letter from the Romano-German Central Museum of Mainz concerning a Roman lens of glass, quartz, or crystal. As far as our museum is concerned, we are sorry we can only give you a negative response: according to the inventory, our museum, the former museum of antiquities for the city of Mainz, has never possessed such a lens. Regarding the lens mentioned by Ernst Mach which was said to have come from 'a Roman grave at Mainz', as far as your ancient origin is concerned, this should be considered with the greatest scepticism, since it certainly was in private possession, in the hands of Herr Mach's informant Professor [R.] von Schneider.

It is interesting that Dr Decker goes out of his way to warn me that I should be highly sceptical. I do not know whether this is because he thought the late Professor R. von Schneider was unreliable, or because the lens was in private hands and thus not to be trusted, or simply because he felt that there could be no such thing as an ancient lens and I shouldn't have such delusions.

The Mainz Lens is now Object Number XI. 835 in the Kunsthistorisches Museum in Vienna. Although the lens was whole when excavated in 1875 and when examined by March in 1913, it is now broken, since the Museum has informed me that the description now is: 'Incomplete, assembled from three fragments.' They also give the official measurements as: 'Diameter, 5.5 cm, thickness, 0.5 cm.' The lens is officially catalogued as a Magnifying Glass, so there is no dispute in Vienna as to the true nature of this lens. The Vienna museum authorities were very helpful, and photographed the lens for me, as there was no previously existing photographic record of it. (See Plate 39.)

Another person who mentions the Mainz Lens is Henry C. King, in an article published in an ophthalmological periodical in 1958. He does this on the basis of having read Mach's report, and says only: 'Ernst Mach, writing in 1913 says that Prof. R. von Schneider showed him a lens, presumably made of glass, found in a Roman grave in Mainz. The diameter was just over two inches. Originally the focal length was about 7 inches, but Mach found the surfaces so laminated and iridescent from exposure to damp earth, as to render the lens quite opaque. In his opinion it served originally either as a visual aid or as a burning glass.'[8]

The last person to mention the Mainz Lens before I tracked it down was my old friend Joseph Needham, in 1962. I worked with Joseph, who was the world's leading sinologist, in the 1980s and I am the only Western colleague of his (apart from his first wife) who ever accompanied him to China. That was in December 1986, on Joseph's last visit to that country.

It must be said that Joseph got his notes muddled when he discussed that lens (many years before I knew him), and he wrote that 'rock-crystal balls, which may or may not have been used as lenses, have been found at sites such as Pompeii, Nola, Mainz, etc.'[9] Obviously it was not crystal balls which were found at these places but actual lenses. However, Joseph was right in believing that objects which 'may have been used as lenses' were found at the places he named. I regret that I never actually discussed this subject with him. I had set ancient optics aside at the time of my prolonged association with him, and I was too busy reading eight-and-a-half million words of Joseph's published and unpublished writings and remembering it all (no time to take notes, I just kept it in my head) in order to write the official popularization of his work on the history of Chinese science. My book on this subject was first published in 1986 and is still in print, although it is the Chinese edition which is of greatest interest to me – an edition translated by a specialist team of 34 translators under the auspices of the Chinese Academy of Sciences.[10]

There are several lessons to be drawn from the above survey. First of all, the Mainz Lens was never discussed in France because the French scholars either could not or would not read German, and from 1875 to 1957, all discussion of the Mainz Lens took place in German (except for the translation of Mach's book into English). Even to this day, no one has ever mentioned the Mainz Lens in French. This highlights the extreme provincialism of both the French and the German scholars, neither of whom took much notice of the other. It is extraordinary, as we have seen repeatedly in this book, how two separate dialogues were going on about ancient optics in the two adjoining countries, but they did not interact. The two countries might as well have been two planets in two different solar systems, which contained scholars of two separate species who had once visited the earth and made a study of some of its ancient texts and a few of its ancient lenses. The French paid great attention to each other, and the Germans paid great attention to each other, but the Germans ignored the French and the French ignored the Germans. How can a subject be discussed sensibly under those circumstances?

Only two people have mentioned the Mainz Lens in English, both of them superficially, and as we have seen, one of them committing a serious error (Forbes). Another point to be made is that two erroneous descriptions of the Mainz Lens were circulated by supposedly reputable scholars, which hardly helped matters. Forbes, said to be one of the world's leading historians of science, got the shape wrong, and von Schneider gave Mach wrong information about the provenance (saying it came from a grave, when it didn't). And I sheepishly have to admit that my old friend Joseph also got the shape wrong, but wrong in a different way from the way in which Forbes did. So the situation became pretty confused.

The discussions of the Mainz Lens have also largely been derivative, with writers taking sparse information from one another in passing but making little if any attempt to find out the facts firsthand. And on the basis of no study at all, cranks like the ophthalmologist Greeff (refer to note 5) had no compunction about insisting that black was white, and that the Mainz Lens was not a lens. Since 1875, only one person took the trouble actually to look at the Mainz Lens and study it in person: the physicist Ernst Mach. But in this respect, the Mainz Lens has been luckier than many others, as we shall see.

This is a frequently mentioned lens which is now lost. It is (or was) a plano-convex glass lens which was excavated at Pompeii and was last seen in the Museo Archeologica Nazionale (National Archaeological Museum) at Naples. However, attempts to locate it there have failed. Perhaps it and the Nola Lens are really both there in the basement somewhere, sitting side by side in a dusty box labelled 'bits of old glass'. If so, it will take a miracle rarer than a statue of the Virgin Mary shedding blood for them to be excavated a second time and see the light of day to discerning eyes. So far I have managed to discover that the 'small glass finds' (an expression which archaeologists use) from Pompeii are meant to be stored in the Reserve Collections of Excavation Stores at Pompeii, *on behalf of* the Naples Museum. My initial efforts to locate the Pompeii Lens were in 1979/1980, and on 21 August 1980, Dr Giuseppina Cerulli Irelli (who had been Director of Pompeii Excavations) wrote to me from Lombardy, to which she had by that time been transferred from the Naples Museum, saying: 'the Civic Museum of Naples has nothing to do with Pompeiian antiquities. . . . I don't believe, however, that the data that you give us regarding this piece will be sufficient for the identification'. And yet, as we shall see, the Pompeii Lens *was* in the Naples Museum in 1884, when it was examined there. So it may well be that it was transferred back to the stores in Pompeii at some unknown date between 1885 and 1980, and still languishes there. It is not easy to sort out archaeological matters in Italy! The Pompeii Lens was apparently first mentioned in 1885 by the French writer Edouard Gerspach, who examined it personally at Naples. He wrote of it:

> The use which Nero made of an emerald for viewing the Circus combats [which we shall consider later] shows that the ancients knew how to appreciate the optical qualities of certain materials. We can cite as a personal example a small glass disc which we studied at the Museum of Naples; it is flat on one side and is ground convex on the other; its diameter is 6.5 centimetres and the highest point of convexity is 12 mm; the circumference has a crimped rim and is prepared for mounting in metal. The glass having been rendered opaque by the onset of decomposition, we have not been able to judge the optical quality, but it was affirmed to us that its dimensions constituted a magnifying glass; it seems also that it was found at Pompeii alongside engraved pieces.[11]

In the same year, 1885, Sir Flinders Petrie published his account of the two Tanis Lenses from Egypt (discussed later), and in doing so remarked (though giving no reference): 'Some lenses have been found at Pompeii in an engraver's shop, . . .'[12] The Pompeii Lens may thus have had companions – otherwise, why would Petrie say that more than one had been found? However, he does not record further details, and his mention is merely in passing to put his own lenses into context. But considering Petrie's professional expertise and high reputation in archaeology, his casual reference should be treated seriously. In 1886, Marquardt mentioned a single Pompeii Lens briefly in the footnote referred to in our discussions of the Mainz (above) and Nola Lenses (in Chapter One). Although Marquardt records that the Lens had been excavated in 1854 and that it is plano-convex and similar (in size – and possibly in having also been mounted in gold?) to the Nola Lens, he gives no reference whatever!

In 1899 Joseph Hirschberg, a truly fanatical sceptic, went out of his way to insist that not only did no ancient lenses exist, but: 'In Pompeii nothing of the kind has been found'.[13] He had clearly not seen any of the three publications in the 1880s which we have just mentioned.

In 1901, Pierre Pansier (in his rare book which is not to be found in the British Library), drawing upon Gerspach, says of the Pompeii Lens:

Some lenses have been excavated in the ruins of Pompeii and of Nola: one of these (found at Pompeii and exhibited at the Museum of Naples) consists of a small plano-convex disc of glass; it is six-and-a-half centimetres in diameter and its greatest thickness of convexity is twelve millimetres; the rim has been worked on a wheel and prepared for mounting.[14]

Although this may seem to be just a repetition of what we already have been told by Gerspach, Pansier goes on to tell us some further fascinating things which he found in writings of Dutens in 1776 (an edition of his work of which there is no copy in the British Library),[15] of Gilberto Govi (in Italian) in 1880, and elsewhere. Pansier quotes Louis Dutens as follows:

Dutens speaks of ancient lenses in these terms: 'I have seen in a cabinet of antiquities of the King of Naples at Portici several magnifying lenses stronger than those which are in use among our engravers: some have only four lines of focus [an obscure statement, presumably meaning they were such powerful magnifiers that only a small area could be seen magnified through them], and I have a less powerful one of them myself which, as a matter of fact, was found at Herculaneum.'

As Pansier also points out, Gilberto Govi was very dismissive of the Pompeii Lens. Who was Gilberto Govi? He was the translator from Greek to Latin of the *Optics* of Claudius Ptolemy (second century AD). In his Introduction (in Italian) to this work, published in 1885,[16] Govi says:

We do not have the entire fifth book of Ptolemy [that is, the fifth book of his *Optics*]; he finishes that part of the demonstration relative to the position and size of images of things seen through a medium ending in a cylindrical surface, where the eye which observes them finds itself in a more refractive medium than that from which the cylinder is made. . . . The mutilation of this fifth book deprives us, for the moment at least, of any means of knowing with certainty whether or not the Ancients had lenticular glasses [lenses], as what Ptolemy tells us of a medium ending in a flat or in a cylindrical surface is not enough to prove that they had them. Indeed the fact that he does not tell us of spherical vessels nor of portions of a sphere is almost an assurance to the contrary. The supposed lens mentioned by some writers as found at Herculaneum or Pompeii and kept at the Portici Museum (now the one at Naples) is not and can never have been a lens. It is a piece of glass which is irregularly plano-convex, twisted, blistered, such, in short, as, even supposing it was originally more regular and less worn by time, could never have provided useful images of the objects seen through it.

The strange mutilation of the manuscript of Ptolemy's *Optics* just at the very point where he was apparently describing a telescope lens is a subject already alluded to in our discussion of the Greek literature on lenses. It appears that the subsequent portion of Ptolemy's *Optics* was in the possession of Roger Bacon, but destroyed when he was accused of black magic. Certainly the mention of 'a more refractive medium than that from which the cylinder is made' seems to refer to a transparent medium such as glass or crystal.

However, this is not for discussion here. There is such an amazing discrepancy between the dismissive description by Govi and the favourable description by Gerspach that I can only imagine that Govi and Gerspach had not inspected the same object, and that there was indeed more than one Pompeii Lens. If the Pompeii Lens inspected by Gerspach had been twisted and blistered, he would have said so, and he would not have commented about its possible use for optical purposes, as to do so would have been ridiculous. All he said was that it had gone opaque because decomposition had commenced. They both inspected plano-convex objects of glass in the 1880s at Naples, but the objects cannot possibly have been the same unless one of the men was mad.

This makes one all the more eager to try and find that box full of bits of old glass which may be sitting around somewhere in Naples. For, as we shall see below, the actual number of lenses found in the vicinity seems really to have been considerable. The pity is that we have no idea what the true number of them is, nor whether any of them survive to the present time. We do not even know how many Pompeiian lenses were in the possession of the King of Naples, for no number is given by Dutens, who saw them with his own eyes (see account below).

Finally, the most informative account of the Pompeii Lens's provenance which exists was published in 1855 by the British archaeologist and antiquary, H. Syer Cuming, who records its discovery only the year before, and who clearly had considerable knowledge of it, perhaps from a colleague. He says:

> To what period or country, and to whom, are we to attribute the invention of spectacles? . . . That the ancients possessed something approaching to the nature of our spectacles, or rather eye-glasses, seems to be a well-established fact, for in the early part of the year 1854 was discovered, in the Stabian-street at Pompeii, a plano-convex lens, about one inch and five-eighths in diameter, with the edge ground as if it had been set in a frame. The colour, like most of the glass found at Pompeii, is a pale green: though the surfaces are so oxidised as to prevent its magnifying powers being tested, no doubt is entertained that it was designed for optical purposes. This treasure is safely deposited in the gem room of the royal museum of Naples.[17]

This vivid description immediately after the Pompeii Lens was found cannot possibly be of the same object described 30 years later by Gilberto Govi as being twisted and blistered. The evidence of Cuming and Gerspach is really conclusive – Govi was either spreading a false report, or he was describing a completely different piece of glass altogether.

THE HERCULANEUM LENS

This lens, which is only mentioned by Louis Dutens and Pierre Pansier (as mentioned above in the account of the Pompeii Lens), was clearly excavated in the 18th century at Herculaneum. In 1776 it was in the private possession of the Rev. Louis Dutens. Dutens was the editor of the works of the philosopher Leibniz and he lived most of his adult life in England, where among other things he was Rector of Elsdon, in the County of Northumberland, a living obviously bestowed upon him by his friends the Percy Family.[18]

In terms of recorded information about the Herculaneum Lens, we also know that it was not a powerful magnifier. For Pansier tells us that Dutens said the King of Naples Lenses (described in a moment) were 'very powerful magnifiers', whereas of his own lens, Dutens said it was 'one of lesser strength which was excavated at Herculaneum'.[19] So it was probably only a 1.5X or 2X magnifier, as so many ancient lenses were. The other ones, the 'very powerful magnifiers' belonging to the King of Naples, were probably about 4X. After all, I have seen so many ancient lenses by now that the slightest description sometimes suffices for me to know which sort people are talking about. The average ancient reading glass magnified 1.5X or 2X, and thus enabled presbyopic people (people past the age of about 45 who have developed long-sightedness and today would require low-strength spectacles) to read comfortably. The Herculaneum Lens was probably one of those simple reading-aids.

THE VENICE LENS

This is only mentioned by Pierre Pansier, and I have found no other record of it. He mentions it as follows:

> With lenses of 7 dioptres, such as those found at Venice and at Pompeii, one can light within seconds from the sun either tinder or a lamp-wick; they were equally sufficient for the cauterisation of the skin.[20]

(Because lenses focus light rays, if one is used to focus sunlight, the focal point very quickly becomes hot and can cause a fire or burn the skin.)

THE KING OF NAPLES LENSES

Louis Dutens knew the King and Queen of Naples well, and discusses them at great length in his enormous five-volume autobiography, *Memoirs of a Traveller, Now in Retirement. Written by Himself. Interspersed with Literary, and Political Anecdotes Relative to Many of the Principal Personages of the Present Age* (1806). He thus had plenty of occasions to view the contents of their curio cabinets. And in one of these, he found several ancient lenses, which he describes as 'very powerful magnifiers – in a cabinet of antiquities of the King of Naples at Portici'.[21]

Just before going to press I managed to buy an odd volume of the second (1776, 'considerably augmented') edition of his work *Origine des Découvertes Attribuées aux Modernes* (*Origin of the Discoveries Attributed to the Moderns*), an edition which is not to be found in the British Library but which contains Dutens's remarks about the King of Naples Lenses. (These are not mentioned in either the first edition or its English translation.) Fortunately the odd volume which I managed to obtain was the correct volume for these comments. Here is a translation of what Dutens has to say:

> Finally I have seen in the cabinet of antiquities of the King of Naples at Portici several magnifying glasses or lenses stronger than those which are ordinarily used amongst our engravers of today. Some of these have [here a puzzling 18th-century expression in French occurs which appears to mean 'magnify fourfold'], and I have one myself – less strong actually – which was found at Herculaneum. Nothing is lacking but just such magnifying glasses to have executed such works as the stone engraved in the cabinet of the King and known under the name of Michelangelo's Seal, upon which the naked eye cannot perceive all the figures which number fifteen in the space of only six or seven lines.[22]

It should be possible for someone familiar with the Italian antiquities scene to locate the former contents of the curio cabinet of the King of Naples in the 18th century. Alas, my resourcefulness falls short at this point. I have seen no recent mention of these ancient lenses, and it is doubtful if anyone who has seen them in modern times knows what they are.

THE CATACOMBS LENS

In the 18th century, a Roman lens was found in the Catacombs, but before that century reached its end, it had already been lost. Pierre Pansier in 1901 tells us of it:

> A celebrated antiquarian from Rome, Francesco di Ficaroni, questioned by [Domenico Maria] Manni on the magnifying glasses possessed by the ancients, replied that he had seen some antique figurines drawn on some precious stones which were so fine and delicate that it was impossible that they had been carved without the aid of a magnifying glass. And he added that upon going down into the Catacombs of San Lorenzo fuori le Mura ['San Lorenzo Outside the Walls' at Rome, seriously damaged by Allied bombing during the Second World War] one day:
> 'Io stesso trovai una lente murate e fermata col gesso o calcina fina; a questa lenti era giusto della grandezza d'un testone, che ingrandeva mirabilabente [*sic* – a misprint, should be 'mirabilamente'] le cose.' ['I myself found a lens embedded in a wall and fixed with chalk or fine mortar; and this lens was the same size as a large head (*testone*), which wonderfully magnified things.'] The antiquary [di Ficaroni] gave it to a friend, who lost it.

Pansier adds in a footnote that this was 'two hundred years ago, about the commencement of the 18th century' (he was writing in 1901).[23]

This is certainly a strange story. Pansier does not give the reference to Domenico Manni, but perhaps, although I cannot find it there (in the 1738 edition), this tale is to be found somewhere in Manni's book *Degli Occhiali da Naso trattato istorico (Historical Tract Concerning Spectacles)*, which he originally published in 1738 at Florence and then reissued at Venice in 1750 apparently with a further volume on the subject of which no copy seems to exist in Britain, so that I have not seen it. In the 1738 volume, which I *have* seen, Manni mentions the famous Emerald of Nero through which Nero used to look at the gladiatorial combats in the arena as an assistance to his eyesight – a subject discussed at length in Chapter Two – and says that he believes it was a lens. He also cites textual evidence about ancient lenses from Seneca, Pliny, and Plautus. This little book of Manni, 84 pages long with engravings, is not widely known, and has featured in little of the literature on ancient optics due to its rarity and the fact that Italian discussions, being in a minority language, have tended to be disregarded by the speakers of English, French, and German.

One person who did *not* ignore Manni's book was the German poet and playwright Gotthold Ephraim Lessing, whose two Antiquarian Letters dealing with ancient optics (published in 1769) I have fully translated from the German and published as Appendix Three to this book.[24] Lessing writes in a flowery 18th-century manner, containing much indirect expression of views (a form of affected politeness at that time). But he was opposed to the idea that the ancients had lenses. Because of specific textual evidence from antiquity that the Romans used glass globes filled with water to magnify things, Lessing could not deny that. But he came to a truly weird conclusion about the further textual evidence that crystal spheres or globes were also used by the Romans to start fires. Lessing insisted that these rock crystal globes must have been hollowed out and also filled with water!

Lessing's reasoning and conclusions about these matters were thus tortuous and bizarre. Only 31 years before the publication of his own treatises on ancient optics, Manni had published his book, so that Lessing was familiar with it. After all, it was a current work at that time. Manni comes into Lessing's discussion in the context of Lessing's discussion of the glass globes filled with water. These, as we saw in our chapter about classical texts (Chapter Two), are explicitly described by the Roman author Seneca (first century AD), who said in his work *Natural Questions*: 'Letters, however tiny and obscure, are seen larger and clearer through a glass ball filled with water,' and also in another place said: 'Everything is much larger when you look at it through water.' (See Chapter Two for references and discussion of these passages.)

Lessing mentions these passages and points out that the early Renaissance poet and writer Francesco Petrarch had commented upon them in his essay 'On the Remedies of Both Fortunes'.[25] And then he adds:

> It is true that Petrarch, with regard to this passage of Seneca [about glass balls filled with water], had without doubt assigned to the ancients the amplification of vision by this medium [i.e. Petrarch accepted Seneca's evidence]: still, I believe it was first explicitly brought out by the modern author Manni, in his treatise on the invention of spectacles, which first appeared in 1738 . . .

After the collapse of the Roman Empire, the first time anyone in the Mediterranean area (as opposed to the British in the Middle Ages) realized that the use of magnifying aids had been discussed in Latin literature was Petrarch, early in the Italian Renaissance. It is therefore not surprising that it was an Italian, Domenico Manni, who picked the idea up from him and carried it further, so that the discussion then entered into the German arena and awareness of the significance of the Seneca texts ceased to be confined to Italy.

This, therefore, was the Manni whose friend found what I call the Catacombs Lens. And the only reason why this find was recorded was because Manni had already formed an interest in ancient optics, so that his friend thought to mention it.

Gone are the days when one can wander down into the Catacombs unattended and chip away at the walls to see what the bulge is, and find a fascinating ancient object which you put in your pocket and take home. The very fact that the Catacombs Lens was ever found at all was only preserved by a chance encounter between Manni and di Ficaroni at the right time. Otherwise the information would have been as lost as the lens is now.

But what exactly was this strange lens which was the same size as a large head? There are only two possibilities which I can think of. Either it was a very large cast-glass lens, probably biconvex, or it was a crystal ball. At first thought one is inclined to think that it was the latter, since a head is round, and a head was mentioned in comparison. But the fact that di Ficaroni and Manni did not say that it was a crystal ball (and after all, crystal balls were not so unusual) but speak of it as a magnifier which was wonderfully effective and speak of its being embedded in a wall makes me uneasy. Very large cast-glass lenses were indeed made by the Romans, so that we know that such things existed. Even in this century some the size of windows were preserved in Germany, and I shall speak of them later. Such a large lens might have had some function underground in a catacomb as a condensing-lens for the intensifying of light from lamps into a more powerful beam to be directed at some sacred object. But this is only speculation, since we have no sufficient description of the object to enable us to decide.

I am not aware of any other lenses having been found in any of the Catacombs, but if they had been, it is doubtful that anyone would have recognized them as such. For all we know, there are drawers full of them and no one knows what they are or thinks them of any significance whatever. Or there may be none at all. But the point of recounting this tale is, that at least we know there was one. And where there is one, there should be more than one.

THE CUMING LENS

In 1855, the British antiquarian Henry Syer Cuming published an account of a Roman glass lens which had been excavated in the City of London, and which he had in his extensive private collection of antiquities. The publication was of a talk which he delivered to the British Archaeological Association in that year, on which occasion he showed the lens to his audience. His account runs:

> I exhibit to the Association about half of a lens of Roman glass, exhumed in the city [the City of London, being the ancient Roman town of Londinium] a few years back, which may have been cast in this form for a similar purpose to the one discovered at Pompeii. It is an omphaloptic lens, both surfaces being slightly convex; and the edge is rounded off,

but not ground. When entire, it must have been rather more than two inches and one-eighth in diameter, and full three-eighths of an inch thick in the centre. It is of the usual pale green colour of the Roman glass of both this country and Italy. It is the only example of an ancient lens I have ever met with; and it is difficult to say for what use it was intended, if not for some optical purpose.[26]

Cuming's enormous collections of curiosities and antiquities now form the basis of a very unusual little museum in London called The Cuming Museum, which very few people have ever heard of. It is today located on the floor above the Newington District Public Library at 155–157 Walworth Road in Southwark, a short distance from the Elephant and Castle round-about. When I contacted it to ask the staff if they had the Cuming Lens, they did not know what I was talking about. They said they were overwhelmed with more than 10,000 objects still needing cataloguing and classifying. No one had seen a lens, but then no one knew there were any ancient lenses, so why would they notice something they didn't think was possible? Did I want to come and help find it? . . .

Having made my appointment, an hour before I was due to arrive I was telephoned by Keith Bonnick of the Museum staff, who said: 'Was the lens you are looking for excavated in Egypt? Because we have found a catalogue entry for one that was.' I was thrilled, for this was a different and new lens discovery. It was *Cuming's Other Lens*. Most museums have more than one – they just don't know it, so the Cuming Museum was no exception to what we could call Temple's First Law, which states: *Any museum in possession of an ancient lens is in possession of more than one ancient lens*. I know of no exceptions to this apparently universal law, unless perhaps the Kunsthistorisches Museum in Vienna really only has the one (Mainz) lens – but I bet if I made a search I would find more.

So I went to the Cuming Museum expecting to find an Egyptian lens but not to be able to find the Cuming Lens. There was no curator at the time, and Keith Bonnick and Ian Carroll seemed to be running the place pretty well without one, frankly. The first thing Bonnick showed me was a small round old cardboard box 1.15 cm high and 1.56 cm in diameter. On the lid it said that it contained object number C.7351, described as 'Eryum Lens. Thebes, Egypt'. However, the sad news was that the lens was no longer in its box. Instead, the box contained a couple of dark pellets. We were deeply depressed. We think the lens is probably still in the basement of the museum, but it will be in one of dozens of boxes full of bits of glass. It was suggested that I come back on a Monday when the Museum is closed and I could go through the countless large boxes and try and find the missing object. So that is a project for a rainy day.

Meanwhile, Olivia had been browsing around the displays and came and told me she had found a lens. And indeed she had. I describe it below as The London 'Counter' Lens.

Keith Bonnick tried to look for some indications in the records of where the missing Cuming Lens might be. No one had seen it since Cuming died in Victorian times, or if they had, they hadn't known what it was. However, Keith was very clever in figuring out that one of the many large boxes full of glass in the basement might be the likely one. I volunteered to go with him, knowing that I could spot a thing like that instantly. Down we went, and the basement turned out to be so stuffed with things that there was almost no room to turn around – there were simply thousands upon thousands of objects packed into boxes on moveable bays. A large whole rhinoceros horn pointed at me as I entered, and we had to move some antlers or horns of some kind out of our way on the floor lest we step on them. Keith figured out that the box in question was in a different bay, and he finally found it. He pulled it out and I suggested I look through all the glass objects, which he was happy for me to do. There seemed to be about 50 or 60 small pieces of glass in the box.

Within about five minutes I spotted the Cuming Lens amongst the other objects, and we took it upstairs to be certain that it was really what we thought it was. It bore the object number C.11306 painted on it in white, so we were able to consult the records under that number.

In the Museum are preserved the catalogue entries of Cuming himself, and in Vol. 3 under C.11306 we found a reference to his further notes of 434 (4). The relevant entry, written in Cuming's tiny script, was:

Half of a Disk of Roman Glass. 2 $\frac{1}{8}$" diameter & $\frac{3}{8}$" thick. Presented by C. R. Smith, Esq. Sept. 27th 1848.

A sticker on the broken lens also written in Victorian handwriting stated: 'London'. I measured the object and its maximum thickness was 0.99 cm and its diameter by my estimation when intact would have been about 5.54 cm. (a little less than half of the lens survives). The measurements essentially correlate with Cuming's expressed in inches, although the estimated diameter is inevitably a matter of judgement and can vary by a tiny amount. The description (greenish glass, half broken away) and provenance (London) being also in agreement, there can be no doubt whatever that C.11306 is the Cuming Lens described by Cuming in the talk and the article. It may be seen in Plate 4.

My study of the Cuming Lens revealed it to be a rather unobvious lens. It seems to have been cast rather than ground, indicating that a considerable number of such objects must have been made. The rim was very smoothly rounded, not at any point ground. The surfaces were extremely smooth all over. The break is very clean, though appears not to be modern, as it has some iridescence and ingrained dirt patches. The larger half of the lens was not recovered, and was presumably crushed.

Cuming was an enthusiast for bits and pieces of ancient detritus, and he was so keen about it that he used to haunt the sites of road excavations and pay the diggers for small objects which they found during their construction work in building, for instance, the New Kent Road. He also paid a small army of mudlarks – the boys who scavenged in the mud of the River Thames at low tide at London – for every interesting object they brought him. A large proportion of the objects in the Cuming Museum came from the Thames, or from road excavations. C. R. Smith was presumably a London builder – one of Cuming's many suppliers of such objects.

The biconvexity of the lens is very slight indeed, and it is nearly a disk, though it is not really flat on the surfaces. If we consider the surface with the label 'London' the superior surface, it is of +2D (dioptres) of curvature measuring parallel to the break; and measuring radially, at right angles to the break, is +6D. The underside is flatter and measures +1D and +5D respectively in the two directions. Such a flat lens would have had a very long focal distance, such as one would get from placing such a lens at the eye if sitting upright and reading something flat on a table. (Elsewhere in this book I have described a crystal lens of this kind which may possibly be of pre-Roman date from Britain. See Appendix Eleven.)

The glass poured into the mould to make this lens was full of bubbles, and the greenish colour of the glass is also pronounced. It may be therefore that this object was intended more as a 'sun-glass', since we know that the Romans appreciated the use of green transparent materials for viewing through – a subject discussed at length when we considered Pliny's account of the green lens through which the Emperor Nero is recorded as having viewed the combats of the gladiators at Rome. The present condition of the glass is that it is translucent and only partially transparent in patches. Considerable portions have been rendered nearly opaque by severe pressure-flawing near the break which has gone dark inside the glass, by severe oxidation and darkening of the surfaces, by surface iridescence, particularly of one of the surfaces, by extensive shallow pitting and heavily ingrained patches of dirt of substantial size in the pits (rather than microscopic pitting such as one gets on crystal), and by very severe scratching of the surfaces. Despite all of this, it is a marvel that in a strong lamplight one can still see one's finger through the glass. Originally, this lens would have been transparent in the manner of a very pale sunglasses lens, and would have magnified in the manner just described. With such a long focal distance, the bubbles in the glass probably would have constituted no nuisance, whereas a lens with a very short focal length could not have been used comfortably with them. (When using a camera with dirt on the lens, the dirt doesn't actually show up on the photo, as all photographers will have noticed.)

It is nothing short of a miracle that we found this tiny item so readily amidst all the thousands of objects stuffed into that claustrophobic basement room. One can suspect the Hand of Cuming behind all of this, guiding us to the right box, since he didn't wish his collections to go to waste.

Although they had nothing new to say about it, and never examined it, the Cuming Lens was referred to in passing in discussions by Marquardt (in German, 1886), Weule (in German, 1912), Theobald (in German, 1935), and Sines/Sakellarakis (in English, 1987), all of whom have already been mentioned above.

It is amusing that when I was trying to locate this lens in the 1980s, I was informed by the Greek and Roman Antiquities Department of the British Museum (who were unaware that a Cuming Museum existed – and I only found out about that later) that: 'We have only one gift recorded from Cuming, a group of iron nails which he presented in 1892. . . . I have also consulted my colleagues in the Department of Greek & Roman Antiquities, to see whether they might have any glass or crystal objects which could be interpreted as lenses, but they do not. As I pointed out on the telephone, even if Cuming's lens does turn up somewhere, you should treat its dating with the greatest caution.' (Letter from Catherine Johns, 11 March 1985.) Of course, I subsequently found a number of lenses in this very Department, but then that is hardly surprising. Nor is it surprising that I was warned off the Cuming Lens by someone who had never seen it, in the way the German museum official tried to warn me off the Mainz Lens which he had not seen either.

I should mention that there is another object in the Cuming Museum, Number C.11204, which I found in the same box with the Cuming Lens, which may have had an optical use. It is of greenish transparent glass, presumably Roman, labelled 'Site of New Post Office. St Martin's le Grand. [London] 1870.' Broken at the top, this small flat-bottomed hollow glass object if filled with water could have stood upon a surface and acted as a standing-magnifier. The Romans made enormous numbers of such hollow glass magnifiers, as discussed in the main text of this book.

THE ERYUM LENS

This small lens excavated at Thebes in Egypt has just been mentioned above, and we know no more about it than the size of its box, until such time as it is found in the Cuming Museum and examined. This may be the lens of which Petrie said in 1885, as reported above, that 'I have heard that one was found in Egypt . . .' See also the discussion of The Tanis Lenses, below.

THE LONDON 'COUNTER' LENS

As I was examining the Cuming Lens in the Cuming Museum, Olivia noticed this small lens in a display case. Because the display case, built in 1902, cannot be conveniently opened on the relevant side, it is impossible to get at this lens to study it properly unless the entire exhibition is removed from the case first. I have been promised that if the Museum staff remove the exhibition, they will notify me and I can rush around and examine the lens. It was not part of Cuming's collection, but is on loan from the London Museum, who have no idea that it is a lens. They think it is a 'counter', and it is on exhibition beside three solid and opaque 'counters' as a rather unconvincing fourth.

The display is under the category of 'Trades', and the objects are labelled 'Four Counters'. Their numbers are 2844, 1645, 2810, and 1529. From what we could gather, the transparent glass one seems to be 2810. Its colour might be described as peridot-green, since it resembles the green colour of the semi-precious stone, peridot. It is plano-convex, round, about an inch-and-a-half in diameter, and has clear evidence around its rim of having been mounted at one time. This alone should have been sufficient to alert the London Museum staff to the fact that it could not be a 'counter'. It is transparent, and through it one can see that the underlying display material is slightly magnified. From my experience of such lenses, I would estimate that the resting magnification is only about 1.25X, and certainly not more than 1.5X, but when raised to a focal point, the magnification would go to between 1.5X and 2X. I only presume it is glass, but it could be a transparent stone. Further details await the opportunity to gain access to the object.

THE TANIS LENSES

Two glass lenses were excavated in Egypt by Sir William Flinders Petrie in 1883–4 and published by him in 1885.[27] They are both preserved in the British Museum, where the intact one is Object 22522 (see Plates 41 and 42) and the broken one is Object 27639, in the Department of Egyptian Antiquities. They were both presented to the British Museum in 1885 by the Egypt Exploration Fund, which was the organization which funded Petrie's dig. They are of Roman date, estimated at about the second century AD. Petrie's description of the two lenses, in the book just referred to, states:

61. Another glass object, nearly as rare [as a glass zodiac which he has just described], is a plano-convex lens, two-and-a-half inches across, and half an inch thick (section in pl. xii. 30). Some lenses have been found at Pompeii in an engraver's shop, and I have heard that one was found in Egypt, but yet this is such an unusual object that we may note the reasons for believing it to be a lens. It is of remarkably clear and colourless glass; it has been highly polished on both sides; and on the middle of the convex face a small patch is worn rough by rubbing about. Now the only other use it can have been applied to is for setting as a boss in a breast-plate, or some such ornament; but if so it would probably be coloured to imitate garnet or emerald, and the wear would be diffused over the face, and not all in one spot as on this. The surface is now all

decomposed by the damp earth, and though retaining its polish is translucent milky white, and liable to scale off. A piece of another lens was also found in this house.

The house referred to is House 44 at the site known in modern Arabic as San el-Hagar, but a site which is generally called by its ancient name of Tanis. Petrie says of it that is had been 'looted and burnt', and its owner 'seems to have been not a native, but a Roman'. In this house, 'the most striking objects . . . have been imported, probably from Magna Graecia [the south of Italy], and (so far as observation at the time went) half or nearly half of the papyri were in Greek . . .' The owner seems to have been 'a wealthy Roman official, a man of taste and refinement, who came from Italy to the administration of Tanis.'[28] (Egypt was at that time, of course, a Roman colony.) A drawing of the intact Tanis lens in section is shown as Item 30 in Plate XII of Petrie's book, and is given in actual size. I reproduce photos of front and side views of this lens in Plates 41 and 42. A photo of the lens fragment is not worth reproducing.

The British Museum has indeed described the objects as lenses, and there has never been any quibble about this.[29]

It seems worthwhile here, even in the context of lenses which are really Roman, to mention one interesting possibility relating to Egyptian hieroglyphics. There are two basic Egyptian hieroglyphs which represent the letter 'r' [strictly speaking, it is not a letter but a syllable]. One is a crouching lion seen from the side. But the more common, and easier to draw, is something which looks like a biconvex lens in section:

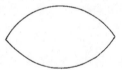

Two of the fundamental meanings of this hieroglyph as a single-syllable word are concepts which are not at variance with the subject of magnification. As a preposition, *er* means 'near to, towards, upon, up to'. And *er* is also used either singly or doubly (in which case two of these signs are drawn on top of one another) as a sign of the comparative, meaning 'more', and thus designating a kind of magnification, as it were, of whatever subject is being mentioned. And it may not be irrelevant to point out once again that two convex lenses together form a basic telescope, which could be depicted by two of these hieroglyphs on top of one another. Certainly a convex lens appears to bring something 'near to' the eye, and its size is thus increased so that it is 'more'. In the absence of further evidence all of this is speculation, but it is worth mentioning in case there may be something to it.

THE KARANIS LENSES

These glass lenses, excavated in Egypt, are preserved in Michigan and in Cairo. Karanis is the ancient Greek name of a site called in Arabic Kom Aushim (also called Kom Ushim), in the Fayum region. They are also of Roman or Roman-inspired manufacture, and are estimated to date from about 100 AD. Two are intact and two are fragmentary. They were excavated between 1924 and 1929 by a team of archaeologists from the University of Michigan. It was one of these which was mentioned above by Harry Taylor as being announced while he was in Cairo looking for lenses in the winter of 1929/1930.

A report on these four lenses was published by Donald B. Harden in 1936, in his book entitled *Roman Glass from Karanis*. In that, he had Section G, of one page, entitled 'Lenses', where he wrote the following:

> These objects were certainly magnifying glasses: that they do not any longer serve that purpose is explained by the clouded state of their surface owing to weathering. Two complete and two fragmentary specimens occurred, all of uniform type.
>
> Similar lenses of Roman date have been found elsewhere in Egypt, e.g. at Tanis and at Hawara by Petrie [for these latter, see below, The Hawara Lenses]. A recent article on early magnifying glasses by H. C. Beck ['Ancient Magnifying Glasses', *The Antiquaries Journal*, London, Vol. VIII, pp. 328–30, where he reproduces a photo of the intact Tanis Lens. However, Beck mistakenly calls it the 'Tunis' Lens and says that it is in the Ashmolean Museum at Oxford, whereas it is of course the Tanis Lens and is in the British Museum in London.] mentions, besides Roman ones, some earlier ones of the sixth to fourth century BC found at Carthage and now in the Lavigerie Museum there [see Plates 2 and 3 and discussion in the main text of this book], while Kisa [already mentioned in connection with the Nola Lens] refers to examples of the Greek period from Nola as well as to Roman pieces found in England [the Cuming Lens], at Pompeii, and elsewhere. Their use was therefore widespread, and began at least as early as the fourth century BC. Beck, indeed, on the analogy of similar lenses made of crystal which have been found in a layer of about 1600–1200 BC in Crete, thinks that glass lenses may also go back to that early period.

> 868.26/B 12 A/R Mich. 5969. [Illustrated in Harden's Plate XXI – a simple section drawing.] Greenish colourless; intact, but chipped and scratched by usage; many pin-prick bubbles and some impurities. D[iameter]. 0.051 m. H[eight; i.e. maximum thickness] in centre 0.011 m. Lens, circular: under side flat, upper side conical: edge ground flat [i.e. for mounting] and *c[irca]* 0.003 m thick, the rest of the surface, both above and below, polished by rotatory motion. [*This lens is preserved in Michigan.*]

869. 24/5011 B/C Cairo J 52787. Greenish colourless; intact; spots of iridescence; many pin-prick bubbles and many black impurities. D[iameter]. 0.05 m. H[eight, i.e. maximum thickness] in centre 0.0075 m. Lens, circular: under side flat, upper side convex; edges sharp and less than 0.001 m. thick; the whole polished by a rotatory motion. [*This lens, the one mentioned by Harry Taylor (above) as being deposited in the Cairo Museum in the winter of 1929/30, is now on display in the Egyptian Museum at Cairo (the modern name for the Cairo Museum). I give my own account of it as 'The Cairo Lens'. See Chapter One and Plate 5.*]

870. 26/B 53 D/D Mich. 5970. Colourless with greenish tinge; almost complete, but badly stain-cracked [as the Cuming Lens is]; good glass, no bubbles. D[iameter]. 0.055 m. Lens, circular: shape as no. 869. [*This lens is preserved in Michigan. See Plate 44.*]

871. 28/B 141 K/E. [Harden does not give this lens's Object Number, which is Mich 25697.] Greenish colourless; half-extant; spots of milky pitting; many pin-prick bubbles. D[iameter]. 0.053 m. H[eight, i.e. maximum thickness] in centre 0.011 m. Lens, circular: shape as no. 869.'
[*This lens is preserved in Michigan.*]

Three of the Karanis Lenses as described above are to be found at the Kelsey Museum of Archaeology, University of Michigan, Ann Arbor, Michigan, USA. *The fourth, Cairo J52787*, is 'The Cairo Lens'.

THE HAWARA LENSES

Sir Flinders Petrie – who has already been mentioned – after his death left his enormous private collection of Egyptian antiquities to form the contents of one of London's most fascinating and least-known museums, the Petrie Museum. This museum is even more obscure and hard to find than the Cuming Museum. In fact, it is upstairs in one of the buildings belonging to University College London – and anyone who has ever attempted to navigate the labyrinthine alleyways and corridors of that building complex will know that even finding the right building is challenging, much less the right *portion* of that building. One enters by a small door in a back alley, and is immediately confronted with a barrier and the demand for a pass. However forbidding this may seem, one must be courageous and utter the magic words 'Petrie Museum' to the guards, and suddenly they let you in after all, directing you upstairs and around various corners. Perhaps I am giving away a dangerous secret, and all the people whom University College wishes to keep out of their library because they could steal books or plant bombs will now use this inside knowledge to gain forbidden entry by saying 'Petrie Museum'. In fact, I have wondered if 'Petrie Museum' might perhaps be a mantra which could be used elsewhere, so that saying those words could, for instance, grant me unquestioned entry to private clubs and other closed premises.

Petrie excavated two glass lenses which he kept in his private collection, and which may now be inspected at the Petrie Museum. Their catalogue numbers there are U.C. 16764 and U.C. 16765. The first of these is biconvex, with a very slightly convex base (measuring +0.5 D [dioptres]) and a smoothly convex upper surface (varying between +8 and +10 D [dioptres] in curvature). The latter has a pointy convex top, so that the upper surface measures +5D except across the point, when the curvature varies to +4D. This lens has a slightly concave base, with a curvature of −1 D.

Lens 16764 is circular, 5.4 cm in diameter, with a small piece broken off the edge. Its maximum thickness is 8 mm. There is no evidence on the rim of this lens ever having been inlaid or mounted. This lens is still transparent but for the dirt and markings which largely cover it.

Lens 16765 is still completely translucent, but only partially transparent. It is nearly round, and its diameter varies between 5 cm along its minor axis and 5.1 cm along its major axis. Its maximum thickness is 1.3 cm. There is a transverse crack across the lens, as if a quarter of it had nearly broken off. The rim is perfectly smooth, just like the surfaces, so that there is no evidence that this lens either was ever mounted.

These two lenses, presumed to be of Roman date, like the Cuming Lens, were evidently cast rather than ground – and Petrie excavated them at the Egyptian site of Hawara, hence their name.

THE BERLIN LENS-PANES

Baron Heinrich von Minutoli has already been mentioned for his published account in 1836 of the Nola Lens. Later in his life, he came into possession of three very remarkable Roman glass lenses of gigantic size, which he left in his will to the Berlin Museum. Unfortunately, these seem to have been destroyed in the Second World War. The only description of them which I have managed to find so far is by Claude du Bois-Reymond (writing in German, despite his French name) in 1905.[30] At that time, the catalogue numbers in the Berlin Museum for these objects were 1780, 1781, and 1782 in the Terra Cotta Inventory, and 2368, 2369, and 2370 in the Glass Inventory. Du Bois-Reymond makes a strong and enthusiastic case for a highly advanced science of optical lens-grinding by the Romans, although he knows only four ancient magnifying lenses (not named) in addition to the three huge Roman plano-convex glass panes left to the Berlin Museum. He says: 'The maker of such enormous lenses was without doubt also capable of making magnifying glasses or spectacles.' And he says that viewing from the appropriate positions, a person who looked through the large window-panes could have his vision corrected for presbyopia [long-sightedness] or astigmatism. Precise measurements of these lens-panes are not given by du Bois-Reymond, and it is hoped that some further details of these extraordinary objects will at some time emerge from the records of one of the post-War museums in Germany. However, the fact that there were evidently Roman glass lenses the size of window panes is most astonishing, and shows how far Roman technology in this area had gone. We have no information of which site or even of which country yielded these objects, although it was probably somewhere in southern Italy, where von Minutoli spent so much time.

THE TYRE LENS

This rock-crystal lens, excavated at the site of the ancient city of Tyre on the coast of present-day Lebanon in the 19th century, is currently lost. It was brought back from Tyre to Athens by Andreas Anagnostakis, Rector of the University of Athens, in the 1870s. On 13 March 1877, Anagnostakis, who was fluent in French, gave a talk at the French School of Archaeology at Athens (the École Française d'Athènes) at which he displayed the lens. This is recorded in the annals of that School, a copy of the relevant page having been kindly supplied to me by Dr Guy Cobolet, the Director of the School. Unfortunately, all that the record shows is that on that occasion Anagnostakis spoke about a *loupe antique découverte à Tyr* – 'an ancient magnifying glass discovered at Tyre'.[31]

The next year, Anagnostakis published at Athens his 28-page pamphlet *Meletai peri tēs Optikēs tōn Arçhaiōn (Studies Concerning the Optics of the Ancients)*, in which he mentioned the Tyre Lens. There is no copy of this pamphlet in Britain or even in several of the major libraries in Athens, and I was fortunate indeed to find a copy in the Bibliothèque Nationale in Paris, of which I made a microfilm (which took months to arrive). This work is not written in the demotic Greek spoken today, but rather in the old-fashioned literary 'modern Greek' of the 19th century known as *katharēvousa*, which only a handful of Greeks alive today can read.

Anagnostakis mentions the Tyre Lens and says that it is of crystal on page 11 of his pamphlet, but he gives no measurements. In insisting that it is a lens, he appeals to the textual evidence of Seneca and others (which we deal with in Chapters Two and Three).[32] He believed the lens to be 2,300 years old, hence dating from about 300 BC. Anagnostakis was convinced that there were many ground lenses in antiquity. Unfortunately, I have found no one in Athens who has any idea where this lens may now be, and there seem to be only a handful of people in the academic community there who have even heard the name of Anagnostakis. I know many Greek professors, but none of them has been able to help on this matter.

Appendix Two

The only further information which I have been able to discover about the Tyre Lens is given by the arch-sceptic Joseph Hirschberg in 1899. Hirschberg actually knew Anagnostakis, as they were contemporaries, and he also inspected the Tyre Lens. But Hirschberg is fanatical in insisting that none of the ancient 'lentoids' were lenses, and he misreads ancient texts almost perversely in pursuit of his preconception. Although Hirschberg admits that the ancients had burning-glasses and burning-globes and admits that they also realized that these magnified, he strangely persists in concluding that 'There is not the slightest trace to be found in any writings of any optical purpose or optical effect of ground glass, or crystal . . .' And he has scathing words to say of his friend Andreas Anagnostakis's views:

> Finally, whoever wishes to read an attractive novel may get hold of my unfortunately recently deceased friend Anagnostakes's [*sic*, an alternative spelling] *Meletai peri tēs Optikēs tōn Archaiōn*, Athens, 1878 – a book of the most beautiful style, of the greatest industry, naturally also showing the greatest love for the ancient Greeks, in which however not a single assertion is actually provable. . . . One [lens], found in the ruins of Tyre, and reputed to be over 2,200 years old, is a button-like object of rock crystal which I have myself seen at Athens, and which Anagnostakes maintained was the oldest magnifying lens of our planet, is just – a button.[33]

Although Hirschberg's fanatical determination to disallow any ancient lens whatever may be discounted, there are some advantages to his account – the fact that he describes the Tyre Lens as being like a button indicates that it must have been biconvex and relatively small, and the fact that Anagnostakis was so keen on its magnifying powers must mean that it was a fairly powerful magnifier, in no case less than 2X, and probably more. Let us hope the Tyre Lens one day comes to light again.

THE PROMETHEUS LENS

This crystal lens is in my own possession at the time of writing. I acquired it from my friend Peter Mitchell, the Nobel Laureate for Chemistry, who in turn got it from an antiquities dealer. This remarkable lens is also mentioned in the discussion of the legend of Prometheus, the 'fire-bringer' whose 'fire from heaven' was really sunlight focused through a lens. Here, I shall merely say that there is a transparent carving on the base of the lens (in no way interfering with its magnifying properties) which is Archaic Greek, and that this enables the carved lens to be dated to no later than the sixth century BC. (Whether the lens was earlier than this and the carving was merely done at this time is unknown.) A photo of this lens is reproduced as Plate 11.

The Crystal Sun

Notes

1. Sacken, Edward Freiherr [Baron] von, 'Neuere Erwerbungen der Antikensammlung des A. h. Kaiserhauses' ('New Acquisitions of the Antiquities Collection of the Kaiserhaus [now part of the Kunsthistorisches Museum of Vienna]', in *Archaeologisch-Epigraphische Mittheilungen aus Österreich* (*Archaeological and Epigraphical Communications of Austria*), ed. by O. Benndorf and O. Hirschfeld, Vienna, pp. 126–52. On p. 151, von Sacken reports Item 25, 'A Roman Magnifying Glass', which is the Mainz Lens.

2. Marquardt, Joachim, *Das Privatleben der Römer* (*Private Life of the Romans*), Vol. VII of *Handbuch der Römischen Alterthümer* (*Handbook of Roman Antiquity*), ed. by Joachim Marquardt and Theodor Mommsen, Leipzig, 1886. The relevant passage is in Part II, pp. 751–2, and the footnotes mentioning the Mainz Lens are Footnote 9 on p. 751 and Footnote 1 on p. 752.

3. Bock, Emil, *Die Brille und Ihre Geschichte* (*Spectacles and Their History*), Verlag von Josef Šafár, Vienna, 1903 (62 pp.); there is an unpublished translation by A. W. Boatman, and I have also translated the relevant sections about antiquity myself.

4. Mach, Ernst, *Principles of Physical Optics: An Historical and Philosophical Treatment*, trans. by J. S. Anderson and A.F.A. Young, Methuen, London, 1926, pp. 50–1. The original German edition of this book was published in 1913.

5. An ill-tempered sceptic, annoyed by the increasing number of reports in German about ancient magnifying glasses, was (Karl) Richard Greeff. In 1916, Greeff attempted to rebut the evidence presented by the four lenses reported in the footnote of Marquardt, including the Mainz Lens, as well as the Layard Lens, and several more which we shall be considering later. He merely mentions the Mainz Lens in passing, in six words, plus giving its diameter at 5.5 cm, obviously knowing no more about it than that. Nevertheless, despite negligible knowledge of the lenses which he lists, he does not hesitate to insist that 'the use of convex lenses for the eyes of presbyopes [long-sighted people] was entirely unknown to (the ancients).' (Greeff, [Karl] Richard, 'Kritische Betrachtungen über Funde von Brillengläsern und Lupen aus dem frühen Altertum' ['Critical Observations concerning the Discovery of Eyeglasses and Magnifying Glasses from Early Antiquity'], in *Zeitschrift für Ophthalmologische Optik* [*Journal of Ophthalmological Optics*], Berlin, Vol. IV, Part 3, pp. 142–6.) Greeff returned to the attack in 1921 in a full-length book, but gave no further information about the Mainz Lens than to say that it was 'from Roman times'; he still seems not to have been bothered to learn any more about it than could be obtained from Marquardt's brief footnote, having failed to consult von Sacken's excavation report and having also pointedly ignored the distinguished physicist Mach's study of the lens. (Greeff, [Karl] Richard, *Die Erfindung der Augengläser* [*The Invention of Eyeglasses*], Berlin, Vol. I of *Optische Bücherei* [*Optical Pamphlets*], 1921, p. 24.) Self-styled 'sceptics' like Greeff have a double duty, for in wishing to dismiss things, they must not only have full knowledge of what they wish to dismiss and impeccable familiarity with all its fine points, but they must not give the impression that they are acting on a preconception where evidence is not important. In this, Greeff fails dismally.

6. Theobald, Wilhelm, 'Zur Geschichte der Lupe' ('On the History of Magnifying Glasses'), in *Forschungen und Fortschritte* (*Researches and Advances*), Berlin, Vol. 11, No. 14, 10 May 1935, pp. 190–1.

7. Forbes, R. J., *Studies in Ancient Technology*, Leiden, Vol. 5, 1957, p. 187. He says the Mainz Lens has a diameter of 5.5 cm and is similar to the Nola plano-convex lens (see discussion of it in Chapter One).

8. King, Henry C., 'Lenses in Antiquity', in *The Optician*, London, 12 September 1958, p. 224.

9. Needham, Joseph; Ling, Wang; and Robinson, Kenneth, Vol. IV, Part 1 (*Physics*) of *Science and Civilisation in China*, Cambridge, 1962, p. 100.

10. My book was originally published in Britain under the title of *China: Land of Discovery and Invention*, Patrick Stephens, Wellingborough, 1986. It was originally published in the USA by Simon and Schuster, New York, as hardback and paperback under the title *The*

Genius of China, 1987. It has three times been republished in Britain by Prion Books, London, as *The Genius of China*, 1991, 1998 and 1999. The book was translated in whole or in part into 43 languages, all of the minor language translations such as Swahili, Basque, and Catalan, having been financed by UNESCO, who promoted the book internationally through their organization and with great enthusiasm.

11. Gerspach, Edouard, *L'Art de la Verrerie* (*The Art of Glassmaking*), Paris, 1885, p. 41.

12. Petrie, (Sir) W. M. Flinders, *Tanis. Part I, 1883–4*, London, 1885, p. 49.

13. Hirschberg, Joseph, *Geschichte der Augenheilkunde im Alterthum* (*History of Ophthalmology in Antiquity*), in *Gräfe-Saemisch Handbuch der Gesamten Augenheilkunde* (*Gräfe-Saemisch Handbook of Complete Ophthalmology*), Leipzig, Vol. XII, Part 2, *Pathologie und Therapie* (*Pathology and Therapy*), 1899, pp. 174–80.

14. Pansier, Pierre, *L'Histoire des Lunettes* (*History of Spectacles*), Paris, 1901, pp. 2–3.

15. Dutens, Louis, *Origine des Découvertes Attribuées aux Modernes* (*Origin of the Discoveries Attributed to the Moderns*; the actual English title given to the translation however was *An Inquiry into the Origin of the Discoveries Attributed to the Moderns*, London, 1769), first edition, Paris, 1766; second edition, 1776 (this is the one which the British Library does not have, and from which Pansier – in a book which the British Library *also* does not have! – quotes), third edition, London, 1796. The third edition contains views on ancient lenses which are diametrically opposed to those expressed in the first edition, for Dutens changed from a complete sceptic who denied the existence of such lenses, to someone who was convinced that they *did* exist. As for the second edition of 1776 in Paris, judging from what Pansier quotes from it (a passage which meanwhile disappeared from the third edition!), Dutens's change of mind happened in the ten years between the first and second editions.

   Just before going to press, I managed to buy an odd volume, namely the second half, Volume II, of the second (1776) editions of Dutens. From its Index I learn that Dutens's comments about magnifying glasses and telescopes appeared in Vol. I, which I have still not seen. But his discussion of burning-mirrors is in Vol. II, as well as the mention of the King of Naples Lenses (in the section on 'Mechanics of the Ancients', sub-section 'The Use of Microscopes by the Ancients'). I have therefore been able to quote the latter remarks in this Appendix, in the section entitled 'The King of Naples lenses'. However, Dutens's account of the Herculaneum Lens is in Vol. I, and it is only mentioned in passing in Vol. II, so that the fuller information on that subject is not yet available.

16. Ptolemy, Claudius (Tolomeo, Claudio), *L'Ottica* (*The Optics*), translated into Latin and introduced by Gilberto Govi, Torino [Turin], 1885. The 'Introduzione' (Introduction) is in Italian, and contains the remarks about the Pompeii Lens on pp. xxxvi-xxxvii.

17. Cuming, H. Syer, 'On Spectacles', in *Journal of the British Archaeological Association*, London, Vol. 11, 1855, pp. 144–5.

18. A very brief biographical notice of Dutens was published in German in 1845 by Georg Lichtenberg, and I have translated it for quoting in full here, as the life of Dutens may have some bearing on the whereabouts of his lens:

> Louis Dutens, born at Tours 1730, went to England, accompanied Lord Algernon [Percy], son of the Duke of Northumberland, on his travels; died in London 1812. Published: *Recherches sur l'Origine des Découvertes Attribuées aux Modernes*, 1766, 2 vols, octavo. Fourth edition 1812, and Leibniz's *Opera Omnia*, Geneva, 6 vols. (Lichtenberg, Georg Christoph, 'Eine Moderne Entdeckung des Herrn Dutens' ['A Modern Discovery of Monsieur Dutens'], in *Vermischte Schriften: Neue Vermehrte, von dessen Söhnen veranstaltete, Original-Ausgabe* [*Miscellanies: Newly Augmented, Prepared by His Sons, Original Edition*], Göttingen, 1845, Vol. VI, pp. 448–50. The brief article was reprinted from the *Taschenkalender* [*Pocket Almanac*], Göttingen, 1798, pp. 176–9.

> The 'modern discovery' referred to in the title is a reference to Dutens's conversion from sceptic to believer in the existence of ancient lenses. The article was thus a review

in a German periodical of the third, 1796, edition, of Dutens's work. And by the way, Lichtenberg got the title of Dutens's book wrong, because it commenced *Origine* and not *Recherches sur l'Origine*.)

Further biographical information is found in the list of members (*Index Biographique*) of the Académie des Inscriptions et Belles-Lettres of Paris, where we are told that Dutens was born at Tours in Touraine on 15 January 1730, made an Academician on 22 January 1775, and died at London on 23 May 1812. (Institut de France, *l'Académie des Inscriptions et Belles-Lettres: Histoire*, Vol. I, Paris, 1924, *Index Biographique*, p. 209. The British Library pressmark for this is Ac.420.c. [Vol. I]; all publications dealing with the French academies are so fantastically difficult to sort out – whether in London or in Paris – that giving the pressmark is advisable for anyone ever hoping to find the work in question and remain sane.)

It is frustrating to know that in 1776 Dutens possessed an ancient Roman lens from Herculaneum, the whereabouts of which is unknown. Since Dutens died in London, it occurred to me that his will would be deposited there, and the dispositions of his effects might be mentioned in it (i.e. 'I leave my collection of antiquities and curios to my good friend Lord Algernon Percy', or something of that kind). I realized that it was not inconceivable that amongst the many curious objects to be found in drawers, attics, and cabinets in a great English country house, there may in one of them – perhaps that of the Percys – be a small glass object which does not look very impressive, and to which no one has paid any attention for two centuries because they do not know what it is. So I commenced a search for the Last Will and Testament of Louis Dutens, which was proved in July 1812, and is three pages long, under the listing PROB 11/1535 in the London Public Record Office.

The will of Louis Dutens is very interesting, but it does not reveal the whereabouts of the Herculaneum Lens. After some financial bequests, I was very excited when I came across bequests of specific antiquities to individuals. Dutens wrote his will in 1807 and said: 'I give and bequeathe to the Countess of Beverley for whose merit I have always entertained the greatest respect my small Oval Snuff Box of Red and Yellow Jasper B . . . tel of Egypt set in Gold. I give and bequeathe to the Earl of Beverley my Antique Ring of a fine Cornelian representing Pompey the Great Sacrificing.' This was just the sort of thing I was expecting. But then imagine my disappointment when I read the following:

I desire that my House ffurniture Books Watches Snuff Boxes Rings Trinkets and all other my Effects may be sold by auction at Mr Christies of Pall Mall and that the rest of the produce of them together with the arrears of my Pension [etc., etc., – quite a lot of pensions, money in the hands of Coutts the bankers, and so forth] . . . the whole to be divided in eight shares which I give and bequeathe to my four Nephewes and four Nieces . . .

Presumably the Herculaneum Lens was thus amongst the 'trinkets' sold at Christies in 1812, along with Dutens's collection of snuff boxes. But hold on – there is a Codicil added in February 1812! In this Codicil, Dutens alters his dispositions of his effects. Suddenly he decides to leave a lot of his household furniture to his servants, and 'my Wearing Apparel including my Shirts &c as also my Canes' to his footman. His housekeeper Mrs Millington gets all his beds and tables. His two housemaids Mary Collinson and Sarah Goodluck are given 'all the Kitchen ffurniture and utensils & every thing in the Kitchen except Silver Plate of every kind'. So, as he was presumably suffering from what was to be a terminal illness, Dutens became more charitable to those around him and who were actually looking after him on a daily basis. The nieces and nephews were far away in France and would not be needing his shirts and walking sticks!

The more interesting parts of the Codicil relate to his especially prized scholarly possessions:

I leave and bequeathe to the Library of the Royal institution all my Volumes of Tracts (above 82 in number) which are bound in 4° [quarto size], 8° [octavo size, smaller than quarto], & 12° [smaller still] and all together in a small Bookcase in my Library the list of which is to be found at the end of my Catalogue in folio as also a small folio Volume . . . with the Genealogy of my ffamily in one of the first blank leaves.

Dutens had evidently become an early member of the Royal Institution, a scientific academy in the centre of London which still preserves the laboratory of Michael Faraday, and has a remarkable library of science books. It is not impossible that Dutens before his death might have given his lens to the RI since it was of antiquarian scientific interest. However, the Royal Institution has assured me that they do not have it and they cannot find any of the 82 volumes either!

19. Pansier, *op. cit.*, p. 2.
20. *Ibid.*, pp. 4–5.
21. *Ibid.*, p. 2. Pansier is quoting the second edition of Dutens, of 1776, of which no copy exists in the British Library.
22. Dutens, Louis, *Origine des Découvertes Attribuées aux Modernes (Origins of the Discoveries Attributed to the Moderns)*, second edition 'considerably augmented', Paris, 1776, Vol. II, pp. 223–4.
23. Pansier, *op. cit.*, p. 3 and n. 3.
24. Lessing, Gotthold Ephraim, 'The 25th Antiquarian Letter' and 'The 45th Antiquarian Letter', in *Briefe, Antiquarischen Inhalts (Antiquarian Letters)*, Berlin, 1769. Lessing's *Antiquarian Letters* have been reprinted at various times in collected editions of Lessing's works, but only in German. They have never been translated into English. It is the second Letter, the 45th, which has the real importance for our subject. I have taken pains to translate these works myself (as I have done with all German material used in this book) owing to the importance of their author in the history of world literature, not because I agree with his opinions or think that his conclusions are valid. However, he gathered much interesting material in his extensive researches, and it all really does need to be freely available in English.
25. Petrarch, Francesco, *De Remediis Utriusque Fortunae (On the Remedies of Both Fortunes)*, Book II, Chapter 83.
26. Cuming, *op. cit.*, pp. 144–50.
27. Petrie, [Sir] W. [William] M. Flinders, *Tanis. Part I., 1883–4*, London, 1885, p. 49b.
28. *Ibid.*, pp. 46b–47a.
29. The intact lens for a long time was exhibited in the 6th Egyptian Room, in the 5th case along, in the extreme right-hand corner. The archaeologist John Cooney wrote the fourth volume, on *Glass*, of the *Catalogue of Egyptian Antiquities in the British Museum* (1976), and in it he records Items 1804 (the intact lens) and 1817 (the lens fragment) and describes the former as having a diameter of 6.6 cm and the fragment as having a width of 6 cm. Of the intact lens he says:

> The form is conventional, a flat base with convex top. The glass is very pale green, almost colourless and almost transparent. The surface is heavily filmed and is full of bubbles and minute cavities.

Of the fragment he says:

> A fragment, about half, of a lens. The metal [*sic*: a misprint for 'glass'!], of greenish cast, is transparent and is of finer quality than the preceding specimen.

I wrote to Cooney, then at the Cleveland Museum of Art, on 22 April 1980, wanting 'to elicit from you any comments you might like to make on these objects.' I received a reply from him dated 10 May 1980, making these strange comments:

The lens[es] excavated by Petrie have not again been commented on so far as I know and that they are lens[es] is only an assumption. I know of no parallels. I have just consulted Harris *Ancient Egy. Materials and Industries* but curiously he has nothing to say on the subject.

There has been much speculation on how the ancients did some of their finest work without the aid of magnification but there is no consensus of opinion and certainly there are no comments on it in ancient literature.

It is almost impossible to get an answer from a letter to the Cairo Museum and photographs are equally difficult to obtain. So very little is known, almost nothing, that I advise you not to go into the subject . . . I'm sorry I have been unable to be of greater assistance but you ask questions that cannot be answered.

I have examined the Tanis Lenses, which are readily accessible in London, and the idea that it is only an 'assumption' that they were lenses is absurd. It is a pity that, like most of the ancient glass lenses which survive, they are no longer transparent. It is much more rewarding to examine the many surviving ancient crystal lenses, for it is possible to measure their magnification directly, as only a few of them have gone opaque due to damage.

30. du Bois-Reymond, Claude, 'Zur Geschichte der Glaslinsen' ('On the History of Glass Lenses'), in *Beiträge zur Augenheilkunde: Festschrift (für) Julius Hirschberg von Schülern und Freunden* (*Contributions to Ophthalmology: A Festschrift for Julius Hirschberg from His Pupils and Friends*), Leipzig, 1905, pp. 103–5.
31. *Bulletin de Correspondance Hellénique*, Athens, 1877, Vol. I, p. 264.
32. Anagnostakis, Andreas, *Meletai peri tēs Optikēs tōn Archaiōn* (*Studies Concerning the Optics of the Ancients*), Athens, 1878.
33. Hirschberg, Joseph, *Geschichte der Augenheilkunde im Alterthum* (*History of Ophthalmology in Antiquity*), in *Gräfe-Saemisch Handbuch der Gesamten Augenheilkunde* (*Gräfe-Saemisch Handbook of Complete Ophthalmology*), Leipzig, 1899, Vol. XII, Part 2, *Pathologie und Therapie* (*Pathology and Therapy*), pp. 174–80.

Appendix Three

Two Essays by Gotthold Ephraim Lessing Relating to Ancient Optics

Translated from the German by Robert Temple

From *Briefe, Antiquarischen Inhalts* (*Antiquarian Letters*) by Gotthold Ephraim Lessing, original publication: Berlin, 1769

THE 25TH ANTIQUARIAN LETTER

But what do I say to the many engraved emeralds which are found in cabinets?

That they are not true emeralds; that they are stones of an inferior kind which to the ancients more or less approximated emeralds. Most of them are probably what the Italians call Plasma of Emerald. Plasma of Emerald, says Herr [Johann Joachim] Winckelmann,[1] is the matrix or outermost rind of the emerald. I will not contest the matter with him here; but I beg to make an etymological footnote on this word 'plasma'. One would be mistaken to take this for the Greek word *plasma*. It is nothing else than the mildly mispronounced 'prasma'; for Zanetti[2] and others always write 'prasma of emerald' instead of 'plasma of emerald'; and Herr [Philipp Daniel] Lippert groundlessly makes 'plasma' and 'prasma' into two different stones.[3] It is also quite false to hold that the Italians understood by 'plasma' a greyish speckled chert. Neither chert nor greyish and speckled! Perhaps it is the case that this is merely a textual error in Herr Lippert and instead we should read 'greyish/greenish'. What he calls 'plasma' must then be the stone which elsewhere he calls 'prasma' and in a third place 'pras'.[4] In brief, 'plasma', 'prasma', and 'pras' are all the same.

But what of it? All three are nothing other than *Prasius*, or the *gemma prasina* of the ancients. In *prasina* the dot over the 'i' was lost, and 'in' read as 'm', and thus arose 'prasma' or 'plasma', which we Germans now shorten to 'pras', after the archaic 'präsem'[5] which has fallen into disuse.

The Greeks and Romans appear to have conceived of all gems of an impure green colour under the name of *prasius* or *prasites*, where the word signifies nothing more than such a colour. But then amongst these there must necessarily be some which approach nearer to the beautiful green of the emerald: and to these the modern gem connoisseurs have given the fabricated name 'prasma of emerald', or 'emerald-*präsem*', which in Latin must then become *smaragdoprasius*, and should in no way have been translated *prasma smaragdinea*, as by Gori.[6] For that would be a corruption of the authorized ignorance, and would ravage the appellation of a superfluous convention.

The ancients knew so many kinds of 'pras', or *gemmis viridantibus*, which each had their particular names! The ancient cut stones which we call emeralds were certainly rather one or the other of these instead of true emeralds. For whereas Pliny has explicitly stated that true emeralds were never engraved, we not only can but we must believe him. [*Translator's note:* This point was mentioned in the preceding, 24th Antiquarian Letter. There, the Pliny reference is given as *Natural History*, 37, 16; Professor D.E. Eichholz tells me he translates this as emeralds were forbidden to be *engraved*, not forbidden to be *cut*.] How could Pliny possibly have had such a notion enter his head, if it were not true? Should he have left to us false information to which every day would have brought before his eyes the refutation?

I find one further circumstance with him which goes to confirm what I have just said. It is namely that emeralds [*smaragdi*] were mostly cut concave:[7] *iidem plerumque et concavi, ut visum colligant*, a shape which is extremely awkward to cut. – I deal in a separate Letter [the 45th, which is also translated for this Appendix] with this question of the concave or convex shapes of ancient gems, where it will be shown that the opinion of Salmasius,[8] that the prohibition against engraving emeralds was confined only to those cut concave, can have no place.

THE 45TH ANTIQUARIAN LETTER

But this same [Francesco] Vettori [mentioned in the preceding, 44th Letter] has found in the passage of Pliny just mentioned something entirely separate. Traces of the magnifying glass.

For there he concerns himself with various ancient engraved gems of such extraordinary minuteness, that one can scarce conceive of how they could have been engraved by the naked eye alone, for by no means would one have been able to distinguish any of it:[9] so he believes that one can hardly be allowed to think that such stones could have been worked by the naked eye. [Domenico Maria] Manni had already judged [in *Degli Occhiali da Naso Trattato Istorico*, Firenze (Florence), 1738] that it could not be absolutely denied that the ancients possessed magnifying glasses or something similar; he especially referred to the glass globes filled with water which are mentioned by Seneca, and [Francesco] Vettori believed that this idea could be still further confirmed by what Pliny says about the emerald: *iidem plerumque et concavi, ut visum colligant* [translation: 'The same stones (*smaragdi*, or emeralds) are generally concave (in shape) so that they collect (or gather together) the vision.' – taking *conligant* as in the Loeb edition instead of *colligant*]. '*Igitur*,' says he [Vettori], '*si concavi plerumque erant apud veteres Smaragdi, ut facile visum colligere possent, sane non nisi arte optica illam cavitatem induissent, quam artem ideo perfecte scivisse praesumendum videtur. Et Neronis Smaragdum, quo ludos gladiatorios spectare consuervant, pari argumento, concavum fuisse, licet arguere.*' [Translation: 'Therefore if emeralds were, for the ancients, mostly concave, so that they could focus the rays, certainly they could not have endowed them with that concavity without the science of optics, which science it seems they can be presumed to have known perfectly. And it is reasonable to argue that the emerald of Nero, with which he used to watch the gladiatorial games, on the same principle was concave.']

But Vettori must have understood little of science, for he believed that the ancients practised this so perfectly. Otherwise he would certainly have known that through a concave lens things appear smaller and not larger; and that the whole advantage provided by concave glasses is only for short-sighted eyes, by refracting the light rays in a suitable manner. But this type of refraction, if it were true that the ancients knew of it, would not exactly be expressed by the words *visum colligere*; but *visum colligere* would rather be what one would say for the refraction of light rays through convex glasses. For, the presbyope [a person who has become far-sighted in middle age, a condition known as presbyopia], who makes use of convex glasses, uses them only therefore to increase the refraction of those rays which in his eyes are too greatly diverging. And this refracting or collecting together into the appropriate place we might rather describe truly as *visum colligere*. As for the myope [a person suffering from myopia, or short-sightedness], on the other hand, who has recourse to concave glasses, he therefore uses them only because the rays converge too soon in his eyes and accordingly he needs to disperse them to compensate so that they will be made to come together a bit later at the correct point. This is really the opposite function and can hardly be called *visum colligere*.

However, it is quite obvious that the ancients can have known nothing of this, and the words of Pliny must be understood as referring not to refracted, but to reflected, rays. They must be explained by catoptrics [the science of mirrors], not by dioptrics [the science of lenses]. In the former, we are instructed that rays reflected by a concave surface converge, so that necessarily the concave mirror must emit the stronger light. And this intensification of the light, and consequently also of the colour, is that which Pliny meant by *visum colligere*, and was why he said that emeralds were usually cut concave.

The emerald of Nero proves nothing. Nero can have used an emerald through which to view the gladiatorial contests, but the emerald may have been cut neither concave nor convex. For Pliny says also that there were emeralds which were entirely flat, and this may have been such a flat emerald, which Nero used as a *'Conservativglass'* [this old German word used by Lessing refers to what we nowadays call sunglasses] principally for its green colour as being beneficial to the eyes. One need but consider the words of Pliny which follow the others, and one could not agree that this is the most natural explanation:

> *Iidem plerumque et contur, ut visam colligant. Quamquam Scythicorum Aegyptiorumque duritia tanta est, ut nequeant vulnerari. Quorum vero corpus extensum est, eadem, qua specula, ratione supini imagines rerum reddunt. Nero princeps gladiatorum pugnans spectabat smaragdo.*

[The above Latin text from Pliny's *Natural History*, xxxvii, 64, is now considered to be erroneous. The text as given in the modern Loeb edition from a better manuscript reads: *'Iidem plerumque concavi, ut visum conligant.'* – Then there is an entire sentence, omitted by or unknown to Lessing, about it being forbidden at Rome to engrave emeralds. – The text then continues, as amended: *'Quamquam Scythicorum Aegyptiorumque duritia tanta est ut non queant volnerari. Quorum vero corpus extentum est, eadem qua specula ratione supini rerum imagines reddunt. Nero princeps gladiatorum pugnans spectabat in smaragdo.'*
Professor D. E. Eichholz has given me a revised private translation of the first sentence above: 'The same stones [*smaragdi*, or emeralds] are generally concave (in shape) so that they collect (or gather together) the vision.' Eichholz has abandoned his published translation of 'concentrate the vision' after thought and discussion. The next sentence of the above passage, in Eichholz's published Loeb translation, is: 'In any case, those of Scythia and Egypt are so hard as to be unaffected by blows.' This is a reference to the engraving of emeralds from those sources being difficult or perhaps even impossible. Eichholz's revised private translation of the rest of the passage is: 'However the stones whose body is stretched out, when (laid) on their backs (*supini*) in the same way as mirrors, do give back the images of things. The Emperor Nero used to look at the fights of gladiators in a *smaragdus*.' Note that this revised translation is quite different from Eichholz's published translation, where, for instance, he gratuitously added the word 'reflecting' (which is not in the Latin) at the end to describe the *smaragdus*, in an attempt, as he told me, to be 'helpful' to his readers. As for Lessing's comments on this passage from Pliny, it is clear that his text was so corrupt, that many of his comments no longer have any relevance. However, we continue with the translation of what Lessing did say:]
If this emerald necessarily must have belonged to one of the aforementioned categories, would one not far sooner have counted it as *quorum corpus extensum est* rather than as the *concavis*? Still, Pliny certainly had not intended to mean either one or the other, if the emerald had in fact been used as a mirror. For a flat emerald which is used as a mirror cannot

possibly at the same time be seen through.

But suppose that it really had had a convex surface, this emerald of Nero; suppose that Nero really had used it as a convex eye-glass, that Nero had clearly seen through it, as with the naked eye, without knowing how or why – also imagining to himself that the clearness of vision must be imputed solely to the material of the stone; supposing all this, I say, nevertheless from another angle I can prove the opposite to the conjecture of Vettori. The emerald of Nero can absolutely not be concave – it must have been ground convex – for, in a word, Nero was presbyopic [long-sighted]. Suetonius describes him to us as *oculis caesiis et hebetioribus*[10] ['his eyes grey and dull'], and Pliny even says explicitly: *Neroni, nisi cum conniveret ad prope admota (oculi) hebetes.*[11] [Translation: 'Nero's eyes were dull of sight except when he screwed them up to look at objects brought close to them.' [Loeb Library edition of Pliny, Vol. 3, p. 523, translation by H. Rackham.]

It would hardly occur to me in such matters to refute so pure an antiquary as Vettori, had I not found that Herr [Philipp Daniel] Lippert had already trodden the same path. Herr Lippert also dares to believe himself permitted to interpret the magnifying glasses of the ancients; and, it is true, from the likelihood of the same grounds as urged by Vettori, only he has developed them somewhat more exactly.

He writes:[12]

There is a footnote which deserves a place here, regarding the extraordinarily subtle work of the ancient gem cutters. Such fine work required more than a sharp eye. The eyes of the ancients weren't any sharper than ours. We must suppose that they afforded their eyes the assistance of magnifying glasses and spectacles, just as our artists do today to achieve their keenest sight. But for these to be fabricated appertains to dioptrics [the science of lenses].

But that dioptrics had been arrived at by the ancients I cannot discover, although it is but a modest surmise. I well realize that Euclid, three hundred years before the birth of Christ, taught mathematics and also optics, and that afterwards Abazen [this must be a misprint for Alhazen] and Vitellio took their laws of optics from him. But that dioptrics specifically was taught I have nowhere found. So much could be the case: namely, that it was included as a part of optics, because we imposed the name *Anaclastica* [dioptrics] upon a science which is to be added to optics, which it presumably would have been. For we have many ancient round ground stones, as Euclid and the other ancients must have realized over the course of more than three thousand years. For one very often finds writing on the stones which is without question specifically in the form of ancient letters, and which are of far greater antiquity than the time of Euclid. Therefore I hold that it is entirely possible that magnifying glasses were very early, and the ancients might have come across them by mere fortuitous chance. A single drop of water which had casually fallen on a small grain would easily have given the occasion for this, without the need for us to conceive that it derived from the articulated laws of dioptric science. For many ancient stones are entirely round or shaped like a tortoise shell or shield ground like microscope lenses; also, the ancients frequently used rock crystal and other stones, particularly beryl, which were every bit as pure and transparent as crystal. It required only a piece of crystal to have been cut in such a lens-like form to discover the magnifying glass. And one knows that Nero used a cut emerald, through which he used to look, when he went to the theatre, for which see [Andreas] Baccius, *De Gemm. Natur.* [*De Gemmarum Natura*], p. 49.[13]

This a fleeting reader would consider sufficient. But consider the following footnotes as far as they may be allowed to hold good for the enquirer.

1. From Pliny I have proved that Nero was presbyopic. When he observed distant objects through his emerald (Herr Lippert says the spectators of the spectacle; Pliny says the spectacle itself), nothing happened to improve the defects of his eyes, but merely when he strained his eyes he was able to soothe the eye-strain itself by holding up before his eyes the agreeable green of the stone. The surface of the emerald did not need to be convex, because he didn't wish to see near objects as if their rays had come from afar; nor could it be concave because then the distant objects at which he looked would have become just as indistinct as the near ones were to his unaided eyes. But the surface must have been flat, and the light rays have passed through at the same angle at which they were incident. As a flat transparent object, therefore, the emerald of Nero had nothing to do with spectacle lenses, except insofar as one would use simple tinted sunglasses which did not in any way sharpen the sight, and indeed that is the account which is given. I find, as does Baccius [i.e. Andrea Bacci] whom Herr Lippert cites, that Pliny had not meant anything else. He [Baccius] writes:

'*Smaragdus Neronis quoque gemma appellatur, quem gladiatorum pugnas Smaragdo, tanquam speculo, spectasse ajunt: et mea quidem sententia, ut ejus aspectu oculorum recrearet aciem, qua ratione nos quoque crystallo, vitrisque viridibus, cum fructu utimur.*' [Translation: 'Another gem is the so-called Emerald of Nero, with which they say he used to watch the fights of gladiators as though in a mirror. And my opinion is that by this use of it he thus reinforced the sharpness of his eyes, for which reason we too now usefully employ crystal and green glass.']

And Herr Lippert dares so little to give the meaning of Baccius as not to have quoted him or the facts themselves. Only, Baccius must have omitted the words *tanquam speculo* ['as though in a mirror']. They strongly contradict the idea of seeing *through*; and Pliny also, as I have already observed, does not say that the use to which Nero put the emerald had been the same as customarily making use of the same stone as a mirror. He mentions these double uses only as being similar to one another; but it could not possibly have occurred to him to explain the one by means of the other. If Baccius had realized that Nero had seen through his emerald, then he could not possibly have said that this had occurred *tanquam speculo* ['as though in a mirror']. He wished however to assume that Nero had *made use of* his emerald *tanquam speculo*; therefore these words must be omitted, for he had thought the stone either entirely opaque or at least reflective on the back side.

2. It would be of small consequence if the ancients had taught their dioptric principles along with their optics, whether under one name or another, considering that in general one could only be conceding them the same thing. And yet still Herr Lippert falsely informs us that they had a separate science under the name of anaclastics [i.e. dioptrics]. Unless I am mistaken, this term *anaclastica*, as even the term *dioptric*, is a late term; at least it is certain that even by the time of Proclus [a Neoplatonic philosopher] in the fifth century AD, no science was known under either the former name or the latter one. The ancients doubtless knew that if light rays passed through media of different thicknesses they underwent an ανακλασιν [*anaklasin*] (refraction). But by what laws this refraction took place – of that they knew nothing. They accounted in general for this refraction – relatively such few phenomena of light-rays passing through various natural media; but they had not carried out actual experiments with their purposely-shaped objects of glass, and it remained a deep mystery to them how these shaped glass objects put it in our power to bring about refraction by means of the differently shaped surfaces.

3. Still Herr Lippert himself finally gives up the theoretical knowledge of the ancients on this, and only believes that they could have had magnifying glasses, without their having been manufactured according to the laws of dioptrics. This is true: in later times, spectacles were used as early as the 1300s, before anybody could clearly explain their principles or remedy this ignorance.[14] But the mere possibility proves nothing; and even the ease with which this possibility could at any moment become verified means nothing. The easiest discoveries need not have been the earliest. After all, this ease might not actually be so great as Herr Lippert makes out. The stones which the ancients cut most frequently were rarely transparent; and if the purest rock crystal had been cut approximately in the shape of a lens it still need not mean that one had discovered a magnifying glass. For an approximately lens-shaped piece of crystal would still only be an approximately lens-shaped piece of crystal, and the shape of an underlying figure would, it is true, be magnified, but would also be distorted. What would he know who observed a magnifying glass and hoped to use it for particular purposes if he were still so far removed from any idea as to what gave rise to the distortion and lessened precision of the image by the spherical surface?

4. Finally, what in general were these fortuitously ground lens-shaped crystals for? For one does not know that the ancients actually had magni-

fying glasses or came any nearer to them than such crystals. The following passages in [Robert] Smith's *Optics* have somewhat surprised me:[15]

> Since the ancients knew the principles of globes for burning, one wonders whether one might find some trace from them that they knew the principles also of magnification by them. Should they have seen nothing through a globe? Herr [Gabriel-Philippe] de la Hire clarifies this. The focal distance of a glass sphere is the fourth part of the diameter computed from the nearest (point of the) surface. If the ancients had had such a sphere of 6 inches (diameter) – and larger than that we dare not assume – it would result in their being able to see clearly if it were one and a half inches away. But it would be more natural that they should have seen things through it which were further away, which would have appeared quite unclear to them. In order to see more distant objects clearly requires either a much larger sphere than could be fashioned, or a section of a great sphere, which we employ with profit at the present time. The ancients presumably did not know how to grind glass; they could only blow it into spheres. [Note by translator: this of course is untrue, as many specimens of ground glass from antiquity have by now been found, and I have examined a large number of them.]
>
> I don't believe that this clarification by de la Hire can be considered very satisfactory, even if the things he seeks to clarify were to be true. If the ancients, through their spheres of 6 inches, looked at distant things, must they have been obliged not to see nearer things? And how easily could they not find exactly an object in the distance which the focal distance of the sphere requires? Truly, it would be quite inconceivable if such a sphere had never even by chance been placed, never by chance been carried or held, so that the eyes had never even by chance seen an object through it where it could, within the limitations of the sphere's diameter, be magnified. It would be inconceivable, I say: but in any case, it is not necessary for us to have to believe this inconceivable thing. For the prerequisite itself is false, and there are indeed traces to demonstrate that the ancients understood the magnifying principles of the glass globe so well as to use them for burning. – What traces! – The explicit testimony of Seneca:[16]
>
> 'Litterae quamvis minutae et obscurae, per vitream pilam aqua plenam majores clarioresque cernuntur.'
>
> [Translation: 'Letters, however tiny and obscure, are seen larger and clearer through a glass ball filled with water.']

This, in my opinion, is much more than just a trace; and it is just a pity that it remained unknown to both Smith and de la Hire. It is true that Petrarch, with regard to this passage of Seneca, had without doubt assigned to the ancients the amplification of vision by this medium: still, I believe it was first explicitly brought out by the modern author [Domenico Maria] Manni, in his treatise on the invention of spectacles, which first appeared in 1738 after de la Hire and Smith had already written.[17] [The casual reference to Petrarch by Lessing is inspired by Manni's book, which on page 29 quotes the above passage of Seneca and then quotes Francesco Petrarch, *De Remediis Utriusque Fortunae ('On the Remedies of Both Fortunes')*, Book II, Chapter 83: '*Visum languidum Ocularibus refovet; qua in re maioribus vestris acutius cogitastis, qui vasculis vitreis aqua plenis (ut Seneca meminit) utebantur, prope delectabilis naturae ludus.*' The translation of this is: 'He restores the failing sight with eyeglasses (*ocularibus*), in which matter you may think it more effective than your ancestors who used to employ glass receptacles filled with water, as Seneca recalls. Practically speaking, a delightful trick of nature.']

But Manni believes that notwithstanding the ancients having had the magnifying globe, which to us would seem more or less the same thing and only a short step from the similar magnifying lens, this was nevertheless a step which they did not take. I might well accept, with de la Hire, that they did not know how to grind glass. I well realize that he means not grinding in general, but grinding a curved surface in a definite arc. However, if this were really unknown to them, how did it come about that they were able straightaway to cast glass in the very same curved form and afterwards to grind it perfectly smooth by hand? Most certainly, if they had made even the smallest surmise, they would have arrived at the facts about convex surfaces. And here, I think, we find the explanation to the whole mystery. For all those many centuries, they didn't progress from water-filled glass globes to magnifying glasses because they believed that the magnification arose not by means of the convexity of the glass but because of the water. That this was the universally accepted belief of the ancients is certain; and to me the preceding words of the recently quoted passage of Seneca prove it:

Omnia per aquam videntibus longe esse majora.
    [Translation: 'Everything is much larger when you look at it through water.' – Seneca, *Natural Questions*, I, 6, 5.]
    [Translator's note: Lessing is wrong here, since we now know that they had so many lenses which contained no water but were merely crystal or glass.]

But shouldn't we think in this case that they specially would have connected the cause of the magnification ascribed to the water, since it was in a hollow convex globe, equally to convex surfaces? No. They simply didn't think of convex surfaces at all. They thought only of a constant slipperiness of the water by means of which the inconstant gaze would thus slip, so – what do I offer as to how and by what means? In a word, this slipperiness was nothing other than a *qualitas occulta* [occult quality], which enabled them to explain the whole phenomenon as one thing. – And

it seems to me that it is almost always the case that when we see the
ancients coming close to a truth or an invention, we must however deny it
to them. They just didn't take the last step to their objective. For the last
step is the hardest. Or because it is directly arranged by Providence that
certain insights should not be discovered before their appointed time. Also,
they did not attain these things because they stood, so to speak, with their
backs towards their objective, and their prejudices seduced them so that
they viewed each objective from an entirely false perspective. Day was
breaking for them, but they besought the rising sun at eventide.

5. Was the glass globe of Seneca, through which one could see such
small and indecipherable letters clearly and enlarged, unique? Why did
others not have them to assist them to distinguish objects difficult by their
minuteness? – Du Cange [Charles Seigneur du Cange du Fresne, the
Byzantine historian and compiler of Greek and Latin dictionaries] commu-
nicates to Ménage [Gilles Ménage, 1613–92, a renowned French classicist]
a passage in a still unpublished poem of Ptochoprodomus, who lived about
1150 [Theodore Prodromus, Byzantine poet and man of letters; died
1166][18] where he refers to the doctors of the [Byzantine] Emperor
Emmanuel [Manuel] Comnenus:

Erkontai, blepousin euthys, kratousi ton sphyg mon tou. Thorousi kai ta
skybala meta tou hyeliou.

[Translation: 'They come, observe him rigid, feel his pulse, and
examine his excrement with a glass.']

[Note: 'with a glass' is *meta tou hyeliou*; this word *hyalos* has an
optical signification extending back millennia before Prodromus, and is
of Egyptian origin, as first noted by Jablonski. I have discussed the
etymology and usage of this word in the main text.]

Ménage was at first not undisposed to understand by this 'glass' a reference
to spectacles, or otherwise a magnifying glass; but in the end he took it as
evident that it meant simply a glass which lay over the vessel in which the
excrement was, for confining the foul smell. Molineux [William Molyneux,
author of *Dioptrica Nova* (1692)] and Smith [Robert Smith, author of *A
Compleat System of Opticks* (1738), mentioned previously] support this
interpretation, and the last with the addition that the passage might really
be best explained by being actually a reference to the inspection of the
urine. Manni himself even said:[19]

As a matter of fact, this is the true sense, as even in our own days one
often finds this in several localities, or one must explain the glass as a
kind of *lente* ['lens' in Italian, which was the language in which Manni
originally wrote; it would appear that the term was left to stand in Italian
in the German translation used by Lessing]; however, I doubt that the
ancients had that type of glass.

But if Manni had more than merely doubted this – if he had been fully convinced that the ancients had absolutely not had such glasses: does the former (i.e. that the glass was a covering over the excrement) necessarily then follow? The ancients had no lens-shaped ground magnifying glasses [translator's note: we obviously now know this to be untrue]; but does it necessarily follow that the glass with which the doctors inspected the excrement was really 'more to protect the nose than to aid the eyes'? A doctor, I should have thought, should not have been so disgusted, and if he could learn something from the closer examination of the excrement, he would sooner have held his nose than allow the closeness of his examination to be sacrificed. The *meta tou heliou* [he here errs, by giving *hyeliou* as *heliou*] also says something more (i.e. than merely looking through a glass covering). And why could we not even understand by it the glass globe of Seneca, which Manni himself knew so well? It surprises me that such a natural thought did not occur to Manni. But it would without doubt have occurred to him if he had known or recalled that such glass globes had been used routinely by ancient doctors for their closer inspections. Pliny says:[20]

> *Invenio Medicos, quae sunt urenda corporum, non aliter utilius id fieri putare, quam crystallina pila adversis posita solis radius.*
>
> [Translation: 'I find that amongst doctors it is thought that parts of the body which have to be cauterized by burning are not otherwise burnt more beneficially than by means of a crystal ball placed in the path of the facing rays of the sun.' – this is the private translation done for me by Professor D. E. Eichholz, which is otherwise unpublished.]

Here Pliny speaks of crystal balls; in another place is likewise mention of a glass globe filled with water. [Lessing does not give this reference or cite the passage, but it is to be found in *Natural History*, Book 36, Section 67: '*Addita aqua vitreae pilae sole adverso in tantum excandescunt, ut vestes exurant.*' The private translation of this passage done for me by Professor D. E. Eichholz is: 'When water has been added, glass balls facing the sun begin to radiate to such an extent that they burn clothes.'] These would have been either of crystal or glass, with or without water: enough that the aforesaid transparent globes, which burned, must also necessarily have magnified, and it is difficult to conceive of how anyone could use them for long for the one purpose without the other becoming obvious. – One circumstance however might strike one with relation to this. That is, namely: if the globe with which the doctor burnt, and through which necessarily things must also be magnified, were not glass, were not hollow, were not filled with water, but were crystal through and through: then the indirect reasoning that the ancients – according to my interpretation – omitted the discovery of true magnifying glasses because they believed the magnification to be an intrinsic characteristic of the water itself, must be quite false. And what then prevented the ancients from realizing the truth which was thus so impossibly much more clear than ever? With regard to this, one can answer: the evidence of Pliny is later than the evidence of Seneca; at the time of Seneca, people burnt and magnified still only through glass globes filled with water; by the time of Pliny, people knew that it was possible to do both also through solid crystal spheres. And that was precisely the step which had been taken in the knowledge of the ancients at this period of time. Or one could even answer what Salmasius [Salmasius is the Latinized name of Claude Saumaise (1588–1653)][21] says on the occasion of another passage of Pliny:

Vitrum pro crystallo accepit Plinius; to krystallophanes anti tes krystallou.
[Translation of this strange half Latin, half Greek passage: 'Pliny takes glass for crystal; i.e. mock-crystal instead of crystal.']

The sphere of which he has read that the doctors made use for cauterization by burning was not of true rock crystal (quartz) but of crystal-glass; it was the same sphere of which Pliny had written elsewhere, and also the same sphere which magnified for Seneca. Also in general it was usual for writers at that time to call all bodies *in candido translucentes* (used for purposes of translucent clarity) [for *candidas* see Pliny, *Natural History*, Book 37, Section 61] by the name of crystal, whether actually of pure glass or really of the precious colourless stone. Still, why only such a half-satisfactory answer? The full answer, I do believe, is this: if the burning-sphere of Pliny were actually of real crystal, who says that it had to be of solid crystal? Crystal can be ground hollow, and the ancients understood how to grind it hollow. What would therefore prevent a true crystal sphere, by means of which the ancients burned and magnified, having been also filled with water? Nothing prevents it. On the contrary, it is found, by the very same reason that we must believe the glass globes were filled with water, equally that the spheres of crystal must also have been. They filled the glass globes with water because they imagined that without the resultant cooling of the water, the glass could not bear the necessary heating by means of the rays of the Sun – that without water it must burst. Pliny says as much explicitly:

Est autem caloris impatiens (vitrum), ni praecedat frigidus liquor: cum addita aqua vitreae pilae solae adverso in tantum excandescant, ut vestes exurant.
[Revised translation by Professor Eichholz: 'It cannot bear heat unless cold fluid goes first, although when water has been added, glass balls facing the sun begin to radiate to such an extent that they burn clothes.' *Natural History*, Chapter 36, Section 67. Professor Eichholz pointed out to me that the above passage was presented as a paradox.]

Therefore, however, they also believed of true crystal that it could so little bear heat and that it was essential to believe this by virtue of the strange idea they held of the origin of crystal.[22] Consequently a similar apprehension gave rise to a similar precaution: if you fill glass burning-globes with water, you must also fill crystal ones with water.

6. And now, to come back to Herr Lippert again: what does he really mean by his conjectures concerning the spectacles and magnifying-glasses of the ancients? Why does he propound these notions? Indeed, why does he propound them just at this point? Without doubt, he does so because he supposes it to be novel, or at least the gist of something novel, that he should take the transparent, convexly ground stones [of the ancients] to be lenses. But why at this juncture? At this point where the account is given of such marvellous close work by the ancient gem cutters? Does Herr Lippert genuinely believe that such work could be done easier and better by the use of magnifying glasses than by the naked eye? I have been told the contrary, and eminent artisans in close work, of whom I know more than one, have assured me that a magnifying glass could not possibly be used for their work because it would magnify stone and hand and instrument all together. It is true that by means of a magnifying glass they could perceive in many instances of their work, if they looked through it after they had finished and wished to be certain, whether there were anything defective. But it would be ridiculous, however, when doing this close artistic work to have the pleasure of seeing it enlarged through a glass: for though one could see through the glass all the defects of one's work, the craftsman only has need to correct such defects as the unaided eye can detect. But in this connection, while it is all very well to have at hand the means to increase his ability to see, it is more important that he can feel what he is doing by touch than see what he is doing. As for the ancient gem engravers, for what reason would they have wished to use the glass magnifying-globe of Seneca or a transparent spherically ground stone? For as I understand it, the glass magnifying-globe could have been known at the time of Pliny without his ever mentioning it on the occasion of his multifarious references to micro-technical work, since on the contrary he precisely noted that the stone cutters especially made use of various means to maintain and strengthen the acuteness of their vision.[23] Other old writers mention still other such means which are still used in our own day, when the use of magnifying glasses has become so universal, unquestionably however so neglected that the question demands clarification as to whether the sense of sight of the ancients was superior to that of the moderns. We see more than the ancients; and yet perhaps our eyes are poorer than the eyes of the ancients: the ancients saw less than we; but their eyes, generally speaking, may have been a little sharper than ours. – I fear that the whole issue of the comparison between the ancients and the moderns arises here.

[Translator's note: we have seen in Plate 40 the ingenious crystal lens from ancient Troy with a hole in the middle to allow an engraving tool through while magnifying all around it. Also, the British lenses described in Appendix Eleven sometimes have what I have named 'resting-points' which enable engraving tools to be inserted beneath the lens. It seems worthwhile to remind the reader of this in the light of Lessing's comments above.]

Notes

1. [Johann Joachim Winckelmann] *Anmerkungen zu der Geschichte der R[ome?]*, p. 18.
2. *Dactyl.*, Zanetti, p. 17.
3. [Philipp Daniel Lippert, *Dactyliothec*] Dactyl. First Thousand, no. 178 and Second Thousand, no. 391.
4. *Ibid.*, First Thousand, no. 270.
5. Boethius, *De Boot ex Recens.*, Adriani Toll, p. 203.
6. *Dactyl*, Zanetti. l. c.
7. [Pliny, *Natural History*,] Book 37, Section 16.
8. *Ad Solinum*, p. 196.
9. [Francesco Vettori,] *Dissert. Glyptogr.*, p. 107. [i.e. *Dissertatio Glyptographice sive Gemmae Duae . . . Quae Exstant . . . in Museo Victorio*, 1739] – *Exstant in Museo Victorio gemmae aliquae ita parvulae, ut lenticulae granum illis duplo majus sit; et tamen in is vel semiexstantes figurae, vel incisae pariter spectantur: opere in area tam parvula sane admirando, quas oculo nudo, vix incisas esse judicaveris.* [Translation of the title of Vettori's book: *Dissertation on Inscriptions* ('*Glyptography*'), *i.e. of Two Gems Which Exist in the Museo Victorio.* Translation of the quotation: 'In the Victoria Museum there exist certain gems which are so small that a grain of lentil would be twice as large, and yet in them there are to be seen drawings which are either half-raised from the surface or engraved in it, worked in an area so small that it is certainly to be wondered at, and one would judge they could hardly have been cut with the naked eye.']
10. [Suetonius,] Chapter 51 of his Life of Nero.
11. [Pliny, *Natural History*.] Book XI, Section 54. Edit. Hard.
12. [Philipp Daniel Lippert, *Dactyliothec, Das Ist Sammlung Geschittenersteine der Alten . . .* (Translation of title: *Dactyliothec, That Is, A Collection of Cut Stones of the Ancients from the Most Principal Museums in Europe for the Use of the Fine Arts and of Artists, in Two Thousand Copies*), no place but possibly Leipzig, 1767.] Foreword, p. xxxv.
13. [Andreas Baccius is the Latinized name of the Italian author Andrea Bacci. The book concerned is *De Gemmis et Lapidus Pretiosis . . . Tractatus . . . Non Solum in Latinum Sermonem Conuersus Verum Etiam . . . Observationibus Auctior Redditus*, Frankfurt, 1603. The reference is to page 49, in Chapter Five *'De Smaragdo'* ('On the Emerald').]
14. See Kaestner, *Lehrbegriff der Optik* ('*System of Optics*'), p. 366. [The Kaestner in question is Abraham Gotthelf Kaestner. He was the German translator of Robert Smith (see next footnote), and Lessing is naughty in referring to Smith's work by Kaestner's name as this cost me much wasted time in searching for a book by Kaestner himself of that title, until I realized that Lessing was referring to: *Vollstaendiger Lehrbegriff der Optik* (*Complete System of Optics*), *nach Herrn Robert Smith's Englischen mit Aenderungen und Zusaetzen ausgearbeitet von Abraham Gotthelf Kaestner* (*prepared by Abraham Gotthelf Kaestner from the English of Mr Robert Smith, with corrections and additions*), Altenburg, 1755. On page 366 there is a mention of de la Hire, whom Lessing is shortly to cite himself.]
15. [Robert Smith, *A Compleat System of Optics*, 1738. Lessing cites page 381 of Kaestner's German translation of which no copy exists in Britain except in a photocopy in my possession; see previous footnote. Since Smith's work is so long, and it proved impossible to locate the passage in question in the original edition, I have had to retranslate it into English from Lessing's German quotation.]
16. [Seneca, *Naturales Quaestiones* (*'Natural Questions'*), Book I, Chapter 6, Section 5. This passage is found at pp. 57–9 of Vol. I of the Loeb Library translation by T. H. Corcoran, Harvard University Press, 1971.]

17. [Lessing does not give the reference, but it is as follows: Domenico Maria Manni, *Degli Occhiali da Naso Inventati da Salvino Armati Gentiluomo Fiorentino Trattato Istorico ('Historical Treatise on Spectacles Invented by Salvino Armati, Gentleman of Florence')*, Firenze (Florence), 1738, 84 pages with engravings; the British Library reference is 717.g.22.]

18. [Many of Prodromus's works are even now unpublished. To him are also attributed, as 'Ptochoprodromus' ('poor Prodromus'), a number of lively poems in the vernacular. But Lessing gives no hint as to which work of Prodromus is here quoted, nor does he give a reference for du Cange, despite the implication that the letter quoted is amongst some published correspondence of some kind. I could locate no published correspondence in Britain under the name of du Cange.]

19. From the German translation in the 7th Part ['Theil'] of the *Allegemeine Magazin*, p. 9. [From this note it is evident that Manni's work had been translated into German and published in instalments in the German periodical mentioned, no copy of which appears to be available for consultation in Britain.]

20. *Natural History*, Book 37, Section 10.

21. *Ad Solinum*, p. 1092, Edit. Paris. [The work referred to here is Salmasius's 1629 commentary on the *Polyhistor* of Solinus, which in turn was largely drawn from Pliny. Gaius Julius Solinus was a Latin grammarian and compiler of the early third century AD. *Polyhistor* is the title of the sixth-century revision of what had originally been entitled *Collectanea Rerum Memorabilium ('Collection of Remarkable Things')*. Salmasius's commentary on Solinus is actually entitled *Plinianae Exercitationes ('Plinian Exercises')*, and would normally today be consulted in the 1895 edition by Mommsen, though Lessing's reference is obviously to an earlier edition published at Paris.]

22. Pliny [*Natural History*], Book 35, Section 9: '*Cristallum glaciem esse certum est – ideo caloris impatiens nisi in frigido potui addicitur.*' [The Latin text given by Lessing is no longer accepted. In the Loeb edition, we find instead: '*e caelesti umore puraque nive id fieri necesse est; ideo caloris impatiens nisi in frigido potu abdicatur.*' Which, translated, is: 'The inevitable conclusion is that rock-crystal is formed of moisture from the sky falling as pure snow. For this reason, it cannot stand heat and is rejected except as a receptacle for cold drinks.']

23. [Pliny, *Natural History*,] Book 20, Section 51, and Book 37, Section 16. [The first reference says, in a discussion of the medical uses of herbs: '. . . engravers and painters use rue as food, with bread or cress, for the sake of their eyes; wild goats also, they say, eat it to improve their vision.' (trans. W. H. S. Jones). The second reference says: 'Indeed, even after straining our sight by looking at another object, we can restore it to its normal state by looking at a *smaragdus* [an emerald]; and engravers of gemstones find that this is the most agreeable means of refreshing their eyes: so soothing to their feeling of fatigue is the mellow green colour of the stone.' (trans. D. E. Eichholz). Both translations are from Loeb Library volumes of Pliny's *Natural History*, Harvard University Press. The first is Vol. 6 (1951), p. 79. The second is from Vol. 10 (1962), p. 213.]

Appendix Four

The Finnish Lenses

There are seven crystal lenses excavated so far in Finland. The following six, all grave finds, are in the National Archaeological Collections in Helsinki. A seventh (Object Number 84060:18), not a grave find, is deposited in the National Historical Collections outside Helsinki, and full details of it are not yet available, as its existence only became known to me when it was too late to inspect it.

1. *Object number*: 19000:11676.
   Provenance: From Mahittula Cemetery in Raisio, Finland.
   Description: BICONVEX, RIDGED CABOCHON, UNMOUNTED. The ridge is fairly sharply defined; it very clearly splits the image underneath. The quartz is very lustrous and clear despite a ghostly longitudinal flaw running the whole length of the major axis on one side and a transverse flaw at one end. There is a very curious facet cut smoothly on one longitudinal side along the rim as if the slight bulge had been shaved off to facilitate mounting; it is important to note that this was done long after the lens had received its chief use, for the surface of this facet is entirely free of any abrasion and merely has a series of vertical striations from the slicing, whereas the superior surfaces of the lens are heavily abraded (though with no ingrained dirt: the lens must have been washed after being excavated). On the opposite longitudinal side a much smaller shaving of a bulge has been made, with the same vertical striations. The rim has received very bad chipping and wear, and some of this chipping (but not any of the abrasion) occurred after the slicing of the facets. The history of the object thus seems to be: (a) unmounted or soft-mounted (in leather?) use as a lens, (b) mounting as either lens or gem, and finally (c) loss of the mounting before burial, as the object was excavated without any sign of an accompanying mounting.
   Condition: As described above. The ridge shows no signs of wear.
   Maximum thickness: 1.44 cm.
   Major axis: 3.09 cm.
   Minor axis: 1.68 cm.
   Magnification when resting horizontally on base: 1.5X either as seen directly or as seen through side at 45°; also 1.5X when resting on ridge vertically and viewing downwards. The lens runs very smoothly along a

line of print, obviating the need for spectacles in the moderately long-sighted (presbyopic) individual.

Magnification when raised: Ineffective.

Status: Excavated from a grave in the 1970s. Deposited in the National Archaeological Collections, Helsinki. Unpublished.

2. *Object number*: 10833:8.

Provenance: From Taskula Cemetery in Turku (formerly called Maaria), Finland.

Context: This and the next lens (Object 10833:9, from the same cemetery) are practically a matching pair.

Description: BICONVEX OVAL WITH SHARP RIDGE, MOUNTED. The silver mounting, with retaining-teeth but no back, is of Viking style (nine-beaded diamond shape on the large teeth, four-beaded on the small teeth for this object and Object 10833:9). This object has only two teeth and about 20 per cent of its mount left. What remains is extremely decayed and fragile. The base of the lens is only slightly convex, but the superior surface is greatly domed with a very pronounced ridge. The crystal appears to taper slightly towards the end with the remaining piece of mounting, but this effect is illusory, an impression enhanced by a bad chip on the rim.

Condition: There is a severe gouge/chip on the rim of the lens 50 mm long, effecting both base and superior surface. The quartz is very clear and lustrous with little abrasion and some slight chipping in the centre of the ridge. Some opacity to the base has occurred as the result of sticky glue used to exhibit the object on a square patch of plastic.

Maximum thickness: 1.83 cm.

Major axis (with half mount): 2.97 cm.

Minor axis (without mount): 2.12 cm.

Magnification when resting: Nearly 2X viewing through most directions, including downwards from above, through side at 45°, and 2X when resting on side.

Magnification when raised: When raised fractionally, the magnification goes to 2.5X before distortion is severe.

Status: Deposited in the National Archaeological Collections, Helsinki. Published by Kivikoski in 1939, in 1947, and in 1973.[1]

3. *Object number*: 10833:9.

Provenance: From Taskula Cemetery in Turku (formerly called Maaria), Finland.

Context: This and the previous object (Object 10833:8, from the same cemetery) are practically a matching pair.

Description: BICONVEX OVAL WITH SHARP RIDGE, MOUNTED. The silver mount is Viking style, and nearly 75 per cent of the mounting survives. The mounting has four unbroken teeth and one broken; the silver is in a very perilous condition. The Viking beading is as described for previous object (Object 10833:8). The base of the lens is only slightly convex, but the superior surface is greatly domed with a very pronounced ridge. There is no tapering or apparent tapering of the object.

Condition: The quartz is extremely clear and lustrous. There is a patch of sticky glue on the base from exhibition on a square of plastic. There is a very serious chip in the centre of the ridge, but the lens otherwise has very little wear or abrasion. The lens has quite a lot of glue on it used in modern times by conservators who have tried to stick the decaying mount tightly to the lens to preserve the mount.

Maximum thickness: 1.91 cm.

Major axis (with half mount): 2.81 cm.

Minor axis (mount both sides): 2.42 cm.

Magnification when resting: Nearly a twin of the above (Object 10833:8), but slightly better. Magnification when resting on base is fractionally better, being easily 2X; the retaining-teeth prevent viewing when resting on side.

Magnification when raised: When raised slightly with base upwards, magnification goes to 2.5X before severe distortion.

Status: Deposited in the National Archaeological Collections, Helsinki. Published by Kivikoski in 1939, in 1947, and in 1973.[2]

4. *Object number*: 8656.H8:1. [Note: the letter 'H' used in this and subsequent object numbers stands for *hauta*, the Finnish word for 'grave'.]

Provenance: From Humikkala Cemetery, Masku, Finland.

Description: OVAL, MOUNTED AND BACKED. This lens is either plano-convex or very slightly convex at the base – it is impossible to tell because of the backing. The superior surface of the lens is smoothly convex and has no ridge. The quartz is very clear and lustrous but has considerable flawing internally. The lens is set in an intact mediaeval silver mount, which is very crudely done.

Condition: The surface of the lens has some chipping but almost no abrasion.

Maximum thickness (with back): 1.18 cm.

Major axis (with mount): 3.21 cm.

Minor axis (with mount): 2.68 cm.

Magnification: Cannot be observed because of back. Probably between 1.5X and 2X if removed from crude mount and back. (This lens seems to have been set into its existing mount and back in phase two of its history.)

Status: Excavated from a male grave (Grave 8) together with an axe and a fire-steel. Deposited in the National Archaeological Collections, Helsinki. Published by Kivikoski in 1947, in 1964, and in 1973.[3]

5. *Object number*: 8656.H14:4.

Provenance: From Humikkala Cemetery, Masku, Finland.

Description: OVAL RIDGED BICONVEX lens extremely crudely

mounted in a decaying mediaeval soft silver mounting with partially lost very crude backing. The high quality of the polished lens contrasts grievously with the miserable mounting, which appears never to have had even rudimentary retaining-teeth. The lens appears upon superficial glance to be of distinctly yellowish quartz, but this is illusory, for upon close inspection, the lens can be seen to be perfectly clear; the yellowish colour emanates from the interior surface of the backing and appears to be gilding (the back and mount themselves are not gilded). Whoever mounted the crystal in the Middle Ages attempted by this device to make the crystal look like a topaz. The crystal would once have been clear and lustrous. It is still amply transparent in the portions where the back has fallen away. The stone has a very prominent ridge.

Condition: The lens is fairly smeared with modern glue to hold the mount together by sticking it firmly to the lens, but under that and in clear patches one can see that this stone is heavily abraded on its superior surfaces and along its very prominent ridge.

Maximum thickness (with thin back): 1.23 cm.

Major axis (with thick mount): 3.0 cm; *attempt to measure without mount*: 2.28 cm.

Minor axis (with thick mount): 2.24 cm; attempt to measure without mount: 1.62cm.

Magnification when resting on base: 1.75X, observed looking directly down and viewed through hole in the backing. The ridge doubles the image. Due to the backing no other viewing angle is possible.

Magnification when raised: 2X through hole in backing.

Status: Excavated from a female grave. Deposited in the National Archaeological Collections, Helsinki. Published by Kivikoski in 1947, in 1964, and in 1973.[4]

6. *Object number*: 8656.H.33:1.

Provenance: From Humikkala Cemetery, Masku, Finland.

Description: OVAL BICONVEX RIDGED CABOCHON. The base is nearly flat. The superior surface has a very prominent ridge, which doubles the image seen through the lens looking directly downwards. At the ends of the major axis, the ridge as it descends to the base bifurcates, indicating a rounding-off at either longitudinal end in the grinding process; this clue may be useful to an expert in crystal polishing for interpretation of techniques and tools used. This lens was formerly mounted and backed in mediaeval silver. Remains of this mounting were found with the lens, with the backing nearly gone. The silver mounting, which is in a terrible disintegrating condition, has entirely fallen away from the lens and is now preserved beside it but detached. The quartz is very clear and would originally have been lustrous.

Condition: Silver powder sticks to the base of this lens from the disintegrated backing, so that about a quarter of the base is rendered opaque by

the powder. The ridge and superior surfaces show signs of significant wear.
  Maximum thickness (without back): 1.35 cm.
  Major axis: 3.01 cm.
  Minor axis: 2.17 cm.
  Magnification resting on base: 1.5X viewing downwards at 45°.
  Magnification when raised: 2X.
  Status: Excavated from a female grave. Deposited in the National Archaeological Collections, Helsinki. Published by Kivikoski in 1947, in 1964, and in 1973.[5]

The following lens was not examined because it was not in Helsinki and could not be fetched before my departure from Finland:

7. *Object number*: 84060:18.
  Provenance: Church of Lempäälä, Finland.
  Description: ROUND, BICONVEX, MOUNTED in silver as a pendant with suspension-loop, with four large and four small retaining-teeth on the superior surface. The mounting is typical Viking style with granulated beading; the suspension-loop bears a Maltese Cross design made of four triangles each of ten beads pointing inwards, another typical motif for these Viking period objects. The object is essentially identical with the similar objects from Gotland in Sweden, but is rather small.
  Condition: The quartz is clear. No information is available concerning abrasion or chipping.
  Maximum thickness: 11 mm.
  Diameter (with mounting): A diameter of 37 mm has been published by Hiekkanen; although the diameters of all of these objects vary between certain maxima and minima, the published diameter may be taken as a mean.
  Magnification: 4X as published by Hiekkanen must be the magnification when raised; he has not recorded the magnification when resting.
  Status: Excavated in 1983 during repair and restoration of the church, approximately two metres west of the choir in the centre of the cross-arms. Deposited in the National Historical Collections. Published by Markus Hiekkanen in 1986.[6]

Ella Kivikoski made a few comments about the lenses which she published, although she altered her views somewhat as the years passed. In her earliest publication which mentioned them in 1939, she stressed that the two Taskula lenses 'display a single manufacture', thereby acknowledging the fact that they were nearly identical. She then says: 'Crystals in the Viking Period were used in Middle Europe for various church objects, but also frequently occur as pendants or other jewellery. Which use applied to the examples from Taskula is difficult to determine, for the mountings, as we said, are broken to bits. Of the examples from Masku, two are evidently broken off from some object, and may perhaps have been objects of booty.' In a footnote she refers to a crystal – 'a suspended ornament' (hence it must have been mounted with a suspension-loop, although she does not say so) from the District of Cesis in Latvia, deposited in the Riga Museum, V. 3356.[7]

In 1947 she says: 'Polished crystals in silver mountings, from Masku-Hummikala, evidently detached from a book, a reliquary, or church object. Crystals in the Viking Period were used in Middle Europe as ornamentation for many objects.'[8]

By 1973, she abandoned the suggestion of the crystals having once been mounted on a book. She says merely: 'From the details of ornament, these evidently were used for an article of church use, probably displayed as an amulet.'[9]

It is most unlikely that the two Taskula lenses were mounted on church objects, because their Viking-style mounts do not accord with such a practice. There are no known Swedish lenses for which evidence exists that they were mounted liturgically, even the mediaeval-mounted ones, and certainly not the Viking-mounted ones. Of all the Scandinavian and Baltic lenses, only some in Denmark are known to survive in liturgical settings, all of them mediaeval and none of them Viking, and these uses are in any case believed to have been secondary to their original purpose, and under the influence of more southerly cultures. Having examined the mountings of the Finnish lenses, I could find no evidence which could be interpreted as demonstrating any liturgical use. On the contrary, the Finnish mountings are of such remarkably poor quality that it is difficult to imagine a liturgical mounting being made either so crude or so weak. The speculations by Kivikoski that the lenses had been mounted liturgically rest on no actual evidence, and are merely her attempt to try and make some sense of the strange objects, of the possible optical nature of which she as yet had no inkling.

Notes

1. Kivikoski, Ella, *Die Eisenzeit im Auraflussgebiet* (in German), Vol. XLIII of *Suomen Muinaismuistoyhdistyksen Aikakauskirja Finska Fornminnesföreningens Tidskrift*, Helsinki, 1939, p. 171, and photo is Plate XLI, 1 and 2. Kivikosi, Ella, *Die Eisenzeit Finnlands: Bilderatlas und Text* (in German), Helsinki, Vol. I, 1947, p. 38, and revised edition, Helsinki, 1973, p. 142 (no photo).
2. *Ibid.*
3. Kivikoski, Ella, *Die Eisenzeit, op. cit.*, 1947, p. 38, and 1973, p. 142 (no photo). Kivikoski, Ella, *Finlands Förhistoria* (in Swedish), Almqvist & Wiksell, Stockholm, Göteborg, and Uppsala, 1964, p. 242 and Fig. 207 (a photo of the three lenses from Masku). This is a Swedish translation of a book which originally appeared in Finnish, *Suomen Esihistoria*, Helsinki, 1961.

4. *Ibid.*, and also *Die Eisenzeit*, 1947, Figure 1083, Plate 138, and *Die Eisenzeit*, 1973, Figure 1155, Plate 128.
5. *Ibid.*, and also *Die Eisenzeit*, 1947, Figure 1082, Plate 138, and *Die Eisenzeit*, 1973, Figure 1154, Plate 128.
6. Hiekkanen, Markus, 'Archaeology of the Medieval Stone Church of Lempäälä in Satakunta, Finland', in *Fennoscandia Archaeologica*, The Archaeological Society of Finland, Helsinki, Vol. III, 1986, pp. 91–101. Figures 7, 8, and 9 are of the pendant. Hiekkanen gives information about a similar Viking-era pendant found in 1938 in the Kostivere Hoard in Harju, Northern Estonia. His article contains considerable discussion of the Gotland lenses and related matters. Strangely, Hiekkanen is unaware of the existence of Object 19000:11676 (our Number One above) from Mahittula Cemetery in Raisio.
7. Kivikoski, 1939, *op. cit.*
8. Kivikoski, 1947, *op. cit.*
9. Kivikoski, 1973, *op. cit.*

Appendix Five

THE WOODWARD LENSES
(in Cambridge, England)

*Three rock crystal objects in the geological
collections of John Woodward, formerly at
the Fitzwilliam Museum, but since 1907 at
the Sedgwick Museum of Geology:
these are two lenses and one crystal ball
of early British provenance*

1. Object A. 7. 11. [Cabinet A, Drawer 7, Object number 11.]
BICONVEX, ROUND.
Maximum thickness: 1.81 cm. (0.8 cm. below rim).
Diameter: varies between 3.49 and 3.58 cm.
Condition: Crystal very clear with one ghostly flaw running through it
at an angle of 45° to the vertical. A chip in the centre of the superior surface
has dirt deeply ingrained, which makes the lens appear less than perfectly
transparent. The rim is very badly chipped (with deeply ingrained dirt),
indicating there may once have been a thin metal rim-mounting. The polish
is very fine indeed.
Magnification when resting: 1.5X resting on base; 2X when resting at an
angle of 45° on superior surface and viewing through base at an angle of
45°; this lens would have made a good reading-glass of 2X magnification
when run along the page in that manner.
Magnification when raised: 2X.
Comments: This lens would seem to be the top left object in the Martin
Lister engraving of five crystals accompanying his article 'An Account of
Certain Transparent Pebles [sic] . . ., *Philosophical Transactions*, London,
Number 201, June, 1693, pp. 773–80.

2. Object A. 7. 12. [Cabinet A, Drawer 7, Object number 12.] CRYSTAL
SPHERE; actually an oblate spheroid.
Description: There is a flattened patch to enable the crystal ball to rest
on a flat surface unaided. The sphere has one almost invisible ghostly

internal flaw. The sphere was originally extremely well polished and wholly transparent.

Condition: The sphere has suffered heavy abrasion, slight chipping, and extreme scratching and striation. These have caused the crystal to appear dark and greyish when resting on a surface. The illusion of opacity vanishes when the object is held and one views anything through it which is more than about a centimetre away.

Diameter: varies; the flattened patch can be taken to define a base, thus defining the horizontal diameters, which vary from 4.97 to 5.04 cm. The vertical diameter from the base is 4.76 cm. Diameters at 45° to these two axes vary between 4.94 and 5.05 cm.

Magnification: When good light is used (owing to its present condition), it may be seen that the resting sphere is an excellent magnifier of about 3X. If raised slightly, the magnification increases to 3.5X before spherical aberration becomes severe.

Comments: This globe would have made an excellent reading glass for a presbyope if run along the page on its basal patch. The apparent tendency to lose transparency is a result of the severe surface damage and would not have been an original feature. The sphere would also have been an excellent burning-globe, and the fact that it has a basal patch means it could have been left sitting in the sun for as long as necessary for ignition of a substance to take place beside it, without the need for anyone to hold it and wait.

3. Object A. 7. 13. [Cabinet A, Drawer 7, Object number 13.]

A PROMINENTLY-RIDGED CABOCHON.

Description: The crystal is clear and lustrous. The base is slightly convex, 5.25 dioptres in the longitudinal axis and 8 dioptres in the minor axis.

Maximum thickness: 3.79 cm.

Major axis: 5.02 cm.

Minor axis: 3.38 cm.

Condition: The base has almost no abrasion but has been severely scratched in the direction of the minor axis at one end only. The rim has been shaved slightly in places and has a few deep chips. There is a very slight, nearly invisible, ghostly flaw in the crystal at one end and three other nearly invisible flaw-planes can barely be discerned. The two superior surfaces are fairly heavily abraded, with pitting. The ridge has one chip but is otherwise lacking in damage or abrasion.

Magnification: When resting on its base, this lens gives a magnification of 1.5X viewed at 45° or of 2X if looking down directly from above. It doubles an image of sufficient size through the cabochon effect. On its base, and run along a page, the lens is an excellent reading aid for a moderate presbyope. However, if resting on a superior surface with view through the base at 45°, the lens reduces an image by 25%, as if it were a concave lens. On the other hand, if the rim is held against a surface, the lens gives a 2X magnification if viewed through the side.

Comments: This is the biggest and heaviest cabochon inspected to date (Nov. 4, 1997). To have abraded superior surfaces but a non-abraded ridge is very unusual and indicates that the abrasion of the surfaces came about through habitual use, indicating a pattern of wear whereby the ridge was not rubbed against a surface and neither was exposed as would be the case in, say, an ornamental mounting. This supports the notion that the lens was a reading aid.

Appendix Six

CRYSTAL BALLS FOR ROMAN LADIES

By Robert Temple

Carl August Böttinger, *Sabina: oder Morgenszenen im Putzzimmer einer Reichen Roemerin* [*Sabina: or, Morning Scenes in the Parlour of a Rich Roman Lady*] Leipzig, 1806.

Translated from the German by Robert Temple

Part II, pp. 185–7:

Then a female slave carried in on a beautifully woven dish two globes, one clear, of the purest, most transparent crystal, and one golden, of amber. These lay on an elegant potpourri-cushion, which was woven of the finest and most delicate threads, and covered with a net of the choicest rose leaves.[1] Sabina immediately chooses the crystal globe, but gestures towards the dish standing nearby, that the amber globe should also be taken. Both globes then serve as cooling-agents for the hands of the aristocratic ladies in turn.[2] In ancient times rock crystal, as indeed the etymology of the Greek word indicates, was universally believed to be a product of the most compacted frost, of ice which could never be broken.[3] Spheres were ground of this fossil, and the ladies took them in their hands with considerable gracefulness in order to cool themselves in the heat of the sun, on their walks and at public pageants, for which in those days ladies' hands were not jealously concealed in gloves. It didn't take long for these globes which could only be purchased for a vast sum to become a great luxury in such a hot climate,[4] as is the case in our winter regions for completely opposite reasons with fur muffs. Every Roman lady wanted to own such a cooling-globe, and as it would have been impossible to produce such quantities from the crystal mines of the Swiss Alps and India, the Alexandrian dealers in fancy goods therefore arranged to supply globes of 'crystal glass' from the glassworks of Egypt[5] which very closely resembled the globes of true crystal. Thus the ostentatious Roman ladies had to think of another contrivance owing to the scarcity of what they really desired; and so amber globes took the place of crystal ones. Also these afforded, although only briefly, an agreeable cooling, and if they became warmed-through, in place of their cooling offered a delightful odour.[6]

Nevetheless the ladies who were truly discerning retained their preference for the genuine crystal globes on account of their lasting coolness, and for that reason Sabina also now exhibited one, as it promised to be a warm day for today's spectacle.

Notes
1. [Omitted as not important]
2. Crystal globes. Propertius, II, xx8, 60. (118?), *manibus dura frigus habere pila*, with Burmann's *Anmerkungen [Observations]*, p. 577, and the chief source is from Pliny, 37, 2, 10–11 [note that this is in error, the 2 should be omitted]. Compare Beckmann's *Anmerkungen [Observations]* for *Marbodi liber lapidum* (Goettingen, 1799), p. 41, p. 71. . . . etc. etc.
3. [Omitted as not important]
4. Twenty such globes have been found at Rome in an alabaster urn, but they are not so much suggestive of this luxury of Roman matrons, as that which this find admirably illustrates, the superstition attaching to transparent crystal. See Brueckmann's *Beitraege zur Abhandlung von den Edelsteinen [Contributions to the Discussions concerning Precious Stones]*, Part II, p. 105.
5. Egypt was noted for its costly glassworks. A large quantity of references to these may be found in Caylus, *Recueil*, and Hamberger's *Historia Vitri, in Commentariis Goetting*, vol. 4, p. 132.
6. Amber globes. etc. etc.

Appendix Seven

RECOGNITION OF VIKING OPTICAL TECHNOLOGY IN 1904

Translated from the German by Robert Temple

From the Evening Edition, Number 390, August 20, 1904, of the *Koeniglich Privilegirte Berlinische Zeitung von Staatsund Gelehrten Sachen und Vossische Zeitung*, Berlin. [*Berlin Gazette, published under Royal Privilege*].

STOCKHOLM. 18 August. From our own Correspondent.

The visit to the Swedish capital by German anthropologists has resulted in the realization that an existing find in the possession of the local Historical Museum is a *magnifying-glass from Viking times*. As Professor Montelius exhibited to the German visitors the gold treasures and silver treasures of the late Iron Age, ornamented with marvellously fine filigree work, the German oculist von Foerster declared that the fastenings with their tiny metal beadings could not possibly have been produced by the unaided eye. This caused the scientific official of the Museum to get out an object which came from the Viking period finds made at Gotland. It is a well-polished, nearly hemispherical piece of rock crystal of 5 cm. diameter, slightly convex on the underside, which proves to be a very good lens producing approximately a double magnification. This old magnifying-glass was found in 1877 at Visby in association with two small bronze balances laid side by side with a money weight which in Viking times would have been used to weigh gold and silver for payment purposes.

Appendix Eight

THE KEY TEXT RELATING TO THE VIKING LENSES

Translated from the German by Robert Temple

Mårten Stenberger
Die Schatzfunde Gotlands der Wikingerzeit [*The Gotland Treasure Finds of the Viking Period*]
Vol. I (Text) was published at Stockholm in 1958, but Vol. II (Description of Finds and Plates) was published earlier, at Lund in 1947.

Vol. I, pp. 200–4:

Before bringing this chapter [he is referring to his own book] to a close, mention must be made of a magnificent pendant type, namely the rock crystal pendants. These have been found in three treasure-finds, of which two are purely jewellery hoards, while the third has rather the nature of a silver hoard. They are Treasure Number 353 from Lilla Rone, Parish of Lye (See Vol. II, Illustrations 248: 1–3, 5); Treasure Number 256 from Hejslunds, Parish of Havdhem (See Vol. II, Illustrations 250: 2–8) and Treasure Number 613 from Domerarve, Parish of Öja (See Vol. II, Illustration 260: 2). The pendants are represented by two types: some are round or oval lenses slightly convex on both sides (Lilla Rone and Hejslunds), some are spherical crystals (Lilla Rone and Domerarve). The crystals are attractively bound in silver fastenings. The fastening bands consist firstly of narrow, beaded frames, from which 4, 5, 6, or 8 symmetrically-distributed triangular teeth with masses of beaded grains protrude. The second form of fastening is a pretty wide band which encircles the crystal spheres, which likewise has teeth which bear imitations of beading. The pendants of the first type were – to judge from appearances – suspended by a short, tubular loop which was constructed together with the frame and exhibits the customary masses of beading like the teeth. Also the crystal spheres are suspended on a loop, perhaps on their own. The frame contrivance consists as described of a band, whose ends are fastened round from a loop-bandlet, which are drawn up beneath in two spirals. This loop springs back and thereby holds the band together. An empty

511

fastening [i.e., without a crystal sphere] of this type was also found in the treasure hoard Number 610 from Petes, Parish of Öja (See Volume II, Illustration 259: 11).

The treasure from Lilla Rone contained eleven round or oval lenses and three spherical crystals, the treasure from Hejslunds contained seven round lenses, and the treasure from Domerarve contained one spherical crystal. [These total 22 objects.] In both of the first two cases the pieces lay together with a great number of silver beads, on which a portion exhibited a beaded decoration of the same sort as the frame loops of the crystal pendants.

Treasures with pendants of this kind are all late and belong to the second half of the 11th century. The treasure of Domerarve was probably deposited about 1080, the other two being somewhat earlier.

To turn one's attention away from the afore-named pieces, there have been found in Gotland further round or oval lenses of rock crystal and – in one case – of amethyst, either fastened in silver or loose. In the second Volume [which appeared eleven years earlier than the first] of this work, on p. 215, under Treasure Number 533 are mentioned 'one large and three smaller ground crystals' from Bryor, Parish of Tingstäde (SHM [Stockholm Historical Museum] 4757:22).[1] It is scarcely to be supposed that these crystals of Treasure Number 533 are worthy of consideration, although they come from the same field; the Treasure is older than the first appearance of rock crystal pendants at Gotland. Three are round, with one side slightly and the second side more pronouncedly convex, the fourth crystal is oval and on the more convex side has a slight ridge. From the parish of Hangvar – without more particulars as to excavation details – has come a biconvex lens of rock crystal, which is extremely convex on one side and slightly so on the other.[2] From Rommunds, Parish of Gammelgarn, come two crystal lenses, one of which is a half-sphere, the second biconvex (SHM 2630). SHM further possesses four crystal lenses without excavation details from Gotland (SHM 2976), which may date to Viking times. And there are the ornamental lenses which have been found in graves in Gotland, which are also important. A find rich in female jewellery from the burial field at Annexhemmanet, in Hemse Parish, which dates to the middle or the second half of the 11th century (SHM 4689), contains a small pendant with an oval polished crystal stone with a silver fastening which is provided with triangular teeth of the same kind as the pendants of the treasure from Lilla Rone. A second female burial find of the same period, from the cemetery of the Parish of Fardhem (SHM 21856), has provided two pendants of the same type: one a round, biconvex amethyst with a simple fastening and a loop with small three-pointed triangles, the other an oval biconvex crystal with a loop which likewise is stamped with triangles. A find from the end of the 11th century comes from the cemetery of Stänga, where three biconvex crystal pendants of oval and round form were also found beside the skeleton portions of three individuals in addition to various other jewels, in silver fastenings which were prettily beaded or ornamented with ordered groups of embossed points, which bore four or eight triangular teeth respectively as well as loops with hourglass-shaped stamps (See Illustration 82).[3] The loop of the largest of these pendants is a variant of the loops of the spherical crystal pendants and consists of a little silver tube which is drawn up under longitudinally as a spiral. A further example of this form is encountered from another grave of the cemetery at Stänga, of the middle or second half of the 11th century. The grave yielded various pieces of female jewellery beneath which was a small biconvex crystal which was fastened in a narrow, beaded silver frame with four teeth and a small suspension loop with hourglass-stampings. The same grave produced yet another oval rock crystal without a fastening. Finally there remain to be mentioned two biconvex crystals in silver fastenings from the large treasure find, probably of the year 1361, from Dune, Parish of Dalhem (SHM 6849).[4] Both belong to the type of Lilla Rone, but whereas the fastening of one has the usual beading, the fastening and loop of the second is decorated with elegant palm-leaf-shaped filigree wire. The treasure of Dune consists of objects, some older and some younger, and af Ugglas dates the crystal pendant in the region of the year 1100.

No pendants of this type are known from Swedish treasure finds of the Viking Period outside Gotland,[5] of all that the other districts of the Scandinavian North have yielded. On the other hand, objects of this type are known in Finland. E. [Ella] Kivikoski discusses two rock crystal lenses in partially preserved silver fastenings from Taskula; both are solitary finds.[6] The fastenings correspond to the pieces from Gotland. That is, we find in their case also triangular beaded teeth. Kivikoski remembers objects from three [Finnish] burial finds from Masku-Humikkala – two female graves and a male grave – which correspond to the examples from Taskula. Also in Lettland a pendant of this type would seem to have been found.[7] Otherwise I can find no counterparts to the Gotland crystal pendants in the literature.

Now I wish to ask whether the crystal pieces with silver fastenings found at Gotland were native products or were imported. One can perhaps not fully reject the possibility that at the end of Viking times they were able to manufacture lenses and spheres of rock crystal themselves. However, one must nevertheless be very doubtful about formulating such a hypothesis on the basis of numerous occurrences of an object type. The silver pendants with fastened crystals appear very suddenly at the end of the tenth century and disappear again just as suddenly. One must therefore conclude that the stones were imported fully polished. And from this follow two questions: From where were they imported? And were the stones imported in their fastenings or was that done on the island? The fastenings of the round and oval stones give all the appearance of having been made outside Gotland – that is, they were already attached to the stones as imports; on the other hand, the fastenings of the spherical crystals are perhaps local work. The former fastenings are decorated with silver beads of insignificant size, which are laid out in rows or in simple or opposite stampings, which seldom occur in Nordic beading-work.[8] This beading pattern comes directly from the silver-plated beads of Lilla Rone. There are ten which in all probability constituted a necklace, since as our illustration (Vol. II, Illustration 248:5) shows, the beads and the pendants alternate with one another. The beads are partly round, partly spool-shaped and with a sole exception, which has filigree rings, are beaded. It is the same fine beading as we find on the pendants. The pattern corresponds: bands and stampings. These beads are not Nordic (see p. 214). They are also clearly different from the fragile silver-plated beads which we associate with the Slavic cultural sphere south of the Baltic Sea, but they do have close parallels in Russian treasure finds. In these circumstances it is most possible that the pendants originate from the same area as the beads and the entire sets of jewellery are imported from there. It is most likely that they originate from the area of west or southwest Russia, although to my knowledge no jewellery pieces of this type have been found there.[9] It follows from this also that the other biconical [sic] crystals set in silver from Gotland stem from there, but they were certainly not manufactured only in the East. Perhaps if these imports were confined to a single locality it could explain the numerous occurrences of the pendants during a brief and limited time at Gotland. The finds of similar pieces of jewellery in the localities of the eastern edge of the Baltic Sea certainly support the theory to a degree, although one cannot dismiss the idea that they could have been re-exported from Gotland. However it must nevertheless be said that rock crystal was remarkably common in West European art at that time.

The fastenings of the spherical crystals of Lilla Rone or Domerarve respectively resemble the biconvex round and oval pendants insofar as their inner margins are curved and provided with triangular tips. But the means of suspension are constructed differently, and the decoration does not correspond. The decoration of the fastening flaps consists of groups of points which are embossed, further of stamped toothed lines, small crosses and points, in addition to which on the band-shaped part of the fastening and on the loop are rows of small triangles.

Similar crystal spheres occur in German grave finds of a much earlier period, although not at Gotland or anywhere else in Sweden. The grave finds of the fourth century AD at Aarslev in Fünen, as well as the pieces recovered of provincial Roman or South European origin, contained also a spherical crystal with a magical inscription in Greek;[10] similar spheres have been found in graves of the same or somewhat later periods in Western Europe and in England.[11] The diameters of these crystals are often nearly the same as that of the sphere from Domerarve, that is, about 3 cm. Where these excavated crystals come from is not established with any certainty. They might be considered as Merovingian work. But it is then exceedingly strange that they should be found at Gotland with the biconvex crystals, which we would sooner trace back to the southeast. In their ultimate origins, the crystal grinding and the form of our crystals go back to antiquity, and with the highest probability the Western European crystal spheres as well as the ones from Gotland come from the East – from Egypt or possibly Persia, where for instance there was a centre for rock crystal production at Basra.[12] On the other hand, I might take it as conceivable that the fastenings of the Gotland crystal spheres are Nordic work, perhaps even Gotlandish, made under the influence of the fastenings for the biconvex, round and oval pendants. The decoration was partially done by an application of customary Nordic stamping techniques and the beading accomplished by an embossed point pattern.

Notes

1. These lenses at the time of writing the text for the second [earlier] Volume of this work could not be located, but have since made their appearance.
2. Otto Ahlström, 'Swedish Vikings Used Optical Lenses', p. 2, Fig. 1, 4. [This article appeared in *The Optician*, London, May 19, 1950, pp. 459–69. When Stenberger refers to 'page 2' he means pages 460–1. No one who was not already familiar with this article could ever possibly have located it from Stenberger's meagre reference!] – F. M. [Franz Maria] Feldhaus, *Die Technik der Vorzeit [Technology of Olden Times, 1914]*.
3. *Månadsblad 1903–05, Tillväxten unter år 1903*, p. 104, Illustrations 150–1. [This publication is by the Kungl. Vitterhets Historie och Antikvitets Akademie, Stockholm.]
4. C. [Carl] R. af Ugglas, *Gotländska Silverskatter från Valdemarstågets Tid* [Stockholm, 1936], p. 19, Plate XVII: 32, 33.
5. I found a small, oval, ground rock crystal in the year 1931 whilst sampling grave contents in the broad culture horizon of Eketorps borg at Öland. See M. Stenberger, *Eketorps borg*, in *Arkeologiska Studier tillagnade H. K. H. Kronprins Hustaf Adolf*, Stockholm, 1932 (pp. 132–40), pp. 139 ff., Illustration 4g. [There is no copy of this publication in Britain but I consulted it in Stockholm.]
6. E. [Ella] Kivikoski, *op. cit.* [although Stenberger does not specify *which* earlier Kivikoski book he means here, the reference is in fact to *Die Eisenzeit im Auraflussgebiet*, Helsinki, 1939, which is Vol. XLIII of the Suomen Muinaismuistoyhdistyksen Aikakauskirja Finska Fornminnesfoereningens Tidskrift], p. 171, Plate 41: 1, 2.
7. E. Kivikoski, *op. cit.*, p. 171, Note 2. [This reference is to the same work as the preceding.]
8. On the richly-beaded, round, gold pendants of the treasure of Dune, small open beading-stampings occur.
9. Two ground, apparently convex, rock crystals without fastenings come from a treasure found in the city of Wladimir [also Vladimir] in 1865. A. S. [Aleksandr Sergievich] Gushchin, *op. cit.*, p. 72, Plate xvii: 8, 19. [The reference is to *Monuments de l'Art Industriel de l'Ancienne Russie X-XIII Siècles*, Moscow and Leningrad, 1936. The work is in Russian, with a Russian title which I cannot reproduce, but with the above French title as well, and a bit of French text. The Plate is in colour. I was able to determine that items 8 and 19, which are two rock crystal lenses, are described (in Russian) in a single sentence on p. 72. Vladimir was a mediaeval Russian kingdom of the 12th century between the Rivers Oka and Volga.]
10. M. B. [Carl Mogens Bellmonn] Mackeprang, *Aarslev-Fundet*, pp. 93 ff. and Illustration 6. [The article is entitled 'Et rigt fynsk gravadstyr fra 4. årh. e. [*efta* = 'before'] Kr[ist].' ('A Rich Grave Assemblage from the 4th century AD'), in *Fra [From the] Nationalmuseet Arbejdsmark-Copenhagen*, Copenhagen, 1940, pp. 87–96.]

11. For instance, W. [Walther] Veeck, *Ein Alamannisches Frauengrab aus Schwenningen,* Plate 6: 9a,b. [This short article is to be found in *Germania Anzeiger,* Berlin, Jahrgang [Vol.] 23, Heft [Part] 1, January 1939, pp. 40–2. (Ac 5388/7 in the British Library.)] – *Reallexikon zur Deutschen Vorgeschichte,* column 277 ff. [This reference work cannot be traced in the British Library and they have no copy of it in the library of the Historiska Museet in Stockholm, so it must have been privately owned by Stenberger. There are many books of similar titles, and we cannot even estimate a date of publication of this mysterious work.] Compare also Parducz, M. [Mihaly], *A Szarmatakor Eml ékei Magyarorszagon* [Part II, in Hungarian and German, Budapest, 1944], Plate XXV: 8. [See also Plate XXIV, 17a–b. In Part III of his work, Budapest, 1950, Parducz in Plate LXXI: 8a – b shows two broken glass globes apparently placed in the grave in a broken condition. The description of the objects in German is found on p. 150, right-hand column.]
12. A. [Andras] Alföldi, *Die Goldkanne von St Maurice d'Agaune* [*The Gold Tankard of St Maurice of Agaune*], p. 25, and the associated literature. [This fascinating work by Alföldi does not exist in Britain, but I obtained a photocopy of it from the library of the Historiska Museet in Stockholm, with the help of Lena Thunmark-Nylén and a determined search by the librarian. It is more concerned with the history of art than archaeological matters. It contains a great deal of extraordinary information.] – Paul Kahle, 'Bergkristall, Glas und Glasflüsse nach dem Steinbuch von el-Bērūni' ['Rock Crystal, Glass, and Glass Paste according to the Book of Stones of el-Bērūni'], in *Zeitschrift der Deutschen Morgenlandischen Gesellschaft,* Vol. 29, Leipzig, 1936, pp. 333 ff.

Appendix Nine

TEXT ABOUT THE
VIKING 'SUN-STONE'

Translation done with the kind assistance of Dr Malin Lindquist

From a large book in Swedish entitled *Vikingen* [*Vikings*] by many authors, published by Tre Tryckare, Cagner & Co., Goteborg, Sweden, 1967, p. 14:

One doesn't know whether the Vikings were familiar with the compass. It began to be known historically around 1300. In the Icelandic sagas there is mention of a navigation instrument, a *solsten*, 'sun-stone'. In one of the epics [a minor Icelandic saga], King Olav the Holy [*Olav den helige*] was on board a ship with the chieftain Sigurd Syr and '. . . asked him if he knew where in the heavens the sun was, as it was cloudy. Sigurd replied that he knew, and indicated the location. The king then held his sun-stone [*solstenen*] up high and observed the manner in which the light streamed from it. And he thus confirmed that the sun was indeed where Sigurd had said.' One doesn't know whether this 'sun-stone' instrument of Sigurd may have been a primitive compass with a magnetic piece of iron floating on water . . .

[This is a reference to an account in the old sagas of the Viking use of the sunstone, which was not a compass at all, but was a transparent stone which polarized the rays of the sun, enabling the location of the sun to be known through cloud. It was by the use of this device that the Vikings were able to reach America. – R.T.]

Appendix Ten

THE OLD LENSES OF GOTLAND
Deposited in the Fornsal Museum, Visby

Until 1931, when Stenberger excavated a small crystal lens at Eketorps Borg on the Island of Öland,[1] old Swedish crystal lenses were believed all to be from Gotland. Commencing in 1964, a series of further crystal lenses were excavated at Eketorps Borg from the Eketorp III Level, and seventeen whole lenses and one lens fragment have now been described from there.[2] The Eketorp lenses are rather small and unimpressive compared to many of the Gotland lenses. Several of them are so tiny that it has been necessary to adopt the nomenclature of 'oval droplet' to describe them, as for instance the smallest known from Eketorps (SHM Y18: 95) has a major axis of only 7.8 mm. and a minor axis of 5.4 mm. Commencing in 1988, several crystal lenses have also been excavated at Sigtuna on the Swedish mainland, and fourteen lenses are now known from there (a fifteenth crystal is not a lens but a gem). These are unpublished, but will be described in a survey of all known Scandinavian and Baltic lenses which I am preparing in English for a future issue of *Fornvännen*. In addition to the many Swedish lenses, there are seven known lenses which have been excavated in Finland (including at least one which appears to have come from Gotland), one in Estonia, six in Latvia, one in Lithuania, and several in Denmark; none are known from Norway.

Amongst the new Sigtuna material, dating from about 1200–1230 AD, are more of the remarkable crystal 'droplets'. Sigtuna is the source for the smallest Swedish crystal droplet of all, Object Number 01134, which has a maximum thickness of 2 mm., a major axis of 6 mm., and a minor axis of 4.4 mm. Its magnifying powers are only 1.2X, but a droplet only slightly larger (a major axis of 6.1 mm.), Object Number 03484, magnifies 1.5X. Since many tiny lenses of this kind have now been recovered at Sigtuna and Eketorps, their discovery can really be regarded as a triumph of Swedish archaeological technique and expertise. Many archaeologists around the world would have overlooked such microscopic artifacts! And they are indeed artifacts, for they are expertly ground and polished and give good magnification. Indeed, the most effective of them, Object

Number SHM M19: 78, from Eketorps, magnifies 3X when raised above the surface to its focal point despite being only 1 centimetre long. The successful retrieval from the soil of these collections of small Eketorps and Sigtuna lenses represents one of Sweden's major contributions to the worldwide history of science, for they constitute the discovery of a genuine *Swedish miniature optical technology* dating from early Mediaeval times, but thought to have originated in the Viking period. These crystal droplets with their excellent magnifying powers whether resting on a surface or raised very slightly above it (when their magnification increases to its maximum, and a small tool can be inserted underneath) would have afforded magnificent assistance to jewellers and other craftsmen engaged in miniature decorative work. The droplets are of course too tiny to have been reading aids in the way that the larger lenses probably often were. It is remarkable that no miniature lenses have yet been found at Gotland, and it is suggested that because so much of the Gotland material was excavated before the rigour of modern techniques came into application, such tiny objects may well have been missed. It would not be surprising if miniature lenses were found on Gotland in future excavations, now that their importance is recognized and modern excavation techniques are in use.

Old lenses in general are a remarkable feature of the tradition of Gotland throughout many centuries. From Viking times through Mediaeval times, Gotland produced large quantities of beautifully ground and polished crystal lenses and crystal balls, many of them magnificently mounted in silver of the highest artistic quality and design. We say 'produced', but we cannot be certain that the production actually took place on Gotland. The truth is that the source of the crystal, the location of the grinding and polishing, and the identity of the metalworkers who mounted many of them, are all unknown. What is certain is that the rock crystal itself did not come from Gotland, which has none, and that Gotland was the trading focal point for this extensive but mysterious industry which still puzzles all experts. A fuller discussion of these problems, as far as they can be elucidated at present, will appear in my forthcoming article in *Fornvännen*, since this is a subject which necessarily involves a consideration of the entire range of distribution of similar objects from Britain and Ireland to Russia, Hungary, and Bulgaria, – a broad sweep of many hundreds of miles. But amidst this vast distribution of crystal lenses the tiny island of Gotland has a remarkable and disproportionate significance which has yet to be explained. It seems inescapable to conclude that the supply of good-sized and high-quality crystal lenses and crystal balls was for some time a very crucial and lucrative trading monopoly of the Island of Gotland. The monetary value of even a single such object must have been vast, as we know from other cultures. These materials were very carefully kept out of the hands of the Norwegian Vikings, and the Danes seem only to have got hold of crystal lenses in the Middle Ages. This monopoly was thus a monopoly of the Swedish Vikings, who excluded the more westward Vikings from any share in it. But in many respects it was not simply a monopoly of trade, but a monopoly of *technology*. For the objects were invaluable in the production of fine metalwork and jewellery because of their ability to allow craftsmen to continue working after the age of 45 when presbyopia (long-sightedness) sets in and otherwise renders such artisans useless just as they reach the peak of their skill. How this strange monopoly came to be secured by Gotland, and from where, is one of the great mysteries of the island's history.

Good-quality rock crystal of any size has always been difficult to obtain until modern times, and it was such a rarity in ancient Rome that even the richest families would boast of having it, and the fashionable Roman ladies who liked to hold it to cool their hands in the hot weather could rarely obtain it and had to make do with Baltic amber as a substitute.[3] What unusual source was tapped by the traders of Gotland? Although some rock crystal exists in Greenland,[4] there is no evidence that the Norwegian Vikings made use of it, since no Norwegian crystal lenses or crystal balls have been found. It is therefore not at all likely that Gotland obtained its crystal from Greenland via Norway, or some traces of this would otherwise be known. The source does seem to lie to the southeast, as suggested by Stenberger in 1958.[5] Two small hoards of uncut raw rock crystal dated to the early 13th century have been found at Sigtuna, as well as a rotary grinding stone of sandstone excavated in 1990–1, of 10.9 cm. diameter (shaft hole diameter 4.23 cm.) which may have been used to manufacture some of the small Sigtuna crystal lenses. But these uncut crystals are small and pathetic, evidently 'leftovers', and neither they nor most of the Sigtuna lenses, which also tend to be very small, indicate the availability at that time on the Swedish mainland of a good supply of crystal such as Gotland had available to it. The conclusion which suggests itself is that a very remote source of good crystal was known to the Gotland traders, that it lay to their east so that the Norwegian and Danish Vikings could not themselves reach it, and that they did not advertise the details of this source to their immediate neighbours.

For those with a special interest in the history of Gotland, a full survey of the Gotland crystal lenses and crystal balls actually deposited in the Fornsal Museum in Visby is much to be desired. The Gotland material is inevitably shared with the Stockholm Historical Museum. In general, a Stockholm Historical Museum object has an object number commencing 'SHM', whereas a Fornsal Museum object has an object number commencing 'C'. But in fact, several SHM objects have now been returned to Gotland, and are thus to be seen not in Stockholm but in Visby.

There have been two or three cases of mistaken or confused identity of these objects over the decades. Recently, a very large and important lens at Visby has been re-identified as Object Number SHM 6104, after having borne the wrong object number apparently since the 1940s when it is believed that it was put back into the wrong box by someone known to have studied it at that time. It is very easy to confuse these small objects, as not all of them have had numbers written onto them. Nor is it necessarily a good idea to write numbers onto crystal lenses, since some small ones are more than half covered with a number and the optical properties are thus partially obscured. However, 'The Case of the Missing SHM 6104' has now at last been solved with the help of an old photograph and some old published descriptions.[6] These matters of identity will be discussed as we proceed.

We shall now give an annotated survey of those crystal lenses and crystal balls which are actually to be found in the Fornsal Museum at Visby. This list, which may be published separately in Swedish, will appear also in English as a self-contained portion of the comprehensive list of all Scandinavian crystal lenses and crystal balls which will appear in my forth-coming survey article in the journal *Fornvännen*. The list of the Fornsal Museum material should thus eventually be available in both languages, so that both local and foreign scholars can use it with equal ease.

1. *Object number:* C. 6066.
   Provenance: From Babos, Parish of Mästerby.
   Description: ROUND, BICONVEX, MOUNTED. This lens, evidently of the Viking period, is mounted in silver and its suspension-loop seems to have broken off in antiquity, leaving a very slight trace. There are six retain-ing-teeth, one with its tip chipped off.
   Condition: The crystal is very clear and lustrous but has several inter-nal pressure-flaws which appear to be due to the object having received widely distributed broad or flat blows on the back which did not cause chipping. There is one serious gouge on the back at the edge, measuring 6 mm. by 8 mm. There is evidence that the object was once 'backed' by silver which has come away; the backing may have been lost with the blows on the back, but on the other hand, the back may have protected the lens against chipping by those blows. It is possible that this large and impressive piece was once the centrepiece of a necklace. As is explained in a careful analysis of a necklace deposited in the Stockholm Historical Museum (to appear in *Fornvännen*), the necklaces can be demonstrated to have been second-generation (or even third-generation) uses of these lenses, with backings added very late in their history; the original lenses were single transparent objects. *Three* usage-generations have been conclusively established for the necklace of Gotland's Lilla Rone Hoard (SHM 8315) in Stockholm.
   Maximum thickness: 1.62 cm.
   Diameter (with mount): varies between 4.68 cm. and 4.77 cm.
   Magnification when resting on base: 1.25X.
   Magnification when raised: 1.5X going to 2X when rotated orthogonally in the horizontal plane; though nearly round, the lens thus behaves as if it were an oval lens with a major axis and a minor axis.

2. *Object number:* SHM 11,948 (I, II, and III: three pieces).
Provenance: From the Cemetery of Stänga.

Piece I:
Description: OVAL, BICONVEX, MOUNTED. Mounted in silver with four retaining-teeth on the superior surface and a suspension-loop. Viking period. The reverse surface of the lens, before it was largely destroyed, was slightly convex.
Condition: The lens has a huge triangular gouge on the back 1 cm. long, destroying nearly half the back surface. The crystal is very clear and lustrous despite the gouge.
Maximum thickness: 7.1 mm. today. (Would have been somewhat more before the damage.)
Major axis (with mount): 2.26 cm.
Minor axis (with mount): 1.71 cm.
Magnification when resting on base with major axis horizontal: 1.25X.
Magnification when raised: 1.5X.
Status: Published in 1903 in *Månadsblad 1903–05, Tillväxten unter år 1903, Kungl. Vitterhets Historie och Antikvitets Akademie*, Stockholm, 1905, p. 104; illustrated as Figure 151.

Piece II:
Description: OVAL, BICONVEX, MOUNTED. The base is slightly convex. Mounted in silver with eight retaining-teeth on the superior surface and a suspension-loop. Viking period.
Condition: The crystal is very clear and lustrous.
Maximum thickness: 1.15 cm.
Major axis (with mount): 2.77 cm.
Minor axis (with mount): 2.42 cm.
Magnification when resting on base: 1.25X.
Magnification when raised: 1.5X.
Status: Published but not illustrated in 1903 (as above).

Piece III:
Description: ROUND, BICONVEX, MOUNTED. The base is nearly flat, so that this comes very close to being a plano-convex lens. The lens is mounted in silver with four retaining-teeth and a suspension-loop. Viking period.
Condition: The crystal is extremely clear and lustrous. There are two gouges on the back: one of 2.5 mm. at the side, and one which is a large chip in the centre.
Maximum thickness: 1.02 cm.
Diameter (with mount): 2.7 cm. constant. The perfect roundness, it must be remembered, is of the mounting, but the lens itself must be nearly so; this seems to be the nearest thing to a perfectly round Viking lens in Sweden.

Magnification when resting on base: 1.25X.
Magnification when raised: 2X.
Status: Published in 1903 as above, and illustrated there as Figure 150.

3. *Object number:* SHM 27754.
Provenance: From the Parish of Fardhem.
Description: ROUND, BICONVEX, MOUNTED. Mounted in silver with four retaining-teeth and typical Viking granulated beading. But this object never had a suspension-loop. The base is almost flat, so that the lens is nearly plano-convex.
Condition: The crystal is clear and moderately lustrous. The lens is badly chipped at the edge of the base and has a chip and some scratching on the centre of the base. The base is also very badly abraded. There is one serious scratch on the superior surface and there are considerable patches which, though transparent, are partially obscured by traces of glue around the retaining-teeth of the mount. Although the glue which is found on some of the Finnish lenses in Helsinki (see account of them in Appendix Four and also the forthcoming survey article in *Fornvännen*) is unquestionably modern, and was definitely used to try and preserve the decaying mounts by glueing them to the lenses, the more nearly transparent glue which is found on several of the Swedish lenses such as this one is only presumed to be modern. The Vikings are known to have used a wood glue named *harts* or *kåda*, but it is doubtful that it was transparent (nor is any modern study of this ancient glue known which could tell us more about it). On balance, it would seem that the nearly-transparent glue found on several of the Swedish lenses was applied in less scrupulous modern times – say, before the Second World War – by conservators who meant well but were less hesitant about such things than we would be today. If there is any chance that the glue might actually be Viking, then it should be analysed. I am inclined to believe the glue to be modern, but would recommend this question to the attention of a suitable expert.
Maximum thickness: 6.9 mm.
Diameter (with mount): Varies between 2.11 and 2.12 cm., so that this lens too approximates closely to perfect roundness, which is unusual.
Magnification when resting on base: 1.25X.
Magnification when raised: 1.75X.

4. *Object number:* C9817:4.
Provenance: From the Kaplanen District (or Quarter) or Visby.
Description: ROUND, BICONVEX, UNMOUNTED. The bottom is slightly convex.
Condition: The quartz is clear and moderately lustrous. But the lens is very dirty and also has pressure flaws rendering about a fifth of it opaque in one quarter from the edge. The inventory number is written on some transparent glue, which suggests that the glue on these lenses is modern.

Maximum thickness: 9.9 mm.
Diameter: Varies between 2.61 and 2.68 cm.
Magnification when resting on base: 1.25X.
Magnification when raised: 2X.
Status: Found in the 19th century.

5. *Object number:* C.10.720:8 (I and II: two pieces).
   Provenance: From Lybska Gränd, a street in Visby.

Piece I:
Description: ROUND, BICONVEX, UNMOUNTED, the base nearly flat.
Condition: The quartz is perfectly clear and lustrous. The rim shows some wear.
Maximum thickness: 5.1 mm.
Diameter: Varies between 1.59 cm. and 1.71 cm.
Magnification when resting on base: ZERO.
Magnification when raised: 1.75X, but with some distortion goes to 2X.

Piece II:
Description: ROUND, BICONVEX, UNMOUNTED.
Condition: The quartz is perfectly clear and lustrous. The rim is quite worn.
Maximum thickness: 7.8 mm.
Diameter: Varies between 1.83 cm. and 1.9 cm.
Magnification when resting on base: ZERO.
Magnification when raised: 1.75X, but with some distortion goes to 2X.

6. *Object number:* SHM 6104. – THIS IS A RE-IDENTIFICATION.
   Comments on the re-identification: Previously this lens was wrongly identified as C 9389:4, from Krasse in the Parish of Guldrupe. The two lenses appear to have been mixed up by being replaced in the wrong boxes in the 1940s. The question of what happened to the real Guldrupe lens will be dealt with later, but does not concern this object. The re-identification was done in the summer of 1997 by Dr Lena Thunmark-Nylén of the Stockholm Historical Museum and myself after very lengthy discussions and consideration of evidence, both photographic and textual. (See below under the heading of *Status*.)
   Provenance: From an unknown site in Visby.
   Description: ROUND, BICONVEX, UNMOUNTED. The rim of the lens is very pronounced. The superior surface is so convex that it is nearly a hemisphere.
   Condition: The very pronounced rim is extremely badly damaged: there is one small clean gouge, a number of chips, and a long portion, constituting about 70% of the circumference, which has been extremely heavily

abraded with the material worn or sheared away, and deep ingraining of dirt. One serious pressure crack rises from a deep chip on the rim and seems to have extended as flaws across the entire lens body. The two surfaces themselves have almost no abrasion. The quartz is otherwise clear and transparent.

Maximum thickness: 3.14 cm.

Diameter: Varies between 4.94 and 5.01 cm.

Magnification when resting on base: 1.75X when looking down directly; when viewing at 45°, this becomes 2.25X.

Magnification when resting on rim, base downwards, and held at 45°: 4X.

Magnification when raised: 3X before distortion of image from spherical aberration becomes severe.

Comments on the magnification possible with this lens: This is a very powerful magnifier indeed, and reaches the limit of magnifying power achieved by the Gotland optical technology. The fact that this lens's greatest magnification of 4X can only be achieved by resting the lens on its rim at an angle is very significant, for this could explain the extreme wear on the rim. The evidence indicates that a severely presbyopic (long-sighted) person (presumably a craftsman over the age of fifty) used this lens and ran it along hard surfaces, such as sheets of metal, on its rim. In that viewing position, the use of the lens allowed plenty of room for a working tool underneath it, the tip of which would similarly be magnified. It is important to note that a pattern of wear occurring on the lens at precisely the location corresponding to its use for maximum magnification purposes – and having no other logical explanation – constitutes significant physical evidence that this lens had an optical purpose. Nor is this the only Swedish lens which offers such indications. But anyone wishing to suggest that the Scandinavian crystals were not used as lenses but were merely ornaments (a line of reasoning which seems to have been abandoned in Scandinavia during the 1940s at the latest) would find his or her view contradicted by this highly specific physical evidence for a pattern of use of the object. Nor does any other possible purpose for this large, carefully crafted, object suggest itself, as it is too large and too clumsily-shaped to function as an ornament in any conceivable context.

Status: This lens was formerly thought to have been misplaced and 'lost' in the museum, but its identity having been established, it is now 'found'.

7. *Object number:* C8726.

Provenance: Grötlingbo.

Description: A large CRYSTAL BALL.

Condition: Very rough condition.

Status: This object is temporarily misplaced. Dr Lena Thunmark-Nylén has inspected this object at Visby in the past, so it is known to be in the museum.

8. *Object number:* SHM 6996. (Treasure Number 256.)
   Provenance: Hejslunds.
   Description: A magnificent necklace of seven mounted ROUND crystals with suspension loops interspersed with 17 silver beads (8 round, 9 spindle-shaped), all wrought with superb workmanship. For numbering purposes, with the necklace lying down, the silver backs of the crystals downward, the crystals can be numbered consecutively I-VII, with IV being the central one. The crystals increase in size from I-IV, and then decrease in size. A strange anomaly is that Crystal Number V is of smoky (though transparent) quartz, whereas all the others are clear; all are lustrous. The backs of the crystals are all inaccessible due to their being mounted, but all are clearly BICONVEX with the possible exception of Crystal VII, which seems to be PLANO-CONVEX or nearly so. Crystals II, V, and VI are ROUNDLY CONVEX and the other MUCH LESS CONVEX.
   Condition: The necklace is in wonderful condition and seems to have been cleaned in modern times; the silver backs even appear to have been polished. Significant abrasion is absent on Crystals I, II, and VII. There is a minuscule chip on Crystal V. Crystals III, IV, and VI are significantly abraded. The central Crystal IV has some almost undetectable flaws. Traces of the transparent 'glue' are evident on all seven crystals without exception, and there seems no doubt that the crystals were glued into their mounts: this is perfectly obvious from the central Crystal IV. (This raises again the question: what was this glue used by the Vikings which was so reliably transparent that it could be used on rock crystal?)
   Maximum thicknesses (with mounts): I: 0.65 cm; II: 1.16 cm; III: 1.11 cm; IV: 1.10 cm; V: 1.26 cm; VI: 1.43 cm; VII: 0.54 cm.
   Diameters: I: 2.26–2.28 cm; II: 2.47–2.48 cm; III: 2.71–2.75 cm; IV: 3.19–3.28 cm; V: 2.91–2.92 cm; VI: 2.71–2.73 cm; VII: 2.02–2.07 cm.
   Comments on the measurements: All the crystals were measured in their mounts, and much of the variation can be considered due to the silver mounts themselves.
   Magnification: There is no doubt that if removed from their mounts all of the crystals would be good magnifiers of 1.5X or 2X.

9. *Object number:* UNNUMBERED AND UNCATALOGUED.
   (I and II: two pieces; more pieces to come in the future as part of this donation from a farming family.)
   Provenance: Farm in the Parish of Fröjel.

Piece I:
Description: A magnificent silver-mounted CRYSTAL BALL, the largest in Sweden. The sphere has a wide, strong mounting with five teeth on each side and a very strong suspension loop.
Condition: The crystal is perfectly clear and lustrous but the surface has suffered minor abrasion in antiquity and far more serious dirt and scuffing

which appear to be due to careless handling and storage by the farmer who hid the object in his freezer and only got it out for the family to see once a year at Christmas!

Diameter: The diameter of the sphere measured without including the mounting varies between 4.74 and 4.81 cm.

Magnification: When resting on a surface, the sphere produces magnification of 2.5X with some distortion, but when raised the distortion becomes severe, and the object is then hopeless for magnifying.

Comments: The sphere was evidently intended as a burning-globe, not as a magnifier.

Piece II:

Description: A silver-backed ROUND, BICONVEX (but with a base only slightly convex) crystal necklace piece with suspension loop donated by the same family as Piece I, who say they have more 'which they will donate eventually'. Judging from this piece and what we know of the Viking necklaces, I should estimate that they may have six more necklace crystals at least, but probably more, judging from the size of this piece, which is larger than any on the Hejslunds Necklace (SHM 6996).

Condition: This piece is of a very heavily-abraded and scuffed deep-yellowish smoky quartz which would originally have been transparent. The silver backing is cracked at the bottom. The piece has not only dirt but what appears to be deeply ingrained household dust around the teeth.

Maximum thickness (including backing mount): 1.7 cm.

Diameter: Varies between 3.62 and 3.68 cm. including the mount.

10. *Object number:* UNNUMBERED AND UNCATALOGUED.

(I, II, and III: three pieces.) It is probable that Piece I is the lost Object Number C8709 from Burge in the Parish of Rune which is no longer in the National Historical Museum at Stockholm; this possibility was discussed with Dr Lena Thunmark-Nylén, and she has now examined the crystal and established its identity.

Provenance: Unknown, but possibly Burge in the Parish of Rune for all three pieces, since Piece I is probably from there.

Piece I (this is almost certainly the 'lost' C8709):

Description: A horizontally-mounted OVAL BICONVEX lens with suspension loop atop the minor axis as with specimens previously considered. This object has a silver mounting of design and pattern like the ones already considered, and ones in the National Historical Museum in Stockholm. There is a rounded ridge running along the major axis on the superior surface, as with many other such specimens.

Condition: The teeth of the silver mounting are all broken off. The crystal is perfectly clear and lustrous. There is one slight chip and minor abrasion at the lower right of the superior surface. Although the silver is in bad condition and falling away, the quartz is in very good condition.

Maximum thickness: 1.07 cm.

Major axis (with mount): 2.48 cm.

Minor axis (with mount): 1.5 cm. (to side of loop).

Magnification: Magnification when resting on base is significant but is spoilt by the ridge. Optical use of the lens is by resting it on the superior surface on the page, with major axis horizontal, and the suspension loop provides a very fine resting-point. This gives magnification of 1.25X. Otherwise, resting on its base and viewed at an angle of 45°, magnification of 1.5X is produced.

Comments: Perhaps these oval ridged or semi-ridged lenses were made for the convenience of seated readers viewing flat writing at an angle of 45°.

Piece II and Piece III:

Description: Silver-mounted OVAL lenses; the smaller, Piece II, is evidently PLANO-CONVEX, and the larger, Piece III, is BICONVEX. But these have mountings which are of wholly different workmanship than all others so far studied. These no longer have the typical Gotland Viking style at all, but on the other hand are morphologically similar in concept and therefore may be considered as later, presumably Mediaeval, work which was directly inspired by and attempted to copy the mounted Viking lenses. The most obvious variation is in the nature of the suspension loops, which are no longer horizontally-oriented long rolls of silver but are simply suspension *rings* such as we use today. I now describe them individually:

Piece II:

Description: This OVAL crystal is mounted in silver with a large suspension ring on the top and, curiously, a small suspension ring below. Unlike the traditional Viking lenses, this object has entirely plain retaining-teeth with no beading or decoration on them. There are eleven teeth. On the reverse, the mounting has the appearance of an oval ring with an oval 'window' or hole in it. This form of mounting in no way interferes with the use of the lens as a magnifier. In fact, the pair of suspension rings could be not only for possible suspension, but for holding the lens by the fingers at either end for frequent and easy use as a magnifier. We can be certain that the lens had a previous history before being mounted because a substantial 'bite' was gouged off the top left edge of the crystal prior to being mounted. This indicates that a seriously damaged crystal was still considered sufficiently precious to be conserved and mounted, or re-mounted, with a great deal of care and trouble in silver. (It also hints that it might originally have been a Viking lens transformed into a Mediaeval lens in its second incarnation.) The crystal itself is perfectly clear and lustrous. From what can be discerned in its mounted state, it is either PLANO-CONVEX or so slightly convex at the base as makes no difference; upon extremely close inspection there does seem to be a slight gentle curve to the surface. The superior surface bears a rounded ridge along the major axis.

Condition: The ridge of the superior surface is somewhat abraded, which the surface of the gouge is not. This indicates that the gouge occurred after the abrasion had taken place.

Maximum thickness (with mount): 0.94 cm.

Major axis (with mount, to side of suspension rings): 2.35 cm.

Minor axis (with mount): 2.02 cm.

Magnification: Magnification of 1.25X is obtained by resting simply at 45° on top and sliding along by holding the attached ring(s). 1.5X is obtained at a steeper angle.

Comments: The 'window' acts as a very convenient delimitation for the effective size of a magnified image, since anything beyond its limits is severely distorted. This is a very clever device, which points to the lens having definitely been an optical magnifier. I can read through it without spectacles very easily, and am slightly presbyopic.

Piece III:

Description: This OVAL BICONVEX crystal is presently mounted with its major axis vertical. At the top of the silver mounting is a silver bulb surmounted by a suspension ring. At the bottom, a small snapped protuberance of silver demonstrates that there was once another ring or small handle. There are 15 retaining-teeth on the top and 19 on the base, wholly unlike traditional Viking workmanship; the teeth are incised in a geometrical semi-arboreal pattern. The quartz is slightly yellowish but wholly transparent. The crystal has a ridge running along the major axis on the superior surface.

Condition: The superior surface bears a significant pressure-crack. Both surfaces are significantly abraded, the superior surface to a far greater extent.

Maximum thickness: 1.48 cm.

Minor axis (with mount): 2.79 cm.

Major axis (with mount, taken to side of suspension ring): 3.52 cm.

Magnification: When resting on its base and viewed through 45°, the lens produces magnification of 1.25X; when tilted to a higher degree on its edge towards the viewer (holding the convenient ring between the fingers), it gives 1.5X. It produces 1.25X if one looks through the base as it is held with top down and the mounting facing one, angle of 45° observation – all of these being with the major axis horizontal. Resting on its base vertically, viewing at an angle of 45° gives 1.5X magnification.

Comments: Because of the ridge on the superior surface, when looking down through the lens from above, a letter is doubled, and when the lens is rotated, the image revolves around itself.

11. *Object number:* UNNUMBERED AND UNCATALOGUED.
    (I, II, III, and IV: four pieces.)

Description: four unmounted crystals, three round and one oval.

Piece I:

Provenance: Unknown.

Description: The smallest of the four, OVAL and BICONVEX. Clear and lustrous, with a ridge along the major axis of the superior surface.

Condition: The ridge is very heavily abraded in the same manner as that of SHM 2976:172, a Gotland lens now in the Stockholm Historical Museum, indicating the same sort of wear (described below).

Maximum thickness: 0.99 cm.

Major axis: 1.94 cm.

Minor axis: 1.54 cm.

Magnification: Magnification of 1.5X is obtained if the lens is held as follows: if you slide the lens along the page ridge downwards, with your thumb on one side of the top and your third finger at the far edge, and look through the inclined base, you can read excellently without spectacles if you are presbyopic.

Comments: The lengthy abrasion along the whole length of the ridge can be seen as verification of the hypothesis of the optical use of this object. For the strange mark lies precisely along the portion of the surface which would be repeatedly rubbed by use as a magnifier – and *only* there. The severity of the abrasion is such that the lens's use only for reading seems inadequate, since even centuries of reading manuscripts could hardly be expected to damage a material as hard as crystal in this way. We may thus conclude that the *wear-mark* (for that is what we must call it) was caused by a rougher material than parchment – and an immediate suspicion falls upon metal, suggesting that this lens and the similar one in Stockholm were used by a metal-worker, stamper, or engraver. This requires the assumption that the beading and stamping of Viking silver was done on flat, not curved, strips of silver, for instance, and that the lens was run along the strip. Since this is the second lens I inspected with clear indications of use for metal-working, I experimented and discovered that this lens design may have been ingeniously produced for the purpose: assuming you are right-handed, if you hold your working tool in the right hand and the little lens in your left with the base towards you, you can view the tip of your tool and the work it is doing with slight (1.25X) magnification, as the tool tip fits under the downward longitudinal side of the domed ridged configuration. If you remove your tool and tilt the lens through 45°, looking through the base, the lens resting on its ridge, you then can view your work at 1.5X. I therefore conclude that these ridged lenses were devised as dual-purpose devices for close-work by artisans.

Piece II:

Provenance: Unknown.

Description: The second smallest, ROUND and BICONVEX.

Condition: The crystal gives the superficial appearance of being slightly cloudy, but upon closer examination, this can be seen to be due to fairly heavy abrasions and ingrained dirt on both surfaces as well as one 'ghost-like' crystalline flaw.

Maximum thickness: 1.16 cm.

Diameter: Varies between 2.54 and 2.62 cm.

Magnification: When resting on base, 1.25X; when raised it becomes 2X.

Piece III:

Provenance: Unknown.

Description: The third smallest, ROUND and BICONVEX.

Condition: The crystal is clear but not lustrous and has extreme dirt-ingrained abrasions on top, resulting in a large nearly opaque patch of 2 cm. diameter, as well as some abrasion and dirt on base. There is also a diagonally transverse 'ghost-like' flaw in the centre of the crystal.

Maximum thickness: 1.62 cm.

Diameter: Varies between 3.66 and 3.68 cm.

Magnification: When resting on base it is 1.5X; when raised it goes to 2X.

Piece IV:

Provenance: Unknown, although possibly Krasse in the Parish of Guldrupe (see below).

Description: The largest, ROUND and BICONVEX. The superior surface has very pronounced convexity.

Condition: There is a substantial gouge on the side of the superior surface which is 1.5 cm. long and 1 cm. wide. The rim is very badly chipped, with another smaller gouge on the rim. Both surfaces are extremely heavily abraded with ingrained dirt, creating semi-opaque patches. Before damage, the crystal would have been clear and lustrous.

Maximum thickness: 2.35 cm.

Diameter: Varies between 4.21 and 4.24 cm.

Magnification: When resting on base it is 1.5X; when raised it goes to 2X.

Status: I believe it highly likely that this is the 'lost' C 9389:4 lens from Krasse in the Parish of Guldrupe, discussed under Item 6. This lens and SHM 6104 were mixed up in the 1940s by being put back into the wrong boxes; this lens lost its identification altogether and became numberless, while SHM 6104 took on this lens's identity by mistake. Both lenses are round, biconvex, and unmounted, and of not dissimilar size, so it was easy to confuse them with one another if they were both set out on a table together for examination.

The following crystal is still believed to be misplaced in the museum at Visby:

12. *Object number:* UNNUMBERED AND UNCATALOGUED.
    Provenance: From the Parish of Hangvar.
    Description: Believed to be ROUND.
    Comments: There are no excavation details.

Additional lenses in Gotland: It should be mentioned that additional old lenses are to be found in Väte Church on the Island of Gotland. A late 12th century crucifix in the Church there incorporates on the head of Christ no less than eight oval ridged cabochons of rock crystal, which are probably old Viking lenses recycled for religious adornment in the Middle Ages. There are many similar ones to be found in Mediaeval Danish religious statuary on display in the Nationalmuseet in Copenhagen.

I wish to thank Malin Lindquist, Lena Thunmark-Nylén, and Jenny Zhu for assistance in this survey.

Notes
1. Stenberger, Mårten, *Eketorps Borg* in *Arkeologiska Studier tillägnade H. K. H. Kronprins Gustaf Adolf*, Stockholm, 1932, pp. 139–40, and Fig. 4g on p. 138 (in Swedish); discussed again in Stenberger, Mårten, *Öland under Äldre Järnåldern*, Stockholm, 1933, p. 219, and Fig. 133g, on p. 218 (in Swedish); discussed once more in Stenberger, Mårten, *Die Schatzfunde Gotlands der Wikingerzeit*, Stockholm, Vol. I, 1958, p. 202 n. 3 (in German).
2. See my report: Temple, Robert K. G., 'Lenses from Eketorps Borg, Öland' (in English), to be published as a supplement to the forthcoming *Finds at Eketorps-III* (otherwise in Swedish), Stockholm, in press.
3. Böttinger, Carl August, *Sabina: oder Morgenszenen im Putzzimmer Einer Reichen Römerin*, 2 vols, Leipzig, 1806; see Vol. II, Eighth Scene, pp. 185–7, and Notes on pp. 208–10.
4. Information from Dr Jan Peder Lamm of the Stockholm Historical Museum.
5. Stenberger, *Die Schatzfunde, op. cit.*, pp. 200–4.
6. The final identification was made in August 1997, by Dr Lena Thunmark-Nylén of the Stockholm Historical Museum, after lengthy discussions between us about this complex issue.

APPENDIX ELEVEN

The Sloane Lenses
in London

Most of the lenses to be described here appear once to have been in the collection of the 18th-century antiquarian Sir Hans Sloane, founder of the British Museum. Hence I have decided to call them the Sloane Lenses in his honour. At one time these lenses were in the British Museum but they were transferred long ago to the Natural History Museum in London, where they are part of the mineralogical collections. There was textual evidence for their existence at an earlier period, but after a very long search I was the one who tracked these lenses down to the unexpected site of the Natural History Museum, where no one had ever recognized their optical significance, and they had been treated simply as cut quartz specimens. They are all of rock crystal. Their cousins are to be found at the Sedgwick Museum of Geology in Cambridge, also in a mineralogical collection, and are described in an earlier Appendix to this book. In this account I present only a physical description of the objects, as a discussion of the vast subject of the history of the objects, the early textual material, the lore, etc., would be too lengthy. A certain amount of this has been discussed in the main text of the book. But I thought it best to put on record the physical descriptions, so that others can have that material at least to hand.

The question as to the dates of these old British lenses can never be answered satisfactorily, since they cannot in themselves be dated. The existing textual material does assist us in having some idea when and how some of these lenses were found, and the association of at least some of them with barrow graves, in the manner of the famous crystal balls, gives us confidence in believing in the antiquity of most of the objects, though as we shall see, there is one I believe not to be ancient.

1. *Object number:* 60869 (a), ('Probably Sloane 756')
   Description: 'Polished oval specimen with a rib along the top' is the Museum's description. It is also described as 'QUARTZ (var, Rock-crystal)'. The old label of 1753 says: '756 (Sloane.) Pretious [precious] stones. A Topaz with a rib rising on its middle [middle].'
   BICONVEX OVAL ridged cabochon. The base is only slightly convex,

8.5 dioptres across the minor axis and 6.75 dioptres across the major axis. The ridge is soft, rounded, gentle. There is a tiny patch of internal flaw at one end of the longitudinal major axis. The ridge actually subsides into nonexistence at either end, so that only about half of the superior surface actually possesses a ridge at all. The crystal is extremely lustrous and wholly transparent.

Condition: There is no pitting and very little abrasion; what there is is circular as if from scrubbing. The ridge has moderate abrasion in the center, with some ingrained dirt. The rim has a few minor chips, but it does not appear that this lens was ever mounted in metal.

Maximum thickness: 2.1 cm.

Major axis: 4.37 cm.

Minor axis: 3.41 cm.

Magnification: If held with one edge (longitudinally) on a page, and raised about 45°, with the ridge towards one, looking through it, it magnifies between 2X and 2.5X; the same is true if the ridge is held away from one. The best way to use this lens as a reading-glass is to hold it with the ridge towards one, resting the lower rim on the page and raising the lens about 45°. A presbyope can thus obtain 2X magnification reliably and without spherical aberration, as the lens is run along a line of writing.

2. *Object number:* 58338.

   Description: CRYSTAL BALL.

   Weight: 208.9 grammes.

   Condition: Wholly transparent but in terrible condition. This ball has often been dropped, giving pock-pressure ring-marks just under the surface; in addition, there is some serious interior pressure-cracking. There is one extended and there are two tiny areas of interior planar ghostly flawing. The ball is moderately abraded all over and shows signs of having been rigorously scrubbed on various occasions. The surface has a small modern sticky patch of adhesive from an earlier display; the plastic base for this is still in the specimen box.

   Measurement and orientation: This crystal has a very prominent double-refraction which disappears along the optical axis. I take this axis as a defining axis for purposes of measurement: thickness at optical axis gives a diameter of 5.30 cm.; at 90° to this diameter it varies in a circle from 5.25 cm. To 5.35 cm.; greatest thickness anywhere on the ball gives a diameter of 5.36 cm.

   Magnification: Only effective when resting and when aligned along optical axis, but can then give up to 5X. When held in the air at correct distance from the eyes, the globe gives a bowed inverted image text; in other words, the image which is the correct way up and magnified when the globe is resting on a surface, quickly inverts when the globe is raised and presents a focused inverted image which is heavily bowed. The awe which such bizarre optical behaviour would have inspired in ancient times is obvious.

3. *Object number:* 60869 (I, II, and III: 3 pieces in one specimen box)

Piece 1:

Description: ROUND, BICONVEX 'button style', with base tapering to a central point, and the superior surface a dome.

Condition: The rim is heavily chipped, demonstrating that the lens was once mounted in metal. The base has several serious deep scratches and striations and is fairly heavily abraded; the central point is severely worn from constant use, abraded and with ingrained dirt. There is only light abrasion on the superior surface.

Maximum thickness: 1.83 cm.

Diameter: varies between 2.58 and 2.63 cm.

Magnification: 2.5X when resting on a surface; 3X when raised, before distortion interferes.

Comments: This lens has the remarkable property of condensing light upon the magnified text underneath, thereby significantly illuminating it. In a dim room, one can therefore more or less double the illumination on the portion of the text one is reading simply by placing the lens upon it and looking through the lens at it. Such a lens should therefore be called a Magnifying Illuminator, or otherwise an Illuminating Magnifier. The value to an early scholar would have been incalculable, and the superstitious awe which could have been aroused by such a device must also have been considerable. It is just such a lens which illustrates the phenomena referred to by the Crystal Sun concept of the Pythagoreans, described in the chapter 'The Crystal Sun', of both condensing and refracting ambient light towards a source.

Piece II:

Description: The conical specimen. ROUND, BICONVEX with one end tapering to a prominent cone, or possibly one should rather say: ROUND, CONICAL SUPERIOR SURFACE, MODERATELY CONVEX BASE.

Condition: There is considerable microscopic pitting containing deeply-ingrained dirt. One bad chip on the rim has created a minor pressure-flaw of 3 mm. The rim is very heavily abraded and shows unmistakable signs of heavy and prolonged wear. The tip of the cone has a very severe chip/gouge with some ingrained dirt at the tip. There are several 'pocks' from the lens having been dropped or hit. The quartz was once flawless and perfectly clear; the dirt and abrasion somewhat cloud it today.

Maximum thickness: 2.61 cm.

Diameter: varies between 3.55 and 3.64 cm.

Magnification: If held on its conical tip on a page and run along a line of print, viewed at 45°, it is a very handy magnifier for reading at 2X with no distortion; if raised, this can go to as much as 4X with little distortion.

Piece III:

Description: ROUND DISC. Perfectly clear quartz but for one tiny 'ghostly flaw' of 5 mm. extending inwards from the rim.

Condition: On the rim there are deep but small dents containing deeply-ingrained dirt. No signs that this lens was ever mounted, unless in soft material (leather, etc.) Very insignificant chipping, and no abrasion.

Maximum thickness: 1.28 cm., the thickness varying from 1.26 to 1.28 cm.

Comment on thickness: The two planar surfaces are thus not perfectly flat.

Diameter: varies between 2.8 and 2.83 cm.

Material: Although it looks like it might be glass, this lens is made of quartz, as proved by its refraction (1.54/1.55 indices).

Optical qualities: This lens is more extraordinary than it appears at first glance. The disc acted as a spectacle lens for my mild presbyopia when I held it up to my eye, with my eye about 51 cm. from the page; then, totally out-of-focus letters were transformed into perfect focus. This object otherwise magnifies if one rests it on a surface and looks down through the 'wheel-rim' – but it magnifies only very small things! When it does, the magnification is 4X but with doubled image. One optical trick which this object accomplishes, if held on a rim on a page leaning at 45° towards the observer and if one looks down through it just over the rim, is that it shifts the apparent image – without magnification – by 1 cm. above its true position. If one then takes a ruler and rests it over the word so that the word is largely obscured from normal view, this disc enables one to 'see under' it slightly; this works even if the top of the disc is *completely covered!* It is thus reminiscent of a periscope, and could jokingly be referred to as 'the lens that sees around corners'. One wonders whether this could possibly be an early telescope lens. It is hard to believe that it is ancient British, and yet its not being made of glass and its being cut and ground with such incredible difficulty and care from rock crystal makes it a puzzling object indeed, for which I am at a loss even to guess a date. From its appearance it looks as if it should be made of glass and date from the 17th century perhaps, but this can hardly be the case for a crystal lens. Such a large clear crystal must have been difficult to find. The lens is too heavy actually to hold for any length of time to one's eye, despite its obvious qualities as a monocle. However, suspended in a soft holder in front of one's face, it would have been an excellent magnifier for a seated reader who wanted to keep both hands free, as long as it could be steadied against dangling. It is surprising that the disc has magnification at all, because it seems to be flat on both surfaces, but the fact that it is not really flat is yet another of this object's 'tricks'.

4. *Object number:* 58339 (b)
   Description: FACETED AND POLISHED SPHERE. *Not a lens.*
   Provenance: From Sir Hans Sloane's collection.
   Diameter: varies between 3.95 and 4.05 cm.

Comments: This object is included here only for the sake of complete-ness, since it is not an optical object. But it seemed a shame to let it continue to languish unloved amongst the uncut minerals or mere gems of the Natural History Museum, when it is a rock crystal sphere cut in myriads of triangular facets of irregular size and shape. One big 'ghostly flaw' trans-verse, and one minor one. One pressure-crack, some dirty pitting at one point. Viewing through it, a kaleidoscopic shattering of images is seen. However impressive this may be, there is no suggestion that this object is earlier than the Renaissance, and it may well be contemporary with Sir Hans Sloane. For anyone who likes cut rock crystal, it is well worth seeing and very showy.

Index

Marbodus, George 307
Marcellus, Life of (Plutarch) 199, 200
Marquardt, Joachim 455–456, 460,
  470
Martin, Thomas Henri 12–13
Masonic symbolism 281, 283
Maspero, Professor Gaston 378
*Math and Music: Harmonious
  Connections* (Garland, T.H. and
  Kahn, C.V.) 357
*Mathematical Sciences in Italy,
  History of* (Libri, G.) 160–161
mathematical significance of Horus'
  Eye 441
Maximilian, Emperor of Mexico 444
Maya, The Ancient (Morley, S.G.)
  411
Mayan codices 411
Mayan observation system 411–412
Ménage, Gilles 492
Métius, Jacques 125
On Mechanical Paradoxes
  (Anthemius) 204, 207
Meetkund en Mystiek (Naber, H.A.)
  372
Megalithic Lunar Observatories
  (Thom, A.) 195
Megalithic Science (Heggie, D.) 174
Megalithic Sites in Britain (Thom, A.)
  175–177
Melchizedek, Zorocothora 112–113
Memoirs of a Traveller (Dutens, L.)
  463
Memphis, White Wall at 368, 421
Menkaure, Pyramid of 375
Mercurialis, Hieronymus 76
merkhet (measuring rod) 411
Metallica, De Re (Agricola, G.) 307
meteorites
  see also loadstones
  divine conception linked with
    286–287
  Egyptian knowledge of 287
  Kaaba Stone 294–295
  lodestone source 285
  manifestation of 303
  predicted 287–288
  ritual significance of 289–295
  rock crystal, confused with

  302–303
  as 'seed' from heaven 288, 294
*Meteorology of Aristotle, Commentary
  on the* (Alexander of Aphrodisias)
  107
Metonic Cycle 173, 175, 177–178
microscopic
  artisanship 57–60
  carvings, Egyptian 86–88
  writings 55–56, 57, 60
Microscopical Society, Journal of the
  10, 11, 15
Mielenz, Klaus 230–231
Mills, Professor Allan 385
miniature optical technology
  (Swedish) 518–519
miniature work *see* microscopic
Minoan lenses 39, 70, 117, 159, 414
Minutoli, Baron Heinrich von 37,
  475–476
mirrors
  see also burning-mirrors
  livers as reflecting 154–155
  reflective systems of 205–206
Miscellanies (Aubrey, J.) 308
misconceptions of ancient times 3–4
Mitchell, Peter 477
Mitchell-Hedges, Anna 451
Molyneux, William 61–62, 492
Moon, On the Face in the (Plutarch)
  260
Moorcock, Michael 6
Moore, Professor G.F. 321
Moralia (Plutarch) 264–266
The Morning Post 416
mummification, golden triangle and
  376
Musaeum Metallicum (Aldrovandi, U.)
  307
Museo Settaliano (Scarabelli) 166
music and harmony 354–360
Music of the Ancients, Thesis on
  (Roussier) 351
Mycenean lenses 39
myopia 70–78, 485
Mythological Papyri (Piankoff, A.)
  365
Myths of Greece Examined and Dated
  (St. Clair, G.) 255